HAESE MATH

Specialists in mathema

Mathematics

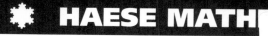

for the international student

8

MYP 3

second edition

Michael Haese

Sandra Haese

Mark Humphries

Edward Kemp

Pamela Vollmar

for use with
IB Middle Years
Programme

MATHEMATICS FOR THE INTERNATIONAL STUDENT 8
MYP 3 second edition

Michael Haese	B.Sc.(Hons.), Ph.D.
Sandra Haese	B.Sc.
Mark Humphries	B.Sc.(Hons.)
Edward Kemp	B.Sc., M.A.
Pamela Vollmar	B.Sc.(Hons.), PGCE.

Haese Mathematics
152 Richmond Road, Marleston, SA 5033, AUSTRALIA
Telephone: +61 8 8210 4666, Fax: +61 8 8354 1238
Email: info@haesemathematics.com.au
Web: www.haesemathematics.com.au

National Library of Australia Card Number & ISBN 978-1-921972-47-8

Published by Haese Mathematics.
152 Richmond Road, Marleston, SA 5033, AUSTRALIA

First Edition	2008
Reprinted	2009 (twice), 2010, 2011, 2012
Second Edition	2014

Cartoon artwork by John Martin. Artwork by Brian Houston and Gregory Olesinski.

Cover design by Piotr Poturaj.

Typeset in Australia by Deanne Gallasch and Charlotte Frost. Typeset in Times Roman 10.

Computer software by Adrian Blackburn, Ashvin Narayanan, Tim Lee, Seth Pink, Nicole Szymanczyk, Brett Laishley, and Linden May.

Production work by Gregory Olesinski, Katie Richer, Anna Rijken, and Robert Haese.

Printed in Singapore by Opus Group.

Acknowledgements: While every attempt has been made to trace and acknowledge copyright, the authors and publishers apologise for any accidental infringement where copyright has proved untraceable. They would be pleased to come to a suitable agreement with the rightful owner.

FOREWORD

MYP 3 second edition has been designed and written for the IB Middle Years Program (MYP) Mathematics framework.

This book may also be used as a general textbook at about 8th Grade level in classes where students complete a rigorous course in mathematics. We have developed this book independently of the International Baccalaureate Organization (IBO) in consultation with experienced teachers of IB Mathematics. The text is not endorsed by the IBO.

It is not our intention that each chapter be worked through in full. Teachers must select carefully, according to the abilities and prior knowledge of their students, to make the most efficient use of time and give as thorough coverage of content as possible.

Each chapter begins with an Opening Problem, offering an insight into the application of the mathematics that will be studied in the chapter. Important information and key notes are highlighted, while worked examples provide step-by-step instructions with concise and relevant explanations. Discussions, Activities, Investigations, Puzzles, and Research exercises are used throughout the chapters to develop understanding, problem solving, and reasoning, within an interactive environment.

One additional chapter is available online:

Chapter 23: Introduction to networks

We understand the emphasis that the IB MYP places on the six Global Contexts, and in response there are online links to ideas for projects and investigations to help busy teachers (see p. 6).

Frequent use of the interactive online features should nurture a much deeper understanding and appreciation of mathematical concepts. The inclusion of our Self Tutor software (see p. 4) is intended to help students who have been absent from classes or who experience difficulty understanding the material.

The book contains many problems to cater for a range of student abilities and interests, and efforts have been made to contextualise problems so that students can see the practical applications of the mathematics they are studying.

We welcome your feedback. Email: info@haesemathematics.com.au

Web: www.haesemathematics.com.au

PMH, SHH, MH, EK, PV

ACKNOWLEDGEMENTS

The authors and publishers would like to thank all those teachers who have read proofs and offered advice and encouragement.

ONLINE FEATURES

There are a range of interactive features which are available online.
With the purchase of a new hard copy textbook, you will gain 15 months subscription to our online product.
This subscription can be renewed annually for a small fee.

COMPATIBILITY

For iPads, tablets, and other mobile devices, the interactive features may not work. However, the electronic version of the textbook and additional chapters can be viewed online using any of these devices.

REGISTERING

You will need to register to access the online features of this textbook.
Visit www.haesemathematics.com.au/register and follow the instructions. Once you have registered, you can:

- activate your electronic textbook
- use your account to make additional purchases.

To activate your electronic textbook, contact Haese Mathematics. On providing proof of purchase, your electronic textbook will be activated. **It is important that you keep your receipt as proof of purchase.**

For general queries about registering and licence keys:

- Visit our Frequently Asked Questions page: www.haesemathematics.com.au/faq.asp
- Contact Haese Mathematics: info@haesemathematics.com.au

ONLINE VERSION OF THE TEXTBOOK

The entire text of the book can be viewed online, allowing you to leave your textbook at school.

The online text contains an additional chapter:

- **Chapter 23: Introduction to networks**

SELF TUTOR

Self tutor is an exciting feature of this book.

The Self Tutor icon on each worked example denotes an active online link.

> Simply 'click' on the Self Tutor (or anywhere in the example box) to access the worked example, with a teacher's voice explaining each step necessary to reach the answer.
>
> Play any line as often as you like. See how the basic processes come alive using movement and colour on the screen.

For example:

Example 1 **Self Tutor**

Plot the points A(3, 5), B(−1, 4), C(0, −3), D(−3, −2), and E(4, −2) on the same set of axes.

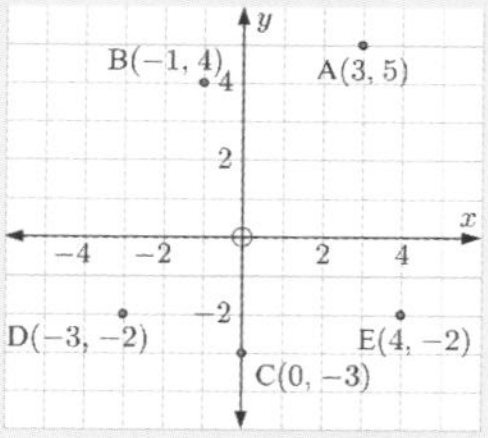

Click here

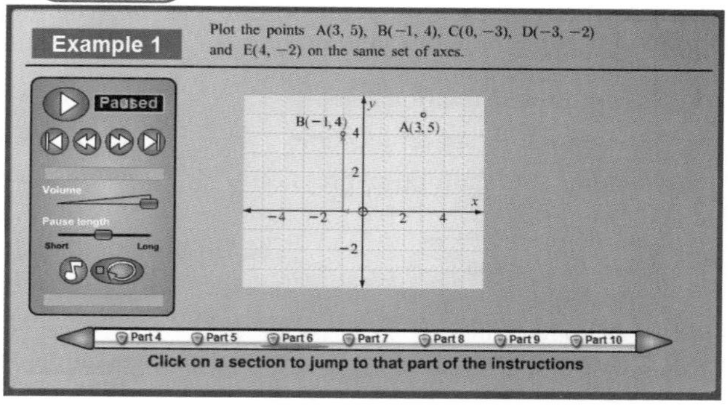

See **Chapter 14**, **Coordinate geometry**, p. 278

INTERACTIVE LINKS

Throughout your electronic textbook, you will find interactive links to:

- Graphing software
- Statistics packages
- Geometry packages
- Games
- Demonstrations
- Printable pages

CLICK ON THESE ICONS ONLINE

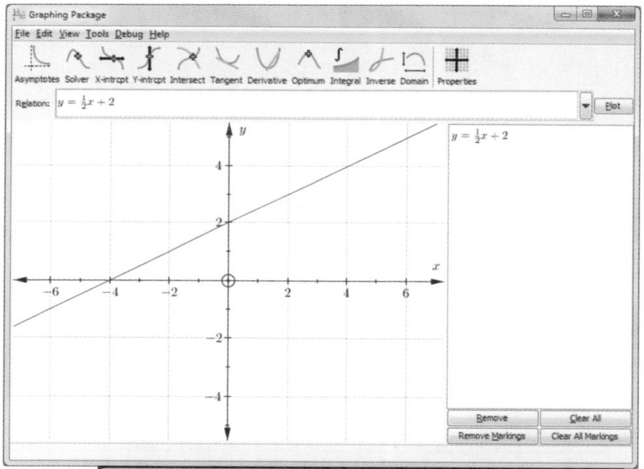

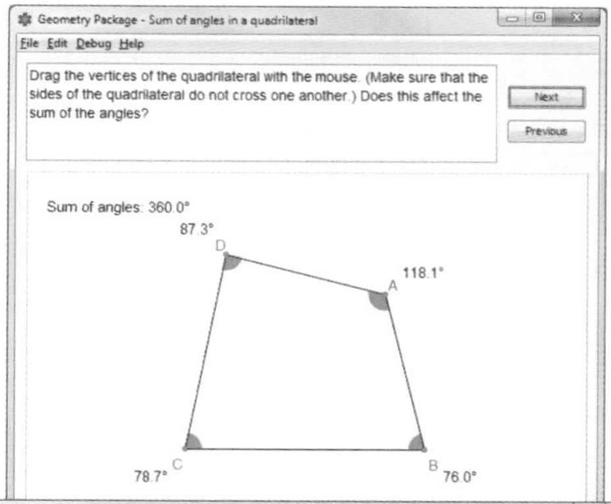

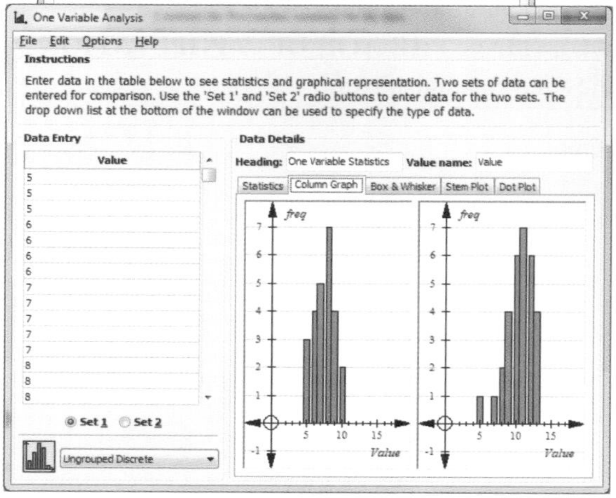

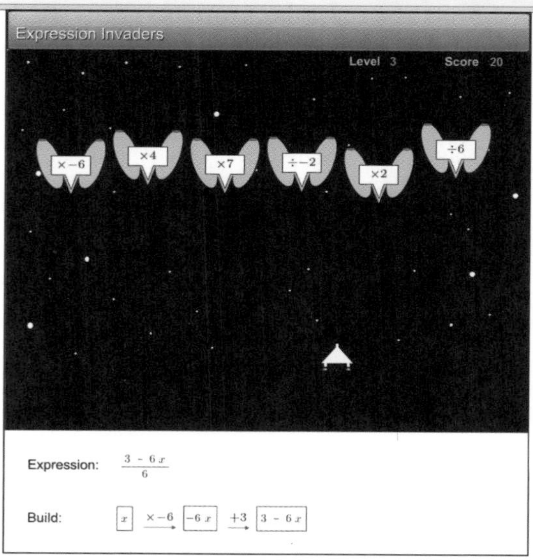

GLOBAL CONTEXTS

The International Baccalaureate Middle Years Programme focuses teaching and learning through six Global Contexts:

- Identities and relationships
- Orientation in space and time
- Personal and cultural expression
- Scientific and technical innovation
- Globalisation and sustainability
- Fairness and development

Click on the heading to access the online link.

The Global Contexts are intended as a focus for developing connections between different subject areas in the curriculum, and to promote an understanding of the interrelatedness of different branches of knowledge and the coherence of knowledge as a whole.

Global context

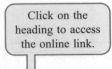

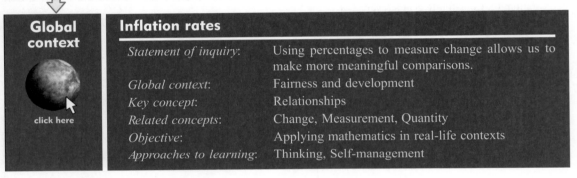

click here

Inflation rates

Statement of inquiry:	Using percentages to measure change allows us to make more meaningful comparisons.
Global context:	Fairness and development
Key concept:	Relationships
Related concepts:	Change, Measurement, Quantity
Objective:	Applying mathematics in real-life contexts
Approaches to learning:	Thinking, Self-management

There are six projects in this book, one for each of the Global Contexts:

Chapter 1:	Number p. 28	**RUSSIAN PEASANT MULTIPLICATION**	Scientific and technical innovation
Chapter 5:	Percentage p. 106	**INFLATION RATES**	Fairness and development
Chapter 7:	Laws of algebra p. 146	**REPRESENTING ALGEBRA**	Orientation in space and time
Chapter 13:	Further measurement p. 272	**ICEBERGS**	Globalisation and sustainability
Chapter 18:	Similarity and congruence p. 379	**CREATE YOUR OWN PYRAMIDS**	Personal and cultural expression
Chapter 20:	Statistics p. 421	**CALCULATING THE AGE OF A POPULATION**	Identities and relationships

Each project contains a series of questions, divided into:

- Factual questions (in green)
- Conceptual questions (in blue)
- Debatable questions (in red).

These questions should help guide the unit of work.

The projects are also accompanied by the general descriptor and a task-specific descriptor for each of the relevant assessment criteria, to help teachers assess the unit of work.

TABLE OF CONTENTS

GRAPHICS CALCULATOR INSTRUCTIONS

Graphics calculator instruction booklets are available for the **Casio fx-9860G Plus**, **Casio fx-CG20**, **TI-84 Plus**, and the **TI-*n*spire**. Click on the relevant icon below.

CASIO fx-9860G Plus | **CASIO fx-CG20** | **TI-84 Plus** | **TI-*n*spire**

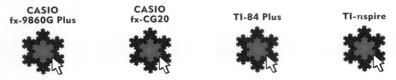

When additional calculator help may be needed, specific instructions are available from icons within the text.

GRAPHICS CALCULATOR INSTRUCTIONS

EXTENSION QUESTIONS

Extension questions are marked in red.

Chapter 1

Number

Contents:

OPENING PROBLEM

A wildlife sanctuary has three shows: 'Brilliant Birds' is 60 minutes long, 'Meet a Monkey' is 90 minutes long, and 'Cuddle a Koala' is 45 minutes long. The shows run continuously throughout the day.

Things to think about:

- **a** What are the *multiples* of 45, 60, and 90?
- **b** If all three shows start together, how long will it be before all three shows again start together?

A NATURAL NUMBERS

People have used numbers since prehistoric times. We know this from ancient writings and drawings.

Today, we live in numbered streets, have telephone numbers, registration numbers, bank account numbers, and tax file numbers. We use numbers to describe the value of things, to measure the universe, and plot courses through time and space. We are "tagged" with a number when we are born, and often after we die. Numbers are thus an essential part of our lives.

NATURAL NUMBERS

The **natural numbers** are the counting numbers $0, 1, 2, 3, 4, 5, 6, 7, 8, 9, ...$

The set of natural numbers is endless. As there is no largest natural number, we say that the set is **infinite**.

FACTORS

The **factors** of a natural number are all the natural numbers which divide exactly into it, leaving no remainder.

For example, the factors of 10 are $1, 2, 5$, and 10.

A number may have many factors. When a number is written as a **product** of factors, we say it is **factorised**.

For example, the number 20 has factors $1, 2, 4, 5, 10$, and 20. It can be factorised into pairs as: 1×20, 2×10, or 4×5.

20 may also be factorised as the product of 3 factors, for example $20 = 2 \times 2 \times 5$.

DISCUSSION

Is it sensible to talk about the factors of zero? If so, what are they?

MULTIPLES

A **multiple** of any natural number is obtained by multiplying it by another natural number.

For example, the multiples of 3 are 3, 6, 9, 12, 15, 18, ... These are obtained by multiplying 3 by each of the natural numbers in turn: $3 \times 1 = 3$, $3 \times 2 = 6$, $3 \times 3 = 9$, $3 \times 4 = 12$, ...

EXERCISE 1A

1. **a** Is 5 a factor of 40? **b** Is 4 a factor of 50? **c** Is 7 a factor of 26?
   d Is 8 a factor of 56? **e** Is 6 a factor of 82? **f** Is 3 a factor of 87?
2. List all the factors of:
   a 6 **b** 15 **c** 13 **d** 24
   e 63 **f** 23 **g** 72 **h** 25
3. Write all the factor pairs of:
   a 45 **b** 48 **c** 72 **d** 100
4. List the numbers which are factors of both 60 and 96.
5. List the first five multiples of:
   a 3 **b** 5 **c** 9 **d** 12
6. Find the:
   a lowest multiple of 7 which is greater than 60
   b highest multiple of 6 which is less than 80.
7. List the numbers between 50 and 100 which are multiples of both 3 and 5.

B INTEGERS

The negative whole numbers, zero, and the positive whole numbers form the set of all **integers**.

...., -5, -4, -3, -2, -1, 0, 1, 2, 3, 4, 5, ...

We can show the integers on a **number line**.

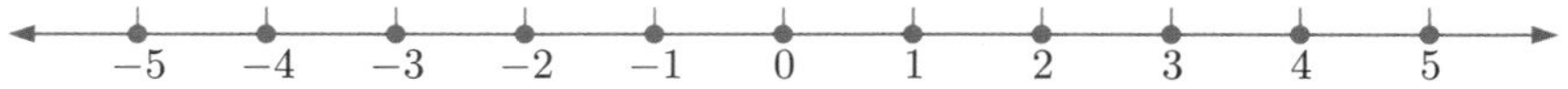

We separate the integers into three categories. Zero is neither positive nor negative.

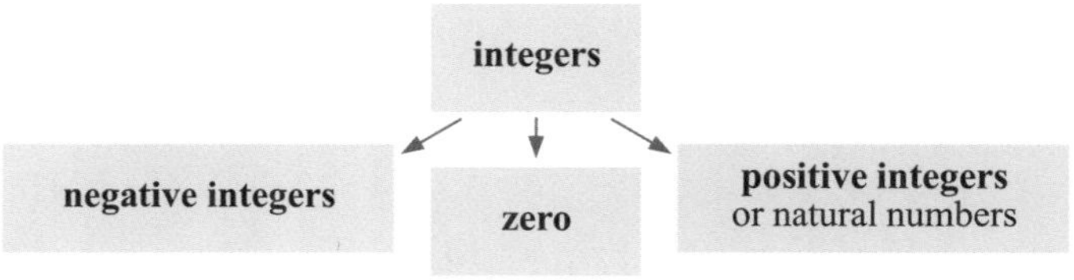

Rules for **addition** and **subtraction** of integers:

+	**(positive)**	gives a	**(positive)**
−	**(positive)**	gives a	**(negative)**
+	**(negative)**	gives a	**(negative)**
−	**(negative)**	gives a	**(positive)**

Example 1 Self Tutor

Simplify:

a $4+-9$ b $4--9$ c $-3+-5$ d $-3--5$

a $4+-9$
$=4-9$
$=-5$

b $4--9$
$=4+9$
$=13$

c $-3+-5$
$=-3-5$
$=-8$

d $-3--5$
$=-3+5$
$=2$

Rules for **multiplication** with integers:

(positive) $\times$ **(positive)** gives a **(positive)**
(positive) $\times$ **(negative)** gives a **(negative)**
(negative) $\times$ **(positive)** gives a **(negative)**
(negative) $\times$ **(negative)** gives a **(positive)**

Example 2 Self Tutor

Find the value of:

a 3×4 b 3×-4 c -3×4 d -3×-4

a $3\times 4=12$ b $3\times -4=-12$ c $-3\times 4=-12$ d $-3\times -4=12$

Rules for **division** with integers:

(positive) $\div$ **(positive)** gives a **(positive)**
(positive) $\div$ **(negative)** gives a **(negative)**
(negative) $\div$ **(positive)** gives a **(negative)**
(negative) $\div$ **(negative)** gives a **(positive)**

Example 3 Self Tutor

Find the value of:

a $14\div 2$ b $14\div -2$ c $-14\div 2$ d $-14\div -2$

a $14\div 2$
$=7$

b $14\div -2$
$=-7$

c $-14\div 2$
$=-7$

d $-14\div -2$
$=7$

EXERCISE 1B

1 Find the value of:

a $14-5$ b $14+-5$ c $14--5$ d $-14+5$
e $-14-5$ f $-14--5$ g $5-14$ h $14+5$
i $13+27$ j $13-27$ k $13+-27$ l $13--27$
m $-13-27$ n $-13+27$ o $-13+-27$ p $-13--27$

2 Find the value of:

a $-3+-8--2$ b $3-8+-2$ c $-3--8--2$
d $-12+7-4$ e $12--7-4$ f $-12--7+4$

3 Find the value of:

a 4×9	**b** 4×-9	**c** -4×9	**d** -4×-9
e 3×11	**f** 3×-11	**g** -3×11	**h** -3×-11
i $4\times 2\times 7$	**j** $4\times -2\times 7$	**k** $4\times -2\times -7$	**l** $-4\times -2\times -7$

4 Find the value of:

a $32\div 8$	**b** $32\div -8$	**c** $-32\div 8$	**d** $-32\div -8$
e $35\div 7$	**f** $35\div -7$	**g** $-35\div 7$	**h** $-35\div -7$
i $54\div 6$	**j** $54\div -6$	**k** $-54\div 6$	**l** $-54\div -6$

5 Determine the missing number in each of the following:

a $7\times \square = -70$	**b** $\square - 3 = -4$	**c** $15+\square = -1$	**d** $25\div\square = -5$
e $\square\times -8 = 40$	**f** $-8+\square = 2$	**g** $\square\div 2 = -20$	**h** $4-\square = 6$
i $-18+\square = 0$	**j** $\square\div -6 = -12$	**k** $\square\times 10 = 100$	**l** $9-\square = 18$

C INDEX NOTATION

Rather than writing $2\times 2\times 2$, we can write such a product as 2^3. We call this **index notation**. We say that 2 is the **base** and that 3 is the **index**, **power**, or **exponent**.

2^3 reads "*two cubed*" or
"*the third power of two*" or
"*two to the power three*".

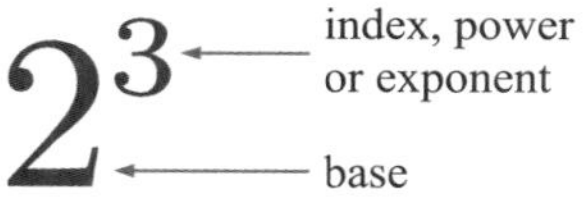

If n is a positive integer, then a^n is the product of n factors of a.

$$a^n = \underbrace{a\times a\times a\times a\times a\times a\times \dots\times a}_{n \text{ factors}}$$

Example 4 — Self Tutor

Find the integer equal to:

a 3^4 **b** $2^4\times 3^2\times 7$

a 3^4
$= 3\times 3\times 3\times 3$
$= 81$

b $2^4\times 3^2\times 7$
$= 2\times 2\times 2\times 2\times 3\times 3\times 7$
$= 1008$

Example 5 — Self Tutor

Simplify:

a -4^2 **b** $(-4)^2$ **c** -2^3 **d** $(-2)^3$

a -4^2
$= -4\times 4$
$= -16$

b $(-4)^2$
$= -4\times -4$
$= 16$

c -2^3
$= -2\times 2\times 2$
$= -8$

d $(-2)^3$
$= -2\times -2\times -2$
$= -8$

You can evaluate powers on your calculator using a special key. Instructions can be found by clicking on the icon.

GRAPHICS CALCULATOR INSTRUCTIONS

EXERCISE 1C

1 Find the integer equal to:

a 2^3 **b** 2^4 **c** 3^3 **d** 2×5^2

e $2^2 \times 5^2$ **f** $3^3 \times 5$ **g** $3^2 \times 5 \times 7$ **h** $2^2 \times 3^3 \times 11$

2 Simplify:

a -3^2 **b** $(-3)^2$ **c** -1^3 **d** $(-1)^3$

e $(-5)^2$ **f** -5^2 **g** $(-2)^4$ **h** -2^4

3 Find, using your calculator:

a 5^6 **b** 9^3 **c** 11^5 **d** $(-3)^8$

e $(-4)^7$ **f** $(-7)^4$ **g** $(-2)^6$ **h** 23^2

4 Find the last digit of 3^{50}.

Hint: Consider $3^1, 3^2, 3^3, 3^4, 3^5, 3^6, ...$ and look for a pattern.

5 Find the last digit of 7^{100}.

D ORDER OF OPERATIONS

Some expressions contain more than one operation. To evaluate these expressions correctly, we use the following rules:

- Perform the operations within **Brackets** first.
- Calculate any part involving **Exponents**.
- Starting from the left, perform all **Divisions** and **Multiplications** as you come to them.
- Restart from the left, performing all **Additions** and **Subtractions** as you come to them.

The word BEDMAS may help you remember this order.

Brackets are **grouping symbols** which are used to indicate a part of an expression which should be evaluated first.

- If an expression contains *one set* of brackets, evaluate that part first.
- If an expression contains *two or more sets* of brackets one inside the other, evaluate the *innermost set* first.
- The division line of fractions also behaves as a grouping symbol. The numerator and the denominator must be found separately before doing the division.

Example 6 — Self Tutor

Simplify:

a $3+7-5$ b $6\times 3\div 2$

a $3+7-5$ {Work from left to right as only $+$ and $-$ are involved.}
$=10-5$
$=5$

b $6\times 3\div 2$ {Work from left to right as only $\times$ and $\div$ are involved.}
$=18\div 2$
$=9$

Example 7 — Self Tutor

Simplify:

a $23-10\div 2$ b $3\times 8-6\times 5$

a $23-10\div 2$ {$\div$ before $-$}
$=23-5$
$=18$

b $3\times 8-6\times 5$ {$\times$ before $-$}
$=24-30$
$=-6$

EXERCISE 1D.1

1 Simplify:

a $4+9-5$ b $4-9+5$ c $4-9-5$
d $3\times 12\div 6$ e $12\div 6\times 3$ f $6\times 12\div 3$

2 Simplify:

a $8+9\times 3$ b $6\times 3+7$ c $14-2\times 4$
d $21-6\times 1$ e $3\times 2-2$ f $30-2\times 2\times 3$
g $30\div 2+6$ h $4+3+2\times 6$ i $12-6\times 3+2$
j $26-9\div 3$ k $5+12\div 2$ l $15\div 3+16\div 2$

Example 8 — Self Tutor

Simplify: $3+(11-7)\times 2$

$3+(11-7)\times 2$ {evaluate the brackets first}
$=3+4\times 2$ {$\times$ before $+$}
$=3+8$
$=11$

3 Simplify:

a $15+(9-3)$ **b** $(15+9)-3$ **c** $(12\div 6)-2$

d $12\div(6-2)$ **e** $(11-8)-3$ **f** $11-(8-3)$

g $36-(9\div 3)$ **h** $(36-9)\div 3$ **i** $24-(6+10)-3$

j $(24-6)+(10-3)$ **k** $(20\div 10)\div 2$ **l** $20\div(10\div 2)$

m $16-(4\times 3)-2$ **n** $30\times 6\div(5-2)$ **o** $28-(3\times 8)\div 6$

Example 9 **Self Tutor**

Simplify: $[12+(9\div 3)]-4^2$

$[12+(9\div 3)]-4^2$ {evaluate the inner brackets first}

$=[12+3]-4^2$ {evaluate the outer brackets}

$=15-4^2$ {evaluate the exponents}

$=15-16$

$=-1$

4 Simplify:

a $9-[(4-3)+2\times 5]$ **b** $[21-(4+5)]\times 2$ **c** $12-[(7+4)+3]$

d $[18-(15\div 5)]+6$ **e** $108\div[2\times(18\div 3)]$ **f** $[(4\times 2)\div(4\div 2)]\times 3$

5 Simplify:

a $5-4^2$ **b** $(5-4)^2$ **c** $2\times(4-7)^2$

d $2\times 4-7^2$ **e** $(3-8)\times(5+2)^2$ **f** $3^2-8\times 5+2^3$

Example 10 **Self Tutor**

Simplify: $\dfrac{12+(5-7)}{18\div(6+3)}$

$\dfrac{12+(5-7)}{18\div(6+3)}$ {evaluate the brackets first}

$=\dfrac{12+(-2)}{18\div 9}$ {simplifying numerator and denominator}

$=\dfrac{10}{2}$

$=5$

The fraction bar acts as a grouping symbol. Evaluate the numerator and the denominator first, *then* perform the division.

6 Simplify:

a $\dfrac{72}{4\times 2}$ **b** $\dfrac{33}{15-4}$ **c** $\dfrac{32\div 4}{6-4}$ **d** $\dfrac{13+7}{11-6}$

e $\dfrac{64-16}{17-5}$ **f** $\dfrac{5\times 2+6}{8}$ **g** $\dfrac{30}{11-(2\times 3)}$ **h** $\dfrac{(4+9)-5}{4+(9-5)}$

7 Using ×, ÷, +, or − only, replace each □ so that correct equations result. Remember that the operations must be evaluated in the correct order.

a $7 \square 3 \square 4 = 6$ **b** $4 \square 6 \square 3 = 21$ **c** $12 \square 4 \square 3 = 9$

8 Insert grouping symbols where necessary to make the following true:

a $9 - 7 \times 4 = 8$ **b** $80 \div 8 \times 2 = 5$ **c** $80 \div 8 \times 2 = 20$

d $4 \times 8 - 7 - 1 = 26$ **e** $4 \times 8 - 7 - 1 = 3$ **f** $4 \times 8 - 7 - 1 = 0$

g $5 + 2 \times 6 - 3 = 39$ **h** $5 + 2 \times 6 - 3 = 11$ **i** $5 + 2 \times 6 - 3 = 21$

ACTIVITY 1

Click on the icon to run the BEDMAS Challenge.

How fast can you go?

BEDMAS CHALLENGE

USING YOUR CALCULATOR TO PERFORM OPERATIONS

In this course it is assumed that you have a graphics calculator. Your calculator already has the **order of operations** built into it. However, you may need to consult the instructions about **negative numbers** and **grouping symbols**, by clicking on the icon.

GRAPHICS CALCULATOR INSTRUCTIONS

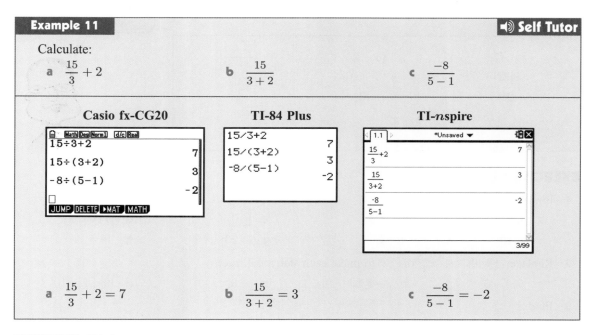

Example 11 **Self Tutor**

Calculate:

a $\dfrac{15}{3} + 2$ **b** $\dfrac{15}{3+2}$ **c** $\dfrac{-8}{5-1}$

Casio fx-CG20

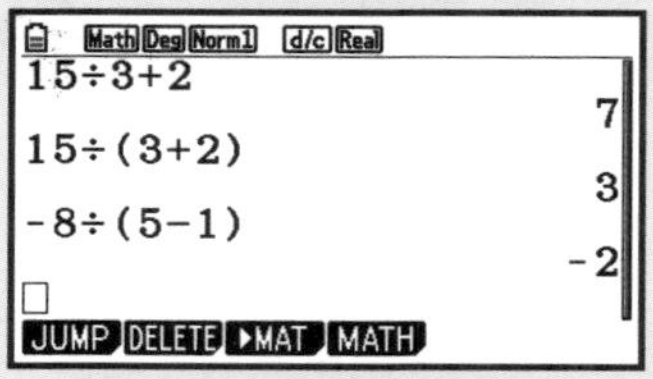

TI-84 Plus

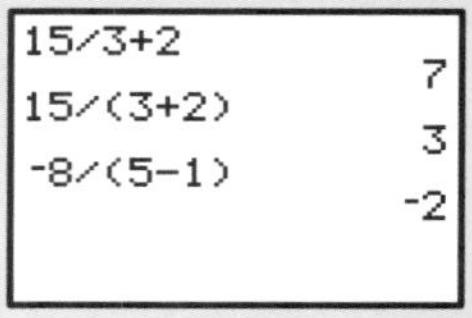

TI-*n*spire

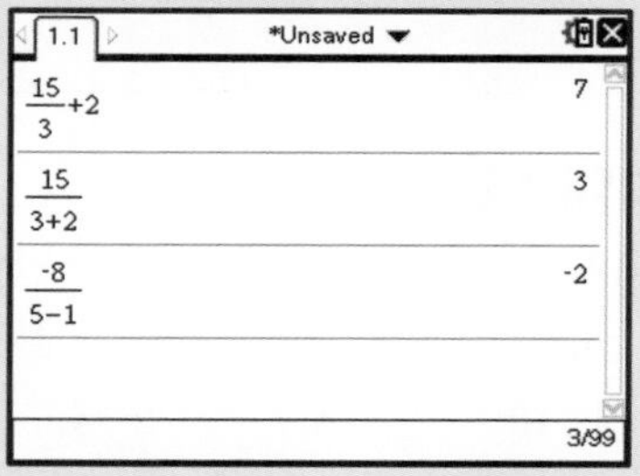

a $\dfrac{15}{3} + 2 = 7$ **b** $\dfrac{15}{3+2} = 3$ **c** $\dfrac{-8}{5-1} = -2$

EXERCISE 1D.2

1 Evaluate using your calculator:

a $16 + 25 \times 9$ **b** $(16 + 25) \times 9$ **c** $112 \div 7 + 7$

d $112 \div (7 + 7)$ **e** 43×-6 **f** $-256 \div -32$

2 Evaluate using your calculator:

a $\frac{39}{3} - 18$ **b** $\frac{139-7}{4\times 11}$ **c** $\frac{-15\times 2}{7-(16\div 8)}$

d $\frac{118+8}{3\times 7}$ **e** $\frac{-240-120}{3\times 4\times 5}$ **f** $\frac{(10-2)\times 3}{32-(4\times 5)}$

E ABSOLUTE VALUE

The **absolute value** of a number is its **size**, ignoring its sign.

For example, the absolute value of 5 is 5, and the absolute value of -4 is 4. We write $|5| = 5$ and $|-4| = 4$.

We can think of the absolute value of a number as its distance from 0 on the number line.

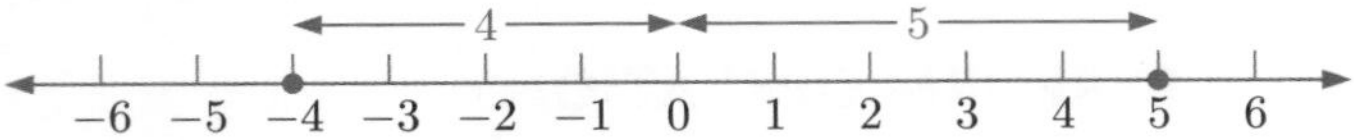

Example 12 **Self Tutor**

Find:

a $|-7\times -3|$ **b** $|3 - 2\times 8|$ **c** $\left|\frac{5+9}{4-6}\right|$

a $|-7\times -3|$
$= |21|$
$= 21$

b $|3-2\times 8|$
$= |3-16|$
$= |-13|$
$= 13$

c $\left|\frac{5+9}{4-6}\right|$
$= \left|\frac{14}{-2}\right|$
$= |-7|$
$= 7$

Evaluate the expression first, then find its absolute value.

EXERCISE 1E

1 Find:

a $|6|$ **b** $|-1|$ **c** $|-9|$ **d** $|11|$

e $|-13|$ **f** $|4|$ **g** $|-23|$ **h** $|0|$

2 Replace □ with $>$, $<$, or $=$ to make each statement true:

a $|7|$ □ $|5|$ **b** $|-4|$ □ $|-9|$ **c** $|-3|$ □ $|3|$ **d** $|9|$ □ $|-10|$

3 Find:

a $|11-4|$ **b** $|5-16|$ **c** $|3\times -8|$

d $|-5\times -9|$ **e** $|54\div 9|$ **f** $|64\div -8|$

4 Find:

a $|4+3\times 6|$ **b** $|8-7\times 4|$ **c** $|10\div 5-4|$

d $|6\times -8+10|$ **e** $|7^2-8|$ **f** $|5\times 4-3^3|$

5 Find:

a $|5 \times (2+4)|$ b $|42 \div (2-5)|$ c $|(7-10) \times (1-5)|$

d $\left|\dfrac{6+12}{7-1}\right|$ e $\left|\dfrac{8 \times 5}{28 \div -7}\right|$ f $\left|\dfrac{(4+2)^2-1}{13-10 \times 2}\right|$

6 Find:

a $3 \times |6-8|$ b $|4-7|+8$ c $\dfrac{|3-12|}{3}$

Absolute value signs act as grouping symbols.

F SQUARE NUMBERS AND SQUARE ROOTS

SQUARE NUMBERS

When a number is multiplied by itself, we say that the number is **squared**.

For example, since $4 \times 4 = 16$, we say "four squared is equal to sixteen". Using index notation, we write $4^2 = 16$.

When a whole number is squared, the result is a **square number** or **perfect square**.

The first five square numbers are:

$1^2 = 1 \times 1 = 1$
$2^2 = 2 \times 2 = 4$
$3^2 = 3 \times 3 = 9$
$4^2 = 4 \times 4 = 16$
$5^2 = 5 \times 5 = 25$

SQUARE ROOTS

Finding the **square root** of a number is the opposite operation to squaring a number.

The **square root** of the number a is the positive number which, when squared, gives a.

We write the square root of a as $\sqrt{a}$.

$$\sqrt{a} \times \sqrt{a} = a$$

For example: since $4^2 = 16$, $\sqrt{16} = 4$
since $5^2 = 25$, $\sqrt{25} = 5$.

If a number is not a perfect square, then its square root will not be a whole number. In this case, we can estimate the square root of the number by considering the square numbers either side of it.

Example 13 **Self Tutor**

Between which two consecutive integers does $\sqrt{11}$ lie?

$\sqrt{9} = 3$ and $\sqrt{16} = 4$

Now $9 < 11 < 16$

$\therefore \sqrt{9} < \sqrt{11} < \sqrt{16}$

$\therefore 3 < \sqrt{11} < 4$

$\therefore \sqrt{11}$ lies between 3 and 4.

$\sqrt{11}$ lies between $\sqrt{9}$ and $\sqrt{16}$.

You can use your calculator to evaluate square roots.
Click on the icon for instructions.

For example, $\sqrt{11} \approx 3.3166....$ is the number which, when multiplied by itself, will give 11.

GRAPHICS CALCULATOR INSTRUCTIONS

```
√(11)
        3.31662479
```

EXERCISE 1F

1 Without using a calculator, find the 6th, 9th, and 12th square numbers.

2 Use your calculator to find the largest 3 digit square number.

3 Copy and complete:

- **a** "The square of an even number is ......"
- **b** "The square of an odd number is ......"

4 Without using your calculator, find:

a $\sqrt{49}$ **b** $\sqrt{64}$ **c** $\sqrt{121}$ **d** $\sqrt{144}$

5 Use your calculator to find:

a $\sqrt{289}$ **b** $\sqrt{576}$ **c** $\sqrt{1521}$ **d** $\sqrt{2304}$

6 Between which two consecutive integers do the following values lie?

a $\sqrt{12}$ **b** $\sqrt{28}$ **c** $\sqrt{103}$ **d** $\sqrt{150}$

Check your answers using a calculator.

7 Consider the pattern:

$1 \times 3 + 1 = ...$
$2 \times 4 + 1 = ...$
$3 \times 5 + 1 = ...$
$4 \times 6 + 1 = ...$

- **a** Copy and complete the pattern, then add three more rows.
- **b** Use the pattern to find: **i** $19 \times 21 + 1$ **ii** 29×31

8 Explain why $2\,679\,430\,077\,712\,313$ cannot be a perfect square.

INVESTIGATION 1 SUMS OF SQUARE NUMBERS

Most whole numbers can be written as the sum of three or less square numbers.
For example, $70 = 6^2 + 5^2 + 3^2$ and $40 = 6^2 + 2^2$.

What to do:

1 Try to write the numbers from 1 to 25 as the sum of three or less square numbers. Record your answers in a table like the one below. The first five have been done for you.

1	1^2
2	$1^2 + 1^2$
3	$1^2 + 1^2 + 1^2$
4	2^2
5	$2^2 + 1^2$
6	
7	
8	
9	

10	
11	
12	
13	
14	
15	
16	
17	

18	
19	
20	
21	
22	
23	
24	
25	

2 List the numbers that you were not able to write as the sum of three or less square numbers. What do they have in common?

G PRIMES AND COMPOSITES

A **prime number** is a natural number which has **exactly** two distinct factors, 1 and itself.
A **composite number** is a natural number which has more than two factors.

For example:

- 17 is a prime number since it has only 2 factors, 1 and 17.
- 26 is a composite number since it has more than two factors. These are 1, 2, 13, and 26.

Notice that **one** (1) is neither prime nor composite.

Apart from order, every composite number can be written as a **product of prime factors** in **one and only one way**.

For example, $72 = 2 \times 2 \times 2 \times 3 \times 3$ is the only way of writing 72 as the product of prime factors. Using index notation, we write $72 = 2^3 \times 3^2$. We call this a **prime factorisation** and say the number is written in **prime factored form**.

There are two methods we can use for writing a number in prime factored form:

- In **repeated division**, we continue to divide the number by primes until we are left with 1.
- In a **factor tree**, we find a factor pair for the number, and these factors become branches of the tree. We continue finding factor pairs for each branch until we are left only with prime numbers.

Example 14 — Self Tutor

Write 600 as the product of prime factors in index form.

Repeated division *or* **Factor tree**

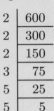

2	600
2	300
2	150
3	75
5	25
5	5
	1

$\therefore\ 600 = 2 \times 2 \times 2 \times 3 \times 5 \times 5$
$= 2^3 \times 3 \times 5^2$

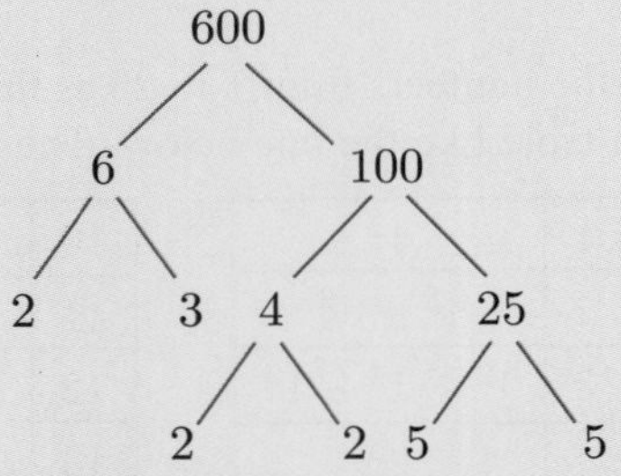

$\therefore\ 600 = 2 \times 3 \times 2 \times 2 \times 5 \times 5$
$= 2^3 \times 3 \times 5^2$

EXERCISE 1G

1. List the set of all primes less than 30.
2. Find two consecutive odd numbers between 60 and 80 which are both prime.
3. A number between 20 and 30 has 2 prime factors and 3 composite factors. Find the number.
4. Write the following as powers of a prime:
   - **a** 8 **b** 27 **c** 125 **d** 128
   - **e** 343 **f** 729 **g** 361 **h** 1331
5. Express the following as the product of prime factors in index form:
   - **a** 54 **b** 108 **c** 360 **d** 228
   - **e** 196 **f** 756 **g** 936 **h** 1225
   - **i** 588 **j** 945 **k** 910 **l** 1274
6. The **most abundant** number in a set of numbers is the number which has the highest power of 2 as a factor.
   For example:
   - the most abundant number of $\{1, 2, 3, 4, 5, 6, 7, 8, 9, 10\}$ is 8 as $8 = 2^3$
   - the most abundant number of $\{41, 42, 43, 44, 45, 46, 47, 48, 49, 50\}$ is 48 as $48 = 2^4 \times 3$.

   Find the most abundant number of the set $\{151, 152, 153, 154, 155, 156, 157, 158, 159, 160\}$.
7. **a** Write 1960 as the product of prime factors in index form.
   b How many prime factors does 1960 have?
   c Explain why $2^2 \times 7 = 28$ is a factor of 1960.

GAME

Click on the icon to play a game which involves writing numbers as the product of prime factors. See if you can get the highest score in your class.

GAME

ACTIVITY 2 HIGHLY COMPOSITE NUMBERS

A number is composite if it has any factors other than 1 and itself.

A **highly composite** number is a number which has more factors than any other number before it. The first highly composite number is 1.

For example, the factors of 12 are 1, 2, 3, 4, 6, and 12, so 12 has 6 factors. The numbers from 1 to 11 inclusive all have less than 6 factors.
So, 12 is a highly composite number.

What to do:

1 There is one highly composite number that is also prime. What is it?

2 Find all highly composite numbers less than or equal to 100.

H HIGHEST COMMON FACTOR

A number which is a factor of two or more other numbers is called a **common factor** of these numbers.

For example, 7 is a common factor of 28 and 35.

The **highest common factor (HCF)** of two numbers is the largest number which is a factor of *both* of these numbers.

For example: The factors of 18 are 1, 2, 3, 6, 9, and 18.

The factors of 45 are 1, 3, 5, 9, 15, and 45.

The *common* factors of 18 and 45 are 1, 3, and 9, so the highest common factor is 9.

The highest common factor of two numbers can be found by expressing each number as a product of prime factors. We multiply all the factors which are common to both numbers, to find the highest common factor.

Example 15 **Self Tutor**

Find the highest common factor (HCF) of 18 and 24.

$$\begin{array}{r|r} 2 & 18 \\ \hline 3 & 9 \\ \hline 3 & 3 \\ \hline & 1 \end{array} \qquad \begin{array}{r|r} 2 & 24 \\ \hline 2 & 12 \\ \hline 2 & 6 \\ \hline 3 & 3 \\ \hline & 1 \end{array}$$

$\therefore\ 18 = \mathbf{2} \times \mathbf{3} \times 3$
and $24 = \mathbf{2} \times 2 \times 2 \times \mathbf{3}$

$\mathbf{2} \times \mathbf{3}$ is common to the factorisations of both 18 and 24.

So, the highest common factor of 18 and 24 is $2 \times 3 = 6$.

EXERCISE 1H

1 Find the highest common factor of:

a 12 and 16	**b** 9 and 15	**c** 14 and 56
d 16 and 40	**e** 24 and 60	**f** 35 and 50
g 55 and 121	**h** 24 and 42	**i** 28 and 70
j 80 and 96	**k** 64 and 288	**l** 169 and 208
m 90 and 189	**n** 252 and 490	**o** 280 and 308

2 Farmer Giles has a field $45 \text{ m} \times 60 \text{ m}$. He wishes to divide it into square yards of equal size. What is the biggest size the yards could be?

3 Two pieces of copper pipe 315 cm and 225 cm long will be cut into sections. All sections must have equal length. What is the greatest possible length of each section?

4 A florist has 30 lilies, 42 gerberas, and 36 roses to make bouquets with. Each bouquet must be identical. What is the largest number of bouquets that can be made using all of the flowers?

INVESTIGATION 2 — THE 3-DIGIT PROBLEM

What to do:

1 Choose any three different digits from 1 to 9.

2 Write down the six possible two digit numbers which can be formed using these digits. For example, if we chose the digits 2, 7, and 8, we would write down 27, 28, 72, 78, 82, and 87.

3 Find the **sum** of these six numbers, and write their sum in prime factored form. Record your results in a table:

Digits chosen	*Numbers*	*Sum of 6 numbers*	*Sum in prime factored form*
2, 7, 8	27, 28, 72, 78, 82, 87	374	$2 \times 11 \times 17$
⋮	⋮	⋮	⋮

4 Find the HCF of all of the sums.

5 Repeat the process above for two other three digit numbers.

6 Prove that you will always obtain this HCF for all possible choices of 3 different digits.
Hint: Any two digit number with digits a and b has the form $10a + b$.
For example, $37 = 10 \times 3 + 7$.

I LOWEST COMMON MULTIPLE

A number which is a multiple of two or more other numbers is called a **common multiple** of these numbers.

For example, 60 is a common multiple of 5 and 6.

The **lowest common multiple** or **LCM** of a set of natural numbers is the smallest multiple which is common to all of them.

Example 16 — Self Tutor

Find the lowest common multiple of 9 and 12.

The multiples of 9 are: 9, 18, 27, **36**, 45, 54, 63, **72**, 81, ...

The multiples of 12 are: 12, 24, **36**, 48, 60, **72**, 84, ...

$\therefore$ the common multiples are 36, 72, ... and 36 is the smallest of these

$\therefore$ the LCM is 36.

Another method for finding lowest common multiples is to write each number as the product of its prime factors. By writing these products one above the other, we include in the LCM only those factors that are necessary.

Example 17 — Self Tutor

Find the LCM of: **a** 9 and 12 **b** 15, 20, and 24.

a

$$\begin{array}{r|l} 3 & 9 \\ \hline 3 & 3 \\ \hline & 1 \end{array} \qquad \begin{array}{r|l} 2 & 12 \\ \hline 2 & 6 \\ \hline 3 & 3 \\ \hline & 1 \end{array}$$

$$\begin{array}{rr} \text{Prime factors of 9:} & 3 \times 3 \\ \text{Prime factors of 12:} & 2 \times 2 \times 3 \\ \hline \text{Prime factors of LCM:} & 2 \times 2 \times 3 \times 3 \end{array}$$

$\therefore$ LCM = 36

b

$$\begin{array}{r|l} 3 & 15 \\ \hline 5 & 5 \\ \hline & 1 \end{array} \qquad \begin{array}{r|l} 2 & 20 \\ \hline 2 & 10 \\ \hline 5 & 5 \\ \hline & 1 \end{array} \qquad \begin{array}{r|l} 2 & 24 \\ \hline 2 & 12 \\ \hline 2 & 6 \\ \hline 3 & 3 \\ \hline & 1 \end{array}$$

$$\begin{array}{rccccccccc} \text{Prime factors of 15:} & & & & & & & 3 & \times & 5 \\ \text{Prime factors of 20:} & & & 2 & \times & 2 & & & \times & 5 \\ \text{Prime factors of 24:} & 2 & \times & 2 & \times & 2 & \times & 3 & & \\ \hline \text{Prime factors of LCM:} & 2 & \times & 2 & \times & 2 & \times & 3 & \times & 5 \end{array}$$

$\therefore$ LCM = 120

EXERCISE 1I

1. Find the LCM of:
   - **a** 5 and 8
   - **b** 4 and 6
   - **c** 8 and 10
   - **d** 15 and 18
   - **e** 12 and 15
   - **f** 14 and 20
   - **g** 12 and 27
   - **h** 42 and 45
2. Find the LCM of:
   - **a** 2, 3, and 4
   - **b** 5, 7, and 10
   - **c** 4, 6, and 8
   - **d** 5, 8, and 9
   - **e** 8, 10, and 12
   - **f** 9, 15, and 20
   - **g** 14, 18, and 21
   - **h** 20, 25, and 30

3 Find the smallest positive integer which is exactly divisible by 15 and 25.

4 Chris has a piece of rope. It can be cut exactly into either 10 metre or 18 metre lengths. Find the shortest length that Chris' rope could be.

5 Answer the **Opening Problem** on page **12**.

6 Gloria is an avid coffee drinker. Every day, she drinks a coffee at each of these stores:

Keen Beans:	"Buy 5 coffees, get 1 free!"
The Caffeine Club:	"Buy 7 coffees, get 1 free!"
Expresso Yourself:	"Buy 9 coffees, get 1 free!"

Today, Gloria had a free coffee at each of the stores. How long will it be before she next has:

a 2 free coffees in one day

b 3 free coffees in one day?

Global context

click here

Russian peasant multiplication

Statement of inquiry:	Different methods can be used to perform a calculation.
Global context:	Scientific and technical innovation
Key concept:	Form
Related concepts:	Equivalence, Representation
Objectives:	Knowing and understanding, Investigating patterns
Approaches to learning:	Self-management, Research

REVIEW SET 1A

1 List the factors of:

a 21 **b** 32 **c** 37

2 Write all of the factor pairs of 66.

3 Find the value of:

a $4 + -7$ **b** -8×9 **c** -3×-12 **d** $54 \div -6$

4 Simplify:

a $24 \div 3 \times 2$ **b** $13 - 5 \times 2 - 4^2$ **c** $5 \times (8 - 2)$

d $8 \div (5 - 1) \times 3$ **e** $15 - [3 \times (8 - 6) - 2]$ **f** $\dfrac{29 - 8}{10 - (6 - 3)}$

5 Using $\times$, $\div$, $+$, or $-$ only, replace each $\square$ so that correct equations result.

a $3 \square 5 \square 4 = 11$ **b** $8 \square 6 \square 3 = 6$

6 Find the integer equal to:

a 4^3 **b** $2^3 \times 5^2$ **c** $2^1 \times 5^2 \times 7^1$

7 Find:

a $|-12|$ **b** $|5^2 - 11|$ **c** $|3 \times (2-7)|$

8 Between which two consecutive integers does $\sqrt{75}$ lie?

9 List the prime numbers between 40 and 50.

10 Express as the product of prime factors in index form:

a 450 **b** 212

11 Find the lowest common multiple of:

a 6 and 15 **b** 4 and 11 **c** 5, 8, and 10

12 Find the HCF of:

a 12 and 14 **b** 24 and 56 **c** 18, 27, and 45

13 A passenger train goes through a 2-track level crossing every 8 minutes. A freight train goes through the same level crossing every 52 minutes.
A passenger train and a freight train go through the level crossing at the same time. How long will it be before a passenger train and a freight train next pass through the level crossing together?

REVIEW SET 1B

1 List the first five multiples of 8.

2 Write 54 as the product of prime factors in index form.

3 Find three consecutive odd numbers less than 100, which are all composite.

4 Simplify:

a $6^2 + 3 \times 5$ **b** $12 - 8 \div 2 + 1$

5 Find the value of:

a $15 - -9$ **b** $-6 + 7 - -3$

6 Find the last digit of 9^{60}.

7 Insert brackets where necessary to make the following true:

a $12 \div 6 - 2 = 3$ **b** $6 + 4 \div 2 + 3 = 2$ **c** $18 \div 1 + 2 \times 4 = 2$

8 Use your calculator to evaluate:

a $200 \div (13 + 12)$ **b** $\dfrac{-7 - 23}{5 - (2 \times 4)}$ **c** $\dfrac{156 - 24}{(2-4) \times 2}$

9 For the numbers 18 and 30, find:

a the highest common factor **b** the lowest common multiple.

10 List the square numbers between 700 and 800.

11 Find:

a $|77 \div -7|$ **b** $|12 - 4 \div 2|$ **c** $\left|\dfrac{8 \times 12}{10 \div -5}\right|$

12 A greengrocer sells nectarines by the bag, and each bag contains the same number of nectarines. The greengrocer sold 126 nectarines yesterday, and 198 nectarines today. What is the greatest number of nectarines that could be in each bag?

13 Amy has some lollies in a bag, which she will share with her friends at a party. She knows she can share them equally whether there are four, five, or six children present. What is the smallest number of lollies Amy could have?

Chapter 2

Sets and Venn diagrams

Contents:

OPENING PROBLEM

There are 30 students on a school bus, and 17 of them are girls. 7 of the students are in Year 8. 4 of the students are girls in Year 8.

Things to think about:

a How can we display this information in a diagram?

b How many students on the bus are:

i boys **ii** girls, but not in Year 8 **iii** boys in Year 8?

The students on the bus in the **Opening Problem** can be placed into different groups. We call these groups **sets**.

In this chapter we will look at some properties of sets, and how we can describe relationships between sets. We will also study **Venn diagrams**, which we use to display sets and to solve problems.

A SETS

A **set** is a collection of objects or things.

The colours of the French flag are blue, white, and red. We can write these colours as the set $C = \{\text{blue, white, red}\}$.

We say "C is the set of colours of the French flag."

The objects or things in a set are called the **elements** or **members** of the set.

In the example above, red is an element of the set C.

The elements of a set can take almost any form, including colours, numbers, letters, and symbols.

For example, the set of all multiples of 4 which are less than 30 can be written as the set $M = \{4, 8, 12, 16, 20, 24, 28\}$.

SET NOTATION

$\in$	means	'*is a member of*' or '*is in*'
$\notin$	means	'*is not a member of*' or '*is not in*'
$n(A)$	means	'*the number of elements in set* A'.

For example, if $M = \{4, 8, 12, 16, 20, 24, 28\}$ then $12 \in M$, $19 \notin M$, and $n(M) = 7$.

EQUAL SETS

Two sets are **equal** if they contain exactly the same elements.

SUBSETS

Set P is a **subset** of set Q if every element of P is also an element of Q. We write $P \subseteq Q$.

For example, if $A = \{1, 3, 6\}$ and $B = \{1, 2, 3, 5, 6, 7\}$, then every element of A is also an element of B. We say that A is a subset of B, and write $A \subseteq B$.

EMPTY SET

The **empty set** $\varnothing$ or $\{\ \}$ is a set which contains no elements.

An example of an empty set is the set of multiples of 5 between 1 and 4.

The empty set is a subset of all other sets.

Example 1 **Self Tutor**

Let P be the set of all multiples of 6 less than 20, and Q be the set of all even numbers less than 20.

a List the elements of P and Q.

b True or false? **i** $10 \in P$ **ii** $10 \notin Q$ **iii** $12 \in P$

c Find: **i** $n(P)$ **ii** $n(Q)$.

d Is $P \subseteq Q$?

a $P = \{6, 12, 18\}$, $Q = \{2, 4, 6, 8, 10, 12, 14, 16, 18\}$

b **i** 10 is not an element of P, so $10 \in P$ is false.
ii 10 is an element of Q, so $10 \notin Q$ is false.
iii 12 is an element of P, so $12 \in P$ is true.

c **i** $n(P) = 3$ $\{P$ has 3 elements$\}$
ii $n(Q) = 9$ $\{Q$ has 9 elements$\}$

d Every element of P is also an element of Q, so $P \subseteq Q$.

EXERCISE 2A

1 List the elements of the set A which is the set of the:

a days of the week
b letters which make up the word FOOTBALL
c prime numbers less than 20
d vowels
e factors of 21
f colours of keys on a piano
g positive whole numbers between 40 and 50
h multiples of 5 less than 40.

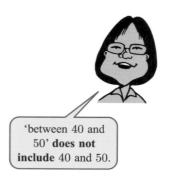

'between 40 and 50' **does not include** 40 and 50.

2 Find $n(A)$ for each of the sets in **1**.

3 Let $S = \{2, 3, 5, 8, 11, 12\}$ and $T = \{2, 4, 5, 12\}$.

a Find: **i** $n(S)$ **ii** $n(T)$.

b True or false?

i $5 \in S$ **ii** $5 \in T$ **iii** $12 \notin T$ **iv** $4 \notin S$

c Is $T \subseteq S$?

4 Suppose $A = \{\text{positive square numbers less than } 10\}$, $B = \{\text{composite numbers less than } 20\}$, and $C = \{\text{factors of } 36\}$.

a List the elements of: **i** A **ii** B **iii** C.

b Find: **i** $n(A)$ **ii** $n(B)$ **iii** $n(C)$.

c Is $A \subseteq B$?

d Is $A \subseteq C$?

5 List all the subsets of:

a $\{8, 9\}$ **b** $\{p, q, r\}$

6 Let A be the set of colours on spinner 1, and B be the set of colours on spinner 2.

a List the elements of A and B.

b Is green $\in B$?

c Find: **i** $n(A)$ **ii** $n(B)$.

d Is $A \subseteq B$?

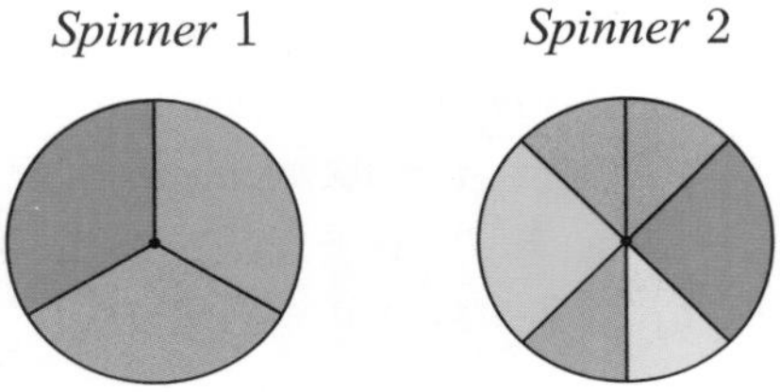

7 Suppose $F = \{2, 3, 5, 6, 7, 10, 11, 12\}$, $G = \{10, 5, x, 2, 12\}$, and $G \subseteq F$. What possible values could x have?

B COMPLEMENT OF A SET

When we are dealing with sets:

> The **universal set** U is the set of all elements we are considering.

For example, if we are considering the letters of the English alphabet, the universal set is:

$U = \{a, b, c, d, e, f, g, h, i, j, k, l, m, n, o, p, q, r, s, t, u, v, w, x, y, z\}$

From this universal set we can define subsets of U, such as $V = \{\text{vowels}\} = \{a, e, i, o, u\}$ and $C = \{\text{consonants}\} = \{b, c, d, f, g, h, j, k, l, m, n, p, q, r, s, t, v, w, x, y, z\}$.

> The **complement** of a set A is the set of all elements of U that are not elements of A.
>
> The complement of A is written A'.

For example:

- if $U = \{1, 2, 3, 4, 5, 6, 7, 8, 9\}$ and $A = \{2, 3, 5, 7\}$, then $A' = \{1, 4, 6, 8, 9\}$
- if $U = \{\text{letters of the English alphabet}\}$, $V = \{\text{vowels}\}$, and $C = \{\text{consonants}\}$, then V is the complement of C, and C is the complement of V.

Example 2 — Self Tutor

Let $U = \{0, 1, 2, 3, 4, 5, 6\}$. Find A' if A is:

a $\{0, 2, 5, 6\}$ **b** {factors of 6} **c** {numbers less than 3}

a $A = \{0, 2, 5, 6\}$
$\therefore\ A' = \{1, 3, 4\}$

b $A = \{1, 2, 3, 6\}$
$\therefore\ A' = \{0, 4, 5\}$

c $A = \{0, 1, 2\}$
$\therefore\ A' = \{3, 4, 5, 6\}$

EXERCISE 2B

1 Let $U = \{1, 2, 3, 4, 5, 6, 7, 8, 9\}$. Find the complement of:

a $A = \{2, 4, 6\}$
b $B = \{1, 3, 5, 7, 9\}$
c $C = \{8, 4, 7, 3\}$
d $D = \{1, 2, 3, 7, 8, 9\}$

2 Suppose U = {whole numbers between 0 and 20}, P = {factors of 12}, and Q = {prime numbers between 10 and 20}. List the elements of:

a P **b** Q **c** P' **d** Q'

3 Alongside is a list of sports played at a school.
Let K be the set of sports that involve hitting a ball with a bat or racquet.

a List the elements of:
i U **ii** K **iii** K'

b What do the elements of K' represent?

SPORTS
Rugby
Athletics
Volleyball
Baseball
Cricket
Archery
Netball
Tennis

4 Consider the letters of the English alphabet. Let X be the set of the letters which make up the word "INHABITANT", and Y be the set of letters which make up the word "MILLION". List the elements of:

a X **b** Y **c** X' **d** Y'

5 Let U = {whole numbers between 0 and 10}, A = {positive even numbers less than 10}, and B = {prime numbers less than 10}.

a List the elements of:
i U **ii** A **iii** A' **iv** B **v** B'

b Find:
i $n(U)$ **ii** $n(A)$ **iii** $n(A')$ **iv** $n(A) + n(A')$
v $n(B)$ **vi** $n(B')$ **vii** $n(B) + n(B')$

c Copy and complete:
"For any set A within a universal set U, $n(A) + n(A') = n(....)$."

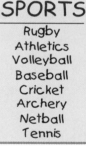

C INTERSECTION AND UNION

Sam and Tess are planning a trip around the world together.

Sam can speak English, French, German, and Spanish.

Tess can speak English, German, and Japanese.

We let $S = \{\text{English, French, German, Spanish}\}$ be the set of languages Sam can speak, and $T = \{\text{English, German, Japanese}\}$ be the set of languages Tess can speak.

INTERSECTION

To determine the languages in which Sam and Tess can communicate, we need to know which languages are spoken by *both* of them.

By inspecting the sets S and T, we can see that Sam and Tess can both speak English and German.

The set $\{\text{English, German}\}$ is called the **intersection** of sets S and T.

The **intersection** of two sets A and B is the set of elements that are in **both** set A **and** set B.

The intersection of sets A and B is written $A \cap B$.

For example, if $A = \{2, 5, 7, 9\}$ and $B = \{3, 5, 9, 10\}$, then $A \cap B = \{5, 9\}$.

Two sets A and B are **disjoint** if they have no elements in common. In this case $A \cap B = \varnothing$.

UNION

When deciding which countries to visit on their trip, Sam and Tess want to make sure that *at least* one of them can speak the native language.

By inspecting the sets, we can see that between them Sam and Tess can speak English, French, German, Spanish, and Japanese.

The set $\{\text{English, French, German, Spanish, Japanese}\}$ is called the **union** of sets S and T.

The **union** of two sets A and B is the set of elements that are in **either** set A **or** set B.

The union of sets A and B is written $A \cup B$.

For example, if $A = \{2, 5, 7, 9\}$ and $B = \{3, 5, 9, 10\}$, then $A \cup B = \{2, 3, 5, 7, 9, 10\}$.

Elements in both A and B **are included** in the union of A and B.

Example 3 — Self Tutor

Let $P = \{b, c, f, g, h\}$ and $Q = \{c, d, g, i\}$. Find:

a $P \cap Q$ **b** $P \cup Q$.

a $P \cap Q = \{c, g\}$ $\{c$ and g are elements of both sets$\}$

b $P \cup Q = \{b, c, d, f, g, h, i\}$ {elements of either P or Q}

EXERCISE 2C

1 Suppose $A = \{1, 3, 5, 7\}$ and $B = \{3, 5, 6, 9\}$. Find:

a $A \cap B$ **b** $A \cup B$.

2 Find $P \cap Q$ and $P \cup Q$ for:

a $P =$ {Dragons, Tigers, Roosters, Raiders}, $Q =$ {Tigers, Storm, Dragons, Knights}

b $P = \{1, 3, 6, 10, 15\}$, $Q = \{1, 4, 9, 16\}$

c $P = \{d, e, g, k, m\}$, $Q = \{g, h, l, m, p\}$

3 Let $A =$ {blue, green, yellow}, $B =$ {green, red, pink}, and $C =$ {orange, blue, black}. Which pair of sets is disjoint?

4 Suppose $X =$ {prime numbers less than 20} and $Y =$ {factors of 20}.

a List the elements of X and Y.

b Find:

i $X \cap Y$ **ii** $n(X \cap Y)$ **iii** $X \cup Y$ **iv** $n(X \cup Y)$.

5 Sarah has gardenias and roses in her garden in New Zealand. Her gardenias flower every year from September to December, and her roses flower from October to March. Let G be the set of months when the gardenias flower, and R be the set of months when the roses flower.

a State the universal set U in this case.

b List the elements of G and R.

c Find $G \cap R$. What does this set represent?

d Find $G \cup R$. What does this set represent?

e Find $(G \cup R)'$. What does this set represent?

6 Suppose $A =$ {multiples of 4 which are less than 10} and $B =$ {factors of 16}.

a List the elements of A and B.

b Is $A \subseteq B$?

c Find: **i** $A \cap B$ **ii** $A \cup B$.

d Copy and complete: "If $A \subseteq B$, then $A \cap B =$ ...... and $A \cup B =$ ......"

7 Holly is baking scones and cake for a morning tea. The ingredients needed for her recipes are shown below:

Let S be the set of ingredients needed to make the scones, and C be the set of ingredients needed to make the cake.

a List the elements of S and C.

b Find $S \cap C$. What does this set represent?

c Find $S \cup C$.

d How many different ingredients will Holly use in her baking?

D VENN DIAGRAMS

We can represent sets visually using Venn diagrams.

A **Venn diagram** consists of a universal set U represented by a rectangle, and sets within it that are usually represented by circles.

For $A = \{1, 4, 8\}$ and $U = \{1, 2, 3, 4, 5, 6, 7, 8, 9\}$, the Venn diagram is:

Place the elements of A inside the circle, and all other elements outside it.

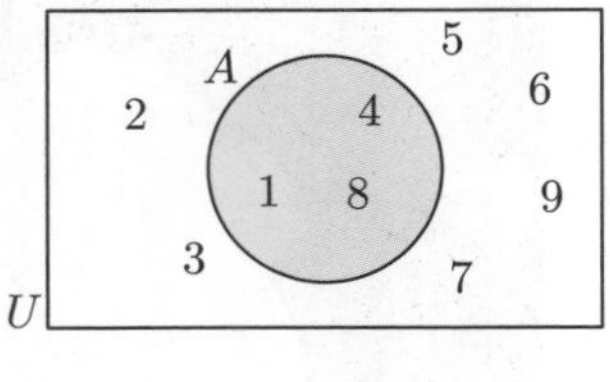

The **complement** of a set A is represented by the region outside the circle which represents A.

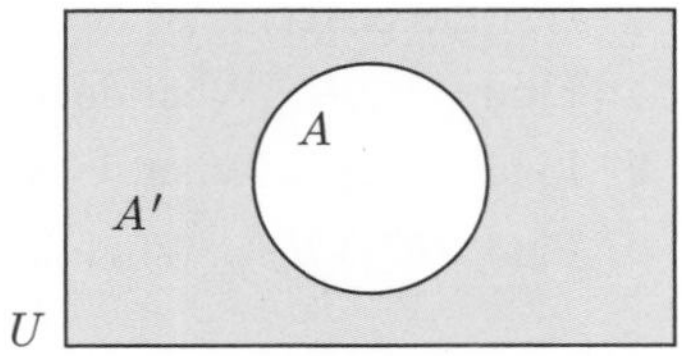

If A is a **subset** of B, we place a circle representing A completely within the circle representing B. This indicates that every element of A is also an element of B.

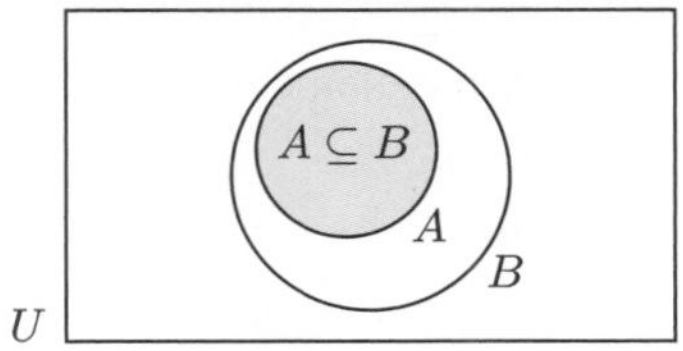

The **intersection** of two sets A and B is represented by the region where the circles representing A and B overlap. Elements in this region are elements of both A and B.

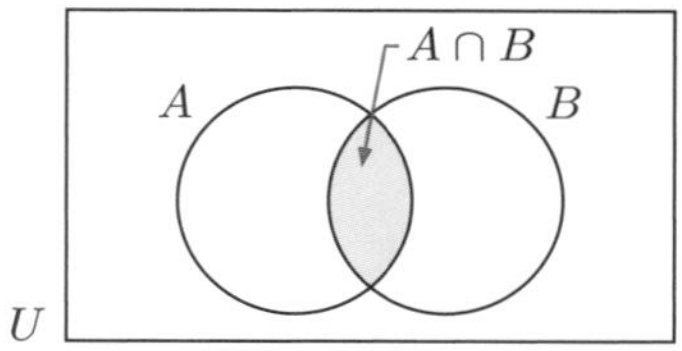

The **union** of two sets A and B is represented by the region inside one or both of the circles representing A and B. Elements in this region are elements of either A or B.

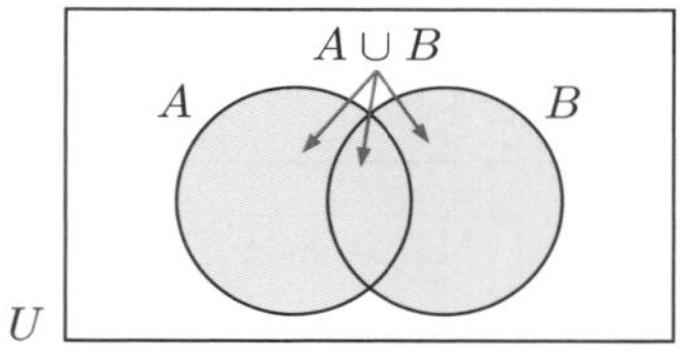

Disjoint sets A and B are represented by two circles which do not overlap. There are no elements in both A and B.

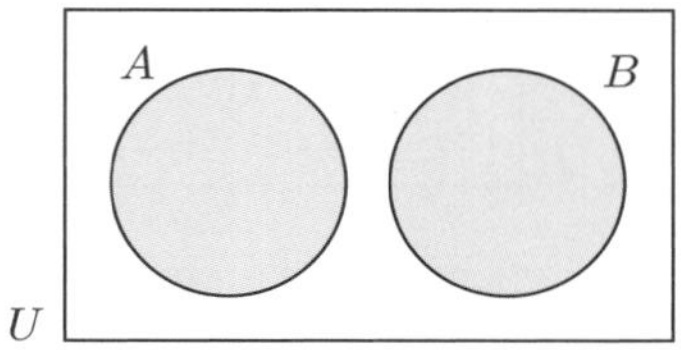

Example 4 — Self Tutor

Let $U = \{1, 2, 3, 4, 5, 6, 7, 8\}$.
Draw a Venn diagram to represent:

a $C = \{2, 3, 7\}$ **b** $A = \{1, 3, 4, 6\}$, $B = \{2, 3, 6, 8\}$

a $C = \{2, 3, 7\}$
$C' = \{1, 4, 5, 6, 8\}$

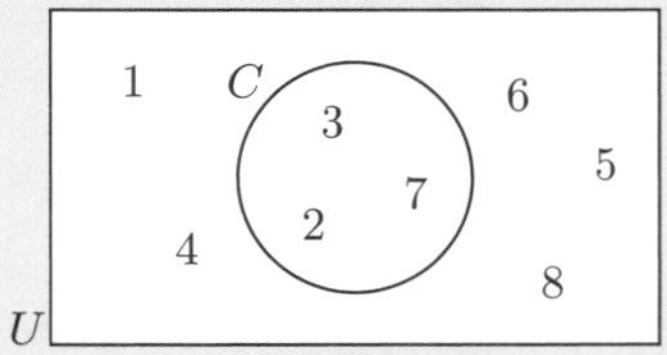

b $A \cap B = \{3, 6\}$
$A \cup B = \{1, 2, 3, 4, 6, 8\}$

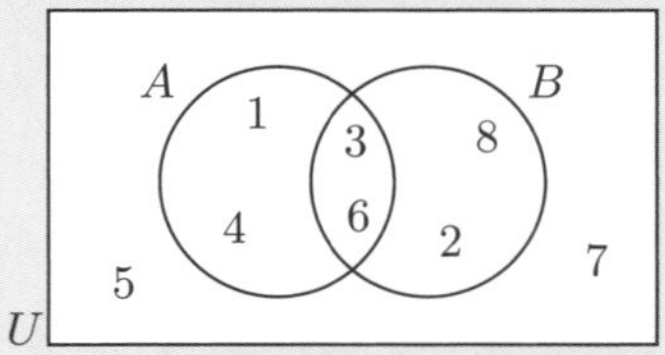

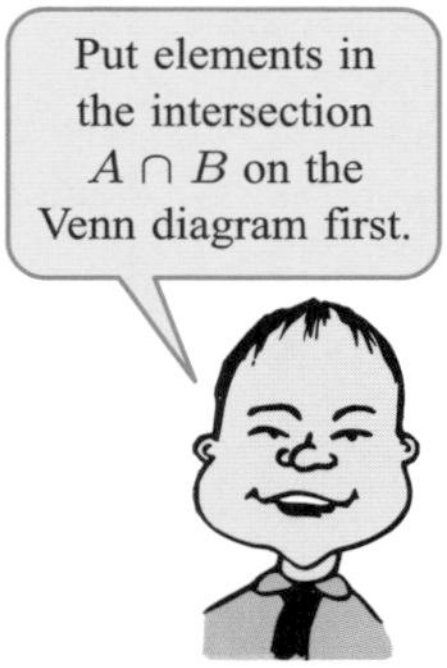

Put elements in the intersection A ∩ B on the Venn diagram first.

Example 5 — Self Tutor

Let $U = \{1, 2, 3, 4, 5, 6\}$. Draw a Venn diagram to represent:

a $A = \{2, 5\}$, $B = \{1, 2, 4, 5, 6\}$ **b** $A = \{1, 3, 6\}$, $B = \{2, 4\}$

a Every element in A is also in B, so $A \subseteq B$.

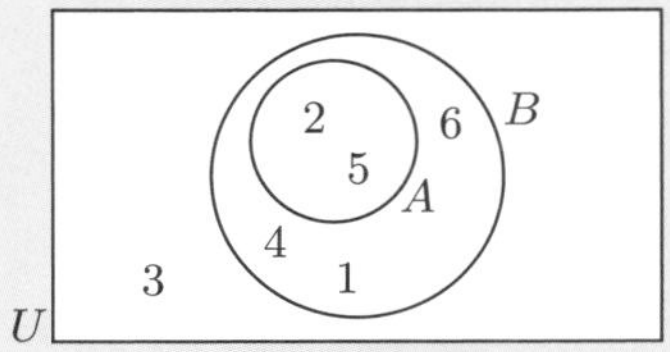

b $A \cap B = \varnothing$, so A and B are disjoint sets.

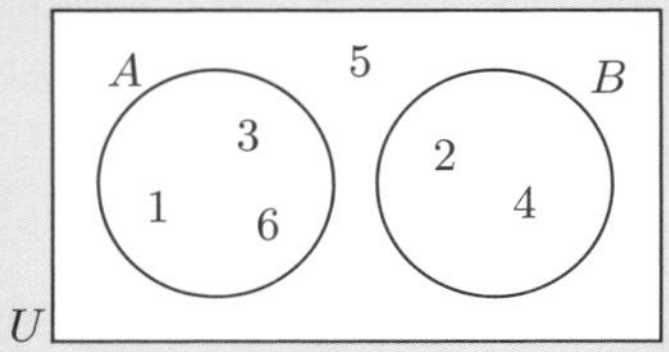

Example 6 | Self Tutor

Shade the region of a Venn diagram representing:

a in A and B **b** in A but not in B.

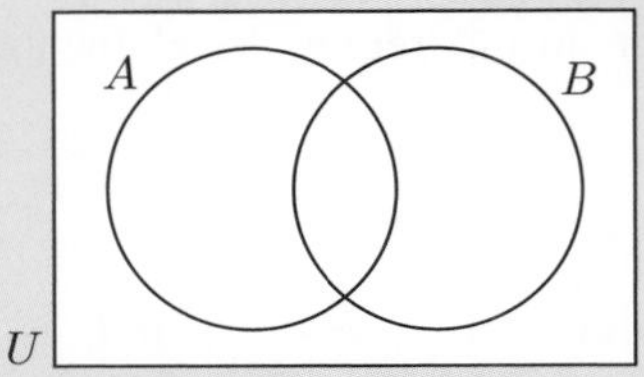

a

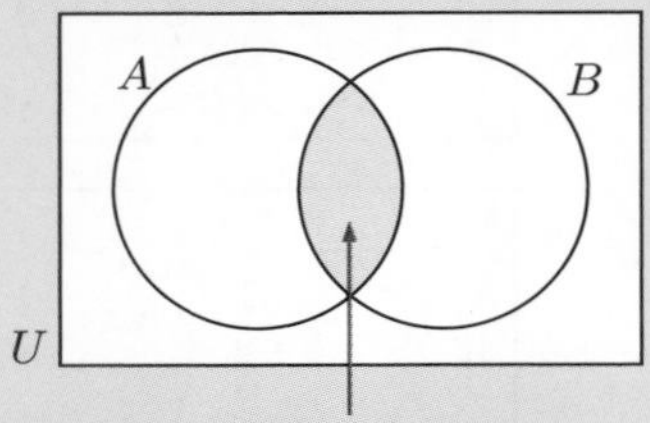

Elements in this region are in both A and B.

b

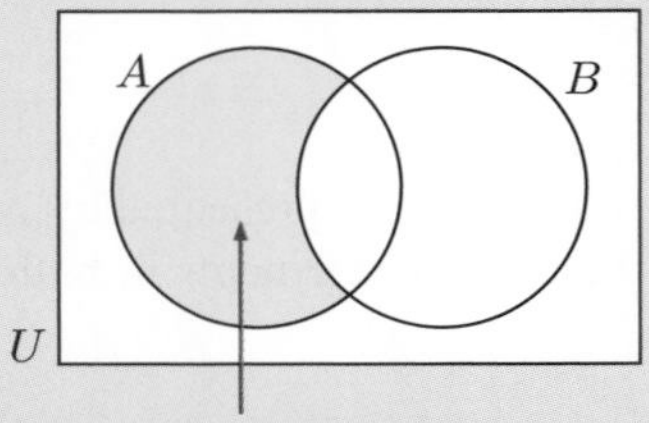

Elements in this region are in A but not in B.

EXERCISE 2D.1

1 Consider the Venn diagram alongside.
List the elements of:

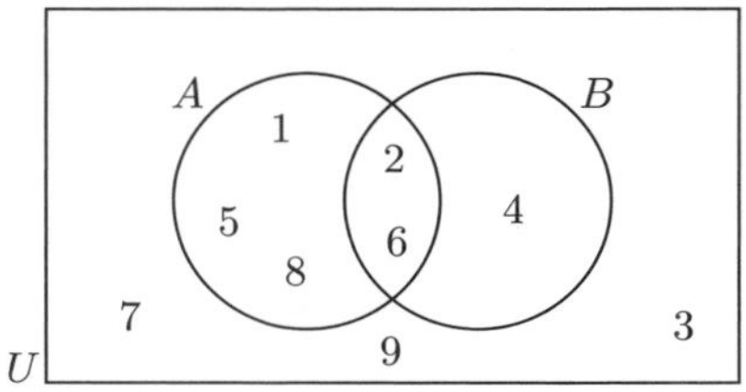

a A **b** B
c $A \cap B$ **d** $A \cup B$
e A' **f** B'
g U

2 Let $U = \{1, 2, 3, 4, 5, 6, 7, 8, 9\}$. Draw a Venn diagram to represent:

a $A = \{3, 5, 6, 8\}$ **b** $A = \{1, 3, 5, 7\}$, $B = \{2, 3, 5, 8\}$
c $A = \{2, 3, 4, 5\}$, $B = \{4, 5, 6, 7, 8\}$ **d** $A = \{1, 4, 9\}$, $B = \{2, 6, 8\}$

3 Let $U = \{a, b, c, d, e, f, g, h, i, j\}$. Draw a Venn diagram to represent:

a $P = \{c, e, f, g, i, j\}$, $Q = \{j, i, g\}$ **b** $P = \{b, e, a, d\}$, $Q = \{c, a, g, e\}$

4 George's cricket team has training on Mondays and Thursdays, and matches on Saturdays. Hugh's cricket team has training on Tuesdays and Thursdays, and matches on Sundays.
Let G be the set of days that George plays cricket, and H be the set of days that Hugh plays cricket.

a List the sets G and H.
b Draw a Venn diagram to illustrate G and H.
c List the elements of G'. Explain what this set represents.
d List the elements of $G \cap H$. Explain what this set represents.

5 Let $U = \{$whole numbers from 1 to 10$\}$, $A = \{$prime numbers less than 10$\}$, and $B = \{$factors of 10$\}$.

a List the elements of A and B.

b Illustrate the sets on a Venn diagram.

c List the elements of:

i $A \cup B$ **ii** $(A \cup B)'$

6 On separate Venn diagrams like the one illustrated, shade the region representing those members:

a not in A **b** in B

c in B but not in A **d** in either A or B.

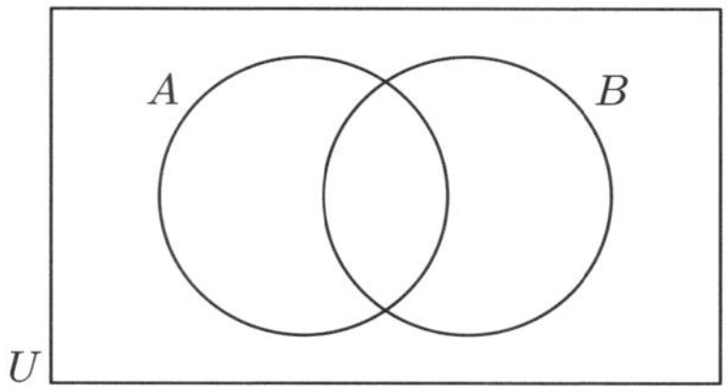

PRINTABLE VENN DIAGRAMS

7 Describe, in words, the shaded region:

a

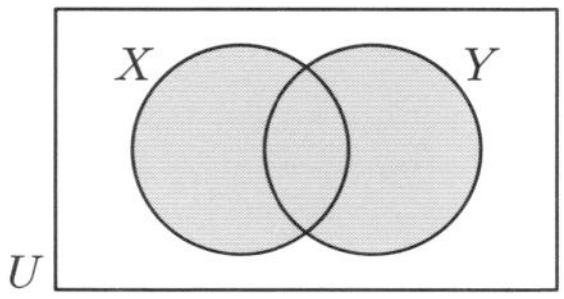

b

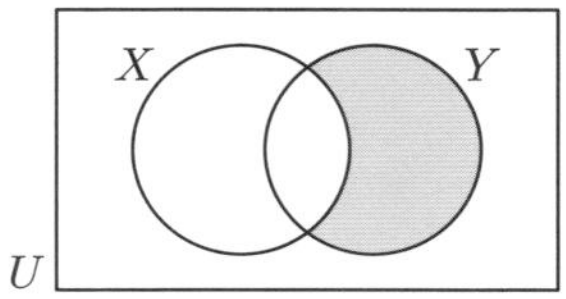

c

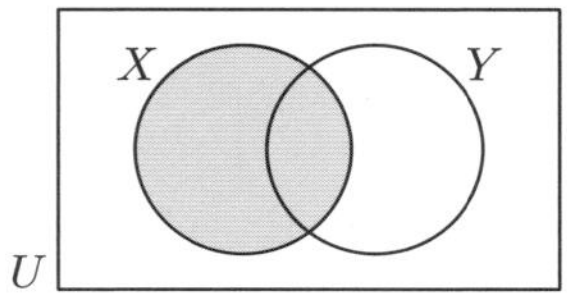

8 Suppose $U = \{$whole numbers from 2 to 12$\}$, $X = \{$multiples of 2 up to 12$\}$, and $Y = \{$prime numbers less than 13$\}$.

a List the elements of X and Y.

b Find: **i** $X \cap Y$ **ii** $X \cup Y$.

c Draw a Venn diagram to illustrate the sets.

d How many elements are in:

i Y but not in X **ii** Y **iii** X or Y?

9 Students must choose five of the subjects listed alongside for their Year 8 studies.
Ruth chooses Mathematics, English, Geography, Art, and Music.
Shelley chooses English, Science, Chinese, Art, and Woodwork.
Let R be the set of subjects chosen by Ruth,
and S be the set of subjects chosen by Shelley.

a Illustrate R and S on a Venn diagram.

b List the subjects chosen by:

i both Ruth and Shelley **ii** Ruth or Shelley, but not both.

c How many subjects were chosen by:

i Shelley but not Ruth **ii** neither Ruth nor Shelley?

SUBJECTS

Mathematics
English
Science
Geography
History
Chinese
Art
Music
Woodwork

NUMBERS IN REGIONS

In many situations there are too many elements to list on a Venn diagram, and we are more interested in the **number of elements** in each region.

To indicate how many elements are in each region of a Venn diagram, we place brackets around the numbers.

For example, the Venn diagram alongside indicates there are 5 elements in both A and B, 2 elements in A but not B, 4 elements in B but not A, and 1 element in neither A nor B.

In total there are $2+5=7$ elements in A, and $5+4=9$ elements in B.

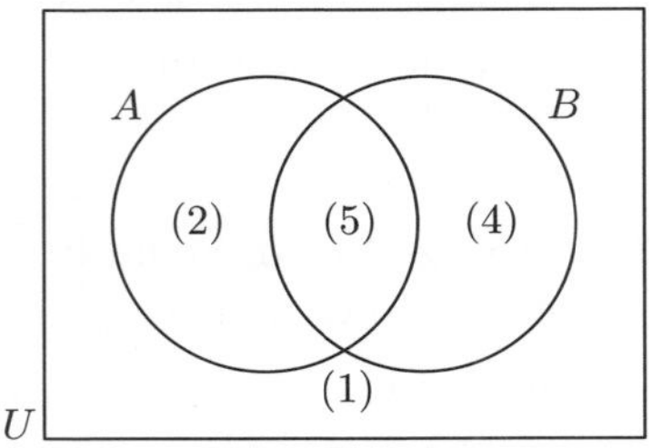

Example 7 Self Tutor

How many elements are there in:

- **a** A
- **b** B
- **c** A, but not B
- **d** B'
- **e** $A \cup B$
- **f** U?

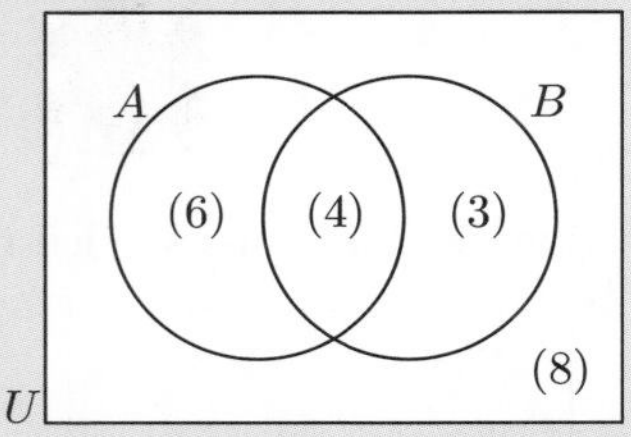

- **a** $n(A) = 6+4 = 10$
- **b** $n(B) = 4+3 = 7$
- **c** $n(A, \text{ but not } B) = 6$
- **d** $n(B') = 6+8 = 14$
- **e** $n(A \cup B) = 6+4+3 = 13$
- **f** $n(U) = 6+4+3+8 = 21$

EXERCISE 2D.2

1 For the Venn diagram alongside, determine the number of elements in:

- **a** A
- **b** B
- **c** $A \cap B$
- **d** $A \cup B$
- **e** A, but not B
- **f** U

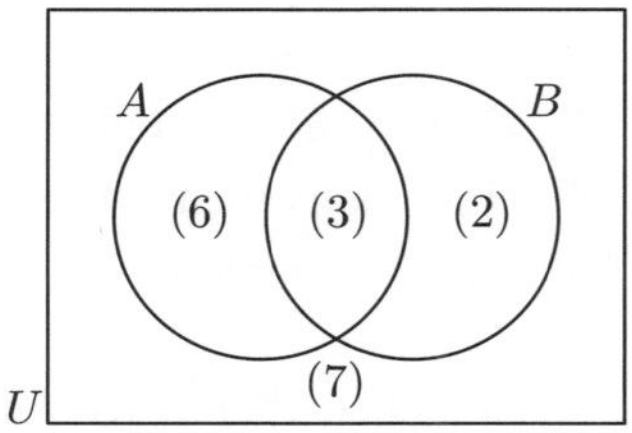

2

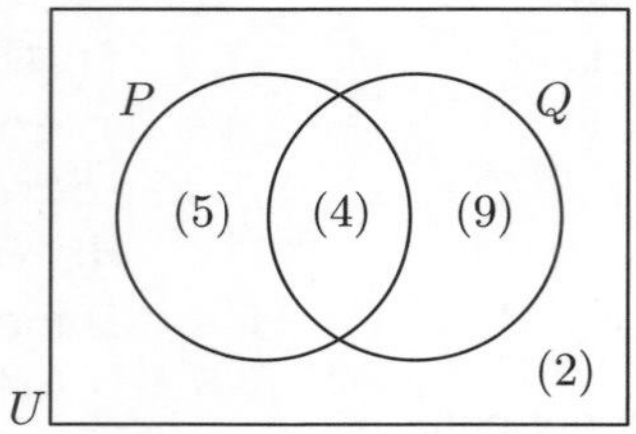

Determine the number of elements in:

- **a** P
- **b** Q'
- **c** Q, but not P
- **d** $P \cup Q$
- **e** P or Q, but not both.

Example 8 **Self Tutor**

Suppose $n(A) = 11$, $n(B) = 15$, $n(A \cap B) = 6$, and $n(U) = 24$. Copy and complete the Venn diagram.

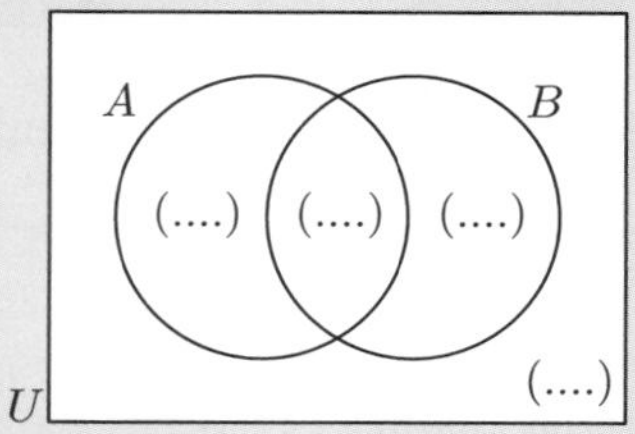

① $n(A \cap B) = 6$

② $n(A) = 11$ and $5 + 6 = 11$.
$\therefore$ there are 5 elements in this region.

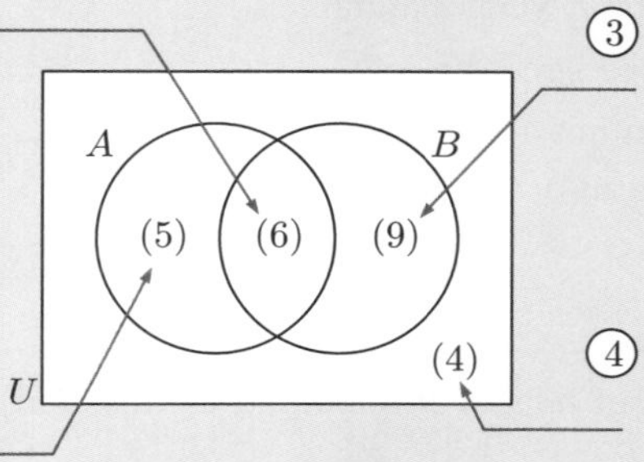

③ $n(B) = 15$ and $9 + 6 = 15$.
$\therefore$ there are 9 elements in this region.

④ $n(U) = 24$ and $5 + 6 + 9 + 4 = 24$.
$\therefore$ there are 4 elements in this region.

3 Suppose $n(A) = 9$, $n(B) = 12$, and $n(U) = 20$. Copy and complete the Venn diagram.

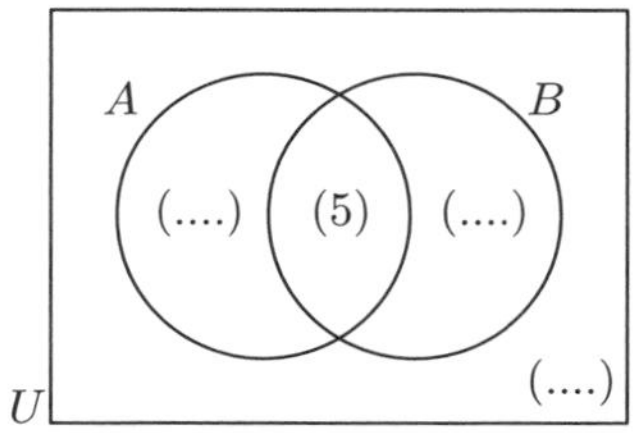

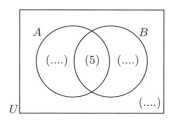

4 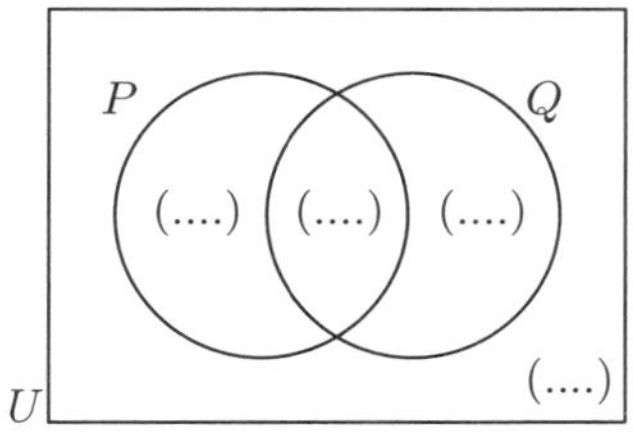

Suppose $n(P) = 14$, $n(Q) = 8$, $n(P \cap Q) = 3$, and $n(U) = 30$. Copy and complete the Venn diagram.

5 Suppose $n(A) = 10$, $n(B) = 13$, $n(A \cap B) = 6$, and $n(U) = 20$.

a Represent this information on a Venn diagram.

b Hence, find the number of elements in:

i B, but not A ii $A \cup B$.

6 Suppose $n(A) = 12$, $n(B) = 17$, $n(A \cup B) = 21$, and $n(U) = 25$.

a Represent this information on a Venn diagram.

b Hence, find the number of elements in:

i B, but not A ii $A \cap B$.

E PROBLEM SOLVING WITH VENN DIAGRAMS

By considering the number of elements in different regions, we can use Venn diagrams to solve problems.

Example 9 **Self Tutor**

There are 30 houses on a street. 16 of the houses have a burglar alarm, 22 houses have a security door, and 10 houses have both a burglar alarm and a security door.

a Place this information on a Venn diagram.

b How many houses on the street have:

  i a burglar alarm but not a security door

  ii either a burglar alarm or a security door?

a Let B represent the set of houses with burglar alarms, and S represent the set of houses with security doors.

① We write (10) in the intersection to indicate 10 houses have both.

② 16 houses have burglar alarms, and $6 + 10 = 16$.
$\therefore$ there must be 6 houses in B but not S.

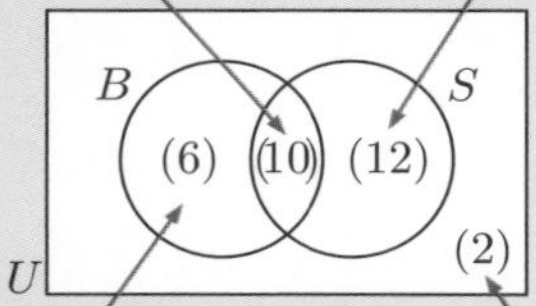

③ 22 houses have security doors, and $12 + 10 = 22$.
$\therefore$ there must be 12 houses in S but not B.

④ There are 30 houses in total, and $6 + 10 + 12 = 28$.
$\therefore$ there must be 2 houses in neither B nor S.

b **i** There are 6 elements in B but not in S.
$\therefore$ 6 houses have a burglar alarm but not a security door.

ii There are $6 + 10 + 12 = 28$ elements in either B or S.
$\therefore$ 28 houses have either a burglar alarm or a security door.

EXERCISE 2E

1 A group of 26 people are discussing which drinks they like. 18 of them like iced tea, 20 of them like water, and 13 of them like both of these drinks.

a Place this information on a Venn diagram.

b How many people in the group:

  i like iced tea or water

  ii like water but not iced tea

  iii like iced tea but not water

  iv like neither iced tea nor water?

2 Nicola was inspecting her 45 apricot trees after a pest outbreak. She found that 17 trees had snails and 26 had aphids. 9 of the trees had both snails and aphids.

a Place this information on a Venn diagram.

b How many trees:

i had snails but not aphids **ii** were not affected by either pest

iii had snails or aphids, but not both?

3 Answer the **Opening Problem** on page **32**.

4 A pizza shop sells 15 types of pizza. 6 of them are vegetarian, and 5 are gluten free. 3 of them are both vegetarian and gluten free.

a Represent this information on a Venn diagram.

b How many pizza types are:

i vegetarian but not gluten free **ii** neither vegetarian nor gluten free

iii either vegetarian or gluten free, but not both?

5 In a class of 26 students, 13 own a smartphone, 9 own a laptop, and 5 own both items.

a Place this information on a Venn diagram.

b How many students in the class own:

i a smartphone but not a laptop **ii** neither a smartphone nor a laptop

iii a smartphone or a laptop?

6 Of the 32 nations that competed in the 2010 Soccer World Cup, 13 were European. 6 European nations advanced to the final 16 knockout stage of the World Cup.

a Represent this information on a Venn diagram.

b How many non-European nations competed in the World Cup?

c How many European nations were eliminated before the knockout stage?

d How many non-European nations advanced to the knockout stage?

7 In one night, a hospital admitted 43 emergency patients. 24 patients required stitches, and 21 patients required an X-ray. 6 patients required neither stitches nor an X-ray.

a Illustrate this information on a Venn diagram.

b How many of the patients required:

i both stitches and an X-ray

ii stitches but not an X-ray

iii either stitches or an X-ray, but not both?

ACTIVITY — 3 CIRCLE VENN DIAGRAMS

So far we have considered 2 circle Venn diagrams which show 2 sets within a universal set. We can add a third set by drawing an extra circle which overlaps both of the other two.

In this Activity you will construct your own 3 circle Venn diagram using information about what school activities the students in your class are involved in.

What to do:

1 Survey the students in your class to find out who:

PRINTABLE ACTIVITY

- plays a sport for the school
- plays a musical instrument at school
- is a member of a school club such as debating or drama.

Record your results in the table which you can print by clicking on the icon. Don't forget to include yourself!

2 Print the blank Venn diagram. Let:

S represent the students who play a sport for the school
M represent the students who play a musical instrument at school
C represent the students who are a member of a school club.

a Describe what the universal set U is.
b List individually the elements of S, M, and C.
c State in words, the meaning of $S \cap M \cap C$.
Write $n(S \cap M \cap C)$ in the centre region of the Venn diagram.
d State in words, the meaning of $(S \cup M \cup C)'$.
Write $n((S \cup M \cup C)')$ in the outer region of the Venn diagram.

3 Carefully fill in the other regions of the Venn diagram, by finding the number of students who:

a play sport and music, but are *not* in a club
b play sport and are in a club, but do *not* play music
c play music and are in a club, but do *not* play sport
d play sport but *not* music, and are *not* in a club
e play music but *not* sport, and are *not* in a club
f are in a club, but do *not* play sport or music.

4 Check your results with others in the class.

REVIEW SET 2A

1 Suppose $A = \{\text{factors of } 12\}$ and $B = \{\text{multiples of 2 less than } 10\}$.

a List the elements of A and B.
b Find: **i** $n(A)$ **ii** $n(B)$
c Is $B \subseteq A$?
d True or false? **i** $8 \in B$ **ii** $8 \in A$ **iii** $10 \notin A$

2 For the following sets, determine whether $X \subseteq Y$:

a $X = \{2, 4, 8\}$, $Y = \{1, 2, 3, 4, 6, 8\}$
b $X = \varnothing$, $Y = \{a, b, c, d, e\}$
c $X = \{\$, £, !, @\}$, $Y = \{\$, £, €, ¥, @\}$
d $X = \{\text{prime numbers between 10 and 20}\}$, $Y = \{\text{odd numbers between 10 and 20}\}$
e $X = \{\text{cats, dogs, ferrets, birds}\}$, $Y = \{\text{birds, cats, dogs, ferrets}\}$

3 Suppose $G = \{\text{multiples of 4 between 10 and 30}\}$, $H = \{\text{even numbers between 10 and 30}\}$, and $U = \{\text{whole numbers between 10 and 30}\}$.

a List the elements of: **i** G **ii** H.

b Find:

i $G \cap H$ **ii** $G \cup H$ **iii** $n(G \cap H)$ **iv** $n(G \cup H)$

c True or false?

i $22 \in G$ **ii** $24 \in G \cap H$ **iii** $18 \in G \cup H$ **iv** $26 \in G'$

4 List all subsets of $\{2, 4, 6\}$.

5 Suppose $S = \{\text{positive square numbers less than 50}\}$ and $E = \{\text{even numbers less than 20}\}$. Find $S \cap E$ and $S \cup E$.

6 Consider the set of whole numbers from 1 to 15.
Let $A = \{\text{factors of 15}\}$ and $B = \{\text{multiples of 3 less than 16}\}$.

a List the elements of:

i A **ii** B **iii** $A \cap B$ **iv** $A \cup B$

b Illustrate the sets A, B, and U on a Venn diagram.

7 Let $U = \{1, 2, 3, 4, 5, 6, 7, 8, 9\}$. Draw Venn diagrams to illustrate the following sets:

a $P = \{2, 5, 8, 9\}$ **b** $P = \{1, 4, 5, 6, 8\}$, $Q = \{2, 4, 6, 7\}$

c $P = \{3, 7\}$, $Q = \{1, 3, 4, 7, 8\}$ **d** $P = \{2, 6, 7\}$, $Q = \{1, 4, 9\}$

8 On separate Venn diagrams, shade the regions representing:

a in Y but not in X

b in neither X nor Y.

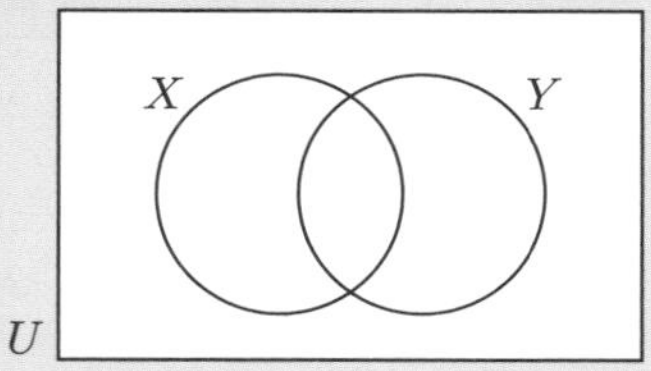

9

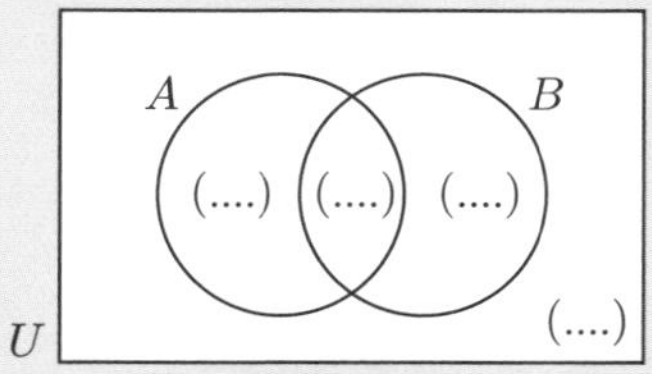

Suppose $n(A) = 12$, $n(B) = 10$, $n(A \cap B) = 3$, and $n(U) = 26$. Copy and complete the Venn diagram.

10 A class of 40 students attended their school's swimming and athletics carnivals. 28 students competed in swimming events, and 37 competed in athletics events. 25 students competed in both swimming and athletics events.

a Display this information on a Venn diagram.

b How many students competed in:

i the athletics carnival only

ii either swimming events or athletics events, but not both

iii none of the events?

REVIEW SET 2B

1 List the elements of the set of all:

a multiples of 6 between 0 and 50 **b** factors of 40.

2 Consider the set of uppercase letters in the English alphabet:

A B C D E F G H I J K L M N O P Q R S T U V W X Y Z

Let A be the set of letters which consist of straight edges only. Let V be the set of vowels.

a List the elements of: **i** A **ii** V.

b Find $A \cap V$.

3 List all subsets of $\{x, y\}$.

4 Suppose $C = \{\text{composite numbers less than or equal to } 20\}$. Find $n(C)$.

5 Let $U = \{1, 2, 3, 4, 5, 6, 7, 8, 9\}$, $A = \{3, 5, 7\}$, and $B = \{2, 3, 4, 5, 6, 7\}$.

a Find the complement of: **i** A **ii** B.

b Is $A \subseteq B$?

c Is $B' \subseteq A'$?

6 Suppose $A = \{3, 4, 5, 8\}$, $B = \{1, 3, 5, 9\}$, $C = \{2, 4, 6, 8\}$, and $D = \{1, 2, 6, 9\}$.
Which pairs of sets are disjoint?

7 Describe in words the shaded region:

a

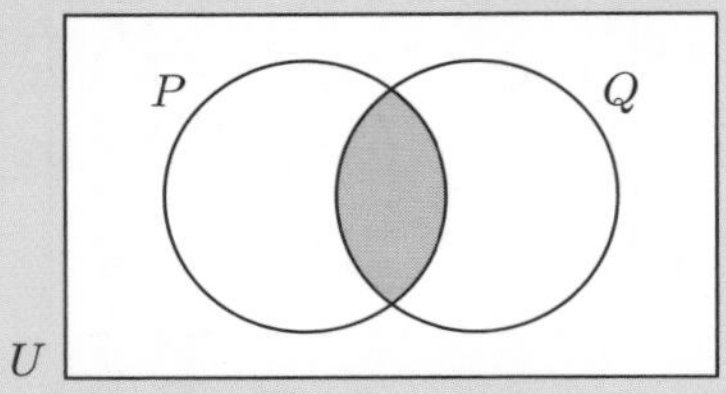

b

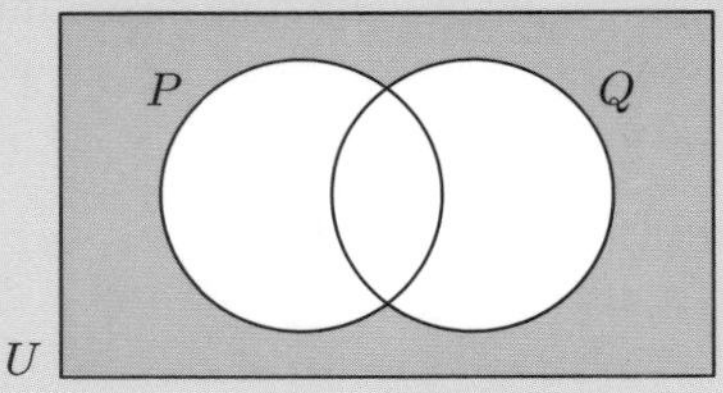

8 Suppose $S = \{\text{positive square numbers less than } 40\}$
and $P = \{\text{prime numbers less than } 40\}$.

Find: **a** $S \cup P$ **b** $S \cap P$.

9 Suppose $A = \{2, 3, 4, 5, 7, 9, 12, 15\}$, $B = \{2, 12, x, 9\}$, and $B \subseteq A$.
What possible values could x have?

10 In one week, an inspector visited 56 hotels.
12 of the hotels had fleas, and 7 of the hotels had rats. 40 hotels were free of these pests.

a Represent this information on a Venn diagram.

b How many hotels had:

i both fleas and rats

ii rats, but not fleas

iii either fleas or rats, but not both?

Chapter 3

Real numbers and ratio

Contents:

OPENING PROBLEM

Qi-Zheng has a circular pond with radius 1 m. He wants to know its surface area, so he asks his family for help. Their responses are given in the table below:

	Area (m^2)
Dad	3.14
Mum	$\frac{22}{7}$
Brother Qi-Ren	$\approx 3.141\,592\,653\,5\ldots$

Things to think about:

a Can all of the answers be illustrated on a number line?

b Use your calculator to write $\frac{22}{7}$ as a decimal. Can you write this decimal so it is *exactly* $\frac{22}{7}$?

c Consider the three answers in decimal form. In which answer does the decimal:

i keep repeating in a pattern **ii** stop or terminate

iii go on forever without repeating?

The set of **real numbers** includes all numbers which can be placed on the number line. It includes the set of whole numbers or **integers**, as well as the **fractions** and **decimals** between them.

In this chapter we first revise fractions and decimals. We will then see how the set of real numbers can also be divided into two groups: **rational** and **irrational**. Finally, we will study **ratios** which, like fractions, can be used to divide a whole into equal portions.

A FRACTIONS

In previous years we have seen how **fractions** are obtained when we divide a whole into equal portions.

The fraction $\frac{a}{b}$ means we divide a whole into b equal portions, and then consider a of them.

The division $a \div b$ can be written as the **fraction** $\frac{a}{b}$.

$\frac{a}{b}$
- a ← the **numerator** is the number of portions considered
- — ← the **bar** indicates division
- b ← the **denominator** is the number of portions we divide a whole into

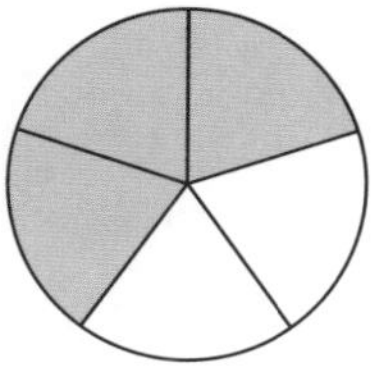

$\frac{3}{5}$ is shaded

A fraction written in the form $\frac{a}{b}$ is called a **common fraction**.

TYPES OF FRACTIONS

$\frac{2}{3}$ is called a **proper fraction** as the numerator is less than the denominator.

$\frac{4}{3}$ is called an **improper fraction** as the numerator is greater than the denominator.

$2\frac{1}{2}$ is a **mixed number** which represents $2+\frac{1}{2}$.

When we perform calculations involving mixed numbers, it is often useful to first convert the mixed number to an improper fraction.

Example 1 — Self Tutor

Convert $2\frac{1}{2}$ to an improper fraction.

$2\frac{1}{2}$

$= 2+\frac{1}{2}$

$= \frac{4}{2}+\frac{1}{2}$ {writing with equal denominators}

$= \frac{5}{2}$

NEGATIVE FRACTIONS

In **Chapter 1** we saw that whenever we divide a positive by a negative, or a negative by a positive, the result is a negative.

Since the bar of a fraction indicates division:

- the fraction $\frac{-1}{2}$ means $(-1) \div 2 = -\frac{1}{2}$
  (−1): negative, 2: positive, $-\frac{1}{2}$: negative
- the fraction $\frac{1}{-2}$ means $1 \div (-2) = -\frac{1}{2}$
  1: positive, (−2): negative, $-\frac{1}{2}$: negative

So, $\frac{-1}{2}=\frac{1}{-2}=-\frac{1}{2}$, and in general $\frac{-a}{b}=\frac{a}{-b}=-\frac{a}{b}$

PLACING FRACTIONS ON A NUMBER LINE

We can represent fractions on a **number line** by dividing each whole into the number of parts in the denominator. By extending the number line either side of zero, we can represent positive and negative fractions.

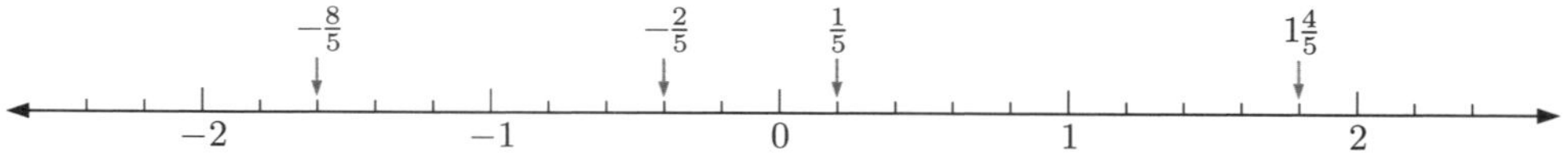

EXERCISE 3A.1

1 Describe the following as proper fractions, improper fractions, or mixed numbers:

a $\frac{2}{7}$ b $\frac{8}{5}$ c $\frac{7}{8}$ d $5\frac{1}{3}$ e $\frac{10}{9}$ f $1\frac{1}{2}$

2 Convert these mixed numbers to improper fractions:

a $1\frac{3}{4}$ **b** $3\frac{1}{2}$ **c** $4\frac{1}{5}$ **d** $2\frac{3}{8}$ **e** $-1\frac{1}{3}$ **f** $-3\frac{1}{5}$

3 Plot these fractions on a number line:

a $\frac{1}{3}, -\frac{2}{3}, \frac{5}{3}, -1\frac{1}{3}$ **b** $\frac{3}{7}, \frac{6}{7}, -\frac{2}{7}, 1\frac{4}{7}, -\frac{10}{7}$

4 Write as a division and hence evaluate:

a $\frac{-6}{3}$ **b** $\frac{6}{-3}$ **c** $-\frac{6}{3}$

EQUAL FRACTIONS

When we multiply or divide the numerator and denominator of a fraction by the same non-zero number, we obtain an **equal** or **equivalent** fraction.

For example, $\frac{1}{3} \overset{\times 2}{=} \frac{2}{6} \overset{\times 3}{=} \frac{6}{18}$, and $\frac{15}{20} \overset{\div 5}{=} \frac{3}{4}$.

Example 2 — Self Tutor

Express: **a** $\frac{3}{4}$ with denominator 32 **b** $\frac{24}{33}$ with denominator 11

a To convert the denominator to 32, we need to multiply by 8.
We must also multiply the numerator by 8.

$$\frac{3}{4} \overset{\times 8}{=} \frac{24}{32}$$

b To convert the denominator to 11, we need to divide by 3.
We must also divide the numerator by 3.

$$\frac{24}{33} \overset{\div 3}{=} \frac{8}{11}$$

SIMPLIFYING FRACTIONS

We can **simplify** a fraction by dividing the numerator and denominator by their **highest common factor**. When we have simplified a fraction in this manner, we say it is in **lowest terms**.

Example 3 — Self Tutor

Express in lowest terms: **a** $\frac{10}{25}$ **b** $-\frac{3}{24}$

a
$$\frac{10}{25}$$
$$= \frac{10 \div 5}{25 \div 5} \quad \{\text{HCF} = 5\}$$
$$= \frac{2}{5}$$

b
$$-\frac{3}{24}$$
$$= -\frac{3 \div 3}{24 \div 3} \quad \{\text{HCF} = 3\}$$
$$= -\frac{1}{8}$$

EXERCISE 3A.2

1 Write with denominator 20:

a $\frac{7}{10}$ **b** $\frac{3}{4}$ **c** $\frac{26}{40}$ **d** $\frac{15}{100}$

2 **a** Write the fractions $\frac{7}{10}$, $\frac{3}{5}$, and $\frac{2}{3}$ with denominator 30.

b Hence write the fractions in order from smallest to largest.

3 Express in lowest terms:

a $\frac{8}{12}$ **b** $\frac{15}{18}$ **c** $\frac{25}{15}$ **d** $\frac{21}{35}$ **e** $-\frac{2}{12}$

f $\frac{-5}{15}$ **g** $\frac{36}{48}$ **h** $\frac{8}{-20}$ **i** $\frac{22}{32}$ **j** $\frac{-42}{28}$

4 An enclosure at the zoo contains 16 meerkats. 6 are asleep and 10 are awake.
Find, in lowest terms, the fraction of meerkats that are:

a asleep **b** awake.

©iStockPhoto.com/pjmalsbury

5 27 beginners, 25 amateurs, and 8 professionals competed in a golf tournament.

a How many players competed in the tournament?

b Find, in lowest terms, the fraction of competitors who were:

i amateur **ii** professional **iii** either amateur or professional.

B OPERATIONS WITH FRACTIONS

ADDING AND SUBTRACTING FRACTIONS

To add or subtract fractions, we convert them to fractions with the **lowest common denominator**. This is the lowest common multiple of the original denominators. We then add or subtract the new numerators.

Example 4 Self Tutor

Find: **a** $\frac{3}{8}+\frac{1}{2}$ **b** $\frac{3}{4}-\frac{2}{3}+\frac{1}{2}$

a
$$\begin{aligned}&\frac{3}{8}+\frac{1}{2}\\ &=\frac{3}{8}+\frac{1\times 4}{2\times 4}\\ &=\frac{3}{8}+\frac{4}{8} \quad \{\text{LCD} = 8\}\\ &=\frac{7}{8} \quad \{\text{adding numerators}\}\end{aligned}$$

b
$$\begin{aligned}&\frac{3}{4}-\frac{2}{3}+\frac{1}{2}\\ &=\frac{3\times 3}{4\times 3}-\frac{2\times 4}{3\times 4}+\frac{1\times 6}{2\times 6}\\ &=\frac{9}{12}-\frac{8}{12}+\frac{6}{12} \quad \{\text{LCD} = 12\}\\ &=\frac{9-8+6}{12}\\ &=\frac{7}{12}\end{aligned}$$

Mixed numbers should be written as improper fractions before the addition or subtraction is performed.

Example 5 — Self Tutor

Find: $2\frac{1}{2} - 1\frac{2}{5}$

$$\begin{aligned} & 2\frac{1}{2} - 1\frac{2}{5} \\ &= \frac{5}{2} - \frac{7}{5} && \{\text{write as improper fractions}\} \\ &= \frac{5 \times 5}{2 \times 5} - \frac{7 \times 2}{5 \times 2} && \{\text{LCD} = 10\} \\ &= \frac{25}{10} - \frac{14}{10} \\ &= \frac{11}{10} \text{ or } 1\frac{1}{10} \end{aligned}$$

EXERCISE 3B.1

1 Find:

a $\frac{2}{9} + \frac{5}{9}$ b $\frac{8}{11} - \frac{3}{11}$ c $\frac{3}{5} + \frac{1}{10}$ d $\frac{1}{3} - \frac{1}{4}$

e $\frac{5}{8} + \frac{3}{4}$ f $\frac{5}{6} - \frac{3}{4}$ g $\frac{4}{7} + \frac{4}{5}$ h $\frac{1}{2} - \frac{5}{9}$

2 Find:

a $\frac{7}{9} + \frac{2}{3} - \frac{2}{9}$ b $\frac{7}{4} - \frac{7}{8} + \frac{1}{2}$ c $\frac{19}{15} - \frac{4}{5} + \frac{3}{10}$ d $\frac{1}{5} + \frac{1}{4} - \frac{1}{3}$

3 Find:

a $1 - \frac{3}{7}$ b $-\frac{1}{2} + \frac{3}{4}$ c $1\frac{1}{4} + \frac{5}{8}$ d $-\frac{5}{7} + \frac{1}{3}$

e $3 - 1\frac{3}{5}$ f $1 - \frac{1}{6} - \frac{3}{8}$ g $2\frac{2}{5} - 1\frac{4}{9}$ h $2 - \frac{3}{4} - \frac{4}{5}$

4 Carter read $\frac{1}{5}$ of a book during a flight from Quebec to Calgary, and another $\frac{3}{8}$ of the book during the flight back.

a What fraction of the book has Carter read?

b What fraction of the book remains for Carter to read?

5 A recipe requires $\frac{2}{3}$ cup of self-raising flour, and $1\frac{1}{2}$ cups of plain flour.

a In total, how much flour is used in the recipe?

b How much more plain flour is used than self-raising flour?

6 Use your calculator to evaluate:

a $\frac{1}{5} + \frac{1}{6} + \frac{1}{7}$ b $\frac{1}{8} + \frac{7}{10} - \frac{29}{30}$

MULTIPLYING AND DIVIDING FRACTIONS

To **multiply** two fractions, we multiply the numerators together and multiply the denominators together.

$$\frac{a}{b} \times \frac{c}{d} = \frac{a \times c}{b \times d}$$

Example 6 — Self Tutor

Find: **a** $\frac{3}{7} \times \frac{2}{5}$ **b** $1\frac{1}{3} \times \frac{3}{5}$

a $\frac{3}{7} \times \frac{2}{5}$
$= \frac{3 \times 2}{7 \times 5}$
$= \frac{6}{35}$

b $1\frac{1}{3} \times \frac{3}{5}$
$= \frac{4}{\cancel{3}_1} \times \frac{\cancel{3}^1}{5}$
$= \frac{4}{5}$

We cancel any common factors in the numerator and denominator before completing the multiplication.

For any fraction $\frac{a}{b}$, we notice that $\frac{a}{b} \times \frac{b}{a} = 1$.

$\frac{a}{b}$ and $\frac{b}{a}$ are called **reciprocals** because their product is one.

The reciprocal of any fraction is obtained by swapping its numerator and denominator.

To **divide** by a fraction, we multiply by the **reciprocal** of that fraction.

$$\frac{a}{b} \div \frac{c}{d} = \frac{a}{b} \times \frac{d}{c}$$

Example 7 — Self Tutor

Find: **a** $4 \div \frac{1}{3}$ **b** $1\frac{1}{3} \div \frac{2}{5}$

a $4 \div \frac{1}{3}$
$= 4 \times \frac{3}{1}$
$= 4 \times 3$
$= 12$

b $1\frac{1}{3} \div \frac{2}{5}$
$= \frac{4}{3} \div \frac{2}{5}$
$= \frac{{}^2\cancel{4}}{3} \times \frac{5}{\cancel{2}_1}$
$= \frac{10}{3}$
$= 3\frac{1}{3}$

EXERCISE 3B.2

1 Find:

a $\frac{2}{3} \times \frac{4}{5}$ **b** $\frac{3}{4} \times \frac{5}{7}$ **c** $4 \times \frac{3}{5}$ **d** $\frac{1}{4} \times 5$

e $1\frac{1}{2} \times \frac{2}{7}$ **f** $1\frac{5}{8} \times \frac{3}{10}$ **g** $\left(\frac{1}{2}\right)^2$ **h** $\left(\frac{2}{3}\right)^3$

i $\left(2\frac{1}{5}\right)^2$ **j** $\left(\frac{1}{3}\right)^2 \times 6$ **k** $8 \times \left(\frac{1}{2}\right)^3$ **l** $1\frac{1}{2} \times 2\frac{2}{3}$

2 Evaluate:

a $\frac{3}{4} \div \frac{5}{7}$ **b** $\frac{1}{3} \div \frac{1}{8}$ **c** $\frac{11}{12} \div \frac{2}{3}$ **d** $\frac{5}{6} \div 3$

e $8 \div \frac{4}{5}$ **f** $1\frac{1}{3} \div \frac{3}{4}$ **g** $\frac{3}{5} \div 1\frac{1}{2}$ **h** $1\frac{2}{3} \div 2\frac{3}{4}$

3 Find:

a $-\frac{4}{5} \times \frac{2}{3}$ **b** $2\frac{1}{4} \times \left(-\frac{1}{3}\right)$ **c** $-\frac{3}{7} \div \frac{5}{6}$ **d** $-2\frac{1}{3} \div \frac{4}{5}$

Example 8 **Self Tutor**

During a season, Joe hit $\frac{2}{5}$ of the home runs for his team.

How many home runs did he hit if there were 40 scored in total?

Joe hit $\frac{2}{5}$ of $40 = \frac{2}{5} \times 40$

$= \frac{2 \times \cancel{40}^{8}}{\cancel{5}_{1}}$

$= 16$ home runs.

Remember that 'of' means '×'.

4 Find:

a $\frac{2}{5}$ of 50 **b** $\frac{3}{8}$ of 24 **c** $\frac{5}{7}$ of 35

d $\frac{1}{4}$ of \$60 **e** $\frac{5}{6}$ of 30 m **f** $\frac{7}{10}$ of 80 kg

5 Lee is travelling 700 km from Barcelona to Monaco. He stops at Marseille, having travelled $\frac{7}{10}$ of the way. How far has Lee travelled?

6 $\frac{2}{5}$ of the money raised at a charity event is given to the local hospital. The hospital spends $\frac{3}{4}$ of their money on a new X-ray machine. What fraction of the total money raised by the charity was spent on the X-ray machine?

7 Tina uses $\frac{2}{3}$ tablespoon of butter to make an apricot loaf. How many loaves can she make with 4 tablespoons of butter?

BUTTER
FLOUR

8 Trevor ate $\frac{1}{9}$ of a lasagne. Eleanor ate $\frac{1}{6}$ of what remained.

- **a** What fraction of the lasagne did Eleanor eat?
- **b** What fraction of the lasagne now remains?

9 Emma buys two identical bottles of shampoo. She uses $\frac{3}{8}$ of one of them at home, and uses $\frac{7}{10}$ of all of the remaining shampoo while she is on holidays. In total, how much shampoo remains?

10 Use your calculator to evaluate:

a $5\frac{1}{9} \div \frac{2}{3}$ **b** $\dfrac{\frac{1}{3}+\frac{2}{5}}{6-\frac{4}{7}}$ **c** $\left(\frac{2}{3}\right)^4$

C DECIMAL NUMBERS

A **decimal number** is a number which contains a decimal point. We can use decimal numbers to display fractions of whole numbers.

For example:

- 4.63 is a quick way of writing $4+\frac{6}{10}+\frac{3}{100}$. This number can also be written as the **improper fraction** $\frac{463}{100}$ or as the **mixed number** $4\frac{63}{100}$.
- 14.062 is a quick way of writing $14+\frac{6}{100}+\frac{2}{1000}$.

Expansions of decimals like those above are referred to as **expanded fractional form**.

Example 9 **Self Tutor**

a Write 5.704 in expanded fractional form.

b Write $3+\frac{2}{10}+\frac{4}{100}+\frac{1}{10\,000}$ in decimal form.

c State the value of the digit 6 in 0.036 24

a $5.704 = 5+\frac{7}{10}+\frac{4}{1000}$

b $3+\frac{2}{10}+\frac{4}{100}+\frac{1}{10\,000} = 3.2401$

c In 0.036 24, the 6 stands for $\frac{6}{1000}$.

CONVERTING DECIMALS TO FRACTIONS

We can use our knowledge of decimal place values to convert decimals to fractions.

Example 10 **Self Tutor**

Write as fractions:

a 0.6 **b** 0.045

a $0.6 = \frac{6}{10}$

$= \frac{6 \div 2}{10 \div 2}$

$= \frac{3}{5}$

b $0.045 = \frac{45}{1000}$

$= \frac{45 \div 5}{1000 \div 5}$

$= \frac{9}{200}$

PLACING DECIMALS ON A NUMBER LINE

To represent decimal numbers on a number line, we choose the scale according to the lowest decimal place value.

For example, when representing $\{0.2, 0.9, 1.3, 1.8\}$, the lowest place value is tenths. We divide each whole into tenths.

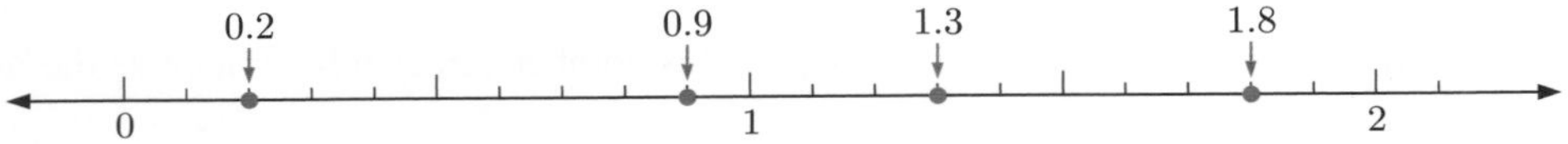

Extending the number line in both directions allows us to represent **negative decimal numbers**:

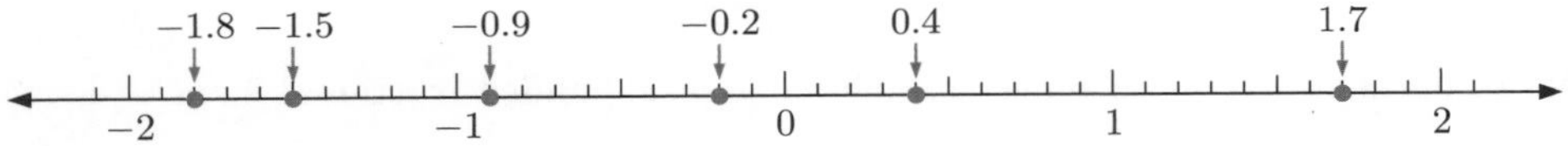

EXERCISE 3C.1

1 Write in expanded fractional form:

a 1.2 **b** 1.02 **c** 1.0234 **d** 9.0909 **e** 0.0382

2 Write in decimal form:

a $4 + \frac{5}{10}$ **b** $2 + \frac{6}{10} + \frac{9}{100}$ **c** $\frac{5}{10} + \frac{2}{1000}$

d $\frac{3}{100} + \frac{8}{1000}$ **e** $2 + \frac{5}{1000}$ **f** $4 + \frac{1}{100} + \frac{4}{10\,000}$

3 State the value of the digit 7:

a 7295 **b** 571 **c** 0.724 **d** 0.078 **e** 0.000 237

4 Write as fractions in simplest form:

a 0.2 **b** 0.17 **c** 0.74 **d** 0.04

e 0.025 **f** 0.008 **g** 0.625 **h** −0.8

5 Place these decimal numbers on a number line:

a 0.4, 0.7, 1.1, 1.5 **b** 0.5, −0.3, −0.6, 1.2, −1.4 **c** 0.1, 0.35, 0.6, 0.95

ROUNDING DECIMAL NUMBERS

We often round decimal numbers to a certain level of accuracy.

For example, if you wish to record your weight in kilograms, you will probably round the result to the nearest whole number, or to 1 decimal place.

In general, decimal numbers can be rounded to a certain number of **decimal places**, or to a certain number of **significant figures**.

RULES FOR ROUNDING

- If the digit after the one being rounded is **less than 5**, we round **down**.
- If the digit after the one being rounded is **5 or more**, we round **up**.

Example 11 Self Tutor

Round 39.748 to:

a the nearest whole number **b** 1 decimal place **c** 2 decimal places.

a $39.748 \approx 40$ {the first decimal place is 7, so round up}
b $39.748 \approx 39.7$ {the second decimal place is 4, so round down}
c $39.748 \approx 39.75$ {the third decimal place is 8, so round up}

Example 12 Self Tutor

Round:

a 4.3765 to 3 significant figures
b 503.4171 to 4 significant figures
c 0.080 51 to 2 significant figures.

a $4.3765 \approx 4.38$ {the fourth significant figure is 6, so round up}
b $503.4171 \approx 503.4$ {the fifth significant figure is 1, so round down}
c $0.080\,51 \approx 0.081$ {the third significant figure is 5, so round up}

We count significant figures from the first non-zero digit.

EXERCISE 3C.2

1 Round to the nearest whole number:
a 6.326 **b** 7.543 **c** 18.72 **d** 199.6

2 Round to 1 decimal place:
a 4.21 **b** 6.39 **c** 11.54 **d** 6.87

3 Round to 2 decimal places:
a 7.542 **b** 3.967 **c** 2.1649 **d** 8.995

4 Round to 3 significant figures:
a 5.2374 **b** 37.1356 **c** 0.2409 **d** 0.019 25

5 Round to 4 significant figures:

 a 27.0394 **b** 0.257 24 **c** 4.001 87 **d** 0.010 200 38

6 **a** Use your calculator to find the value of $\frac{2}{43}$.

 b Round this value to: **i** 4 decimal places **ii** 2 significant figures.

7 **a** Round 0.945 to 1 decimal place.

 b Round 0.945 to 2 decimal places, and then the *result* to 1 decimal place.

 c Discuss your results with your class.

D OPERATIONS WITH DECIMAL NUMBERS

ADDING AND SUBTRACTING DECIMAL NUMBERS

To add or subtract decimal numbers, we write the numbers under one another so that the decimal points line up. We then add or subtract as we do with whole numbers.

The zero at the end of 15.3 is added so the numbers have the same number of decimal places.

Example 13	◄)) Self Tutor

Find $15.3 + 9.26$.

$$
\begin{array}{r}
1\,5\,.\,3\,0 \\
+\ \ \ 9\,.\,2\,6 \\
\scriptstyle 1 \\
\hline
2\,4\,.\,5\,6
\end{array}
$$

Example 14	◄)) Self Tutor

Find: **a** $4.632 - 1.507$ **b** $8 - 0.706$

All of the decimal points must line up.

a
$$
\begin{array}{r}
{\scriptstyle 2\ 12} \\
4\,.\,6\,\cancel{3}\,\cancel{2} \\
-\ 1\,.\,5\,0\,7 \\
\hline
3\,.\,1\,2\,5
\end{array}
$$
Place the decimal points directly under one another and subtract as for whole numbers.

b
$$
\begin{array}{r}
{\scriptstyle 7\ \ 9\ 9\ 10} \\
\cancel{8}\,.\,\cancel{0}\cancel{0}\cancel{0} \\
-\ 0\,.\,7\,0\,6 \\
\hline
7\,.\,2\,9\,4
\end{array}
$$
We insert .000 after the 8 so we have the same number of decimal places in both numbers.

EXERCISE 3D.1

1 Find:

 a $2.31 + 4.57$ **b** $4.9 + 6.3$ **c** $14.2 + 8.64$

 d $19.876 + 5.1$ **e** $3.2 + 5.1 + 4.8$ **f** $21.3 + 4.78 + 3.9$

 g $3.92 + 4.076$ **h** $22.019 + 9.3042$ **i** $37.9 + 1.576 + 0.49$

2 Find:

a $7.84-3.22$	**b** $9.8-5.36$	**c** $11.58-3.7$
d $17-4.85$	**e** $14-9.227$	**f** $26.702-18.8$
g $47.08-3.942$	**h** $1.9-0.137$	**i** $0.032-0.005\,79$

3 For an interstate holiday, Tony has packed a suitcase weighing 11.6 kg, and a backpack weighing 6.75 kg. Find the total weight of Tony's luggage.

4 In a long jump competition, Samantha jumped 5.23 m. This was 1.37 m further than Theresa's jump. How far did Theresa jump?

5 At the supermarket, Margaret bought a tub of margarine for \$2.49, a carton of milk for \$1.86, and a bottle of sunscreen for \$14.90.

a How much did Margaret spend?

b How much change will she receive from a \$20 note?

MULTIPLYING AND DIVIDING BY POWERS OF 10

When **multiplying** by a power of 10, we shift the decimal point to the **right**.

When **dividing** by a power of 10, we shift the decimal point to the **left**.

For example: $0.38\times 10=3.8$ $\quad$ $0.38\div 10=0.038$

$0.38\times 100=38$ $\quad$ $00.38\div 100=0.0038$

MULTIPLICATION AND DIVISION OF DECIMAL NUMBERS

To **multiply** decimal numbers, we multiply the numbers as though they were whole numbers, then divide by the appropriate power of 10.

Example 15 — Self Tutor

Find 0.3×0.15.

$$\begin{aligned}0.3\times 0.15&=(3\div 10)\times(15\div 100)\\&=(3\times 15)\div(10\times 100)\\&=45\div 1000\\&=0.045\quad\{\text{shifting the decimal 3 places left}\}\end{aligned}$$

To **divide** decimal numbers, we write the division as a fraction, then multiply the numerator and denominator by the same power of 10 to make the denominator a whole number. We then perform the division.

Example 16 — Self Tutor

Find:

a $2.7 \div 0.3$ b $0.002 \div 0.08$

a $2.7 \div 0.3$

$= \dfrac{2.7 \times 10}{0.3 \times 10}$

$= \dfrac{27}{3}$

$= 9$

b $0.002 \div 0.08$

$= \dfrac{0.002 \times 100}{0.08 \times 100}$

$= \dfrac{0.2}{8}$

$= 0.025$

$$8 \overline{)\,0.2\,0^{4}0\,} = 0.025$$

EXERCISE 3D.2

1 Find:

a 5.7×10 b 0.046×100 c $0.06 \times 10\,000$
d $0.000\,01 \times 1000$ e $7 \div 100$ f $3.2 \div 1000$
g $0.022 \div 10$ h $0.091 \div 10\,000$ i $2.005 \div 10\,000$

2 Find:

a 6×0.8 b 0.7×9 c 0.9×0.4
d 1.2×0.7 e 0.6×0.15 f 0.08×0.11
g -0.5×12 h $0.3 \times (-0.4)$ i $(-0.9) \times (-0.8)$

3 Find:

a $1.6 \div 0.2$ b $4 \div 0.8$ c $0.56 \div 0.07$
d $2 \div 0.05$ e $0.03 \div 0.2$ f $0.006 \div 0.03$
g $0.0008 \div 0.05$ h $-1.7 \div 0.1$ i $(-4.2) \div (-0.7)$

4 Dominic drank 2.2 litres of water each day for 8 days. How much water did he drink in this time?

5 A mother duck weighs 2.8 kg. Her baby duckling weighs 0.7 kg. How many times heavier is the mother than her baby?

6 Each kilogram of beef contains 0.8 grams of cholesterol. How many grams of cholesterol are in a 0.250 kg serving of beef?

7 A drinks machine contains 90 litres of water. How many 0.3 litre cups of water can be filled from the machine?

8 Bernard buys 4 bottles of water costing \$2.35 each, and 3 fruit bars costing \$1.15 each. How much money has Bernard spent altogether?

INVESTIGATION 1 — DIVISION BY ZERO

When we divide by positive numbers greater than 1, the result is always smaller than the original number we divided.

For example, when we divide 12 by 2, the result 6 is smaller than the original number 12.

In this Investigation we consider what happens when we divide by positive numbers smaller than 1, and what happens as this number gets closer and closer to zero.

What to do:

1 Evaluate:

a $1 \div \frac{1}{2}$ **b** $1 \div \frac{1}{5}$ **c** $1 \div \frac{1}{10}$ **d** $1 \div \frac{1}{100}$

2 Evaluate:

a $2 \div 0.4$ **b** $2 \div 0.1$ **c** $2 \div 0.05$ **d** $2 \div 0.001$

3 Copy and complete:
As the number we are dividing by gets smaller and smaller, the result gets ......

4 **a** Copy and complete:
i Since $\frac{6}{3} = 2$, $3 \times 2 = ...$
ii Since $\frac{6}{2} = 3$, $2 \times 3 = ...$
iii Since $\frac{6}{1} = 6$, $1 \times 6 = ...$
iv If $\frac{6}{0} = a$, $0 \times a = ...$

b In **iv** above, we are saying that if $\frac{6}{0}$ is equal to some number a, then $0 = 6$.
Do you agree with this deduction?

c What can we conclude from **b**?

E RATIONAL NUMBERS

A **rational number** is a number that can be written in the form $\frac{a}{b}$, where a and b are integers and $b \neq 0$.

Proper fractions such as $\frac{2}{5}$, improper fractions such as $\frac{7}{4}$, and mixed numbers such as $1\frac{1}{2} = \frac{3}{2}$ are all examples of rational numbers.

Whole numbers such as 5 and -3 are also rational, since $5 = \frac{5}{1}$ and $-3 = \frac{-3}{1}$.

DECIMAL REPRESENTATION OF RATIONAL NUMBERS

We can express any rational number in decimal form. For example, we can write $\frac{1}{2}$ as 0.5.

When we convert rational numbers to decimal form, the result may either be a **terminating decimal** or a **recurring decimal**.

TERMINATING DECIMALS

A **terminating decimal** has only a finite number of non-zero digits after the decimal place.

For example, 4.256 is a terminating decimal, as it finishes or terminates after 3 decimal places.

When written in lowest terms, a rational number will convert to a **terminating decimal** if its denominator has no prime factors other than 2 or 5.

For example, $\frac{7}{20}$ has denominator $20 = 2^2 \times 5$, which has only 2 and 5 as its prime factors.

So, $\frac{7}{20}$ converts to a terminating decimal. In fact, $\frac{7}{20} = 0.35$.

We can convert fractions like these to terminating decimals by first writing the fraction so its denominator is a power of 10.

Example 17 — Self Tutor

Write the following in decimal form:

a $\frac{3}{5}$ **b** $\frac{7}{25}$ **c** $\frac{5}{8}$

a $\frac{3}{5} = \frac{3 \times 2}{5 \times 2} = \frac{6}{10} = 0.6$

b $\frac{7}{25} = \frac{7 \times 4}{25 \times 4} = \frac{28}{100} = 0.28$

c $\frac{5}{8} = \frac{5 \times 125}{8 \times 125} = \frac{625}{1000} = 0.625$

RECURRING DECIMALS

If you enter $1 \div 3$ into your calculator, your calculator will give the answer $\frac{1}{3} = 0.333\,333\,333$. Your calculator can only show a finite number of digits, but the series of 3s after the decimal actually continues forever. This is an example of a **recurring decimal**.

Recurring decimals repeat the same sequence of digits without stopping.

A rational number in lowest terms will convert to a **recurring decimal** if its denominator has at least one prime factor other than 2 or 5.

For example, $\frac{8}{11} = 0.727\,272\,72....$ is a recurring decimal since the denominator has the prime factor 11.

We indicate a recurring decimal with a line over the repeated digits.

For example, $\frac{1}{3} = 0.\overline{3}$ and $\frac{8}{11} = 0.\overline{72}$.

There may be some non-repeating digits in the decimal before the repeating digits start.

For example, $\frac{5}{6} = 0.833\,33.... = 0.8\overline{3}$.

Example 18 **Self Tutor**

Write as decimals: **a** $\frac{7}{9}$ **b** $\frac{5}{11}$

a $\frac{7}{9}$

$= 0.7777....$

$= 0.\overline{7}$

$$9\,\overline{)\,7\,.\,0\,^{7}0\,^{7}0\,^{7}0\,....}\quad = 0\,.\,7\,7\,7\,7\,....$$

b $\frac{5}{11}$

$= 0.454\,545....$

$= 0.\overline{45}$

$$11\,\overline{)\,5\,.\,0\,^{6}0\,^{5}0\,^{6}0\,^{5}0\,....}\quad = 0\,.\,4\,5\,4\,5\,4\,....$$

Some decimals take a long time to recur. For example,
$\frac{1}{17} = 0.\overline{0588235294117647}$

EXERCISE 3E

1 Show that the following numbers are rational by writing them in the form $\frac{a}{b}$, where a and b are integers.

a $1\frac{1}{3}$ **b** 7 **c** $\sqrt{36}$ **d** -4

e 0.3 **f** $-2\frac{3}{4}$ **g** $\frac{\sqrt{49}}{\sqrt{9}}$ **h** 0.01

2 Without converting them, state whether these rational numbers will convert to a terminating decimal or a recurring decimal.

a $\frac{3}{10}$ **b** $\frac{2}{3}$ **c** $\frac{4}{25}$ **d** $\frac{13}{40}$

e $\frac{2}{7}$ **f** $\frac{5}{16}$ **g** $\frac{4}{45}$ **h** $\frac{75}{81}$

3 Use your calculator to convert each fraction in **2** to a decimal, and hence check your answers.

4 Convert each fraction to a terminating decimal:

a $\frac{9}{10}$ **b** $\frac{17}{20}$ **c** $\frac{2}{5}$ **d** $\frac{3}{25}$ **e** $\frac{31}{50}$ **f** $\frac{3}{8}$

5 Convert each fraction to a recurring decimal:

a $\frac{1}{3}$ **b** $\frac{7}{9}$ **c** $\frac{4}{11}$ **d** $\frac{1}{6}$ **e** $\frac{4}{7}$

6 Use your calculator to write each fraction as a recurring decimal:

a $\frac{6}{37}$ **b** $\frac{20}{27}$ **c** $\frac{13}{30}$ **d** $\frac{15}{22}$ **e** $\frac{123}{185}$

7 Oliver notices that $\frac{9}{15}$ has a prime factor of 3 in the denominator, so he thinks the fraction will convert to a recurring decimal.
However, when he enters it into his calculator, he finds that $\frac{9}{15} = 0.6$.
Can you explain Oliver's mistake?

DISCUSSION

We have seen that $0.\overline{3} = \frac{1}{3}$. What can we say about $0.\overline{9}$?

F IRRATIONAL NUMBERS

An **irrational number** is a number that **cannot** be written in the form $\frac{a}{b}$, where a and b are integers.

An example of an irrational number is $\sqrt{2} \approx 1.414\,213\,56.....$ The fraction $\frac{99}{70} = 1.4\overline{142\,857}$ is sometimes used to *approximate* $\sqrt{2}$, but it is not exact.

Another example of an irrational number is $\pi \approx 3.141\,59....$, read as 'pi'.

In the **Opening Problem**, Qi-Zheng was calculating the surface area of a circular pond with radius 1 m. His family helped him with different approximations, but the exact answer he wanted was π m^2. Interestingly, the distance around the boundary of the pond is actually 2π m!

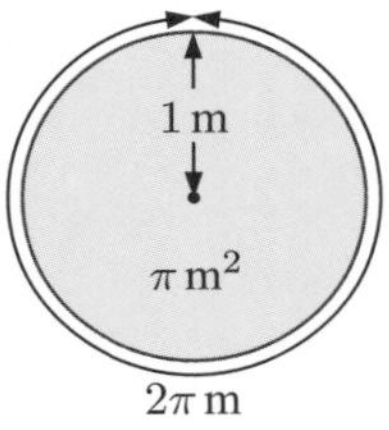

Together, the rational numbers and irrational numbers make up the set of all **real numbers** which can be placed on a number line.

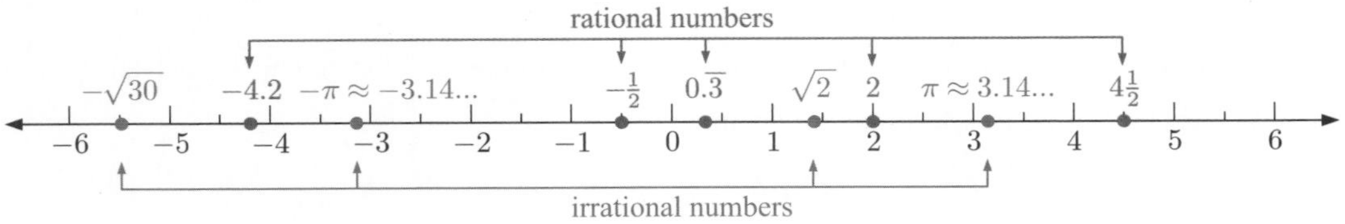

DECIMAL REPRESENTATION OF IRRATIONAL NUMBERS

In **Section E**, we saw that a rational number converts to either a terminating decimal or a recurring decimal.

The decimal representation of an irrational number neither terminates nor recurs.

For example, the first 30 decimal places of π are:

$\pi \approx 3.141\,592\,653\,589\,793\,238\,462\,643\,383\,279.....$

We could keep writing these digits forever, and they would never terminate nor get into a loop of repeating digits.

A computer has been used to calculate π to 5 trillion decimal places!

INVESTIGATION 2 DECIMAL REPRESENTATION OF $\sqrt{20}$

In this Investigation we will consider the decimal representation of $\sqrt{20}$, which is an irrational number.

$\sqrt{20}$ is the number which, when squared, gives 20.

Now, $4^2 = 16$ and $5^2 = 25$, so $\sqrt{20}$ is between 4 and 5.

Also, $4.4^2 = 19.36$ and $4.5^2 = 20.25$, so $\sqrt{20}$ is between 4.4 and 4.5. Thus, $\sqrt{20} \approx 4.4.....$

What to do:

1. Show that $\sqrt{20}$ is between 4.47 and 4.48, and so $\sqrt{20} \approx 4.47.....$
2. Find the first 6 decimal places of $\sqrt{20}$. Check your answer by evaluating $\sqrt{20}$ on your calculator.
3. Can you see how we could keep finding more decimal places indefinitely?

EXERCISE 3F

1. State whether the following numbers are rational or irrational. It may help to view the numbers in decimal form using your calculator.
   - **a** $\frac{5}{6}$
   - **b** $\sqrt{5}$
   - **c** $0.\overline{2}$
   - **d** π
   - **e** $\sqrt{4}$
   - **f** $\pi - 2$
   - **g** -3
   - **h** $\sqrt{2} - 2$
2. Place the numbers in **1** on a number line.
3. Suppose a certain number is irrational. Are the following statements true or false?
   - **a** The negative of the number must also be irrational.
   - **b** 3 more than the number must also be irrational.
   - **c** Double the number must also be irrational.
   - **d** The square of the number must also be irrational.
4. Give an example of an irrational number between 0 and 1.
5. Is the sum of two irrational numbers always irrational? Explain your answer.

DISCUSSION

- Can you show that there are infinitely many rational numbers?
- Are there infinitely many irrational numbers?
- Are there more rational numbers than irrational numbers?

G RATIO

A **ratio** is an ordered comparison of quantities of the **same kind**.

Ned wants to paint his fence green. He is told to mix "two parts blue paint with one part yellow paint". So, he mixes two cans of blue paint with one can of yellow paint.

We say that the **ratio** of blue paint to yellow paint is 2 : 1, or "2 is to 1".

The actual quantities of blue paint and yellow paint used are not important. As long as the paints are combined in the correct *ratio*, Ned will get the correct shade of green paint.

Ratios may involve more than two quantities.

For example, to make a certain strength of concrete, you need 1 bucket of cement, 2 buckets of sand, and 4 buckets of gravel.

The ratio of cement to sand to gravel is 1 : 2 : 4, which we read as "1 is to 2 is to 4".

Example 19 **Self Tutor**

Express as a ratio: 9 mm is to 2 cm.

$$9 \text{ mm} : 2 \text{ cm} = 9 \text{ mm} : 20 \text{ mm}$$
$$= 9 : 20$$

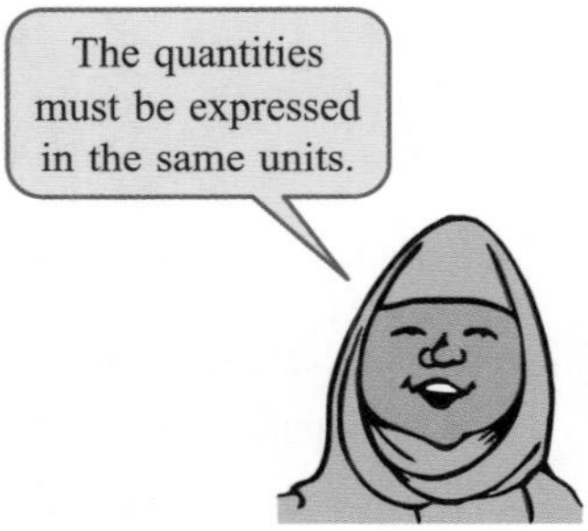
The quantities
must be expressed
in the same units.

EXERCISE 3G.1

1 Express as a ratio:

a 6 mL is to 11 mL
b 5 kg is to 2 kg
c 12 m is to 25 m
d \$1 is to \$3 is to \$8
e 2 kg is to 5 kg is to 9 kg

2 Find the ratio of:

a pens to pencils

b knives to forks to spoons

3 What is the ratio of vowels to consonants in the English alphabet?

4 Express as a ratio:

 a 93 cm is to 1 m

 c 14 mm is to 3.1 cm

 e 23 seconds is to 2 minutes

 b 3 years is to 11 months

 d 4 hours is to 80 minutes

 f 300 g is to 0.006 kg

1 m = 100 cm
1 cm = 10 mm
1 kg = 1000 g

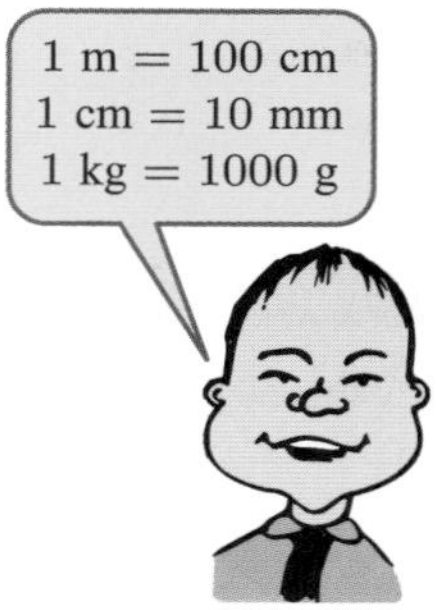

EQUAL RATIOS

> If we multiply or divide both parts of a ratio by the same non-zero number, we obtain an **equal ratio**.

For example,

$$2 : 3 \overset{\times 2}{\underset{\times 2}{=}} 4 : 6 \qquad \text{and} \qquad 21 : 15 \overset{\div 3}{\underset{\div 3}{=}} 7 : 5$$

Ratios can be expressed in **simplest form** by writing an *equal* ratio with integer parts that are as small as possible.

Example 20　　　　　　　　　　　　　　　　　　　　　　　　◀» **Self Tutor**

Write the following ratios in simplest form:

 a $45 : 15$　　　　　　　　**b** $2\frac{1}{2} : \frac{1}{2}$　　　　　　　　**c** $0.4 : 1.4$

 a　$45 : 15$
$= 45 \div 15 : 15 \div 15$
$= 3 : 1$

 b　$2\frac{1}{2} : \frac{1}{2}$
$= \frac{5}{2} : \frac{1}{2}$
$= \frac{5}{2} \times 2 : \frac{1}{2} \times 2$
$= 5 : 1$

 c　$0.4 : 1.4$
$= 0.4 \times 10 : 1.4 \times 10$
$= 4 : 14$
$= 4 \div 2 : 14 \div 2$
$= 2 : 7$

EXERCISE 3G.2

1 Write in simplest form:

 a $3 : 12$　　　**b** $16 : 8$　　　**c** $5 : 30$　　　**d** $6 : 9$　　　**e** $35 : 15$

 f $24 : 40$　　　**g** $63 : 49$　　　**h** $80 : 90$　　　**i** $600 : 800$　　　**j** $250 : 120$

2 Write in simplest form:

 a $\frac{2}{3} : \frac{5}{3}$　　　　　**b** $\frac{5}{2} : \frac{1}{2}$　　　　　**c** $1 : \frac{1}{4}$　　　　　**d** $2 : \frac{2}{7}$

 e $\frac{1}{8} : 3$　　　　　**f** $2 : \frac{1}{2}$　　　　　**g** $4\frac{1}{2} : 9$　　　　　**h** $1\frac{1}{5} : 2\frac{1}{5}$

3 Write in simplest form:

- **a** 0.1 : 0.3
- **b** 0.4 : 0.7
- **c** 1.1 : 0.9
- **d** 0.4 : 0.8
- **e** 1.6 : 0.4
- **f** 1.2 : 1.8

Example 21 **Self Tutor**

Write as a ratio in simplest form: 10 days is to 2 weeks.

$$\begin{aligned} 10 \text{ days} : 2 \text{ weeks} &= 10 \text{ days} : 14 \text{ days} \\ &= 10 : 14 \\ &= 10 \div 2 : 14 \div 2 \\ &= 5 : 7 \end{aligned}$$

Convert to the same units, then simplify.

4 Write as a ratio in simplest form:

- **a** 8 mm is to 1 cm
- **b** 16 months is to 2 years
- **c** 90 cm is to 2.1 m
- **d** 45 minutes is to 4 hours
- **e** 3.6 kg is to 900 g
- **f** 80 min is to 2 h 20 min

PROPORTIONS

A **proportion** is a statement that two ratios are equal.

For example, the statement that $6 : 15 = 12 : 30$ is a proportion.

Example 22 **Self Tutor**

Find $\square$ to complete the proportion $3 : 5 = 18 : \square$.

$3 : 5 = 18 : \square$

$\therefore\ 3 : 5 = 18 : \square$ (×6 from 3 to 18, ×6 from 5 to $\square$)

$\therefore\ \square = 5 \times 6 = 30$

To get from 3 to 18 we multiply by 6.
We therefore multiply by 6 to get the second number.

EXERCISE 3G.3

1 Find the missing number in each proportion:

- **a** $3 : 4 = 6 : \square$
- **b** $3 : 6 = 12 : \square$
- **c** $5 : 8 = \square : 40$
- **d** $1 : 3 = \square : 27$
- **e** $30 : 18 = 5 : \square$
- **f** $56 : 21 = 8 : \square$
- **g** $3 : 4 = 1\frac{1}{2} : \square$
- **h** $0.5 : 0.9 = \square : 9$
- **i** $1 : 6 = \square : 1$
- **j** $20 : \square = 4 : 3$
- **k** $2 : \square = 6 : 9$
- **l** $\square : 12 = 8 : 3$

Example 23 — Self Tutor

The ratio of prefects to students on a grade 5 excursion is $3:10$.

12 prefects are going on the excursion. How many grade 5 students are going with them?

prefects : students $= 3:10$

$$\therefore\ 3:10 = 12:\square \quad (\times 4)$$

$$\therefore\ \square = 10 \times 4 = 40$$

$\therefore$ 40 grade 5 students are going on the excursion.

2 A group of people auditioning for a quiz show consists of men and women in the ratio $11:2$.
   a If there are 33 men auditioning, find the number of women.
   b If there are 12 women auditioning, find the number of men.

3 A street stall sells chicken kebabs and beef kebabs in the ratio $3:8$. If 96 beef kebabs were sold, how many chicken kebabs were sold?

4 Marion is training for a duathlon. Her time spent running and cycling is split in the ratio $3:2$. If she spends 10 hours cycling in one week, how long does she spend running?

5 Pedro makes drinks for his soccer teammates by mixing cordial and water in the ratio $2:9$. If he has 0.4 litres of cordial, how much water should he add?

6 Sue invested money in stocks, shares, and property in the ratio $6:4:5$. If she invested €36 000 in property, how much did she invest in the other two areas?

USING RATIOS TO DIVIDE QUANTITIES

Quantities can be divided in a particular ratio by considering the total **number of parts** the whole quantity is to be divided into.

Example 24 — Self Tutor

There are 35 lollies to be divided between Michelle and Wade in the ratio $3:4$. How many lollies does each person receive?

The ratio contains $3+4=7$ parts in total.

Michelle receives $\frac{3}{7}$ of the lollies, and Wade receives $\frac{4}{7}$ of the lollies.

$\therefore$ Michelle receives $\frac{3}{7}$ of 35 $= \frac{3}{7} \times 35 = 15$ lollies

and Wade receives $\frac{4}{7}$ of 35 $= \frac{4}{7} \times 35 = 20$ lollies

To find a fraction of a quantity, we need to multiply.

EXERCISE 3G.4

1 20 DVDs are divided between Celena and Drew in the ratio $2:3$.

  a What fraction of the DVDs does: **i** Celena **ii** Drew receive?

  b How many DVDs does: **i** Celena **ii** Drew receive?

2 At a pro-am tournament involving 60 golfers, the ratio of professionals to amateurs is $5:7$. How many amateurs are playing in the tournament?

3 Divide \$450 in the ratio $5:4$.

4 Chris is making the ground for the enclosure for his pet tortoise. He mixes soil and sand in the ratio $7:3$. How much of each will Chris need to make:

  a 20 kg **b** 50 kg of ground?

Example 25 **Self Tutor**

To make standard concrete, I mix gravel, sand, and cement in the ratio $5:3:1$.

I wish to make 18 tonnes of concrete. How much gravel, sand, and cement must I purchase?

There are $5+3+1=9$ parts.

$\therefore$ I need $\frac{5}{9}\times 18$ tonnes $=10$ tonnes of gravel

$\frac{3}{9}\times 18$ tonnes $=6$ tonnes of sand

and $\frac{1}{9}\times 18$ tonnes $=2$ tonnes of cement.

5 An alloy is made from tin, zinc, and lead in the ratio $15:4:1$. How much tin is required to make 5 tonnes of the alloy?

6 Toby is applying for a home loan for the full value of the house he is purchasing, and all of the related fees.

The ratio of house price : stamp duty : setup fee is $85:3:2$.

The bank lends Toby a total of £360 000.

  a What is the price of the house? **b** How much stamp duty does Toby pay?

  c What is the setup fee?

PUZZLE

One full glass contains vinegar and water in the ratio $1:3$. Another glass with twice the capacity of the first, has vinegar and water in the ratio $1:4$. If the contents of both glasses are mixed together, what is the ratio of vinegar to water?

REVIEW SET 3A

1 Place the fractions $\frac{3}{4}$, $-\frac{1}{4}$, $-\frac{7}{4}$, $2\frac{1}{4}$ on a number line.

2 Express in lowest terms:

a $\frac{3}{18}$ **b** $\frac{16}{40}$ **c** $\frac{49}{28}$ **d** $\frac{42}{46}$ **e** $\frac{-8}{36}$

3 Find:

a $\frac{1}{6}-\frac{1}{4}$ **b** $7-2.36$ **c** $1\frac{1}{4}\times\frac{5}{9}$

d 0.012×0.6 **e** $9\div 2\frac{1}{3}$ **f** $0.0028\div 0.4$

4 State the value of the digit 5 in:

a 25.7 **b** 1.252 **c** 0.0005 **d** 4.502

5 **a** Use your calculator to find the value of $\frac{20}{17}$.

b Round this value to:

i 2 decimal places **ii** 4 significant figures.

6 Show that the following numbers are rational by writing them in the form $\frac{a}{b}$, where a and b are integers.

a 8 **b** 0.7 **c** $-1\frac{1}{2}$ **d** $\sqrt{81}$

e $6\frac{2}{3}$ **f** -3.5 **g** 0.91 **h** 0.137

7 Write the following rational numbers as terminating decimals:

a $\frac{4}{5}$ **b** $\frac{19}{20}$ **c** $\frac{11}{25}$ **d** $\frac{27}{50}$ **e** $\frac{3}{40}$

8 Is the product of two rational numbers always rational? Explain your answer.

9 Betty baked a lemon slice on Saturday. She ate $\frac{1}{6}$ of it, and her greedy brother ate $\frac{3}{5}$.

a What fraction of the slice has been eaten?

b Express the portion Betty ate as a fraction of the portion her brother ate.

10 At Gary The Greengrocer, watermelons are sold in halves and quarters, as well as whole melons.

a Gary has $7\frac{1}{2}$ melons that he wishes to cut into quarter melons. How many quarter melons will he have?

b The sales of watermelons one day were:

whole melons	5
half melons	9
quarter melons	13

How many watermelons did Gary sell in total?

11 Express as a ratio in simplest form:

a $22 : 30$ **b** 60 cm to 4 m **c** $\frac{1}{4} : 3$

12 In a school the ratio of students playing football and basketball is $8 : 5$. If 96 students play football, how many students play basketball?

REVIEW SET 3B

1 Place the decimals 0.2, 0.6, -0.4, 1.1, -1.3 on a number line.

2 Find $3\frac{2}{5} + 1\frac{2}{3}$.

3 Determine whether the following numbers are rational or irrational, giving reasons for your answers:

a π **b** $3.141\,59$ **c** $\sqrt{25}$ **d** $0.\overline{37}$

4 Find the total cost of buying 0.9 kg of bananas priced at \$2.50 per kilogram, and 0.75 kg of pears priced at \$3.20 per kilogram.

5 Find: **a** $3.6 \div 6$ **b** $3.6 \div 0.6$

6 **a** Write $\frac{9}{20}$ in decimal form. **b** Is this a terminating or recurring decimal?

7 **a** Without using your calculator, determine whether the following rational numbers will convert to a terminating decimal or a recurring decimal.

i $\frac{4}{9}$ **ii** $\frac{21}{40}$ **iii** $\frac{16}{37}$ **iv** $\frac{1}{200}$

v $\frac{7}{12}$ **vi** $\frac{5}{16}$ **vii** $\frac{119}{250}$ **viii** $\frac{29}{88}$

b Use your calculator to write the numbers in **a** as terminating or recurring decimals.

8 Ken had $4\frac{1}{2}$ cans of paint left in his shed. After painting his house, he only had $1\frac{2}{3}$ cans of paint left. How much paint did Ken use?

9 Without using your calculator, write $\frac{5}{9}$ as a recurring decimal.

10 $\frac{7}{8}$ of Yousef's garden beds are used to grow fruit and vegetables. Of these, $\frac{1}{4}$ of the growing space is taken up by eggplants. What fraction of Yousef's garden beds is taken up by eggplants?

11 Find the missing numbers in the following proportions:

a $4 : 7 = 12 : \square$ **b** $5 : 12 = \square : 24$ **c** $\square : 0.4 = 13 : 8$

12 Each year, Giorgio donates money to his three favourite charities in the ratio $7 : 6 : 3$. He donated a total of €320 this year. How much did each charity receive?

Chapter 4

Algebraic operations

Contents:

OPENING PROBLEM

Nadia's brother Tim is 2 years younger than she is. Her mother Melanie is three times Nadia's age. Nadia's father Peter is 4 years older than Melanie.

Things to think about:

a Suppose we use the variable n to represent Nadia's age. How could we represent:
 i Tim's age **ii** Melanie's age
 iii Peter's age?

b If Nadia is 13 years old, how old is Peter?

Algebra is a powerful tool used in mathematics. In algebra we use letters or **pronumerals** to represent unknown values or **variables**. The variables are used in mathematical **expressions**.

For example, the area of any rectangle is found by multiplying its length by its width.

If someone asked you to draw a rectangle, you would probably respond by asking how big the rectangle should be.

The length and width of the rectangle are unknown or variable. We let l represent the length of the rectangle, and w represent its width.

Using algebra, the area of the rectangle can be written as $l \times w$, or lw.

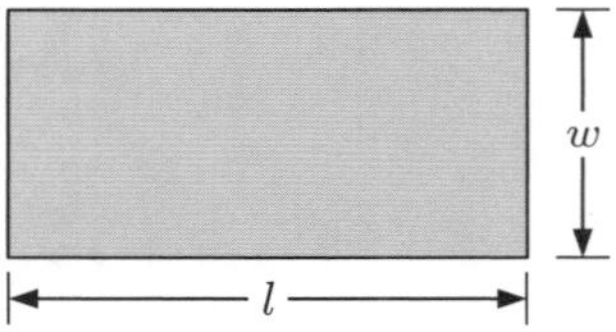

A ALGEBRAIC NOTATION

In algebra the variables are included in expressions as though they were numbers.

However, we obey some rules which help make algebra easier.

In algebra we agree:

- to **leave out** the "$\times$" signs between multiplied quantities
- to write **numerals (numbers) first** in any product
- where products contain two or more letters, we write them in **alphabetical order**.

For example:
- $3b$ is used rather than $3 \times b$ or $b3$
- $3bc$ is used rather than $3cb$.

Example 1 — Self Tutor

Write in product notation:

a $t \times 6s$ **b** $4 \times k + m \times 3$ **c** $3 \times (r + s)$

a $t \times 6s$
$= 6st$

b $4 \times k + m \times 3$
$= 4k + 3m$

c $3 \times (r + s)$
$= 3(r + s)$

WRITING SUMS AS PRODUCTS

Sums of identical terms can be written using product notation.

For example, $3+3+3+3=4\times 3$ {4 lots of 3}

$\therefore\ b+b+b+b=4\times b=4b$ {4 lots of b}

Example 2 Self Tutor

Simplify:

a $r+r+r+s+s$

b $d+d-(a+a+a+a)$

a $r+r+r+s+s$
$=3r+2s$

b $d+d-(a+a+a+a)$
$=2d-4a$

INDEX NOTATION

We can use **index notation** to simplify algebraic expressions in the same way as we did for numbers.

For example, $3\times 3\times 3\times 3=3^4$ and $b\times b\times b\times b=b^4$.

Example 3 Self Tutor

Simplify:

a $8\times b\times b\times a\times a\times a$

b $k+k-3\times d\times d\times d$

a $8\times b\times b\times a\times a\times a$
$=8a^3b^2$

b $k+k-3\times d\times d\times d$
$=2k-3d^3$

EXERCISE 4A

1 Simplify using product notation:

a $5\times x$ **b** $c\times 2$ **c** $q\times 7$
d $f\times 4g$ **e** $6q\times p$ **f** $r\times 9s$
g $2a\times 3b$ **h** $m\times 4n$ **i** $a\times 5\times b$
j $q\times 2\times p$ **k** $j\times k\times l$ **l** $p\times h\times d$

2 Simplify:

a $p\times q+r$ **b** $4\times x+5\times y$ **c** $2\times a-b$
d $b\times a-c$ **e** $b-a\times c$ **f** $f-g\times 7$
g $c\times a+d\times a$ **h** $12-r\times s\times 6$ **i** $3\times(x+y)$
j $5\times(d-1)$ **k** $(w-x)\times 8$ **l** $p\times q\times(r-2)$

3 Simplify using product notation:

a $b+b$ **b** $q+q+q$ **c** $x+x+y+y+y+y$
d $c+c+c+e$ **e** $3+z+y+y$ **f** $a+a+a+a+7$
g $g+g+2+g+g$ **h** $3-(d+d+d)$ **i** $s-t+t$
j $s-(t+t)$ **k** $4+r+r+r+1$ **l** $2+a+a+b+b$

4 Write in expanded form:

a a^4 b f^2 c $4p^3$ d $3t^5$

e $5x^2y$ f $7f^2g^3$ g $(5a)^2$ h $5a^2$

i p^2+2q j p^3-3q^2

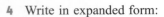

We use indices and product notation to simplify the look of an expression.

5 Write in simplest form:

a $3\times k\times k$ b $4\times a\times a\times a$

c $2\times d\times d\times d\times d$ d $4\times p\times q\times q$

e $3\times f\times g\times f\times g$ f $w\times w\times x\times y\times y\times y$

g $m+m\times m$ h $n\times n\times n+n$

i $y\times y-z\times z\times z\times z$ j $a\times a+7\times a$

k $8\times b-b\times b\times b$ l $2\times p\times q\times q+6\times r\times r\times s$

m $h\times h\times 2-h\times j$ n $3\times x+5\times x\times x\times x$

o $a\times a+2\times b\times b\times b-a\times b\times b$

B THE LANGUAGE OF MATHEMATICS

Some **key words** used in algebra are:

Word	*Meaning*	*Example(s)*
variable	an unknown value that is represented by a letter or symbol	$P=2l+2w$ has variables P, l, and w.
expression	an algebraic form consisting of numbers, variables, and operation signs	$2x+y-7$, $\frac{2a+b}{c}$
equation	an algebraic form which contains an $=$ sign	$3x+8=-1$, $\frac{x-1}{2}=-4$
terms	algebraic forms which are separated by $+$ or $-$ signs, the signs being included	$3x-2y+xy-7$ has four terms. These are $3x$, $-2y$, xy, and -7.
like terms	terms with exactly the same variable form	In $4x+3y+xy-3x$: • $4x$ and $-3x$ are like terms • $4x$ and $3y$ are unlike terms • xy and $3y$ are unlike terms.
constant term	a term which does not contain a variable	In $3x-y^2+7+x^3$, 7 is a constant term.
coefficient	the number factor of an algebraic term	In $4x+2xy-y^3$: • 4 is the coefficient of x • 2 is the coefficient of xy • -1 is the coefficient of y^3.

Example 4 — Self Tutor

Consider $4y^2 - 6x + 2xy - 5 + x^2$.

a Is this an equation or an expression?
b How many terms does it contain?
c State the coefficient of: **i** x **ii** x^2.
d State the constant term.

a There is no = sign present, so this is an expression.
b The expression contains five terms: $4y^2$, $-6x$, $2xy$, -5, and x^2.
c **i** The coefficient of x is -6. **ii** The coefficient of x^2 is 1.
d The constant term is -5.

EXERCISE 4B

1 State the coefficient of x in the expression:

a $3x$ **b** $-8x$ **c** x **d** $-x$
e $3 + 4x$ **f** $xy - 5x$ **g** $3x - 4x^2$ **h** $2x^2 - 2x + 1$

2 State the coefficient of y in the expression:

a $5y$ **b** $-5y$ **c** $14y$ **d** $-7y$
e $3x - y$ **f** $2x + 6y - 3$ **g** $y^2 + 2xy + 3y$ **h** $3y^2 - 2y + 5$

3 Consider $2x^2 + 5x - 7xy + 5y^2 - 2y + 1$.

a Is this an equation or an expression?
b How many terms does it contain?
c State the coefficient of:
i x^2 **ii** y^2 **iii** xy **iv** y.
d What is the constant term?

4 State the number of terms in the expression:

a $4x^2 + 4x + 1$ **b** $p^2 + q^2 - 5pq + 17$ **c** $x^3 - 2x^2 + 5x - \frac{1}{x} - 1$

5 Which of the following are equations, and which are expressions?

a $xy + 2x + 1$ **b** $4x - y = 13$ **c** $4x - 5 = 1$
d $\frac{x}{2} = \frac{6}{x}$ **e** $\frac{x^2}{3} - 2x^2$ **f** $x^2 + 7x + 10$

6 Identify the like terms in each of these expressions:

a $3x + 2 + 5x$ **b** $4x + 2y - 3 - 3y$
c $x^2 + 2x - 5x - 10$ **d** $xy + 3x^2y - 2xy + x^2y$
e $5x - 3x^2 + \frac{x}{2} - 1$ **f** $3x^2y^2 + 7 - xy^2 - 2 + x^2y^2$

C COLLECTING LIKE TERMS

We have seen that **like terms** are algebraic terms which contain the same variables to the same indices.

For example:

- $2xy$ and $-5xy$ are **like terms**
- a^2 and $-3a$ are **unlike terms** because the indices of a are not the same.

Algebraic expressions can often be simplified by adding or subtracting like terms. This is sometimes called **collecting like terms**.

Consider $2a + 4a = \underbrace{a + a}_{\text{"2 lots of } a\text{"}} + \underbrace{a + a + a + a}_{\text{"4 lots of } a\text{"}}.$

In total we have 6 lots of a, and so $2a + 4a = 6a$.

Example 5 — Self Tutor

Simplify, where possible, by collecting like terms:

a $3x + 2x$ **b** $7a - 3a$ **c** $-2x + 3 - x$

d $3bc + bc$ **e** $2x - x^2$

a $3x + 2x$
$= 5x$

b $7a - 3a$
$= 4a$

c $-2x + 3 - x$
$= -3x + 3$
$\{-2x$ and $-x$ are like terms$\}$

d $3bc + bc$
$= 4bc$

e $2x - x^2$ is in simplest form
$\{2x$ and $-x^2$ are unlike terms$\}$

EXERCISE 4C

1 Simplify, where possible, by collecting like terms:

a $2 + x + 4$ **b** $q + 5 + 6$ **c** $b + 3 + b + b$
d $a + a + 7$ **e** $d + d$ **f** $q + 1 + q + 4$
g $5y - 3y$ **h** $4z - z$ **i** $g^2 + g^2$
j $5x + 5$ **k** $5w^2 - 4w^2$ **l** $3x - 3x^2$
m $3x - x$ **n** $3ab + 6ab$ **o** $m + m + m + m$

2 Simplify, where possible:

a $8p - 8p$ **b** $8p - p$ **c** $8p - 8$
d $7pq - pq$ **e** $ab + 3ab$ **f** $3q^2 - q^2$
g $3w + 4w + 5w$ **h** $8xy + 5yx$ **i** $2z + 5z - 4z$
j $2m + 3m - 5m$ **k** $5d + 4d - 9$ **l** $3g + 4g - 7g^2$
m $s + 3s + 4s^2$ **n** $2x^2 + 2x + 2$ **o** $2a^2 - b^2$

3 Simplify, where possible:

a $7x+x$	**b** $7x-x$	**c** $-7x-x$
d p^2+2p	**e** $k+4k-5$	**f** $n-6n-5n$
g $-11m-4m$	**h** $4j-9j+4$	**i** $-y--8y$
j $8y-y$	**k** $8y--y$	**l** $y--4y$

Example 6 Self Tutor

Simplify, by collecting like terms:

a $2+3a-3-2a$ **b** $x^2-2x+3x-2x^2$

a $2+3a-3-2a$
$=3a-2a+2-3$
$=a-1$
{$3a$ and $-2a$ are like terms, 2 and -3 are like terms}

b $x^2-2x+3x-2x^2$
$=x^2-2x^2-2x+3x$
$=-x^2+x$
{x^2 and $-2x^2$ are like terms, $-2x$ and $3x$ are like terms}

4 Simplify, where possible:

a $x+5-3x-6$	**b** $8t+4-3t-1$
c $x+5y-6y-3x$	**d** $pq+3+5pq-7$
e $-cd+2cd+9cd$	**f** $2a-6+6-3a$
g $12x^2+5-7x^2-7$	**h** $-5n+3+2n-6$
i $2v-7v+w-6w$	**j** $-3x^3-2x^2+3x^3-x^2$
k $4a-3b--a-4b$	**l** $-2z-3-3z-4$
m $2p+pq-3pq-p$	**n** $-6mn+3m-mn-5m$

D GENERALISING ARITHMETIC

To find algebraic expressions for many real world situations, we first think in terms of numbers or numerical cases. We then proceed to more general cases.

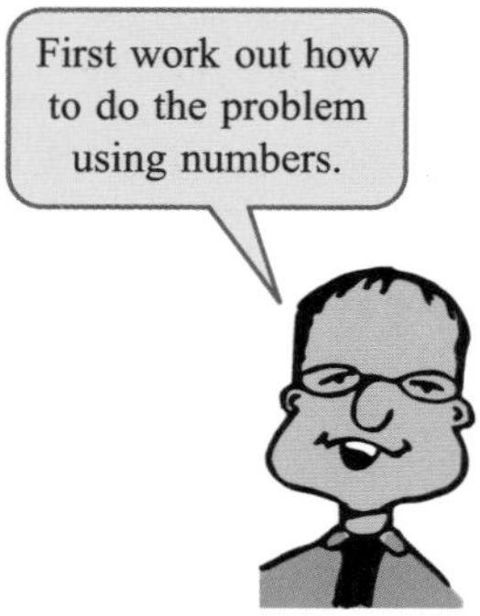

First work out how to do the problem using numbers.

For example, suppose we are asked to find the total cost of x plants which each cost $\$y$.

We could start by finding the total cost of 6 plants which each cost $10. This makes it easier to understand that we need to *multiply* the quantities.

The total cost is $6\times\$10=\$60$.

In the same way, the total cost of x plants at $\$y$ each is $x\times\$y=\$xy$.

Example 7 — Self Tutor

Find: **a** the cost of x bananas at 30 cents each

b the change from \$50 when buying y books at \$6 each.

a The cost of 7 bananas at 30 cents each is 7×30 cents.

$\therefore$ the cost of x bananas at 30 cents each is $x \times 30 = 30x$ cents.

b The total cost of 5 books costing \$6 each is 5×6 dollars.

$\therefore$ the change from \$50 when buying 5 books costing \$6 each is $50 - (5 \times 6)$ dollars.

$\therefore$ the change from \$50 when buying y books costing \$6 each is

$50 - (y \times 6)$ dollars $= 50 - 6y$ dollars.

EXERCISE 4D

1 Find the total cost of buying:

a 5 caps at \$20 each **b** a caps at \$20 each **c** a caps at \$$d$ each.

2 Rick is now 14 years old. How old was he:

a 6 years ago **b** x years ago?

3 Find the change from \$100 when buying:

a 3 hammers at \$15 each **b** h hammers at \$15 each **c** h hammers at \$$p$ each.

4 Patrick decided to go jogging each morning. As a result, he lost 6 kg. If he initially weighed w kg, how much does he weigh now?

5 There were 20 people at a party, then m more people arrived and n people left. How many people are now at the party?

6 Laura buys a apricots and p peaches. Find the total cost (in dollars) if each apricot costs 60 cents and each peach costs 90 cents.

7 Tia is walking to her friend's house, 600 m down the road. Each step she takes is 80 cm long. Tia has walked x steps.

a How far has she walked? **b** How far is she from her friend's house?

8 **a** A cyclist travels at an average speed of 15 km per hour for 3 hours. How far has the cyclist travelled?

b How far would the cyclist travel at an average speed of s km per hour for t hours?

9 **a** Jan has 96 cupcakes to share amongst 8 tables. How many cupcakes does each table receive?

b If Jan had c cupcakes to share amongst n tables, how many cupcakes would each table receive?

10 Frank buys b balls at \$$m$ each and r racquets at \$$n$ each. Find the total cost of these items.

E ALGEBRAIC SUBSTITUTION

In **Exercise 4D** we found algebraic expressions for some real world situations.

Suppose a triangle has base b units and height h units. Its area is given by the expression $\frac{1}{2}bh$ units^2.

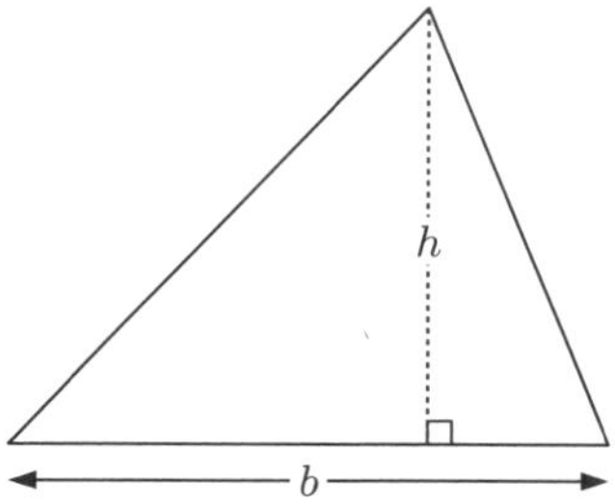

If we are given the base and height of a triangle, we substitute the given values into the expression to find the area.

For example, if the base of a triangle $b = 5$ cm and the height of the triangle $h = 2$ cm, then the area of the triangle is $\frac{1}{2} \times 5 \times 2 = 5$ cm^2.

To **evaluate** a mathematical expression, we **substitute** particular numerical values for the variables and hence find the value of the expression.

If we substitute a negative value, we place it in brackets. This helps us to evaluate the signs in the expression correctly.

For example, consider the expression $5a + 3b$.

If $a = -2$ and $b = 4$, then
$$\begin{aligned} 5a + 3b &= 5 \times (-2) + 3 \times 4 \\ &= -10 + 12 \\ &= 2 \end{aligned}$$

Example 8 — Self Tutor

If $a = 2$, $b = -1$, and $c = 3$, evaluate:

a $3a - 2b$ **b** $c^2 + b$

a
$$\begin{aligned} &3a - 2b \\ &= 3 \times 2 - 2 \times (-1) \\ &= 6 + 2 \\ &= 8 \end{aligned}$$

b
$$\begin{aligned} &c^2 + b \\ &= 3^2 + (-1) \\ &= 9 - 1 \\ &= 8 \end{aligned}$$

We place negative substitutions inside brackets.

EXERCISE 4E

1 If $f = 2$, $g = 4$, and $h = 1$, evaluate:

a $f + h$ **b** $3g$ **c** $h - g$ **d** $7 + 4f$
e $2 - gh$ **f** $fg - h$ **g** $5(g - h)$ **h** $2g^2$

2 If $w = 3$, $x = -1$, $y = 4$, and $z = -2$, evaluate:

a $w + x$ **b** $5z$ **c** $2x + y$ **d** $4w - z$
e x^2 **f** $7 - w^2$ **g** $5x + 2y$ **h** $3z^2$
i $yz + 2w$ **j** $2(y - z)$ **k** $y^2 - wz$ **l** $z(y - 3x)$

Example 9 **Self Tutor**

If $p = 3$, $q = -2$, and $r = -4$, evaluate:

a $\dfrac{p-q}{r}$ **b** $\dfrac{q^2+pr}{p+r}$

a $\dfrac{p-q}{r} = \dfrac{3-(-2)}{(-4)} = \dfrac{3+2}{-4} = \dfrac{5}{-4} = -\dfrac{5}{4}$

b $\dfrac{q^2+pr}{p+r} = \dfrac{(-2)^2+3\times(-4)}{3+(-4)} = \dfrac{4-12}{-1} = \dfrac{-8}{-1} = 8$

3 If $j = 5$, $k = -3$, $l = 2$, and $m = 4$, evaluate:

a $\dfrac{m}{l}$ **b** $\dfrac{2j+l}{m}$ **c** $\dfrac{j}{l-k}$ **d** $\dfrac{k-j}{l}$

e $\dfrac{j-l}{2m}$ **f** $\dfrac{l+k}{j+m}$ **g** $\dfrac{3l}{j+6}$ **h** $\dfrac{15-m}{k-1}$

i $\dfrac{k^2}{5l+m}$ **j** $\dfrac{j+k}{l^2+3}$ **k** $\dfrac{6-k}{lm-5}$ **l** $\dfrac{l^2m}{j^2-21}$

4 Evaluate the expression $a(b^2-4)$ for:

a $a = 2$, $b = 3$ **b** $a = 4$, $b = 2$ **c** $a = -1$, $b = 5$ **d** $a = 7$, $b = -4$

5 Answer the **Opening Problem** on page **76**.

6 The area of a triangle with base length b cm and height h cm, is given by the expression $\frac{1}{2}bh$ cm^2. Find the area of the triangle with base 6 cm and height 9 cm.

7 The *density* of an object is given by the expression $\dfrac{m}{V}$, where m is the mass in grams, V is the volume in cm^3, and the units of density are g/cm^3.

a Find the density of an object weighing 130 g and with volume 26 cm^3.

b A block of iron has the dimensions 3 cm by 5 cm by 2 cm. If the block weighs 234 g, what is its density?

8 A stone is dropped off a cliff. Its speed after travelling s m is given by the expression $\sqrt{19.6s}$ m/s.

a Use your calculator to find the speed of the stone, correct to 2 decimal places, after it has travelled:

i 1 m **ii** 5 m.

b The cliff is 12 m high. What is the stone's speed just before it hits the ground?

INVESTIGATION — EQUAL EXPRESSIONS

We can use substitution to give us a better understanding of whether two different looking algebraic expressions are equal.

We choose some values for the variables, and substitute these values into both expressions. If the results are always equal no matter what values we choose for the variables, then the expressions are equal.

For example:

- $2(x+3)$ and $2x+6$ are **equal expressions** because no matter what value of x is substituted, the expressions will be equal for this value of x.
- $2(x+3)$ and $2x+3$ cannot be equal, because when $x=1$,

$$\begin{aligned} &2(x+3) \\ &= 2(1+3) \\ &= 2\times 4 \\ &= 8 \end{aligned} \qquad \text{whereas} \qquad \begin{aligned} &2x+3 \\ &= 2\times 1+3 \\ &= 2+3 \\ &= 5 \end{aligned}$$

One **counterexample** is sufficient to show that two expressions are not equal.

What to do:

1 Copy and complete the following table of values:

a	b	$a+\frac{b}{4}$	$\frac{a+b}{4}$	$\frac{a}{4}+b$	$\frac{a}{4}+\frac{b}{4}$
8	4				
3	5				
6	-2				

2 From the table, which of the four expressions are likely to be equal, and which are definitely not equal?

3 Use a table like that in **1** or use a spreadsheet to test the following for equality:

a $\frac{1}{2}x$ and $\frac{x}{2}$ using $x=4, 6, -8$

b $180-(a+b)$ and $180-a-b$ using:
  i $a=20,\ b=30$ **ii** $a=40,\ b=75$

c $(2x)^2$ and $2x^2$ using $x=0, 1, 2, 3$

d $(x+y)^2$ and x^2+y^2 using:
  i $x=1,\ y=2$ **ii** $x=3,\ y=5$

e $(x-y)^2$ and $x^2-2xy+y^2$ using:
  i $x=3,\ y=1$ **ii** $x=4,\ y=-1$

F ALGEBRAIC PRODUCTS

Algebraic products are products which contain at least one variable.

$3 \times 2x$ and $a^2 \times 2ab$ are examples of algebraic products.

Algebraic products can often be simplified using these steps:

- Calculate the **coefficient** of the final product by multiplying all the numbers.
- **Simplify** the unknowns using index notation where appropriate. The unknowns should be written in alphabetical order.

Example 10 Self Tutor

Simplify:

a $2a \times 3a$ b $-3x^2 \times 4xy$

a $2a \times 3a$
$= 2 \times a \times 3 \times a$
$= 6 \times a^2$ $\{2 \times 3 = 6,$ and there are 2 factors of $a\}$
$= 6a^2$

b $-3x^2 \times 4xy$
$= -3 \times x \times x \times 4 \times x \times y$
$= -12 \times x^3 \times y$ {3 factors of x, 1 factor of y}
$= -12x^3y$

With practice, you should not need to write all of these steps.

EXERCISE 4F

1 Simplify the following algebraic products:

a $5 \times 4k$ b $x^2 \times x^3$ c $4x \times 7x^2$
d $5z \times 6z$ e $m \times 8m^3$ f $2g^2 \times 5g^2$
g $(5y)^2$ h $3x \times x \times 4$ i $4x \times 3x^2 \times 2x$

2 Simplify:

a $-2x \times 4x$ b $5a \times ab$ c $6c \times (-c)$
d $m^2 \times 3mn$ e $-4a^2b \times 3b$ f $(-4p) \times (-5p)$
g $7x^2 \times (-5x)$ h $(4g)^2 \times g$ i $8x^2y^2 \times 3xy$
j $7 \times (-x^3)$ k $(-3x)^2$ l $s^2 \times (-2st)$
m $x^3 \times (-x^2)$ n $5r \times (-r)^2$ o $(-3x^2) \times (-2x)$
p $9xy^3 \times 3x^2y$ q $5a^2b \times 6ab$ r $4xy \times (-3x^2)$
s $(2y)^3$ t $(-2z)^3$

G ALGEBRAIC FRACTIONS

Algebraic fractions are fractions which contain at least one variable.

$\frac{a}{3}$, $\frac{5}{x}$, $\frac{2}{y-5}$, and $\frac{a^2}{b-c}$ are examples of algebraic fractions.

Algebraic fractions can be simplified by cancelling common factors in exactly the same way as for numerical fractions.

For example, just as $\frac{8}{12} = \frac{2\times\cancel{4}}{3\times\cancel{4}} = \frac{2}{3}$,

$$\frac{2x^2}{x^5} = \frac{2\times\cancel{x}\times\cancel{x}}{x\times x\times x\times\cancel{x}\times\cancel{x}} = \frac{2}{x^3}.$$

Example 11 — Self Tutor

Simplify:

a $\frac{6x^3}{3x}$ b $\frac{4xy^2}{12x^2y}$

a $\frac{6x^3}{3x}$

$= \frac{{}^2\cancel{6}\times x\times x\times \cancel{x}^1}{{}_1\cancel{3}\times\cancel{x}_1}$

$= \frac{2x^2}{1}$

$= 2x^2$

b $\frac{4xy^2}{12x^2y}$

$= \frac{{}^1\cancel{4}\times\cancel{x}^1\times y\times\cancel{y}^1}{{}_3\cancel{12}\times\cancel{x}_1\times x\times\cancel{y}_1}$

$= \frac{y}{3x}$

EXERCISE 4G.1

1 Simplify:

a $\frac{10x}{5}$ b $\frac{12}{4x}$ c $\frac{5a}{a}$ d $\frac{9k}{15k}$

e $\frac{x^2}{x}$ f $\frac{x}{x^2}$ g $\frac{2c^2}{c}$ h $\frac{3m}{m^3}$

2 Simplify:

a $\frac{x^5}{x^2}$ b $\frac{5x^3}{x}$ c $\frac{x^5}{3x^3}$ d $\frac{6x}{x^2}$

e $\frac{xy}{x}$ f $\frac{a}{ab}$ g $\frac{2cd}{c^2}$ h $\frac{8x^2}{10xy}$

i $\frac{a^3}{a^3}$ j $\frac{2mn^2}{14m^2n^2}$ k $\frac{15p^3q}{3p}$ l $\frac{3x^2y}{9y^3}$

m $\frac{12s^2t^2}{8s^2t}$ n $\frac{k^5}{k^5}$ o $\frac{x^2y^3z}{xyz^2}$ p $\frac{10a^2bc^3}{12ab^2}$

DISCUSSION

Is there a way of simplifying algebraic products such as $x^3 \times x^5$ and algebraic quotients like $\frac{x^5}{x^2}$ without writing out all of the factors?

MULTIPLYING AND DIVIDING ALGEBRAIC FRACTIONS

The rules used for multiplying and dividing algebraic fractions are identical to those for numerical fractions.

To **multiply** two fractions, we multiply the numerators together to give the new numerator, and multiply the denominators together to give the new denominator.

$$\frac{a}{b} \times \frac{c}{d} = \frac{a \times c}{b \times d} = \frac{ac}{bd}$$

Example 12 Self Tutor

Simplify:

a $\frac{x}{5} \times \frac{y}{2}$ **b** $\frac{a^2}{6} \times \frac{3}{a}$

a
$$\frac{x}{5} \times \frac{y}{2} = \frac{x \times y}{5 \times 2} = \frac{xy}{10}$$

b
$$\frac{a^2}{6} \times \frac{3}{a} = \frac{a^2 \times 3}{6 \times a} = \frac{{}^1\cancel{a} \times a \times \cancel{3}^1}{{}_2\cancel{6} \times \cancel{a}_1} = \frac{a}{2}$$

Always look for common factors to cancel.

To **divide** by a fraction, we multiply by its **reciprocal**.

$$\frac{a}{b} \div \frac{c}{d} = \frac{a}{b} \times \frac{d}{c}$$

Example 13 Self Tutor

Simplify:

a $\frac{x}{5} \div \frac{y}{3}$ **b** $\frac{8}{m} \div \frac{2}{m}$

a
$$\frac{x}{5} \div \frac{y}{3} = \frac{x}{5} \times \frac{3}{y} = \frac{x \times 3}{5 \times y} = \frac{3x}{5y}$$

b
$$\frac{8}{m} \div \frac{2}{m} = \frac{8}{m} \times \frac{m}{2} = \frac{{}^4\cancel{8} \times \cancel{m}^1}{{}_1\cancel{m} \times \cancel{2}_1} = 4$$

EXERCISE 4G.2

1 Simplify:

a $\frac{a}{3} \times \frac{b}{4}$ **b** $\frac{x}{y} \times \frac{x}{7}$ **c** $\frac{10}{m} \times \frac{m}{2}$ **d** $\frac{5}{x} \times \frac{6}{y}$

e $\frac{p^2}{6} \times \frac{2}{p}$ **f** $\frac{a}{b^2} \times \frac{b}{4}$ **g** $\frac{x}{y^2} \times \frac{y}{x^2}$ **h** $\frac{t^3}{r} \times \frac{r}{t}$

2 Simplify:

a $\frac{a}{7} \div \frac{b}{4}$ **b** $\frac{5}{x} \div \frac{y}{8}$ **c** $\frac{c}{2} \div \frac{4}{c}$ **d** $\frac{p}{q} \div \frac{q}{6}$

e $\frac{x}{2} \div \frac{x}{3}$ **f** $\frac{k^2}{4} \div \frac{k}{j}$ **g** $\frac{3}{t} \div \frac{t^2}{s}$ **h** $\frac{x^2}{y} \div \frac{x^2}{y}$

3 Simplify:

a $\frac{2x}{y} \times \frac{x}{8}$ **b** $\frac{x^2}{6} \times \frac{3y}{x}$ **c** $\frac{a^2}{4} \div \frac{5}{3a}$ **d** $\frac{11}{k^2} \div \frac{5k}{m}$

e $\frac{4x}{y} \times \frac{x}{6y^2}$ **f** $\frac{12a}{b^2} \div \frac{9b}{a^2}$ **g** $\frac{x^2}{3y} \times \frac{6y^3}{5}$ **h** $\frac{(3a)^2}{5} \div \frac{2b}{a}$

REVIEW SET 4A

1 Simplify using product notation:

a $7 \times a \times 3 \times a \times b$ **b** $b \times b \times b + b + b$ **c** $2 \times d \times d \times d - 3 \times d \times d$

2 Write in expanded form:

a $7t^4$ **b** $(3b)^3$ **c** $2b^2 - 3c^3$

3 State whether each of the following is an equation or an expression:

a $3x = 5$ **b** $2x^2 - 4x + 7$ **c** $(x-2)^2$ **d** $xy + 2y = -7$

4 Consider the expression $5g + 12gh - 2h + 3gh + 4$.

a How many terms are present? **b** State any like terms.

c State the coefficient of h. **d** State the constant term.

e If possible, simplify the expression.

5 Gina bought a bag of 18 apples. How many apples will be left in the bag if she eats:

a 2 apples per day for the next 3 days **b** a apples per day for the next 3 days

c a apples per day for the next d days?

6 If $p = -2$, $q = 6$, and $r = -3$, find:

a r^2 **b** p^2qr **c** $\frac{p-r}{2q}$

7 The force acting on an object with mass m kg and acceleration a m/s^2 is given by the expression ma Newtons. Find the force acting on:

a a bicycle with mass 8 kg and acceleration 9 m/s^2

b an arrow with mass 54 g and acceleration 5 m/s^2.

8 Simplify by collecting like terms:

a $7k + 6k - 6$ **b** $9f + 3g - (-8f) - 8g$

9 Simplify:

a $5x^2 \times 4x$ **b** $\dfrac{t^6}{t^6}$ **c** $\dfrac{5x^4y}{10xy^3}$ **d** $\dfrac{14a^2b}{8b^4}$

10 Simplify:

a $\dfrac{m}{4} \times \dfrac{10}{m^2}$ **b** $\dfrac{2}{x} \div \dfrac{x}{3}$ **c** $\dfrac{5n}{p^2} \times \dfrac{2n^2}{7}$

REVIEW SET 4B

1 If $a = 3$, $b = -1$, and $c = -4$, evaluate:

a a^2b **b** $(a - c)^2$

2 Simplify by collecting like terms:

a $3z - 8z + 2$ **b** $t + 5u - 6t + 7u$

3 Simplify:

a $(3d)^2$ **b** $\dfrac{14a^2b}{4ab^2}$

4 Write $a^3 - 7a^2b^3$ in expanded form.

5 Consider the expression $3x^2 + 4x - 7x + 5$.

a What are the like terms in this expression?

b How many terms will the *simplified* expression have?

6 Find the change from \$20 when buying:

a 3 icecreams at \$2 each **b** 3 icecreams at \$$p$ each **c** c icecreams at \$$p$ each.

7 **a** Simplify $\dfrac{15a^3}{3a}$. **b** *Hence* evaluate the expression when $a = -2$.

8 A cake stall had 20 muffins. n customers bought 2 muffins each, then a new batch of m muffins arrived. How many muffins does the stall now have?

9 Evaluate the expression $\dfrac{x^2 - 1}{x}$ for:

a $x = 1$ **b** $x = 2$ **c** $x = -3$.

10 Simplify:

a $(-4x) \times (-5x^2y)$ **b** $\dfrac{a^2}{b} \times \dfrac{b}{3a}$ **c** $\dfrac{(2c)^2}{d} \div \dfrac{c}{14d}$

Chapter 5

Percentage

Contents:

OPENING PROBLEM

At a kitchenware store, frying pans usually sell for $82.50. On the weekend, the store is having a 20% off sale.

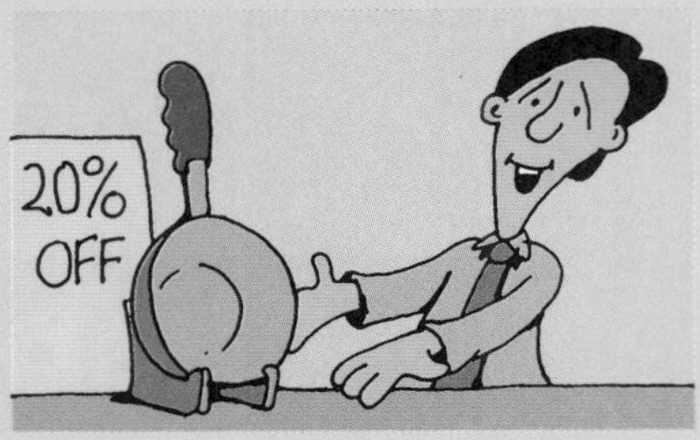

Things to think about:

a How much discount is being offered on the marked price of the frying pan?

b How much will each frying pan cost now?

c During the sale, the store is selling toasters for $48. How much do the toasters usually sell for?

Percentages are used every day around us, so it is important to understand what they mean and how to use them.

We may see headlines like:

- Imports taxed at 10%.
- 40% off sale this week.
- Earn 6.5% interest in our saver account.
- Football attendances down by 8%.
- 68% of children are overweight.

A PERCENTAGE

We use percentages to compare an amount with a whole. We refer to one whole as 100%.

% reads "**per cent**" which is short for *per centum*.

Loosely translated from Latin, per cent means "in every hundred".

If an object is divided into one hundred parts, then each part is called 1 per cent, written 1%.

Thus, $1\% = \frac{1}{100}$

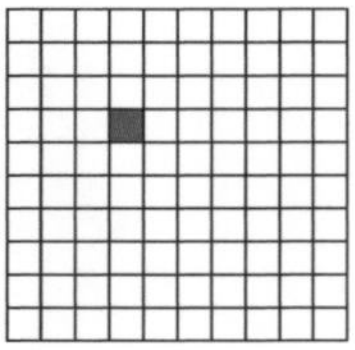

and $100\% = \frac{100}{100}$

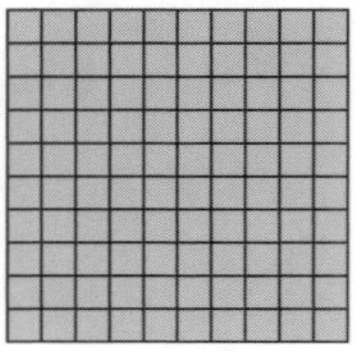

So, a percentage is like a fraction which has denominator 100.

$$x\% = \frac{x}{100}$$

CONVERTING FRACTIONS AND DECIMALS INTO PERCENTAGES

To convert a fraction or decimal into a percentage, we multiply by 100%.

Since $100\% = \frac{100}{100} = 1$, we are not changing the value of the number.

For some fractions, we may end up with a percentage with many decimal places. In this case we often round the percentage to 1 or 2 decimal places.

Example 1 **Self Tutor**

Write as a percentage:

a $\frac{3}{5}$ **b** 0.042 **c** $\frac{1}{6}$

a $\frac{3}{5}$
$= \frac{3}{5} \times 100\%$
$= 60\%$

b 0.042
$= 0.042 \times 100\%$
$= 4.2\%$

c $\frac{1}{6}$
$= \frac{1}{6} \times 100\%$
$= \frac{100}{6}\%$
$= 16\frac{2}{3}\%$
$\approx 16.7\%$

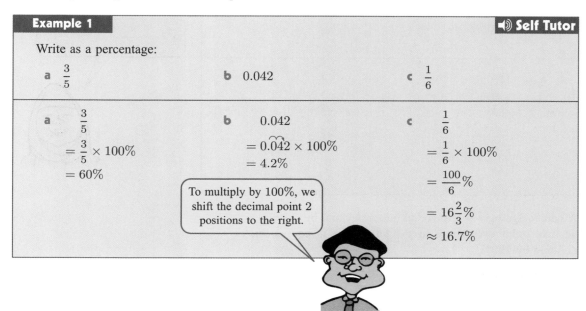

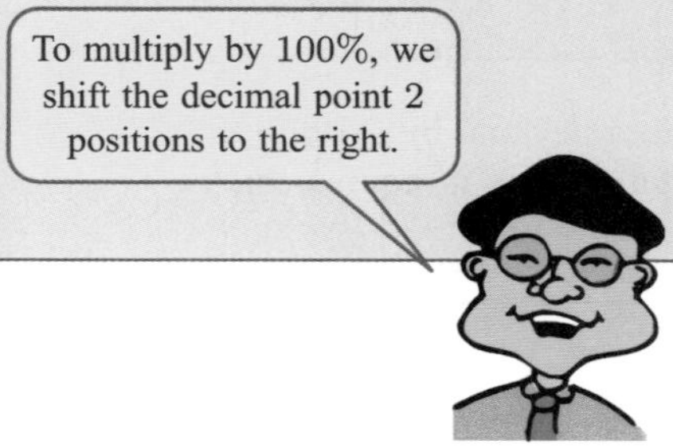

To multiply by 100%, we shift the decimal point 2 positions to the right.

EXERCISE 5A.1

1 Write as a percentage:

a $\frac{3}{10}$ **b** $\frac{9}{50}$ **c** $\frac{21}{25}$ **d** $\frac{1}{4}$
e 2 **f** $\frac{13}{20}$ **g** $\frac{4}{5}$ **h** $\frac{17}{40}$

2 Write as a percentage:

a 0.02 **b** 0.4 **c** 0.37 **d** 0.65
e 1.25 **f** 0.015 **g** 0.333 **h** 5.005

3 Convert into a percentage, giving your answer exactly:

a $\frac{3}{4}$ **b** 0.18 **c** 1.025 **d** $1\frac{1}{2}$
e $\frac{2}{3}$ **f** 2.1 **g** $\frac{4}{25}$ **h** 0.983
i 1 **j** $0.8\overline{3}$ **k** $\frac{2}{9}$ **l** $\frac{8}{125}$

4 Use your calculator to write these fractions as percentages rounded to 1 decimal place:

a $\frac{3}{7}$ **b** $\frac{8}{13}$ **c** $\frac{6}{89}$ **d** $\frac{18}{17}$

CONVERTING PERCENTAGES INTO FRACTIONS AND DECIMALS

To convert a percentage into a fraction, we divide by 100%.

This is often achieved by first writing the percentage with a denominator of 100, then expressing it in its lowest terms.

Example 2 — Self Tutor

Write as a fraction in lowest terms:

a 115% **b** $12\frac{1}{2}\%$

a $115\% = \frac{115}{100} = \frac{115 \div 5}{100 \div 5} = \frac{23}{20}$

b $12\frac{1}{2}\% = \frac{25}{2} \div 100 = \frac{{}^{1}\cancel{25}}{2} \times \frac{1}{\cancel{100}_{4}} = \frac{1}{8}$

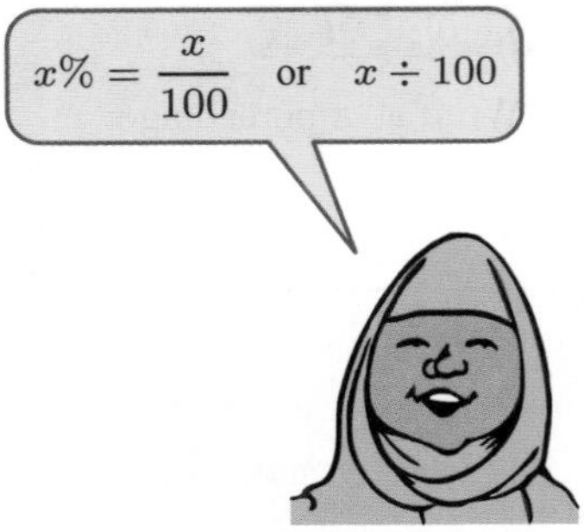

A percentage may be converted into a decimal by shifting the decimal point two places to the left. This is equivalent to dividing by 100%.

Example 3 — Self Tutor

Write as a decimal:

a 88% **b** 116%

a $88\% = 088.\% = 0.88$

b $116\% = 116.\% = 1.16$

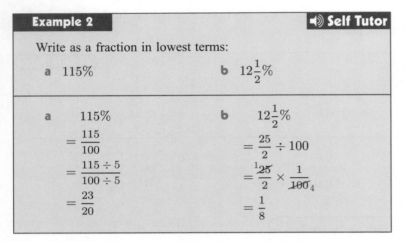

To divide by 100%, we shift the decimal point 2 positions to the left.

EXERCISE 5A.2

1 Write as a fraction in lowest terms:

a 55%	**b** 32%	**c** 210%	**d** 16%
e 72%	**f** $37\frac{1}{2}\%$	**g** $3\frac{1}{4}\%$	**h** 144%
i $33\frac{1}{3}\%$	**j** 120%	**k** 0.01%	**l** 0.75%

2 Write as a decimal:

a 48%	**b** 110%	**c** 101%	**d** 62.5%
e 4.9%	**f** 2%	**g** 552%	**h** 0.1%
i 1000%	**j** 0.0025%	**k** 235.2%	**l** 27.3%

B EXPRESSING ONE QUANTITY AS A PERCENTAGE OF ANOTHER

We can *compare* quantities using percentages.

To find one quantity as a percentage of another, we write the first as a fraction of the second, then multiply by 100%.

Example 4 **Self Tutor**

Express as a percentage:

a Mike ran 10 km out of 50 km

b Rani spent 5 months of the last two years overseas.

a 10 km out of 50 km $= \frac{10}{\cancel{50}_1} \times \cancel{100}^2\%$ {cancelling}

$= 20\%$

So, Mike ran 20% of 50 km.

b 5 months out of the last two years

= 5 months out of 24 months {must have the same units}

$= \frac{5}{24} \times 100\%$

$\approx 20.8\%$ {using a calculator}

So, Rani spent about 20.8% of the last two years overseas.

EXERCISE 5B

1 Express as a percentage:

a 17 marks out of 20 marks
b \$10 out of \$25
c 8 km out of 60 km
d 9 months out of 3 years
e 4 L out of 25 L
f 800 g out of 30 kg
g 3 hours out of 2 days
h 20 cm out of 1.2 m

2 Of the 40 passengers on a tour bus, 12 are from South Africa. What percentage of the passengers are South African?

3 Last week, Jemima was given \$15 pocket money, and Henry was given \$18. Of this money, Jemima saved \$6 while Henry saved \$7. Who saved the greater percentage of their pocket money?

4 At the cinema, Michael spent €15 on his movie ticket, €8 on popcorn, and €3 on a drink. He paid for these things out of the €30 he had in his wallet. What percentage of his money did Michael spend on:

a the ticket
b a drink
c popcorn
d his outing?

5 Every year, firefighters take part in The Sky Tower Climb in Auckland, New Zealand. There are 1103 steps in the climb. The progress of four firefighters is shown in the table below.
Copy and complete the table by finding the percentage of the race each person has run, and the percentage he or she has remaining.

Name	*Steps climbed*	*% already run*	*% remaining*
Marcel	813		
Ariel	672		
Shane	901		
Emma	866		

INVESTIGATION — SPORTING INJURIES

The graphs below show the number of players involved in eight different sports in England, and the number of injuries suffered by players involved in those same eight sports.

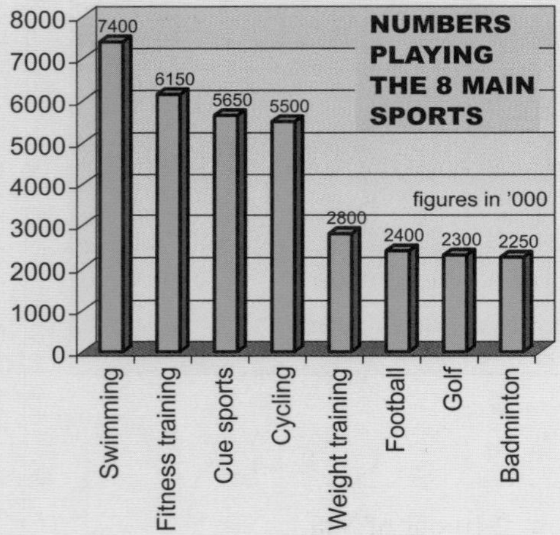

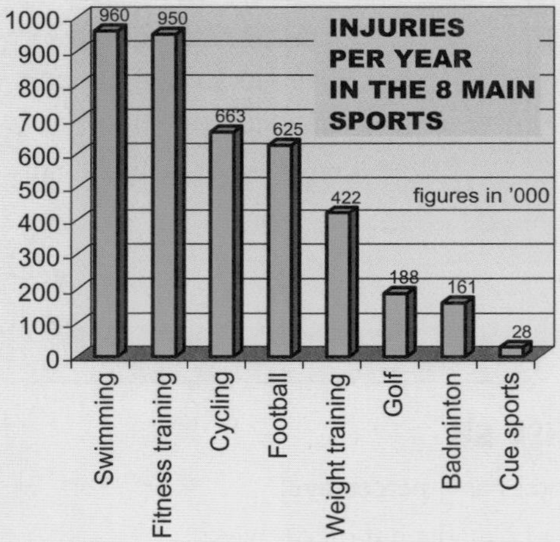

What to do:

1 Find, using your calculator:

a the total number of injuries per year in all eight sports

b the injuries per year for each of the sports, expressed as a percentage of total injuries per year

c the total number of people in England playing these sports

d the percentage of the total number of players playing each sport

e the *injury rate* for each sport using

$$\text{injury rate} = \frac{\text{number of injuries per year}}{\text{number playing that sport}} \times 100\%.$$

2 Use the injury rates to decide which sport appears to be the:

a most dangerous **b** safest.

C FINDING A PERCENTAGE OF A QUANTITY

To find a percentage of a quantity, we convert the percentage to a fraction or a decimal, and then **multiply**.

Example 5 Self Tutor

Find:

a 6% of 150 kg

b 4.5% of \$210

a 6% of 150 kg

$= \frac{6}{{}_2 100} \times 150^{3}\text{ kg}$

$= 9$ kg

b 4.5% of \$210

$= 0.045 \times \$210$

$= \$9.45$

The word 'of' tells us to multiply!

Example 6 Self Tutor

Sandra scored 86% in her exam out of 150. What mark did she score?

Sandra scored 86% of 150

$= 0.86 \times 150$

$= 129$

So, Sandra scored 129 marks.

EXERCISE 5C

1 Find:

a 80% of 30
b 15% of 60
c 25% of 110 kg
d 70% of 400 m
e 35% of \$250
f 6% of 30 L
g 7.5% of 12 km
h 85% of 8 m
i 38.5% of £360
j $4\frac{1}{2}$% of ¥6 400 000
k 0.5% of 3500 kg
l $8\frac{1}{4}$% of \$900

2 Annette spends 32% of her wage on her mortgage. If Annette earns \$52 000 a year, how much does she spend on her mortgage?

3 A mixture of water and lime cordial concentrate contains 12% cordial concentrate. How much water is required to make 6 litres of this lime cordial mixture?

4 Tax on vehicles imported into a country is 6.5%. If the total value of vehicles imported is €2 560 000, how much tax will be charged?

5 A whitegoods manufacturer receives 35% of the sale price of their goods sold by a department store. How much does the manufacturer receive if the store sells whitegoods worth:

a \$45 000
b \$70 000?

6 Nicki and Terry are part of a syndicate that owns racehorses. Nicki owns 28% of a horse, and Terry owns 16% of the horse. Last week the horse won \$18 600 in the derby.

a How much did Nicki receive from this win?
b How much more did Nicki receive than Terry?

7 A petroleum company claims that cars using their new premium unleaded fuel will travel 112% of the distance travelled on regular unleaded. If Geoff can travel 584 km on a tank of regular fuel, how far should he be able to travel using the premium unleaded?

8 On public holidays, a restaurant adds a 10% surcharge to each bill. Jack and Jill buy food and wine to the value of $54 on a public holiday. How much will they have to pay:

a for the surcharge **b** in total?

D THE UNITARY METHOD IN PERCENTAGE

Michelle and Brigette own a business. Brigette receives 25% of the profits each month. Last month, Brigette received $2080. How can she work out the total profit made by the business last month?

The **unitary method** can be used to solve this problem. We first find 1%, then multiply by 100 to find the whole amount.

Example 7 **Self Tutor**

Find 100% of a sum of money if 25% is $2080.

25% of the amount is $2080

$\therefore$ 1% of the amount is $\$2080 \div 25 = \$83.20$

$\therefore$ 100% of the amount is $\$83.20 \times 100$

$\therefore$ the whole amount is $8320

From the **Example** above, we see that the total profit made by Michelle and Brigette's business last month was $8320.

The unitary method can also be used to find other percentages of a quantity.

Example 8 **Self Tutor**

18% of the students at a school are in Year 8, and 16% of the students are in Year 9. If the school has 126 Year 8 students, determine the number of Year 9 students.

18% is 126 students

$\therefore$ 1% is $\frac{126}{18} = 7$ students

$\therefore$ 16% is $7 \times 16 = 112$ students

So, the school has 112 Year 9 students.

EXERCISE 5D

1 Find 100% if:

- **a** 10% is 40 mL
- **b** 45% is 225 g
- **c** 6% is €72
- **d** 70% is 49 kg
- **e** 53% is $159
- **f** 95% is 38 minutes

2 22% of students at a school ride their bikes to school. If 132 students ride their bikes to school, how many students attend the school?

3
- **a** Find 40% of an injection if 5% of the injection is 7 mL.
- **b** Find 84% of a packet of nuts if 14% of the packet is 21 g.
- **c** Find 72% of the contents of a bottle if 9% of the contents is 80 mL.
- **d** Find 18% of a wage if 54% of the wage is $630.

4 An alloy contains 15% manganese and 85% iron. 37.5 kg of manganese is used to make the alloy.

- **a** How much alloy is produced?
- **b** How much iron is used?

5 The area of Wales is approximately 20 800 km^2, which is about 9% of Great Britain. Estimate the total area of Great Britain.

6 When Vivian bakes cookies, she always burns 20% of them. How many cookies does Vivian need to bake so that she finishes with 28 unburnt cookies?

7 When churning cream to make butter, 48% of the cream comes out as butter, and the remainder as buttermilk.

- **a** How much butter will you get from 3.5 kg of cream?
- **b** Amy needs 120 g of butter for a recipe. How much cream does she need to churn?

8 Maddie operates an ice cream van. The table alongside shows the sales for each flavour in the last week, expressed as a percentage of the total number of ice creams sold.

Flavour	*% of sales*
Chocolate	36%
Vanilla	31%
Strawberry	22%
Mint	7.5%
Banana	3.5%
Total	100%

- **a** What percentage of ice creams sold were strawberry flavoured?
- **b** Given that Maddie sold 124 vanilla ice creams, determine:
  - **i** the number of chocolate ice creams sold
  - **ii** the number of mint ice creams sold
  - **iii** the total number of ice creams sold.

9 The children at a camp each chose one of canoeing, hiking, or swimming for their afternoon activity. 45% of the children chose canoeing, 18 children chose hiking, and 15 children chose swimming. How many children were at the camp?

10 Many food and drink packages come with information like the chart below.

This chart indicates that a serve of this food contains 4.5 g of protein, which is 9% of the recommended Daily Intake (DI) of protein.

Use the chart to find the recommended Daily Intake of:

- **a** energy
- **b** protein
- **c** saturated fat
- **d** sodium.

E PERCENTAGE INCREASE AND DECREASE

Changes in quantities are often expressed as a *percentage* of the original quantity.

For example:

- Class sizes have increased by 10%.
- House prices have dropped by 12%.
- Carbon emissions must fall 25% by the year 2020.

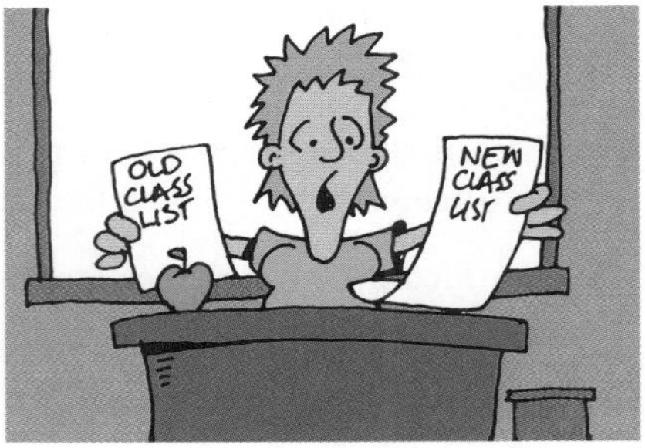

There are two different methods which can be used to solve percentage increase or decrease problems.

METHOD 1: WITH TWO STEPS

Step 1: Find the size of the increase or decrease.

Step 2: Apply the change to the original quantity by addition or subtraction.

Example 9 — Self Tutor

A fruit grower picked 1720 kg of apples last year. This year she expects her crop to be 20% bigger. How many kilograms of apples does the grower expect to pick this year?

Step 1: size of increase
$= 20\%$ of 1720 kg
$= 0.2 \times 1720$ kg
$= 344$ kg

Step 2: new amount
$= 1720 + 344$ kg
$= 2064$ kg

The fruit grower expects to pick 2064 kg of apples.

EXERCISE 5E.1

1 Perform these operations using two steps:

a increase \$30 by 10%
b decrease 50 kg by 20%
c increase 60 m by 25%
d decrease 400 L by 1%
e increase 50 000 people by 2.3%
f decrease 45 minutes by 4%.

2 Katie grows spinach in her garden. Last year she harvested 6 kg. This year her harvest increased by 30%.

a How much extra spinach did Katie harvest this year?
b Find the total weight of Katie's harvest this year.

3 Last year there were 2075 students enrolled in Grade 12 Physics. Enrolments decreased by 4% this year.

a Find the decrease in enrolments.
b How many students enrolled in Grade 12 Physics this year?

METHOD 2: WITH ONE STEP USING A MULTIPLIER

To **increase** an amount by 15%, we start with 100% of the amount, then add 15% of the amount to it. We now have $100\% + 15\% = 115\%$ of the amount.

So, to increase an amount by 15% in one step, we multiply the amount by 115% or 1.15. The value 1.15 is called the **multiplier**.

To **decrease** an amount by 15%, we start with 100% of the amount, then subtract 15% of the amount from it. We now have $100\% - 15\% = 85\%$ of the amount.

So, to decrease an amount by 15% in one step, we multiply the amount by 85% or 0.85. The value 0.85 is called the **multiplier**.

Example 10 — Self Tutor

a Increase 312 kg by 22%, giving your answer to 3 significant figures.
b Decrease $183 by 7%.

a To increase by 22%, we multiply by $100\% + 22\% = 122\%$, which is 1.22.

$\therefore$ the new amount $= 1.22 \times 312$ kg
≈ 381 kg

b To decrease by 7%, we multiply by $100\% - 7\% = 93\%$, which is 0.93.

$\therefore$ the new amount $= 0.93 \times \$183$
$= \$170.19$

EXERCISE 5E.2

1 Find the multiplier corresponding to:
  a an increase of 25%
  b a decrease of 10%
  c a decrease of 19%
  d an increase of 8.2%
  e a decrease of $7\frac{1}{2}\%$
  f an increase of 150%.

2 Use a multiplier to perform the following, giving answers to 3 significant figures where appropriate:
  a increase $50.40 by 20%
  b decrease 46 cm by 13%
  c decrease 230 kg by 55%
  d increase 35 minutes by 7.5%
  e decrease 81 L by 4.5%
  f increase €67 by 250%

3 A Pacific island has an area of 850 km^2. Due to rising sea levels, its area is predicted to decrease by 7% by 2030.
Estimate the area of the island in 2030.

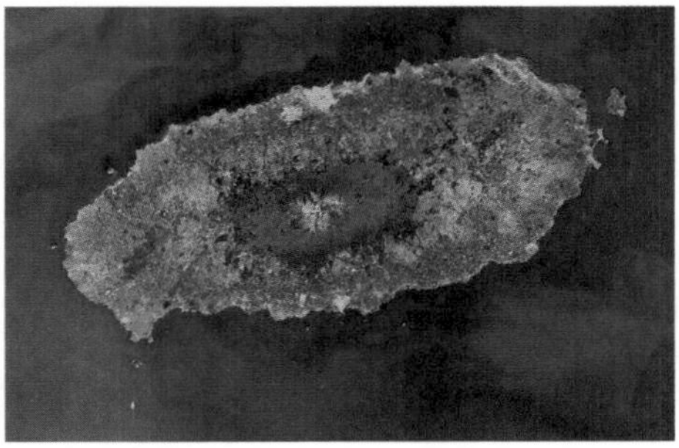

4 Ed is 160 cm tall. His sister Peggy is 8.5% taller than he is. How tall is Peggy?

5 In the year 2000, it was estimated that there were 361 million internet users worldwide. In the next ten years, that number increased by 445%. Estimate the number of internet users worldwide in 2010.

6 Jessi's rent increases by 5% at the end of each year. If she currently pays \$220 per week, how much rent will Jessi be paying:

- **a** one year from now
- **b** two years from now?

7 On Monday, the value of Rijken Industries shares were \$7.50. The price increased by 6% on Tuesday, decreased by 1.5% on Wednesday, and decreased by 2% on Thursday. Find the value of the shares when trade opened on Friday.

FINDING A PERCENTAGE CHANGE

When the size of a quantity changes, the multiplier for the change is calculated by:

$$\text{multiplier} = \frac{\text{new amount}}{\text{original amount}}$$

We can then use the multiplier to determine the percentage change.

Example 11 Self Tutor

Determine the percentage change when:

- **a** 50 kg is increased to 70 kg
- **b** \$160 is decreased to \$120.

a $\text{multiplier} = \dfrac{\text{new amount}}{\text{original amount}} = \dfrac{70 \text{ kg}}{50 \text{ kg}} = 1.4$

This corresponds to a 40% increase.

b $\text{multiplier} = \dfrac{\text{new amount}}{\text{original amount}} = \dfrac{\$120}{\$160} = 0.75$

This corresponds to a 25% decrease.

EXERCISE 5E.3

1 Find the percentage change when:

- **a** \$20 is increased to \$22
- **b** 80 mL is decreased to 68 mL
- **c** 45 g is decreased to 27 g
- **d** 90 cm is increased to 1.35 m.

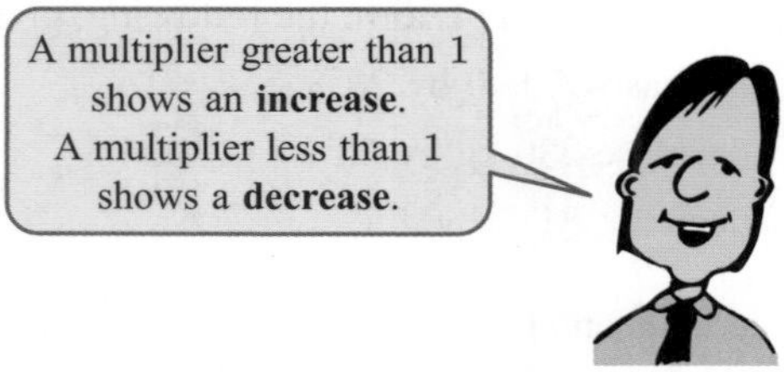

A multiplier greater than 1 shows an **increase**.
A multiplier less than 1 shows a **decrease**.

2 Describe the percentage change in the following situations:

- **a** The price of a haircut last month was \$30. It has since risen to \$34.50.
- **b** 150 people attended a community picnic last year. It rained this year, so only 108 people attended.
- **c** Arthur bought a house for 3 200 000 pesos. It is now worth 3 600 000 pesos.
- **d** At her school's sports day, Casey threw the javelin 56.33 m, breaking the previous school record of 52.40 m.
- **e** John completed a half-marathon in 1 hour and 52 minutes, improving on his previous best time of 2 hours and 8 minutes.

3 Harriot really loves snakes. For her birthday in 2011, she was given a pet carpet python by her uncle. Since then, she has measured its length on her birthday each year.

Year	2011	2012	2013	2014
Length	58 cm	79 cm	94 cm	1.07 m

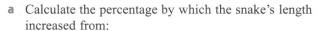

a Calculate the percentage by which the snake's length increased from:

i 2011 to 2012 **ii** 2012 to 2013 **iii** 2013 to 2014.

b Calculate the overall percentage increase for the 3-year period.

4 The following table shows the populations of some European countries, in millions of people, in 2002 and 2012:

	Germany	Italy	France	Spain	Greece	Poland	Ukraine
2002	82.5	57.2	61.8	41.8	11.0	38.2	48.2
2012	81.5	60.9	65.7	47.3	11.3	38.5	45.6

a Calculate the percentage change in population from 2002 to 2012 for each country.

b Which country had the:

i largest percentage increase **ii** largest percentage decrease in population?

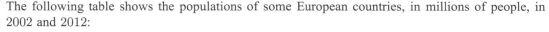

F FINDING THE ORIGINAL AMOUNT

Given an original amount and a certain percentage change, we have seen how to obtain a new amount.

It is also useful to be able to solve the reverse problem, so that if we know the percentage change and the new amount, we can calculate the original amount.

We *multiplied* the original amount by the multiplier to obtain the new amount. Reversing this process, we *divide* the new amount by the multiplier to obtain the original amount.

Example 12 **Self Tutor**

An electrical goods store buys a TV set at a wholesale price. The price of the TV is increased by 25% for sale by the store. Its selling price is now \$550.
For what price did the store buy the TV set?

cost price $\times$ multiplier = selling price

$\therefore$ cost price $\times$ 1.25 = \$550 $\{100\% + 25\% = 125\% = 1.25\}$

$\therefore$ cost price = $\frac{\$550}{1.25}$ = \$440

So, the television set cost the store \$440.

EXERCISE 5F

We *divide* the new amount by the multiplier to find the original amount.

1 Find the original amount given that:

- **a** after an increase of 20%, the length was 24 cm
- **b** after a decrease of 15%, the mass was 51 kg
- **c** after an increase of 3.6%, the amount was \$129.50
- **d** after an increase of 130%, the capacity was 9200 L
- **e** after a decrease of 0.8%, the attendance was 49 600 people.

2 In 2014, 88 nations participated in the Winter Olympics. This was a 10% increase from the 2006 Winter Olympics. How many nations participated in the 2006 Winter Olympics?

3 A clothing store is having a 15% off sale. The price of a coat has been reduced to £119. How much does the coat usually cost?

4 Answer the **Opening Problem** on page **92**.

5 From 1993 to 2013, the recorded number of black rhinoceroses has increased by 97.2% to 4880. Estimate the black rhinoceros population in 1993.

6 Joan has just received an electricity bill of \$283.50. This is 32.5% less than her previous bill. How much was Joan's previous bill?

DISCUSSION

- If an amount is *increased* by 18%, and the resulting amount is then *decreased* by 18%, do we return to the original amount?
- A new model car is 18% more expensive than the model it replaces. What percentage discount must a salesman give in order to sell the new model car at the old model price?

G SIMPLE INTEREST

If you **borrow** money from a bank, you must repay the loan in full, and also pay an additional charge called **interest**.

One method for calculating interest is called **simple interest**.

Simple interest is interest that is calculated each year as a fixed percentage of the original amount borrowed.

The fixed percentage is called the **interest rate**, and is usually written as a percentage **per annum**, which means "per year".

For example, suppose €4000 is borrowed at 10% per annum simple interest.

Each year, the simple interest charge is 10% of €4000 = €400.

Example 13 — Self Tutor

Find the simple interest payable on a loan of \$60 000 borrowed at 9% p.a. for:

a 4 years b 5 months

The simple interest charge each year $= 9\%$ of \$60 000
$= 0.09 \times \$60\,000$
$= \$5400$

a The simple interest for 4 years
$= \$5400 \times 4$
$= \$21\,600$

b 5 months is $\frac{5}{12}$ of a year
$\therefore$ the simple interest for 5 months
$= \frac{5}{12} \times \$5400$
$= \$2250$

Example 14 — Self Tutor

Find the total amount needed to repay a loan of \$40 000 borrowed at 9% p.a. simple interest for 5 years.

The simple interest charge each year $= 9\%$ of \$40 000
$= 0.09 \times \$40\,000$
$= \$3600$
$\therefore$ the simple interest for 5 years $= \$3600 \times 5$
$= \$18\,000$
$\therefore$ the total to be repaid $= \$40\,000 + \$18\,000$
$= \$58\,000$

Total to be repaid = original amount + interest.

EXERCISE 5G

1 Find the simple interest charged when:
  a \$5000 is borrowed for 1 year at 12% per annum simple interest
  b £2500 is borrowed for 2 years at 8% p.a. simple interest
  c €40 000 is borrowed for 5 years at 11% p.a. simple interest
  d \$250 000 is borrowed for 9 months at 20% p.a. simple interest.

p.a. means "per annum".

2 Find the total amount needed to repay a loan of:
  a €2400 borrowed for 3 years at 10% p.a. simple interest
  b \$8000 borrowed for 7 years at 12% p.a. simple interest
  c £7500 borrowed for $2\frac{1}{2}$ years at 8% p.a. simple interest
  d \$23 000 borrowed for 4 months at 15% p.a. simple interest.

3 Kyle borrows \$25 000 at 6% p.a. simple interest for 4 years.
  a Find the total amount needed to repay the loan.
  b Calculate the monthly repayment required to pay this loan off in 48 equal instalments.

Global context

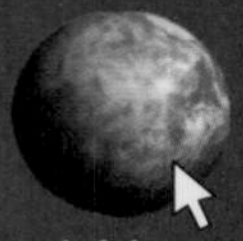

click here

Inflation rates

Statement of inquiry:	Using percentages to measure change allows us to make more meaningful comparisons.
Global context:	Fairness and development
Key concept:	Relationships
Related concepts:	Change, Measurement, Quantity
Objective:	Applying mathematics in real-life contexts
Approaches to learning:	Thinking, Self-management

REVIEW SET 5A

1 Write as a decimal:

a 83% **b** 27.4% **c** 152% **d** 0.4%

2 Write as a percentage:

a 0.6 **b** $\frac{3}{4}$ **c** 0.08 **d** 2

3 In a Mathematics competition, the top 0.3% of participants are awarded a prize. Last year 600 000 students took part. How many students were awarded a prize?

4 From a class of 30 students, 6 had visited the Great Wall of China. What percentage of the class had visited the Great Wall?

5 Find the percentage change when:

a \$80 is increased to \$85

b 3.5 litres is decreased to 2.5 litres.

6 Jillian has repaid \$700 of a \$1500 debt. What percentage of the debt has been repaid?

7 Henri has memorised 60% of a piece of music. If the piece of music takes 5 minutes to play, how long is the section that Henri has memorised?

8 A hospital has 36 doctors, who together make up 24% of the total hospital staff. How many people work at the hospital?

9 As a result of a cyclone, the price of bananas rose 85% to \$9.99 per kg. How much did bananas cost before the cyclone?

10 A football stadium normally has a maximum capacity of 60 000 people. However, one stand is under renovation, so the stadium's capacity has been reduced by 8.5%. How many people can the stadium currently hold?

11 Find the simple interest charged when £5000 is borrowed for 6 years at 7% p.a. simple interest.

12 Find the total amount needed to repay a loan of €1800 borrowed for $4\frac{1}{2}$ years at 5% p.a. simple interest.

REVIEW SET 5B

1 Write as a fraction in lowest terms:

a 48% **b** 15% **c** $5\frac{1}{2}\%$ **d** 0.1%

2 Vince brought 25 pumpkins to the market, and sold 18 of them. What percentage of his pumpkins did Vince sell?

3 An elephant eats 5% of its body weight in vegetation each day. Find the weight of vegetation eaten each day by:

a a 3000 kg elephant

b a 5000 kg elephant.

4 Express as a percentage:

a 75 marks out of 80 **b** $65 out of $104

5 On Tuesday, petrol was sold at 132.5 cents per litre. On Wednesday, the price was 121.9 cents per litre. Describe the percentage change in the price.

6 As part of a road safety campaign, fines for all traffic offences will increase by 5%. Copy and complete the table alongside, showing the changes to each fine.

Offence	*Old fine*	*New fine*
Speeding	$200	
Drink driving	$840	
Not wearing seatbelt		$273
Illegal parking		$52.50

7 Find the simple interest charged when $8000 is borrowed for 6 months at 12% p.a. simple interest.

8 Anwen scored 82% in her last test. Her friend Bree scored 76%, which was 38 marks.

a How many marks did Anwen score? **b** How many marks were in the test?

9 In 2012, the price of a theatre ticket was $50. The price rose 5% in 2013, and then a further 8% in 2014. Find the cost of a theatre ticket in :

a 2013 **b** 2014.

10 A soufflé increases in height by 125% while in the oven. If the finished height is 13.5 cm, how tall was the soufflé when it was placed in the oven?

11 Angas borrows €15 000 at 4% p.a. simple interest for 5 years.

a Find the total amount needed to repay the loan.

b Calculate the monthly repayment required to pay this loan off in 60 equal instalments.

12 A fast food restaurant sells soft drinks. The percentage of each type sold in one week is shown in the table.

Drink	*% of sales*
Cola	35.9%
Diet Cola	15.2%
Orange	12.6%
Lemonade	
Raspberry	8.5%
Total	100%

a What percentage of drinks sold were lemonade?

b The store sold 340 raspberry drinks.

i How many cola drinks were sold?

ii How many drinks were sold in total?

iii The number of orange drinks sold was 10% less than the previous week. How many orange drinks were sold in the previous week?

Chapter 6

Interpreting tables and graphs

Contents:

OPENING PROBLEM

A racing car driver completed one lap of a circuit. The graph below shows the speeds at which he was travelling during the lap.

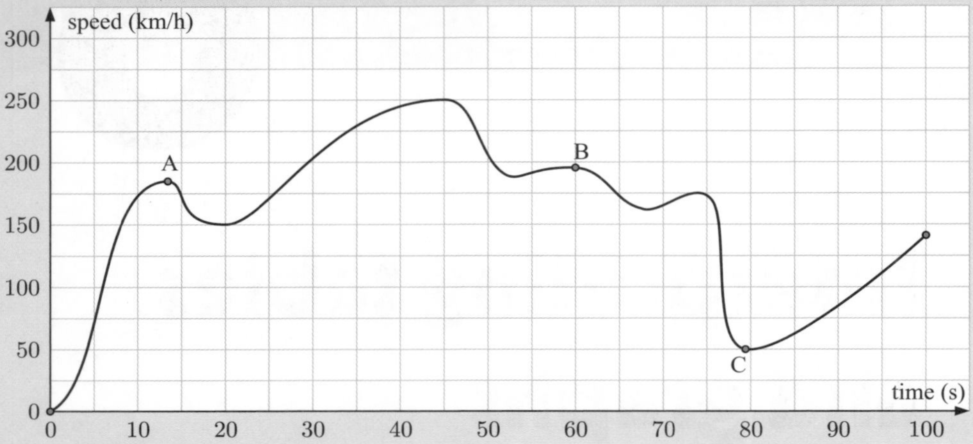

Things to think about:

- **a** How long did the driver take to complete the lap?
- **b** How fast was the car travelling after 20 seconds?
- **c** What was the highest speed the car reached during the lap?
- **d** Which of the labelled points A, B, or C, corresponds to a tight hairpin corner in the circuit?

When we are presented with **tables** and **graphs** containing data, it is important that we interpret and analyse the data correctly. We need to understand the **variables** presented in the table or graph, and what they mean in the real world.

A INTERPRETING TABLES

Tables are often used to display large amounts of data. When answering questions about tables, we need to be able to identify the data which is relevant to the question. We locate the data by using the correct **row** and **column** of the table.

Example 1 Self Tutor

The timetable for trains travelling from Epping Station to Parliament Station in Melbourne, Australia, is shown on the next page.

- **a** At what time does the 7:17 am train from Epping Station arrive at Parliament Station?
- **b** How many of the trains stop at Victoria Park Station?
- **c** Draco gets to Bell Station at 7:18 am. How long will it be before the next train arrives?

Monday to Friday

Wheelchair Accessible Services **Morning (am)/Afternoon (pm)**	am	am	am	am	am	am	am	am	am	am	am	am	am	am	am	am	am
Epping Station (Epping)	6:42	-	6:55	-	7:07	-	-	7:17	-	7:27	-	7:39	-	-	7:49	-	8:00
Lalor Station (Lalor)	6:44	-	6:57	-	7:09	-	-	7:19	-	7:29	-	7:41	-	-	7:51	-	8:02
Thomastown Station (Thomastown)	6:47	-	7:00	-	7:12	-	-	7:22	-	7:32	-	7:44	-	-	7:54	-	8:05
Keon Park Station (Thomastown)	6:49	-	7:02	-	7:14	-	-	7:24	-	7:34	-	7:46	-	-	7:56	-	8:07
Ruthven Station (Reservoir)	6:51	-	7:04	-	7:16	-	-	7:26	-	7:36	-	7:48	-	-	7:58	-	8:09
Reservoir Station (Reservoir)	6:53	-	7:06	-	7:18	-	-	7:28	-	7:38	-	7:50	-	-	8:00	-	8:11
Regent Station (Reservoir)	6:55	-	7:08	-	7:20	-	-	7:30	-	7:40	-	7:52	-	-	8:02	-	8:13
Preston Station (Preston)	6:57	-	7:10	-	7:22	-	-	7:32	-	7:42	-	7:54	-	-	8:04	-	8:15
Bell Station (Preston)	6:59	-	7:12	-	7:24	-	-	7:34	-	7:44	-	7:56	-	-	8:06	-	8:17
Thornbury Station (Thornbury)	7:01	-	7:14	-	7:26	-	-	7:36	-	7:46	-	7:58	-	-	8:08	-	8:19
Croxton Station (Northcote)	7:02	-	7:15	-	7:27	-	-	7:37	-	7:47	-	7:59	-	-	8:09	-	8:20
Northcote Station (Northcote)	7:04	-	7:17	-	7:29	-	-	7:39	-	7:49	-	8:01	-	-	8:11	-	8:22
Merri Station (Northcote)	7:05	-	7:18	-	7:30	-	-	7:40	-	7:50	-	8:02	-	-	8:12	-	8:23
Rushall Station (Fitzroy North)	7:07	-	7:20	-	7:32	-	-	7:42	-	7:52	-	8:04	-	-	8:14	-	8:25
Clifton Hill Station (Clifton Hill)	7:10	7:17	7:23	7:27	7:35	7:37	7:43	7:45	7:49	7:55	7:57	8:07	8:09	8:14	8:17	8:23	8:28
Victoria Park Station (Abbotsford)	7:12		7:25	7:29		7:39		7:47			7:59		8:11		8:19	8:25	
Collingwood Station (Abbotsford)	7:13		7:26	7:30		7:40		7:48			8:00		8:12		8:20	8:26	
North Richmond Station (Richmond)	7:15		7:28	7:32		7:42		7:50			8:02		8:14		8:22	8:28	
West Richmond Station (Richmond)	7:16		7:29	7:33		7:43		7:51			8:03		8:15		8:23	8:29	
Jolimont-MCG Station (East Melbourne)	7:19	7:22	7:32	7:35	7:40	7:45	7:48	7:53	7:55	8:00	8:05	8:12	8:17	8:19	8:25	8:31	8:33
Flinders Street Station (Melbourne City) **ARR**	7:22	7:26	7:35	7:39	7:44	7:49	7:53	7:57	7:59	8:04	8:09	8:16	8:21	8:23	8:29	8:35	8:37
Flinders Street Station (Melbourne City) **DEP**	7:24	7:28	7:37	7:41	7:46	7:51	7:55	7:59	-	8:06	8:11	8:18	8:23	8:25	8:31	8:37	8:39
Southern Cross Station (Melbourne City)	7:27	7:31	7:40	7:44	7:49	7:54	7:58	8:02	-	8:09	8:14	8:21	8:26	8:28	8:34	8:40	8:42
Flagstaff Station (Melbourne City)	7:29	7:33	7:42	7:46	7:51	7:56	8:00	8:04	-	8:11	8:16	8:23	8:28	8:30	8:36	8:42	8:44
Melbourne Central Station (Melbourne City)	7:30	7:34	7:43	7:47	7:52	7:57	8:01	8:05	-	8:12	8:17	8:24	8:29	8:31	8:37	8:43	8:45
Parliament Station (Melbourne City)	7:32	7:36	7:45	7:49	7:54	7:59	8:03	8:07	-	8:14	8:19	8:26	8:31	8:33	8:39	8:45	8:47

Monday to Friday

Wheelchair Accessible Services **Morning (am)/Afternoon (pm)**	am	am	am	am	am	am	am	am	am	am	am	am	am	am	am	am	am
Epping Station (Epping)	6:42	-	6:55	-	7:07	-	-	7:17	-	7:27	-	7:39	-	-	7:49	-	8:00
Lalor Station (Lalor)	6:44	-	6:57	-	7:09	-	-	7:19	-	7:29	-	7:41	-	-	7:51	-	8:02
Thomastown Station (Thomastown)	6:47	-	7:00	-	7:12	-	-	7:22	-	7:32	-	7:44	-	-	7:54	-	8:05
Keon Park Station (Thomastown)	6:49	-	7:02	-	7:14	-	-	7:24	-	7:34	-	7:46	-	-	7:56	-	8:07
Ruthven Station (Reservoir)	6:51	-	7:04	-	7:16	-	-	7:26	-	7:36	-	7:48	-	-	7:58	-	8:09
Reservoir Station (Reservoir)	6:53	-	7:06	-	7:18	-	-	7:28	-	7:38	-	7:50	-	-	8:00	-	8:11
Regent Station (Reservoir)	6:55	-	7:08	-	7:20	-	-	7:30	-	7:40	-	7:52	-	-	8:02	-	8:13
Preston Station (Preston)	6:57	-	7:10	-	7:22	-	-	7:32	-	7:42	-	7:54	-	-	8:04	-	8:15
Bell Station (Preston)	6:59	-	7:12	-	7:24	-	-	7:34	-	7:44	-	7:56	-	-	8:06	-	8:17
Thornbury Station (Thornbury)	7:01	-	7:14	-	7:26	-	-	7:36	-	7:46	-	7:58	-	-	8:08	-	8:19
Croxton Station (Northcote)	7:02	-	7:15	-	7:27	-	-	7:37	-	7:47	-	7:59	-	-	8:09	-	8:20
Northcote Station (Northcote)	7:04	-	7:17	-	7:29	-	-	7:39	-	7:49	-	8:01	-	-	8:11	-	8:22
Merri Station (Northcote)	7:05	-	7:18	-	7:30	-	-	7:40	-	7:50	-	8:02	-	-	8:12	-	8:23
Rushall Station (Fitzroy North)	7:07	-	7:20	-	7:32	-	-	7:42	-	7:52	-	8:04	-	-	8:14	-	8:25
Clifton Hill Station (Clifton Hill)	7:10	7:17	7:23	7:27	7:35	7:37	7:43	7:45	7:49	7:55	7:57	8:07	8:09	8:14	8:17	8:23	8:28
Victoria Park Station (Abbotsford)	7:12		7:25	7:29		7:39		7:47			7:59		8:11		8:19	8:25	
Collingwood Station (Abbotsford)	7:13		7:26	7:30		7:40		7:48			8:00		8:12		8:20	8:26	
North Richmond Station (Richmond)	7:15		7:28	7:32		7:42		7:50			8:02		8:14		8:22	8:28	
West Richmond Station (Richmond)	7:16		7:29	7:33		7:43		7:51			8:03		8:15		8:23	8:29	
Jolimont-MCG Station (East Melbourne)	7:19	7:22	7:32	7:35	7:40	7:45	7:48	7:53	7:55	8:00	8:05	8:12	8:17	8:19	8:25	8:31	8:33
Flinders Street Station (Melbourne City) **ARR**	7:22	7:26	7:35	7:39	7:44	7:49	7:53	7:57	7:59	8:04	8:09	8:16	8:21	8:23	8:29	8:35	8:37
Flinders Street Station (Melbourne City) **DEP**	7:24	7:28	7:37	7:41	7:46	7:51	7:55	7:59	-	8:06	8:11	8:18	8:23	8:25	8:31	8:37	8:39
Southern Cross Station (Melbourne City)	7:27	7:31	7:40	7:44	7:49	7:54	7:58	8:02	-	8:09	8:14	8:21	8:26	8:28	8:34	8:40	8:42
Flagstaff Station (Melbourne City)	7:29	7:33	7:42	7:46	7:51	7:56	8:00	8:04	-	8:11	8:16	8:23	8:28	8:30	8:36	8:42	8:44
Melbourne Central Station (Melbourne City)	7:30	7:34	7:43	7:47	7:52	7:57	8:01	8:05	-	8:12	8:17	8:24	8:29	8:31	8:37	8:43	8:45
Parliament Station (Melbourne City)	7:32	7:36	7:45	7:49	7:54	7:59	8:03	8:07	-	8:14	8:19	8:26	8:31	8:33	8:39	8:45	8:47

© State of Victoria, 2011

a The train leaving Epping Station at 7:17 am arrives at Parliament Station at 8:07 am.

b Trains stop at Victoria Park Station at 7:12 am, 7:25 am, 7:29 am, 7:39 am, 7:47 am, 7:59 am, 8:11 am, 8:19 am, and 8:25 am.
So, 9 of the trains stop at Victoria Park Station.

c Trains stop at Bell Station at 6:59 am, 7:12 am, and 7:24 am.
$\therefore$ the first train to arrive after 7:18 am will be at 7:24 am.
$\therefore$ it will be 6 minutes before the next train arrives.

EXERCISE 6A

1 Use the train timetable in **Example 1** to answer the following questions.

- **a** At what time does the 7:49 am train from Epping Station arrive at Regent Station?
- **b** Keith boards the train leaving Thomastown Station at 6:47 am. Between which two stations will this train be at 7:00 am?
- **c** For how long do the trains stop at Flinders Street Station?
- **d** Celia lives near Clifton Hill Station, and needs to be at Southern Cross Station by 8:10 am. At what time should she get to Clifton Hill Station?

2 The table below indicates the days that certain places open during the end of year holiday period:

	Dec 24	Dec 25	Dec 26	Dec 27	Dec 28	Dec 29	Dec 30	Dec 31	Jan 1	Jan 2
Banks	✓	✗	✗	✗	✓	✓	✓	✓	✗	✗
Supermarkets	✓	✗	✗	✓	✓	✓	✓	✓	✗	✓
Libraries	✓	✗	✗	✗	✗	✗	✗	✗	✗	✓
Department stores	✓	✗	✓	✓	✓	✓	✓	✓	✗	✓

- **a** Are the libraries open on December 29?
- **b** Are the department stores open on December 26?
- **c** On how many days during this period are the banks open?
- **d** On which days are:
  - **i** all of the places open
  - **ii** none of the places open?

3 A furniture store offers a delivery service for its products. The fee depends on the weight of the furniture to be delivered, and the distance the furniture must be transported. The delivery costs are shown in the table below.

		Distance		
		0 - 20 km	20 - 40 km	40 - 60 km
	0 - 50 kg	\$19	\$34	\$50
Weight	50 - 100 kg	\$35	\$62	\$85
	100+ kg	\$50	\$90	\$105

50 - 100 kg includes 50 kg but not 100 kg.

- **a** Suzette bought a cupboard weighing 60 kg. She lives 12 km from the furniture store. How much will it cost Suzette to have the cupboard delivered to her home?
- **b** Jason lives 25 km from the furniture store. He bought a chair weighing 20 kg, a table weighing 35 kg, and a desk weighing 50 kg.
  - **i** Find the total weight of the furniture Jason bought.
  - **ii** Find the cost of delivering these items.
- **c** Lillian lives 47 km from the furniture store. She bought a 70 kg chest of drawers, and had it delivered to her home. A month later, she bought a 45 kg bookshelf, which was also delivered to her home.
  - **i** Find the total cost of the two deliveries.
  - **ii** How much would Lillian have saved if the items had been delivered together?

4 The table below shows the number of internet users per 100 inhabitants in various countries from 2003 to 2012.

	2003	2004	2005	2006	2007	2008	2009	2010	2011	2012
Indonesia	2.39	2.60	3.60	4.76	5.79	7.92	6.92	10.92	12.28	15.36
Japan	48.44	62.39	66.92	68.69	74.30	75.40	78.00	78.21	79.05	79.05
South Korea	65.50	72.70	73.50	78.10	78.80	81.00	81.60	83.70	83.80	84.10
New Zealand	60.96	61.85	62.72	69.00	69.76	72.03	79.70	83.00	86.00	89.51
Philippines	4.86	5.24	5.40	5.74	5.97	6.22	9.00	25.00	29.00	36.24
Russia	8.30	12.86	15.23	18.02	24.66	26.83	29.00	43.00	49.00	53.27
Singapore	53.84	62.00	61.00	59.00	69.90	69.00	69.00	71.00	71.00	74.18
Thailand	9.30	10.68	15.03	17.16	20.03	18.20	20.10	22.40	23.70	26.50
United States of America	61.70	64.76	67.97	68.93	75.00	74.00	71.00	74.00	77.86	81.03
Vietnam	3.78	7.64	12.74	17.25	20.76	23.92	26.55	30.65	35.07	39.49

a How many inhabitants out of 100 used the internet in Singapore in:
 i 2005 **ii** 2010?

b In which years did more than 20 out of 100 Russian inhabitants use the internet?

c Which of the listed countries had the most internet users per 100 inhabitants in:
 i 2007 **ii** 2011?

d Which listed country had the largest increase of internet users per 100 inhabitants from 2003 to 2012?

5 A group of hotel guests were asked to rate the hotel's performance in a number of categories. The results are presented in the table below:

	Excellent	Good	Fair	Poor
Cleanliness	20%	31%	35%	14%
Staff	32%	27%	15%	26%
Restaurant	9%	19%	37%	35%
Value for money	12%	16%	28%	44%
Location	33%	39%	18%	10%
Facilities	27%	34%	26%	13%

a What percentage of people rated the hotel's cleanliness as 'Fair'?

b What percentage of people rated the hotel's staff as 'Good' or 'Excellent'?

c What was the most common response when rating the hotel's value for money?

d 130 people rated the hotel's facilities as 'Fair'. How many hotel guests were surveyed?

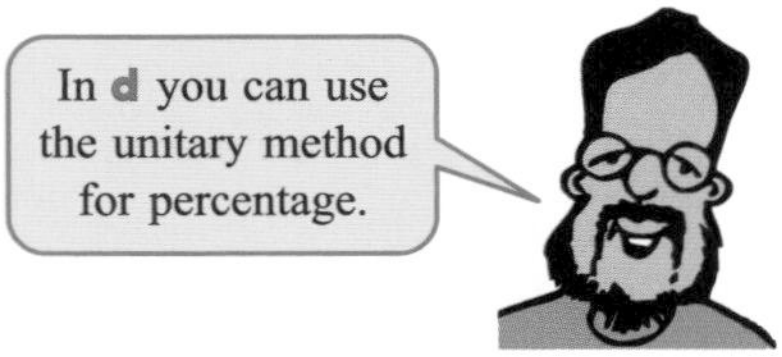

In d you can use the unitary method for percentage.

6 The table below shows the distances in kilometres between cities in the Middle East.

Dubai							
1509	Cairo						
858	809	Baghdad					
997	1311	1244	Sana'a				
539	1021	614	669	Riyadh			
233	1743	1090	1094	751	Muscat		
757	1235	436	1480	808	936	Tehran	
1277	385	466	1348	876	1510	870	Damascus

a Find the distance between:
  i Cairo and Sana'a
  ii Tehran and Baghdad.

b Which of the cities listed is:
  i closest to Damascus
  ii furthest from Baghdad?

c Which two of the cities listed are furthest apart?

d Kay needs to travel from Riyadh to Damascus, and then to Muscat. How far will she travel?

e Use the table to show that the route from Damascus to Muscat passes through Dubai.

7 The table below shows some of the 2011/12 student numbers for higher education qualifications in the United Kingdom, as well as the total percentage changes in student numbers from 2006/07.

Subject area	*Female*	*Male*	*Total*	*Total % change from* 2006/07
Medicine & dentistry	10 650	7555	18 205	30.4
Subjects allied to medicine	68 470	17 280	85 750	1.6
Biological sciences	34 450	20 970	55 420	28.9
Veterinary science	875	255	1130	35.1
Agriculture & related subjects	3635	2255	5890	23.9
Physical sciences	11 110	15 100	26 210	23.6
Mathematical sciences	4720	6765	11 485	30.8
Computer science	5750	24 765	30 515	−2.4
Engineering & technology	8595	42 085	50 680	31.2
Architecture, building & planning	7340	14 405	21 745	28.4
Social studies	46 255	27 485	73 740	22.1
Law	19 585	13 480	33 065	9
Business & administrative studies	69 655	70 370	140 025	43.3
Languages	25 345	11 495	36 840	17.2
Historical & philosophical studies	15 000	13 170	28 170	11.6
Creative arts & design	37 755	23 535	61 290	31.5
Education	61 430	18 915	80 345	11.2

a How many female students studied Law in 2011/12?

b Did more males study Computer Science or Education?

c Which subject listed had the **i** highest **ii** lowest total number of students?

d What percentage of Biological Sciences students were female?

e How many of these subject areas increased their student intake from 2006/07?

f Estimate, to three significant figures, the total number of students studying Social Studies in 2006/07.

ACTIVITY **INTERPRETING TABLES**

What to do:

1. Find a table of information in a newspaper article, on a food label, or in a book.
2. Write three questions which can be answered using the table.
3. Give the table and your questions to a friend in your class to answer.
4. Discuss in your class the most interesting questions.

B INTERPRETING GRAPHS

Many newspapers and magazines use graphs to display information. Graphs are used to make the information more visually appealing and easier to understand.

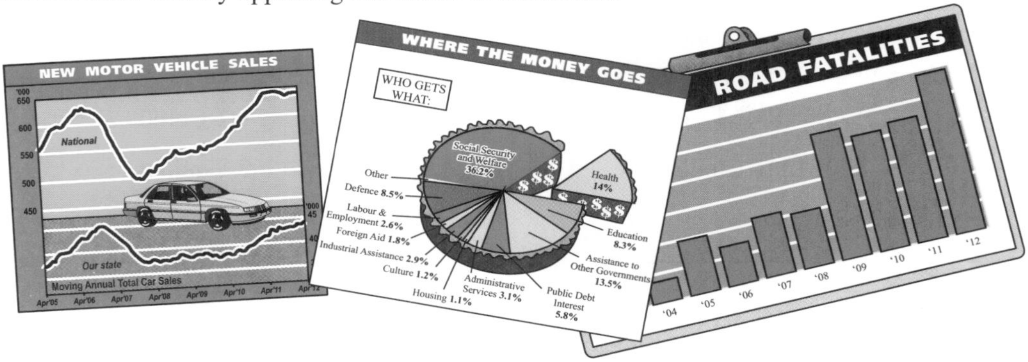

Example 2 **Self Tutor**

The bar graph shows the number of different items sold in an electrical goods store in a given month.

a. How many DVD players were sold for the month?
b. How many more computers were sold than television sets?
c. What percentage of the items sold were cooling fans?

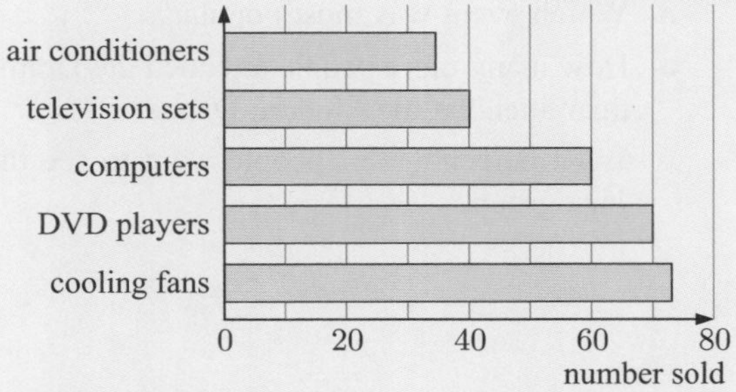

a. 70 DVD players were sold.
b. 60 computers were sold. 40 television sets were sold.
   $\therefore$ 20 more computers than television sets were sold.
c. 34 air conditioners, 40 television sets, 60 computers, 70 DVD players, and 73 cooling fans were sold.
   $\therefore$ the total number of items sold was $34 + 40 + 60 + 70 + 73 = 277$
   $\therefore$ $\frac{73}{277} \times 100\% \approx 26.4\%$ of the items sold were cooling fans.

Example 3 **Self Tutor**

Use the pie chart alongside to answer the following questions regarding the health budget.

a How much money was allocated to the health care budget?

b What percentage of the budget was allocated to mental health services?

c Which service received the most money?

d How much money was spent on:

  i hospital support services

  ii other programs?

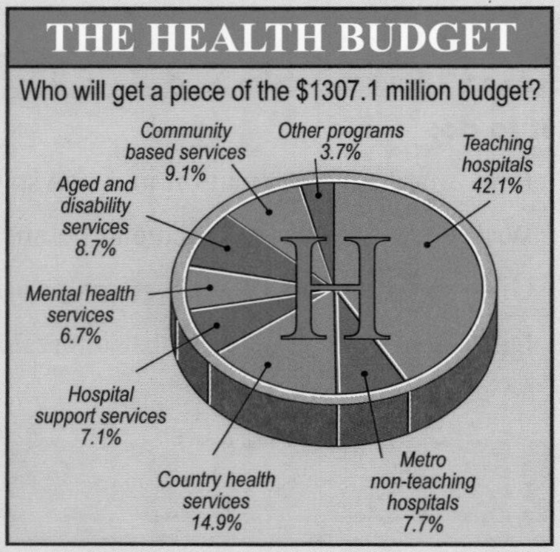

a \$1307.1 million was allocated to the health care budget.

b 6.7% of the budget was allocated to mental health services.

c Teaching hospitals received the most money, with 42.1% of the budget.

d **i** 7.1% of \$1307.1 million
$= \frac{7.1}{100} \times \$1307.1$ million
$\approx \$92.8$ million

ii 3.7% of \$1307.1 million
$= \frac{3.7}{100} \times \$1307.1$ million
$\approx \$48.4$ million

EXERCISE 6B

1 The graph shows the attendances at various Friday night events at an Arts festival.

a Which event was most popular?

b How many more people attended the Drama than attended the Modern Dance?

c What percentage of people went to see the Jazz group?

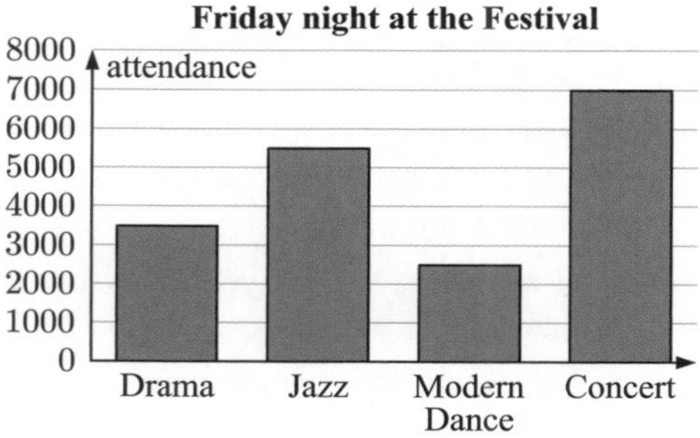

2 **a** Estimate the median house price in 2013 in:

  i Liverpool **ii** Edinburgh.

b How much higher is the median house price in Edinburgh than in Glasgow?

c What percentage is the median Liverpool price of the median Birmingham price?

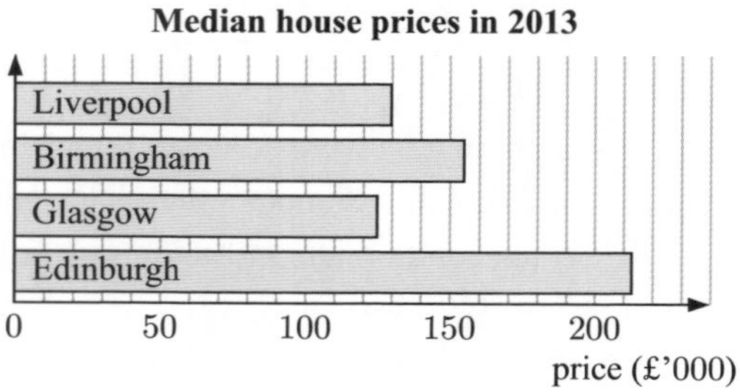

3 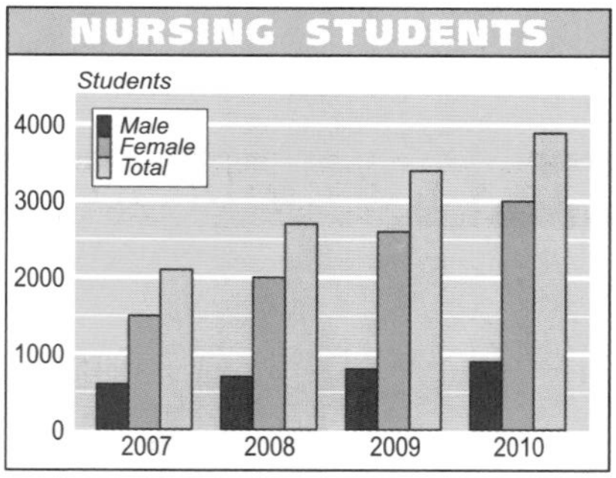

The graph shows the number of students studying nursing over a period of years.

- **a** Estimate the total number of nursing students in 2008.
- **b** Estimate the percentage of the total nursing students in 2008 who were male.
- **c** In which year was the proportion of male students the highest?

4 The graph displays the results of a national poll of 240 children aged six to sixteen, as to what they do at home between 3 pm and 6 pm.

- **a** Estimate the percentage of children who:
  - **i** watch TV, videos, play with computers, or listen to music
  - **ii** spend time with friends, siblings, or pets.
- **b** Of the 240 children surveyed in the poll:
  - **i** how many do schoolwork
  - **ii** how many more spend time on the phone than do chores?

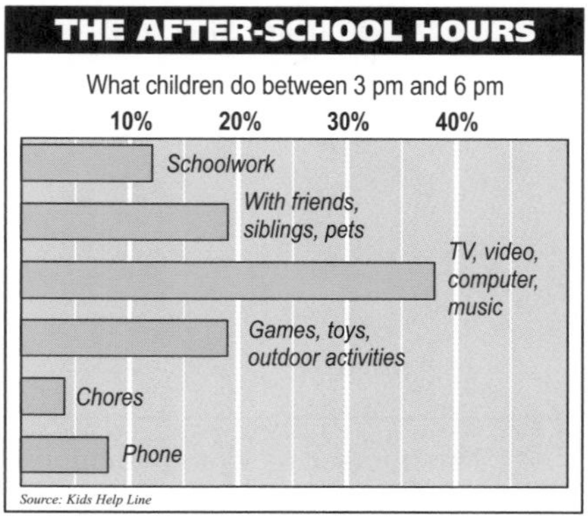

5 The pie chart shows the market share of different wines in the United States of America.

- **a** What percentage of wine sales are from:
  - **i** Muscato
  - **ii** the Sauvignon types?
- **b** What type of wine has the highest market share?
- **c** In 2010, the retail revenue from wine sales in the United States of America was approximately \$30 billion. How much revenue was made in that year from the sale of:
  - **i** White Zinfandel
  - **ii** Merlot?

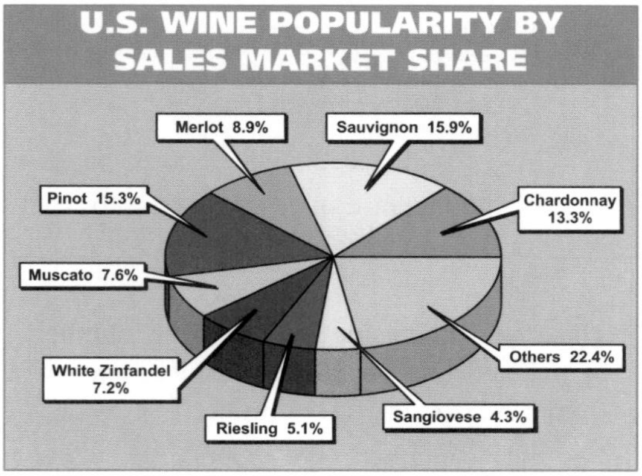

6 Use the pie chart to answer the following questions on the distribution of supermarkets.

- **a** Which supermarket chain accounted for the most supermarkets?
- **b** If the total number of supermarkets is 12 582, find the number of supermarkets which are:
  - **i** Tudor's Foods
  - **ii** Food City
  - **iii** Independent.

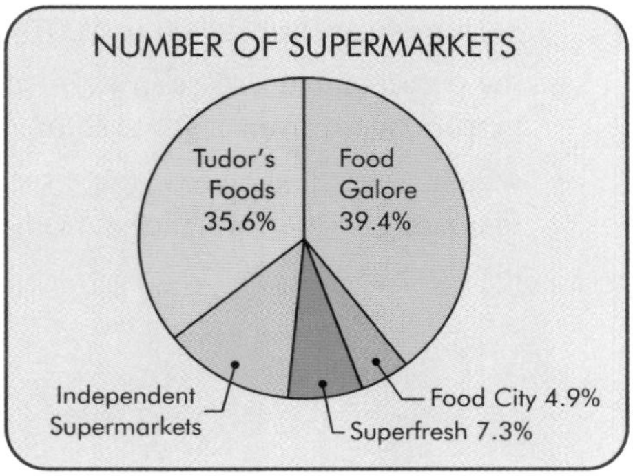

Example 4 **Self Tutor**

The column graph shows the number of women diagnosed with breast cancer from 1999 to 2007. Use the graph to determine:

a the number of women diagnosed in 2007

b how many more women were diagnosed in 2004 than in 2002

c the percentage increase in cases diagnosed from 2001 to 2006.

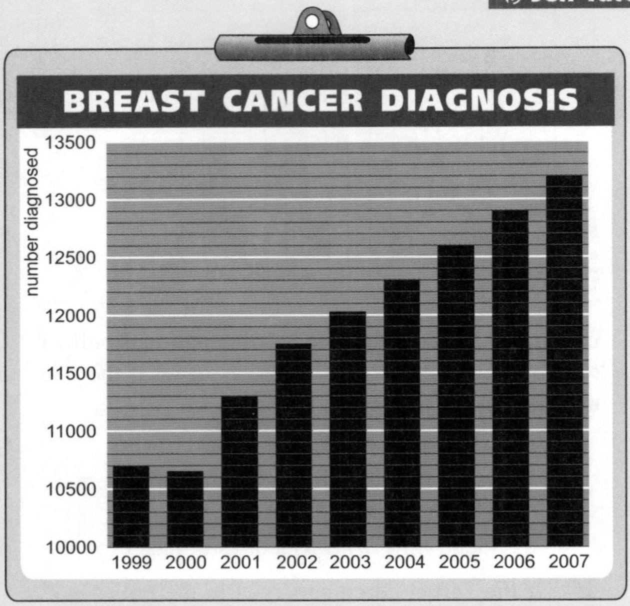

a The number of women diagnosed in 2007 was 13 200.

b The number of women diagnosed in 2004 was 12 300.
The number of women diagnosed in 2002 was 11 750.
$\therefore$ $12\,300 - 11\,750 = 550$ more cases were diagnosed in 2004 than in 2002.

c multiplier $= \dfrac{\text{2006 amount}}{\text{2001 amount}}$
$= \dfrac{12\,900}{11\,300}$
≈ 1.142 which corresponds to a 14.2% increase

So, the increase in cases diagnosed from 2001 to 2006 was approximately 14.2%.

7 The graph alongside indicates the number of ticketed arts performances in Singapore from 1997 to 2007. Determine:

a the number of ticketed arts performances in 1997

b the increase in ticketed arts performances from 2006 to 2007

c the percentage decrease in ticketed arts performances from 2002 to 2003

d which year showed the greatest increase in performances from the previous year.

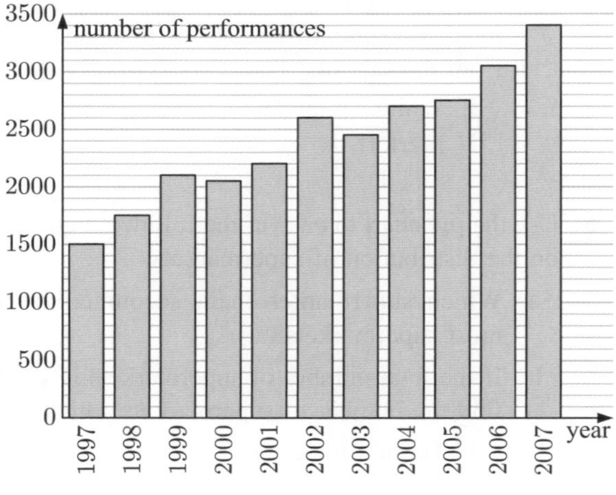

8 The size of Neil's monthly phone bill is displayed in the graph alongside.

a How much was Neil's phone bill in March?

b Find the increase in Neil's phone bill from January to February.

c Describe the percentage change in the phone bill from:

i March to April

ii April to June.

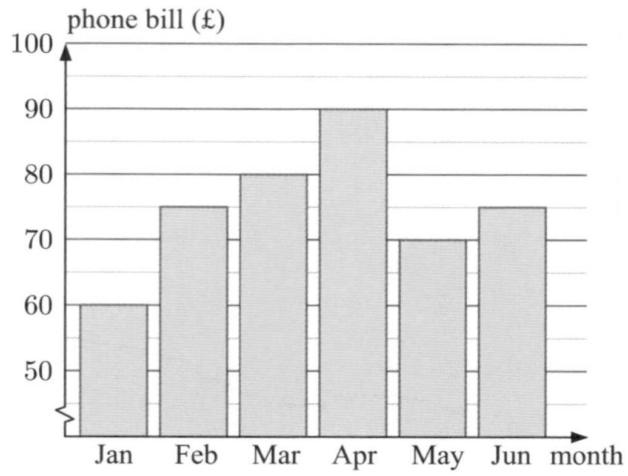

C LINE GRAPHS

A **line graph** consists of a curve, or a series of straight line segments, which shows the relationship between two quantities.

Example 5 — Self Tutor

A chemical engineer is performing a reaction using large quantities of liquid. The line graph shows the volume of liquid in the collection tank over the period of one day. During the day three samples of the liquid were taken for quality control.

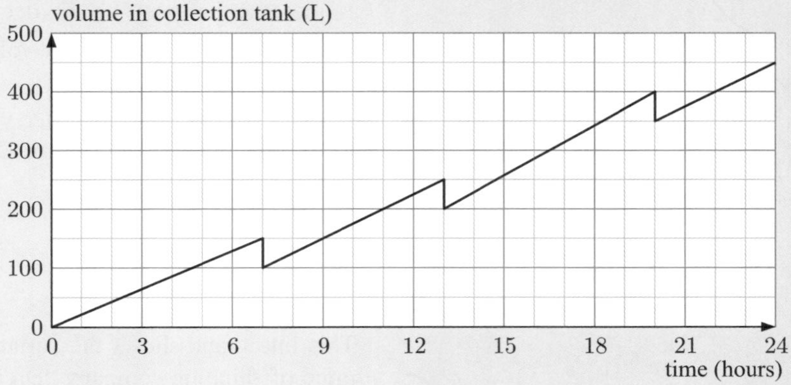

a How much liquid was produced in the first 7 hours?

b How much liquid was sampled each time for quality control?

c What was the total amount of liquid produced by the reaction over the whole day?

a In the first 7 hours, 150 L of liquid was produced.

b 50 L of liquid was sampled for quality control on each occasion.

c After 24 hours, 450 L of liquid was in the collection tank.

3×50 L $= 150$ L of liquid was taken out for quality control.

$\therefore$ the total amount produced by the reaction was 450 L + 150 L = 600 L.

EXERCISE 6C

1 Ebony used a thermometer to measure the temperature in her bedroom from 6 am to 6 pm. The results are shown in the line graph below:

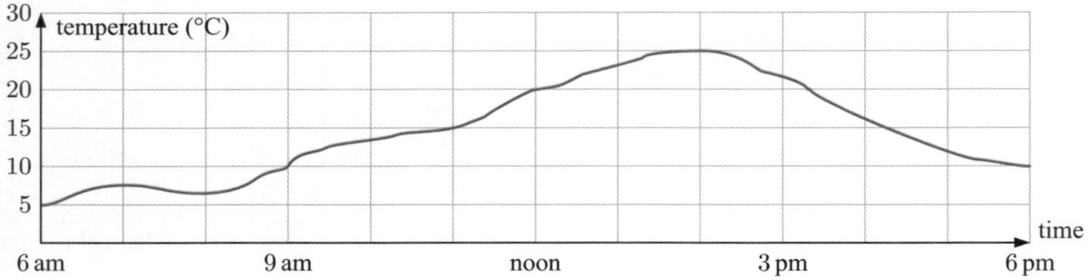

a Find the temperature at 9 am.

b **i** What was the maximum temperature during the day?

ii At what time did this maximum temperature occur?

c Was the temperature increasing or decreasing at 4 pm? Explain your answer.

2

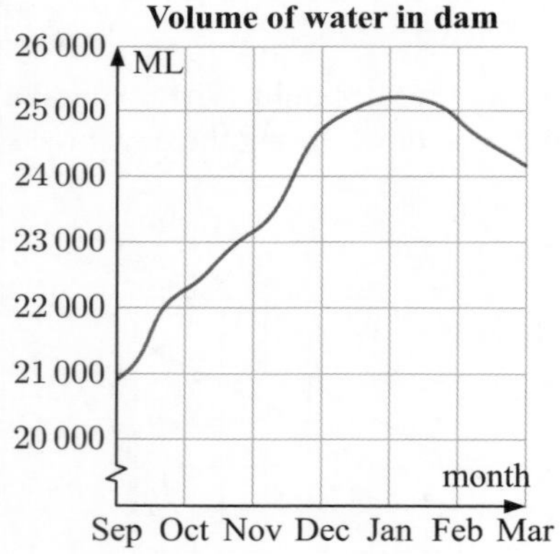

a What information is contained in the graph alongside?

b How much water was in the dam at the start of:

i October **ii** February?

c Over which month did the water volume:

i increase the most **ii** decrease the most?

d What was the maximum water volume during this period?

e What was the increase in water volume from the start of September to the start of December?

3 Answer the **Opening Problem** on page **110**.

4

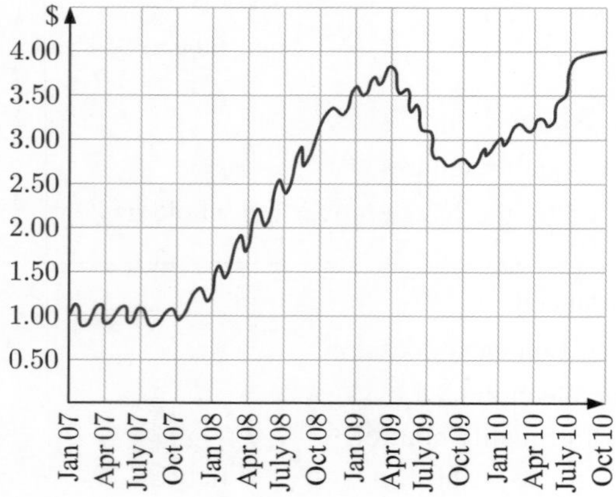

This line graph shows the variation in the share price of shipping company "Dreamboats" over a number of years. Determine:

a the value of the shares in July:

i 2008 **ii** 2010

b the year during which the greatest increase in value occurred

c the percentage increase from the start of 2008 to the end of 2009

d the percentage decrease from April 2009 to October 2009.

5 Match each graph to the corresponding story.

a

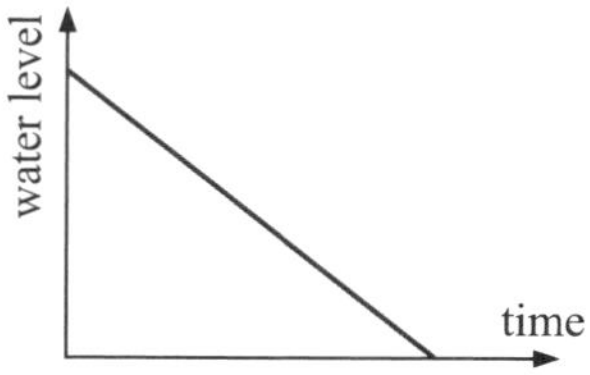

b

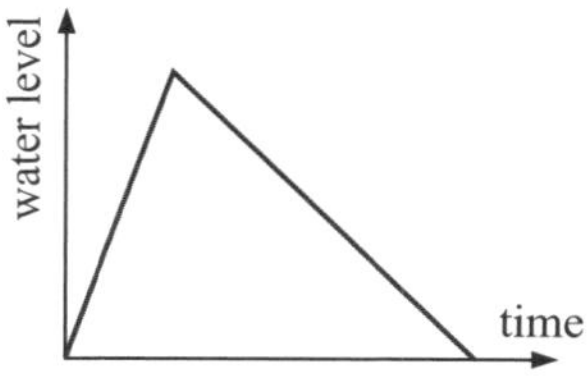

c

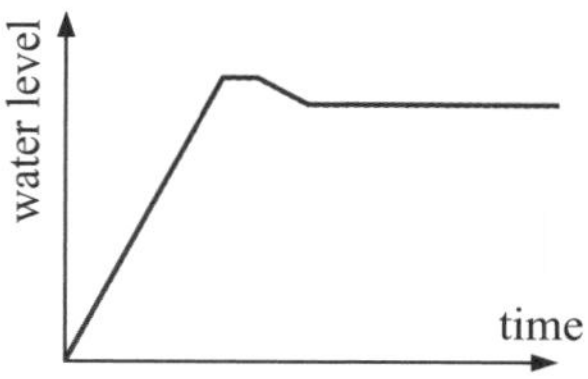

A I fill a bucket with water. After a few minutes my dog has a drink from the bucket. I leave the rest of the water in the bucket in case he wants another drink later.

B I fill a bucket with water, but the bucket has a split and the water runs out.

C I have a full bucket of water. I pour it slowly over my seedlings until the bucket is empty.

D TRAVEL GRAPHS

A **travel graph** for a journey is a line graph which shows the relationship between the distance travelled from a starting point or **origin**, and the time taken to travel it.

Time is the **independent variable**, so is plotted on the x-axis. *Distance* is the **dependent variable**, so is plotted on the y-axis.

An upward sloping section of the graph indicates that the traveller is moving away from the starting point.

A downward sloping section of the graph indicates that the traveller is moving back towards the starting point.

A steep slope on the graph indicates where the speed of travel is fastest.

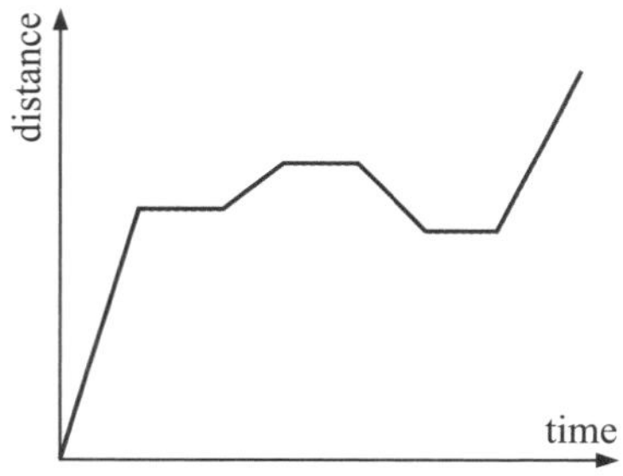

Example 6 **Self Tutor**

This travel graph shows the journey of a sales representative travelling from home to meetings in different towns.

Write a story to describe his journey.

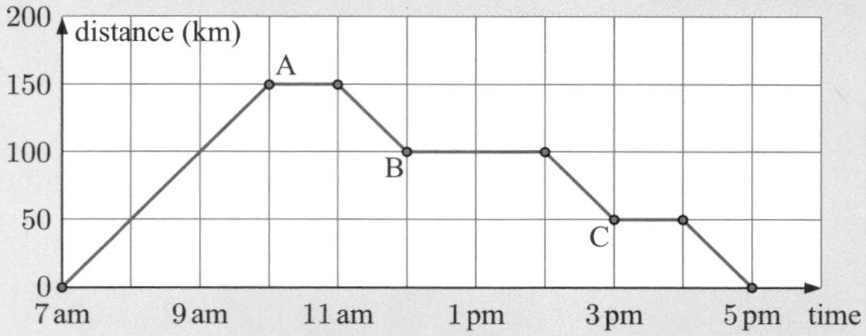

The sales representative leaves home at 7 am and travels 150 km to town A in 3 hours. He spends an hour there with customers.

He then travels 50 km back towards home to town B, where he arrives at 12 noon.

He spends an hour with customers and then has an hour for lunch.

At 2 pm he travels another 50 km back towards home, arriving at town C at 3 pm.

He spends an hour there with customers.

At 4 pm he travels 50 km back to his home, arriving at 5 pm.

EXERCISE 6D

1 Wingyi walks for 30 minutes from her home to the post office, which is 3 km away. She waits in line for 15 minutes, then walks home, taking 45 minutes. Draw a travel graph to illustrate her journey.

2 The travel graph describes the journey of a family travelling from their home in Tokyo to Kanazawa. The total distance is 450 km.

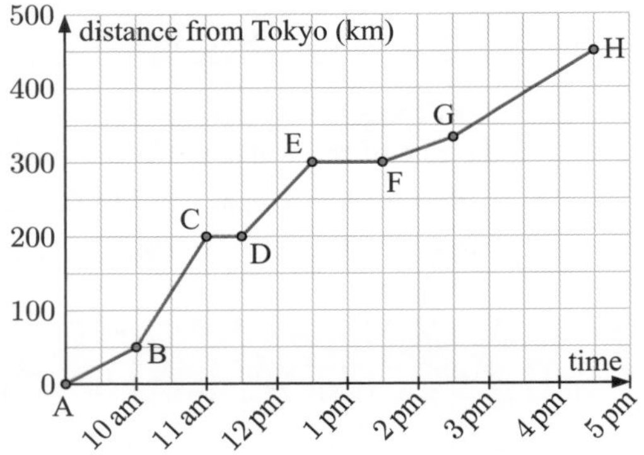

- **a** Write a story to describe their trip.
- **b** Explain where the following comments are made in the journey.
  - **i** "Let's have lunch now."
  - **ii** "This is the fastest section."
  - **iii** "We will have to drive through roadworks."
  - **iv** "We have finally arrived."
  - **v** "Let's stop briefly to stretch our legs."

3 The annual *Hare versus Tortoise* 1 km race took place at the end of spring, so the tortoise was fully awake after his winter hibernation. When the starter's gun fired, the tortoise plodded off at a steady 50 metres per minute, while the hare raced ahead at an amazing 400 metres per minute. Unfortunately, the hare could only do this for 30 seconds at a time, then required a rest for 5 minutes before his next run.

- **a** Construct travel graphs for both the hare and the tortoise. Place time on the horizontal axis and distance on the vertical axis.
- **b** Who won the race?
- **c** Last year the hare only had to rest for 3 minutes after each run. Who won last year?

4 There are three routes from Mt Blanch to Dudley Beach.
Match each travel graph with the appropriate route description:

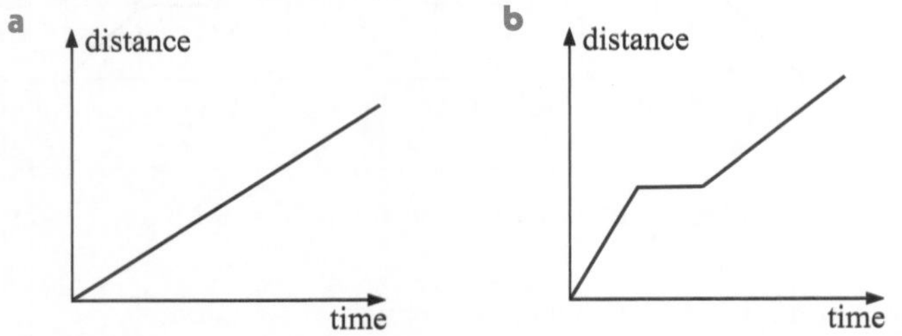

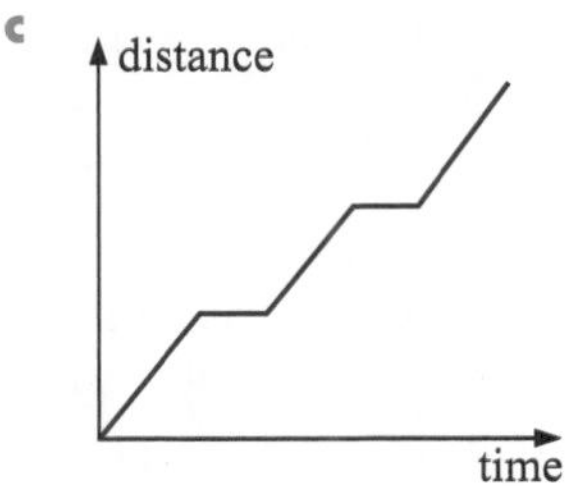

Route A: main roads with 60 km/h speed limits and multiple traffic lights

Route B: a highway with a 110 km/h speed limit, a stop at a train crossing, then an 80 km/h speed limit main road

Route C: a winding road which requires travel at a constant slower speed.

Example 7 **Self Tutor**

The graph alongside shows the distance a homing pigeon travelled from its point of release until it arrived home.

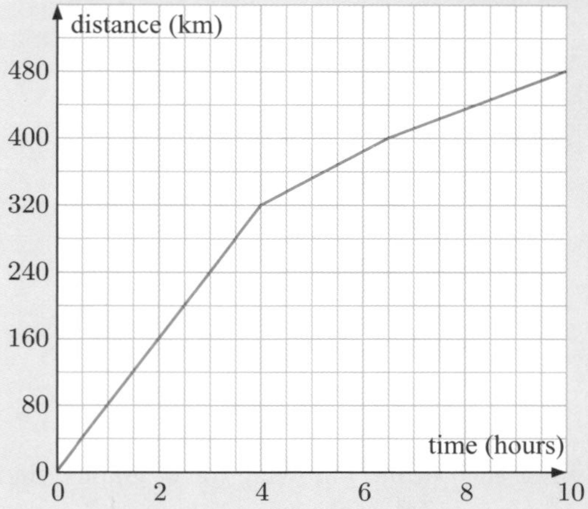

Use the graph to determine:

- **a** the total length of the flight
- **b** the time taken for the pigeon to return home
- **c** the time taken to fly the first 200 km
- **d** the time taken to fly from the 240 km mark to the 400 km mark
- **e** the average speed for the first 4 hours
- **f** the average speed for the whole flight.

- **a** The length of the flight was 480 km.
- **b** It took 10 hours for the pigeon to return home.
- **c** It took $2\frac{1}{2}$ hours to fly the first 200 km.
- **d** It took 3 hours to fly 240 km and $6\frac{1}{2}$ hours to fly 400 km.
  $\therefore$ it took $3\frac{1}{2}$ hours to fly from 240 km to 400 km.
- **e** In the first 4 hours the pigeon flew 320 km.
  $\therefore$ its average speed was $\frac{320}{4} = 80$ km per hour.
- **f** The pigeon travelled 480 km in 10 hours.
  $\therefore$ its average speed was $\frac{480}{10} = 48$ km per hour.

5 The graph alongside shows the journey of a student from home to school. Use the graph to determine:

- **a** the distance to school
- **b** the time taken to get to school
- **c** the distance travelled after 16 minutes
- **d** the time taken to travel the first 8 km
- **e** the average speed for the whole trip, in km/h
- **f** the average speed for the fastest part of the journey, in km/h.

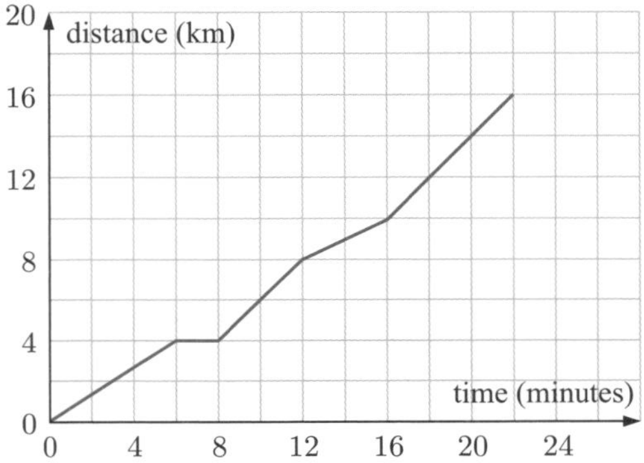

6 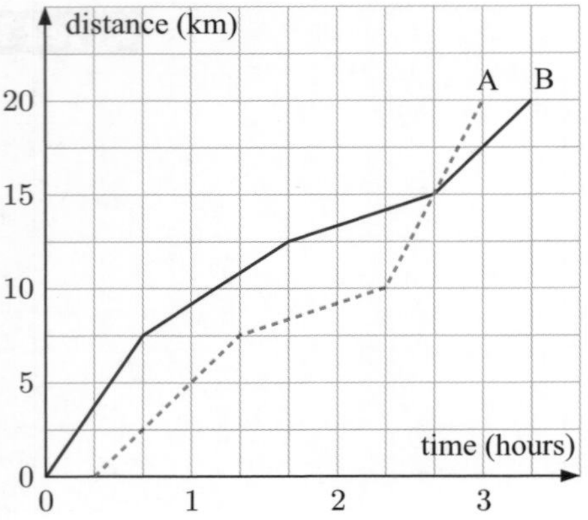

Two yachts set sail from the harbour in a time trial. The travel graph indicates how far each yacht sails over time. Use the graph to determine:

- **a** how many minutes yacht A departed after yacht B
- **b** the distance travelled by each yacht
- **c** how far both yachts had travelled when yacht A caught yacht B
- **d** how long it took each yacht to travel the first 10 km
- **e** how much time elapsed between yacht A and yacht B crossing the finish line
- **f** the average speed of each yacht.

7 For each of the following travel graphs, find:

- **i** the total distance travelled
- **ii** the average speed for the whole trip.

a 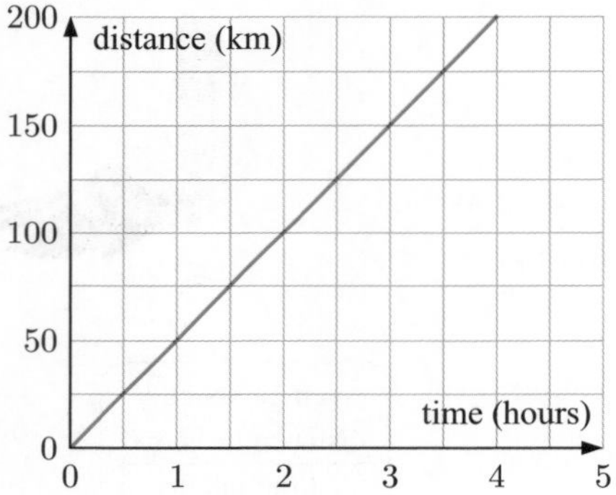

b 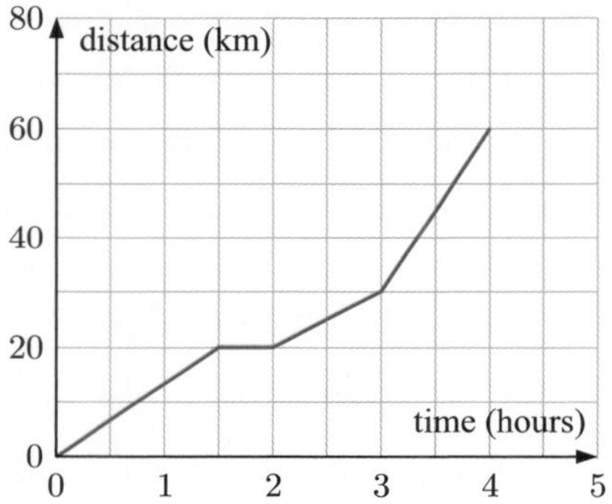

c 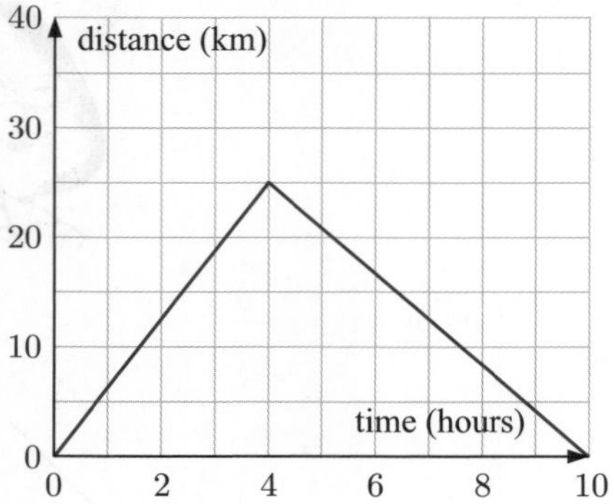

d 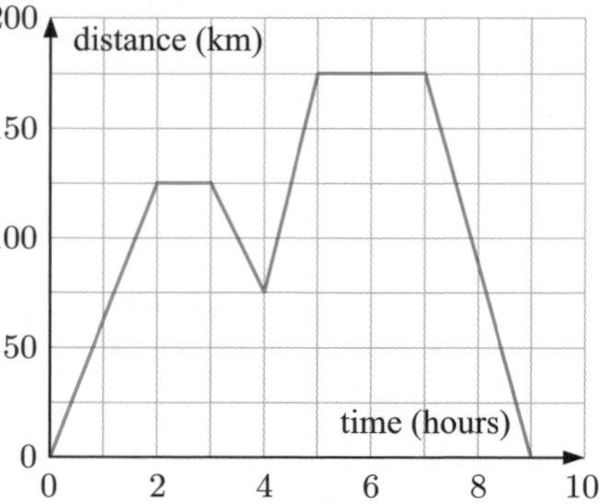

DISCUSSION

- What are the advantages and disadvantages of tables and graphs in displaying information?
- What types of information can different types of graphs represent?

REVIEW SET 6A

1 A local council conducted a survey. They asked their residents to rate, out of five, the standard of different facilities and services in the area. The results are given alongside.

	1	2	3	4	5
Libraries	11%	12%	19%	26%	32%
Public transport	16%	32%	25%	14%	13%
Schools	17%	28%	25%	16%	14%
Shops	7%	16%	20%	35%	22%
Parks	11%	23%	24%	29%	13%
Health services	9%	14%	27%	26%	24%

a What percentage of residents rated health services as 5 out of 5?

b What percentage of residents rated the standard of schools as 4 or above?

c The council will upgrade the facilities and services for which 30% or more of residents gave a rating of 1 or 2. Which facilities and services will the council be upgrading?

2 The cost of sending a parcel depends on the weight of the parcel and the destination. A postal company's prices are given in the table below:

		Weight			
		< 1 kg	1 to 5 kg	5 to 10 kg	> 10 kg
Destination	Within the state	$3	$5	$8	$10
	Interstate	$10	$13	$17	$22
	Overseas	$20	$40	$75	$100

a Danni has a parcel weighing 8 kg which she wants to send interstate. How much will this cost her?

b Owen has 3 parcels, which need to be sent to different locations within the state. The parcels weigh 750 g, 4 kg, and 15 kg. How much will Owen spend on postage?

c Hans is an overseas tourist and needs to send gifts back home. He only has $80 to spend on postage. What is the maximum weight in gifts that Hans can send home?

3

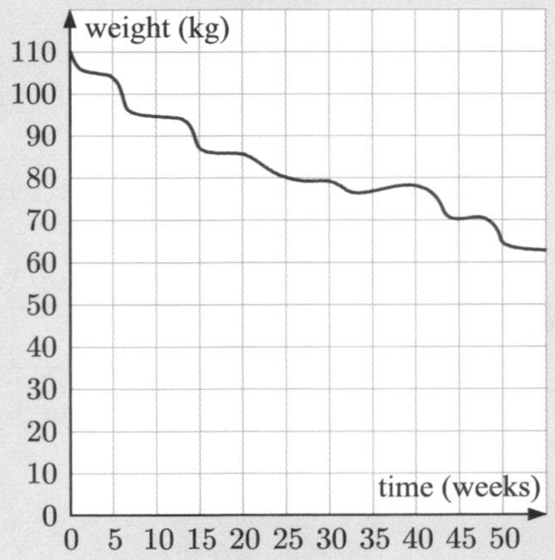

Jodie went on a diet for 50 weeks. The results are shown on the graph alongside.

a What was Jodie's initial weight?

b What was Jodie's final weight after 50 weeks?

c How much weight had Jodie lost after 25 weeks?

d Did Jodie lose weight every week? Explain your answer.

4

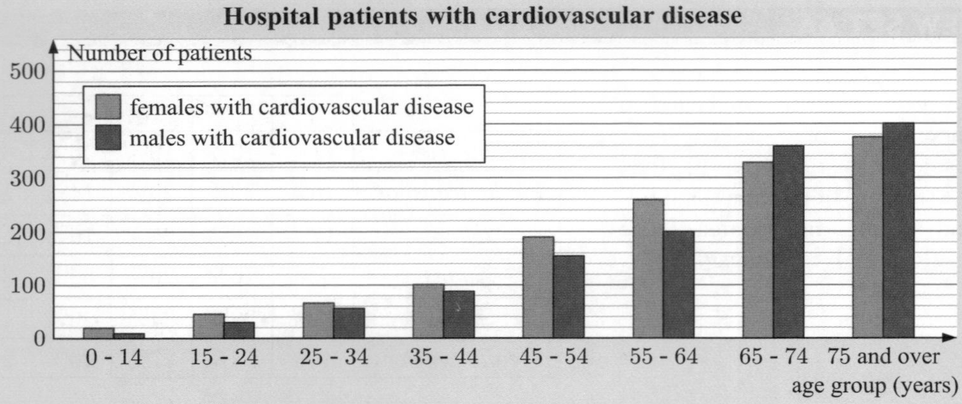

The graph above shows the number of cardiovascular patients admitted to a hospital over 3 months. Use the graph to find:

a how many 55 - 64 year old males were admitted to hospital

b the percentage of the total patients aged 45 - 54 who were female

c which age groups had more male patients than female patients.

5 The graph alongside shows the distance René is from home during a day.

a How far did René travel between:

i 8 am and 9 am

ii 3 pm and 5 pm

iii 8 am and 5 pm?

b For how long was René 35 km from home?

c Describe René's journey.

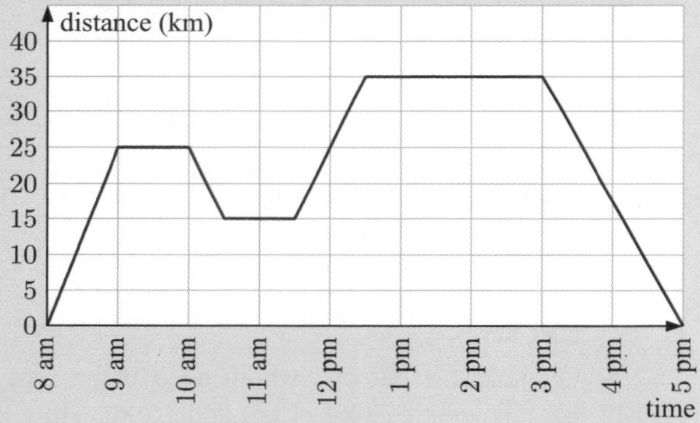

6

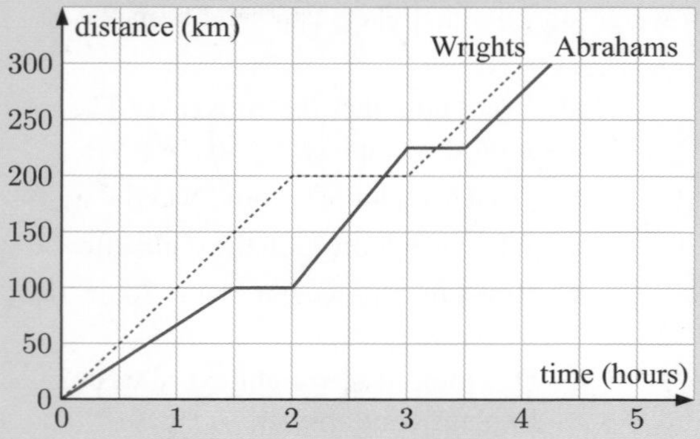

The travel graph shows the distance travelled by two families from Detroit to Indianapolis.

Use the graph to determine:

a the distance from Detroit to Indianapolis

b how long it took each family to complete the journey

c the length of time the Wrights stopped for lunch

d the distances at which the families passed each other on the journey.

REVIEW SET 6B

1 The bar graph shows the crude oil reserves for the top five oil producing countries in the world.

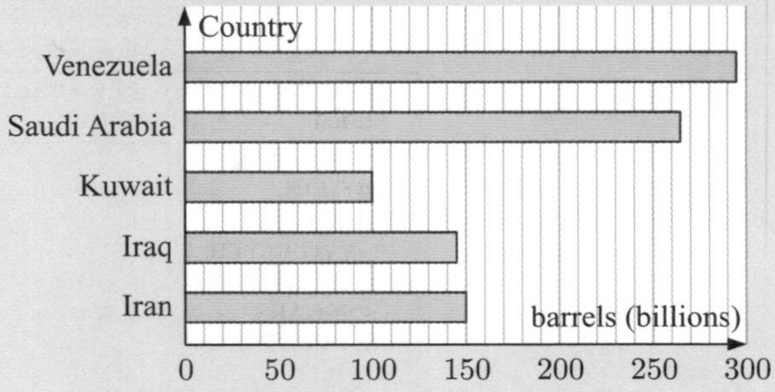

a How many billion barrels of crude oil do these countries have in total?

b How many more barrels can Saudi Arabia produce than Iraq?

c What percentage of the crude oil is held by Iran?

2 The graph below shows the price of gold per ounce, in US dollars, over one year.

a In which month was the price of gold at its

i highest **ii** lowest?

b What was the price of gold per ounce at the beginning of April 2013?

c Which month started with the price of gold at $1400 per ounce?

d During how many months was the price of gold $1360 per ounce?

e Find the percentage increase in the price of gold from the start of August 2012 to the start of November 2012.

3 The travel graph shows the distance travelled by a taxi driver over 8 hours.

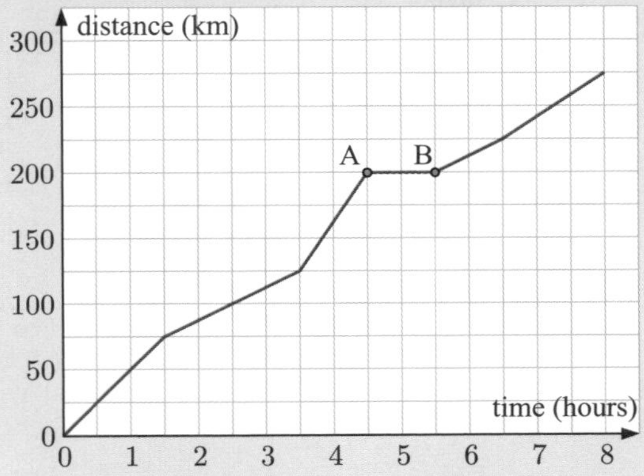

a State the distance the taxi driver had travelled after:

i 2.5 hours **ii** 5 hours

iii 8 hours.

b Find the taxi driver's average speed for the entire trip.

c The taxi driver stopped for a lunch break at point A, and started driving again at point B.

Determine his average speed:

i before the lunch break **ii** after the lunch break.

4 The nutritional information panel from a carton of flavoured milk is shown below.

NUTRITIONAL INFORMATION			
SERVINGS PER PACK: 1			
SERVING SIZE: 600mL	PER 600mL SERVE	%RDI PER SERVE	PER 100 mL
ENERGY	1242 kJ	14%	207 kJ
PROTEIN	19.8 g	40%	3.3 g
FAT, TOTAL	5.4 g	8%	0.9 g
- SATURATED	3.6 g	15%	0.6 g
CARBOHYDRATE	41.4 g	13%	6.9 g
- SUGARS	37.0 g	41%	6.2 g
DIETARY FIBRE	0.6 g	2%	0.1 g
SODIUM	270 mg	12%	45 mg
CALCIUM	750 mg	94%	125 mg

a How much sugar is in the carton?

b How much sodium is in 100 mL of the milk?

c The milk provides 2% of the Recommended Daily Intake (RDI) of a particular nutrient.

i What nutrient is it? **ii** What is the RDI of this nutrient in grams?

5 **a** What information is displayed in the pie chart?

b What factor accounts for the biggest proportion of the cost of a compact disc?

c What factor accounts for the smallest proportion of the cost?

d What percentage of the cost of a CD goes to the artist, composer, publisher, and copyright royalties?

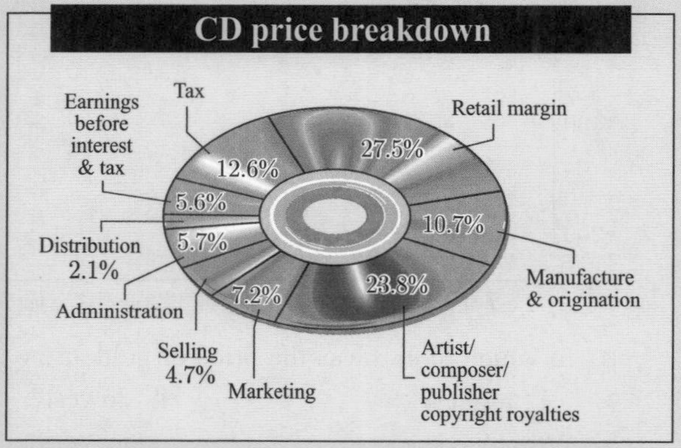

e If you pay $29.95 for a CD in a music shop, how much goes towards:

i marketing **ii** manufacture and origination **iii** tax?

f Add up all the percentages given in the pie chart. Explain your answer.

6

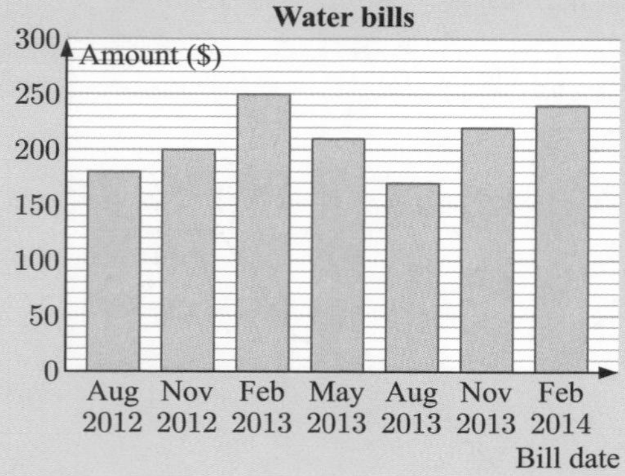

The Brown household gets a water bill every quarter (three months). The column graph shows their recent bills.

a How much was the water bill in November 2013?

b Find the change in the water bill from February 2013 to May 2013.

c Find the percentage change in the water bill from:

i August 2013 to November 2013

ii February 2013 to February 2014.

Chapter 7

Laws of algebra

Contents:

OPENING PROBLEM

Rhonda noticed that when she multiplied the square numbers 4 and 9 together, the result 36 was also a square number.

Things to think about:

- Is this just a coincidence, or will this always happen when two square numbers are multiplied together?
- Can you explain why this occurs?

A INDEX LAWS

We have seen previously that:

> If n is a positive integer, then a^n is the product of n factors of a.
>
> $$a^n = \underbrace{a \times a \times a \times \ldots . \times a}_{n \text{ factors}}$$

We have used this notation to perform simplifications such as:

- $m^3 \times m^4 = \overbrace{(m \times m \times m) \times (m \times m \times m \times m)}^{7 \text{ factors}} = m^7$
- $\dfrac{a^5}{a^3} = \dfrac{\overbrace{a \times a}^{2 \text{ factors}} \times \cancel{a \times a \times a}^{\,1}}{\cancel{a \times a \times a}_{\,1}} = a^2$

We now attempt to discover some **index laws** which allow us to perform simplifications without writing out all of the factors.

INVESTIGATION 1 DISCOVERING INDEX LAWS

WORKSHEET

We can discover some laws for indices by considering several examples and looking for patterns.

1 Copy and complete:

a $2^2 \times 2^3 = (2 \times 2) \times (2 \times 2 \times 2) = 2^5$

b $3^3 \times 3^1 = \boxed{} = \boxed{}$

c $a^3 \times a^4 = \boxed{} = \boxed{}$

In general, $a^m \times a^n = \boxed{}$.

2 Copy and complete:

a $\dfrac{2^5}{2^3} = \dfrac{2 \times 2 \times 2 \times 2 \times 2}{2 \times 2 \times 2} = 2^2$

b $\dfrac{5^4}{5^1} = \boxed{} = \boxed{}$

c $\dfrac{a^5}{a^2} = \boxed{} = \boxed{}$

d $\dfrac{x^7}{x^4} = \boxed{} = \boxed{}$

In general, $\dfrac{a^m}{a^n} = \boxed{}$.

3 Copy and complete:

a $(7^3)^2 = 7^3 \times 7^3 = (7 \times 7 \times 7) \times (7 \times 7 \times 7) = \boxed{}$

b $(3^2)^4 = \boxed{} = \boxed{} = \boxed{}$

c $(a^4)^3 = \boxed{} = \boxed{} = \boxed{}$

In general, $(a^m)^n = \boxed{}$.

From **Investigation 1** you should have found these **index laws** for **positive indices**:

If m and n are positive integers, then:

- $a^m \times a^n = a^{m+n}$ — To **multiply** numbers with the **same base**, keep the base and **add** the indices.
- $\dfrac{a^m}{a^n} = a^{m-n}, \quad a \neq 0$ — To **divide** numbers with the **same base**, keep the base and **subtract** the indices.
- $(a^m)^n = a^{m \times n}$ — When **raising** a **power** to a **power**, keep the base and **multiply** the indices.

Example 1 Self Tutor

Simplify using the laws of indices:

a $2^3 \times 2^2$ **b** $x^4 \times x^5$

a $2^3 \times 2^2$
$= 2^{3+2}$
$= 2^5$
$= 32$

b $x^4 \times x^5$
$= x^{4+5}$
$= x^9$

When multiplying, keep the base and add the indices.

Example 2 — Self Tutor

Simplify using the index laws:

a $\dfrac{3^5}{3^3}$ **b** $\dfrac{p^7}{p^3}$

a $\dfrac{3^5}{3^3}$
$= 3^{5-3}$
$= 3^2$
$= 9$

b $\dfrac{p^7}{p^3}$
$= p^{7-3}$
$= p^4$

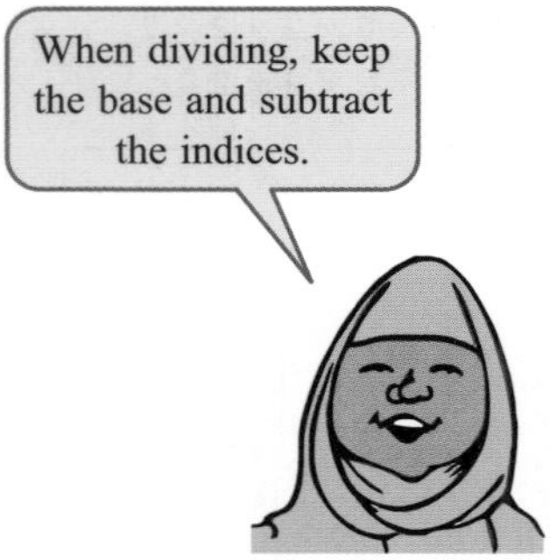
When dividing, keep the base and subtract the indices.

For a power to a power, keep the base and multiply the indices.

Example 3 — Self Tutor

Simplify using the index laws:

a $(2^3)^2$ **b** $(x^4)^5$

a $(2^3)^2$
$= 2^{3\times 2}$
$= 2^6$
$= 64$

b $(x^4)^5$
$= x^{4\times 5}$
$= x^{20}$

EXERCISE 7A

1 Simplify using the index laws:

a $3^2 \times 3^3$ **b** $2^2 \times 2^2$ **c** $5^2 \times 5^4$ **d** $3^4 \times 3^3$
e $a \times a^4$ **f** $n^2 \times n$ **g** $x^3 \times x^6$ **h** $y^3 \times y^5$

2 Simplify using the index laws:

a $\dfrac{2^4}{2^2}$ **b** $\dfrac{3^3}{3}$ **c** $\dfrac{7^5}{7^2}$ **d** $\dfrac{10^4}{10^3}$
e $\dfrac{x^6}{x^2}$ **f** $\dfrac{y^9}{y^5}$ **g** $c^6 \div c^4$ **h** $b^8 \div b^5$

3 Simplify using the index laws:

a $(2^2)^3$ **b** $(10^4)^2$ **c** $(3^3)^2$ **d** $(2^4)^3$
e $(x^5)^2$ **f** $(p^3)^3$ **g** $(t^3)^4$ **h** $(z^2)^6$

4 Simplify using the index laws:

a $c^2 \times c^4$ **b** $b^8 \div b^3$ **c** $(y^5)^3$ **d** $y^4 \times y^6$
e $q \times q^6$ **f** $(z^6)^5$ **g** $t^{10} \div t^7$ **h** $a^2 \times a^n$
i $g^4 \div g$ **j** $n^2 \times n^3 \times n^5$ **k** $(k^4)^2 \div k$ **l** $(p^2)^2 \times p^2$

5 Copy and complete, replacing each $\square$ and $\triangle$ with a number or operation:

a $(7^2)^{\square} = 7^6$ **b** $2^4 \square 2 = 2^3$ **c** $2^2 \square 2^7 = 2^9$

d $(x^{\square})^4 = x^{12}$ **e** $a^5 \square a^5 = a^{10}$ **f** $5^9 \square 5^3 = 5^6$

g $b^4 \square b^3 \triangle b^2 = b^5$ **h** $c^8 \square c^2 \triangle c^3 = c^3$ **i** $(x^3)^{\square} = x^{10} \triangle x^4$

Example 4 — Self Tutor

Simplify using the index laws:

a $2b^2 \times 3a^2b^3$ **b** $\dfrac{6x^4y^3}{3x^2y}$

a
$$\begin{aligned} & 2b^2 \times 3a^2b^3 \\ &= 2 \times 3 \times a^2 \times b^2 \times b^3 \\ &= 6 \times a^2 \times b^{2+3} \\ &= 6a^2b^5 \end{aligned}$$

b
$$\begin{aligned} & \frac{6x^4y^3}{3x^2y} \\ &= \tfrac{6}{3} \times x^{4-2} \times y^{3-1} \\ &= 2x^2y^2 \end{aligned}$$

6 Simplify using the index laws:

a $\dfrac{5a^3}{a}$ **b** $3q^2 \times 5q$ **c** $8x^2y \times 2xy^3$

d $\dfrac{21t^3}{3t^2}$ **e** $\dfrac{24w^2z^4}{6w^2z^3}$ **f** $\dfrac{j^5k^3}{j^4k}$

g $\dfrac{3x^5}{6x^3} \times 2x^2$ **h** $\dfrac{m^{30}}{(m^5)^5}$ **i** $\dfrac{h^{14} \times h^2}{(h^4)^2}$

7 Express as a power of 2:

a $2^2 \times 2^5$ **b** $2^3 \times (2^2)^4$

c $\dfrac{2^3 \times 2^7}{2 \times 2^2}$ **d** $\dfrac{(2^{11})^2 \times 2^3}{(2^6)^3 \times 2^4}$

8 Express as a power of x:

a $x^4 \times x^9$ **b** $\dfrac{x^{11}}{x^2 \times x^3}$

c $(x^6 \times x^7)^2$ **d** $\dfrac{x^{10} \times (x^2)^5}{x}$

Simplify brackets first.

9 Holger says that $3^5 \times 2^3 = 6^8$. Explain why this is not true.

B EXPANSION LAWS

We will now look at index laws for raising a product or quotient to a power.

For example, given $(3a)^4$ or $\left(\dfrac{x}{y}\right)^6$, we need laws which allow us to write the expressions without brackets. We call these **expansion laws**.

INVESTIGATION 2 — DISCOVERING EXPANSION LAWS

WORKSHEET

Look for any patterns as you complete the following Investigation.

1 Copy and complete the following:

a $(ab)^4 = ab \times ab \times ab \times ab \;= a \times a \times a \times a \times b \times b \times b \times b = \square$

b $(ab)^3 = \square = \square = \square$

c $(2a)^5 = \square = \square = \square$

In general, $(ab)^n = \square$.

2 Copy and complete:

a $\left(\frac{a}{b}\right)^3 = \frac{a}{b} \times \frac{a}{b} \times \frac{a}{b} \;= \frac{a \times a \times a}{b \times b \times b} \;= \square$

b $\left(\frac{a}{b}\right)^4 = \square = \square = \square$

In general, $\left(\frac{a}{b}\right)^n = \square$ for $b \neq 0$.

From **Investigation 2** you should have found these **expansion laws** for **positive indices**:

If n is a positive integer, then:

- $\boldsymbol{(ab)^n = a^n b^n}$
- $\boldsymbol{\left(\frac{a}{b}\right)^n = \frac{a^n}{b^n}}$ provided $b \neq 0$.

Example 5 — Self Tutor

Remove the brackets and simplify:

a $(ab)^5$ **b** $(2xy)^3$

a $(ab)^5$
$= a^5b^5$

b $(2xy)^3$
$= 2^3 \times x^3 \times y^3$
$= 8x^3y^3$

Raise each factor to the given power.

EXERCISE 7B

1 Remove the brackets and simplify:

a $(pq)^2$ **b** $(xy)^4$ **c** $(ab)^6$ **d** $(abc)^3$

e $(2a)^3$ **f** $(3d)^5$ **g** $(2k)^5$ **h** $(5gh)^2$

Example 6 — Self Tutor

Remove the brackets and simplify:

a $\left(\dfrac{m}{n}\right)^4$ **b** $\left(\dfrac{2}{b}\right)^3$

a $\left(\dfrac{m}{n}\right)^4 = \dfrac{m^4}{n^4}$

b $\left(\dfrac{2}{b}\right)^3 = \dfrac{2^3}{b^3} = \dfrac{8}{b^3}$

Raise both the numerator and the denominator to the given power.

2 Remove the brackets and simplify:

a $\left(\dfrac{a}{b}\right)^2$ **b** $\left(\dfrac{b}{2}\right)^3$ **c** $\left(\dfrac{j}{k}\right)^4$ **d** $\left(\dfrac{2}{z}\right)^4$

e $\left(\dfrac{4}{x}\right)^2$ **f** $\left(\dfrac{2}{b}\right)^5$ **g** $\left(\dfrac{q}{2}\right)^4$ **h** $\left(\dfrac{3}{b}\right)^3$

3 Find:

a $\left(\dfrac{2}{5}\right)^2$ **b** $\left(\dfrac{3}{4}\right)^3$ **c** $\left(\dfrac{2}{3}\right)^4$ **d** $\left(\dfrac{1}{2}\right)^5$

Example 7 — Self Tutor

Express in simplest form, without brackets:

a $(3a^2)^2$ **b** $(4a^2b)^3$

a $(3a^2)^2$
$= 3^2 \times (a^2)^2$
$= 9a^4$

b $(4a^2b)^3$
$= 4^3 \times (a^2)^3 \times b^3$
$= 64a^6b^3$

4 Express in simplest form, without brackets:

a $(2a^2)^2$ **b** $(3b^3)^3$ **c** $(2c^2)^4$ **d** $(2d^2)^5$

e $(jk^3)^2$ **f** $(xy^2)^3$ **g** $(3g)^2 \times 2g$ **h** $(5r^2s)^2$

i $(8ab^3)^2$ **j** $(3h^2k)^3$ **k** $(2bc^2)^3$ **l** $(7e^3f)^2$

5 Express in simplest form, without brackets:

a $\left(\dfrac{jk}{2}\right)^2$ **b** $\left(\dfrac{2}{cd}\right)^2$ **c** $\left(\dfrac{3p}{q}\right)^3$ **d** $\left(\dfrac{z^2}{5}\right)^2$

e $\left(\dfrac{7d^2}{e}\right)^2$ **f** $\left(\dfrac{w^2}{3v}\right)^2$ **g** $\left(\dfrac{4r}{3s^2}\right)^2$ **h** $\left(\dfrac{5g}{2h^3}\right)^3$

6 Consider the **Opening Problem** on page **130**. Show that when two square numbers are multiplied together, the result is also a perfect square.

C THE ZERO INDEX LAW

For all positive integers n, a^n is defined as the product of n factors of a:

$$a^n = \underbrace{a \times a \times a \times \ldots . \times a}_{n \text{ factors}}$$

But what if $n = 0$? In the following **Investigation** we will discover how to find values such as 2^0 and 5^0.

INVESTIGATION 3 THE ZERO INDEX LAW

What to do:

1 Find the value of:

a $\frac{2}{2}$ **b** $\frac{3}{3}$ **c** $\frac{4}{4}$ **d** $\frac{-8}{-8}$

e $\frac{-5}{-5}$ **f** $\frac{7}{7}$ **g** $\frac{57}{57}$ **h** $\frac{23}{23}$

2 Copy and complete: "When a non-zero value is divided by itself, the result is always ......"

3 Use **2** to complete: $\frac{a^3}{a^3} = \ldots\ldots$

4 Use an index law to show that $\frac{a^3}{a^3} = a^0$.

5 Use **3** and **4** to complete: $a^0 = \ldots\ldots$ for all $a \neq 0$.
Check your answer by evaluating 2^0 and 5^0 on your calculator.

From **Investigation 3** you should have discovered that $\boldsymbol{a^0 = 1}$ for all $a \neq 0$.

EXERCISE 7C

1 **a** Copy and complete: $\frac{3^4}{3^4} = \frac{81}{81} = \ldots\ldots$ **b** Show that $\frac{3^4}{3^4} = 3^0$.

c Use **a** and **b** to find the value of 3^0.

2 Simplify:

a 7^0 **b** 41^0 **c** x^0 **d** 5×2^0

e $8 + 10^0$ **f** $6 - 6^0$ **g** 11×11^0 **h** $p^6 \times p^0$

i $(2^3)^0$ **j** $(2^0)^3$ **k** 7×3^0 **l** $(7 \times 3)^0$

3 Simplify:

a $\frac{k^6}{k^6}$ **b** $\frac{a^3b^2}{b^2}$ **c** $\frac{m^3n^4}{m^3n^2}$ **d** $\frac{pq^3r^2}{pq^2r^2}$

PUZZLE

Click on the icon for a printable copy of the solution grid.

PRINTABLE GRID

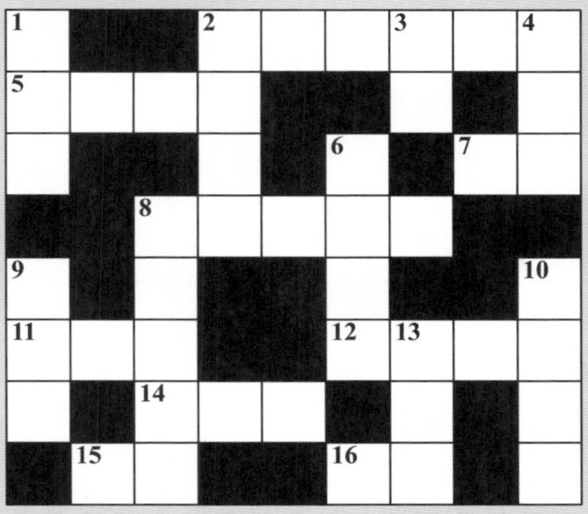

Across

2 $3^8 \times 3^3$
5 $10^4 \div 10$
7 $7^5 \div 7^3$
8 $(11^2)^2$
11 $6^6 \div 6^3$
12 $11^2 \times 11$
14 $3^7 \div 3^2$
15 $6^2 - 6^0$
16 $2^6 - 5^0$

Down

1 $2^5 \times 2^4$
2 $(2^2)^5$
3 $2^{10} \div 2^6$
4 $(3^3)^2$
6 7×7^3
8 $5^4 \times 5^2$
9 $5^6 \div 5^3$
10 $5^2 \times 5^3$
13 $7^7 \div 7^4$

D THE NEGATIVE INDEX LAW

In the following **Investigation** we consider numbers where the index is negative, such as 7^{-2} and 10^{-4}.

INVESTIGATION 4 NEGATIVE INDICES

What to do:

1 Consider the fraction $\dfrac{7^3}{7^5}$.

a By expanding and then cancelling common factors, show that $\dfrac{7^3}{7^5} = \dfrac{1}{7^2}$.

b Use an index law to show that $\dfrac{7^3}{7^5} = 7^{-2}$.

c Hence copy and complete: $7^{-2} = ...$

2 Use the fact that $a^0 = 1$ to copy and complete: $a^{-n} = a^{0-n} = \dfrac{a^0}{\square} = \dfrac{\square}{\square}$.

You should have discovered the following law for **negative indices**:

If a is any non-zero number and n is an integer, then $\boldsymbol{a^{-n} = \dfrac{1}{a^n}}$.

This means that a^n and a^{-n} are **reciprocals** of one another.

In particular, notice that $\boldsymbol{a^{-1} = \dfrac{1}{a}}$.

Example 8 — Self Tutor

Simplify:

a 3^{-1} b 5^{-2} c 10^{-4}

a 3^{-1}
$= \frac{1}{3^1}$
$= \frac{1}{3}$

b 5^{-2}
$= \frac{1}{5^2}$
$= \frac{1}{25}$

c 10^{-4}
$= \frac{1}{10^4}$
$= \frac{1}{10\,000}$

The negative index indicates the **reciprocal**.

EXERCISE 7D

1 Simplify:

a 5^{-1} b 4^{-1} c 8^{-1} d 10^{-1} e 3^{-2}

f 2^{-2} g 11^{-2} h 7^{-2} i 3^{-3} j 2^{-7}

Example 9 — Self Tutor

Simplify, giving answers in simplest rational form:

a $\left(\frac{2}{3}\right)^{-1}$ b $\left(\frac{3}{5}\right)^{-2}$ c $8^0 - 8^{-1}$

a $\left(\frac{2}{3}\right)^{-1}$
$= \left(\frac{3}{2}\right)^{1}$
$= \frac{3}{2}$

b $\left(\frac{3}{5}\right)^{-2} = \left(\frac{5}{3}\right)^{2}$
$= \frac{5^2}{3^2}$
$= \frac{25}{9}$

c $8^0 - 8^{-1}$
$= 1 - \frac{1}{8}$
$= \frac{7}{8}$

"Simplest rational form" means "as a fraction in lowest terms".

2 Simplify, giving answers in simplest rational form:

a $\left(\frac{1}{3}\right)^{-1}$ b $\left(\frac{1}{5}\right)^{-1}$ c $\left(\frac{3}{7}\right)^{-1}$ d $\left(\frac{5}{2}\right)^{-1}$ e $\left(\frac{1}{10}\right)^{-1}$

f $3^0 + 3^{-1}$ g $\left(\frac{5}{6}\right)^{-2}$ h $\left(2\frac{1}{4}\right)^{-2}$ i $\left(\frac{2}{3}\right)^{-3}$ j $5^0 + 5^1 - 5^{-1}$

Example 10 — Self Tutor

Write without brackets or negative indices:

a $8ab^{-1}$ b $8(ab)^{-1}$

a $8ab^{-1} = \frac{8a}{1} \times \frac{1}{b}$
$= \frac{8a}{b}$

b $8(ab)^{-1} = 8 \times \frac{1}{ab}$
$= \frac{8}{ab}$

3 Write without brackets or negative indices:

a $2x^{-1}$ b $(2x)^{-1}$ c $(3q)^{-1}$ d $3q^{-1}$

e $7a^{-2}$ f $(7a)^{-2}$ g $(5z)^{-2}$ h $5z^{-2}$

i st^{-1} j $(st)^{-1}$ k gh^{-3} l $(gh)^{-3}$

m $4cd^{-2}$ n $(4cd)^{-2}$ o $4(cd)^{-2}$ p $(7m^{-3})^{-1}$

4 Write as powers of 10:

a 100 b 1000 c 0.1 d 0.0001

5 Write as powers of 2, 3, 5, or 7:

a 16 b $\frac{1}{16}$ c 25 d $\frac{1}{25}$ e 81

f $\frac{1}{81}$ g 49 h $\frac{1}{49}$ i $\frac{1}{1024}$ j $\frac{1}{343}$

k 1 l $\frac{1}{2^a}$ m $\frac{1}{5^c}$ n $\frac{1}{9 \times 3^x}$ o $\frac{1}{(2^t)^3}$

E THE DISTRIBUTIVE LAW

Over the summer holidays, Jasmin is able to do some jobs. The holidays are 11 weeks long.

Each week, Jasmin earns €5 from her father for washing the family car, and €7 from her grandfather for mowing lawns.

Over the 11 week period, Jasmin earns a total of $11 \times$ €5 from her father, and $11 \times$ €7 from her grandfather.

We could also say that Jasmin earns 11 lots of (€5 + €7), which is $11 \times (5 + 7)$ euros.

Consequently, $11(5 + 7) = 11 \times 5 + 11 \times 7$.

Notice that the factor outside the brackets is multiplied by each term inside the brackets.

$\boldsymbol{a(b + c) = ab + ac}$ is called the **distributive law**.

Example 11 Self Tutor

Expand and simplify:

a $5(x + 4)$ b $4(y - 3)$

a
$$5(x + 4)$$
$$= 5 \times x + 5 \times 4$$
$$= 5x + 20$$

b
$$4(y - 3)$$
$$= 4(y + -3)$$
$$= 4 \times y + 4 \times (-3)$$
$$= 4y - 12$$

Multiply each term inside the brackets by the factor outside the brackets.

Example 12 **Self Tutor**

Expand and simplify:

a $3(2a+7)$ **b** $x(5-4x)$

a $3(2a+7)$
$= 3 \times 2a \ + \ 3 \times 7$
$= 6a + 21$

b $x(5-4x)$
$= x(5 + -4x)$
$= x \times 5 \ + \ x \times (-4x)$
$= 5x - 4x^2$

EXERCISE 7E

1 Expand and simplify:

a $2(x+7)$ **b** $3(x-2)$ **c** $4(a+3)$ **d** $5(a+c)$
e $6(b-3)$ **f** $7(m+4)$ **g** $2(n-p)$ **h** $4(p-q)$
i $3(5+x)$ **j** $5(y-x)$ **k** $8(t-8)$ **l** $6(d+e)$
m $4(10-j)$ **n** $7(y+n)$ **o** $2(n-12)$ **p** $8(11-d)$

2 Expand and simplify:

a $9(2x+1)$ **b** $3(1-3x)$ **c** $5(2a+3)$ **d** $11(1-2n)$
e $6(3x+y)$ **f** $5(x-2y)$ **g** $4(3b+c)$ **h** $2(a-2b)$
i $7(a-5b)$ **j** $12(2+3d)$ **k** $8(3-4y)$ **l** $6(5b+3a)$
m $11(2x-y)$ **n** $7(c-9d)$ **o** $6(m+7n)$ **p** $8(8a-c)$

3 Expand and simplify:

a $x(x+2)$ **b** $x(5-x)$ **c** $a(2a+4)$ **d** $b(5-3b)$
e $a(b+2c)$ **f** $a(a^2+1)$ **g** $x(3-4x)$ **h** $3x(6-x)$
i $5x(x-4)$ **j** $4a(1-a)$ **k** $7b(b+2)$ **l** $a(a+b)$
m $b(3-8b)$ **n** $m(m-3n)$ **o** $c(c-4a)$ **p** $6p(4-7p)$

Example 13 **Self Tutor**

Expand and simplify:

a $-4(x+3)$ **b** $-(2x-4)$ **c** $-a(a+7)$

a $-4(x+3)$
$= -4 \times x \ + \ -4 \times 3$ {-4 is multiplied by x and by 3}
$= -4x - 12$

b $-(2x-4)$
$= -1(2x-4)$ {-1 is multiplied by $2x$ and by -4}
$= -1 \times 2x \ + \ -1 \times (-4)$
$= -2x + 4$

c $-a(a+7)$
$= -a \times a + -a \times 7$ $\{-a$ is multiplied by a and by $7\}$
$= -a^2 - 7a$

4 Expand and simplify:

a $-2(x+2)$	**b** $-3(x+4)$	**c** $-4(x-2)$
d $-5(5-x)$	**e** $-(a+2)$	**f** $-(x-3)$
g $-(5-x)$	**h** $-(2x+1)$	**i** $-3(4-x)$
j $-4(5x-2)$	**k** $-5(3-4c)$	**l** $-2(7-5x)$

5 Expand and simplify:

a $-a(a+1)$	**b** $-b(b+4)$	**c** $-c(5-c)$
d $-x(2x+4)$	**e** $-2x(1-x)$	**f** $-3y(y+2)$
g $-4a(5-a)$	**h** $-6b(3-2b)$	**i** $-xy(2y-x)$

Example 14 **Self Tutor**

Expand and simplify:

a $4+2(x+3)$ **b** $8-3(2y-1)$

a $4+2(x+3)$
$= 4+2\times x+2\times 3$
$= 4+2x+6$
$= 2x+10$

b $8-3(2y-1)$
$= 8+-3(2y-1)$
$= 8+-3\times 2y+-3\times(-1)$
$= 8-6y+3$
$= 11-6y$

With practice you will not need all of these steps.

6 Expand and simplify:

a $3(x+2)+5$	**b** $3x+2(2x+1)$	**c** $7-6(2x-3)$
d $11x-(2+x)$	**e** $6+5(1-2x)$	**f** $11-(3-2x)$
g $16-7(1-3x)$	**h** $x+6+3(4+x)$	**i** $8x+1+2(3-2x)$
j $7-(1-2x)$	**k** $2x-(8+7x)+3$	**l** $8-5(11-3x)$
m $5x+x(x+2)$	**n** $8x+x(x-1)$	**o** $7x-x(x+3)$
p $x^2-x(2-x)$	**q** $4x-x(x-3)+2x^2$	**r** $3x^2-2x(x-5)-6x$

INVESTIGATION 5 "THINK OF A NUMBER"

Algebra is a powerful tool in mathematical problem solving. It can help us describe problems in general terms, and often gives us an insight into *why* something works.

What to do:

1 Play the following 'think of a number' game with a partner:

> Think of a number.
> Double it.
> Subtract 4.
> Halve the result.
> Add 3.
> Subtract your original number.

Repeat the game choosing different starting numbers.

2 We can use algebra to explain why the answer to the game above is always 1. Let x represent the starting number.

Copy and complete the following argument by writing down each step in terms of x:

Think of a number.		x		
Double it.	gives	$2x$		
Subtract 4.	gives	$2x - 4$		
Halve the result.	gives	$\frac{1}{2}(.... - ....)$	or	$.... - ....$
Add 3.	gives	$.... - .... + 3$	or	$.... + ...$
Subtract your original number.	gives	$.... + ... - x$	or	$....$

3 Try the following 'think of a number' game:

> Think of a number.
> Treble it.
> Add 9.
> Divide the result by 3.
> Subtract 3.

What is your answer? Repeat the game using different numbers.

4 For the game above, let x be the starting number. Use algebra to explain how the game works.

5 Make up your own 'think of a number' game. Test it with algebra before you try it with others.

F THE PRODUCT $(a+b)(c+d)$

Consider the large rectangle alongside. It has side lengths $(a+b)$ and $(c+d)$, so the overall area is $(a+b)(c+d)$.

However, this area can also be obtained by adding the areas of the four smaller rectangles.

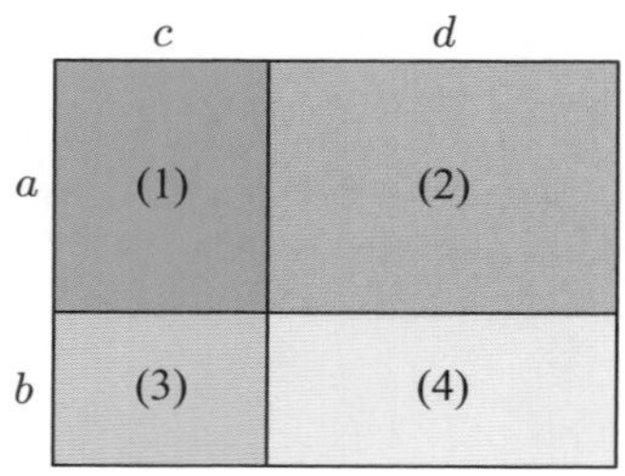

So, $(a+b)(c+d) = \text{area of (1)} + \text{area of (2)} + \text{area of (3)} + \text{area of (4)}$
$= ac + ad + bc + bd$

Hence $$\boldsymbol{(a+b)(c+d) = ac + ad + bc + bd}$$

This expansion rule is sometimes called the **FOIL** rule as:

inners (arrows to b and c)

$$(a+b)(c+d) = \underset{\text{Firsts}}{ac} + \underset{\text{Outers}}{ad} + \underset{\text{Inners}}{bc} + \underset{\text{Lasts}}{bd}$$

outers (arrows to a and d)

Example 15 — Self Tutor

Expand and simplify:

a $(x+3)(x+7)$ b $(x-2)(x+4)$

a $(x+3)(x+7)$
$= x\times x + x\times 7 + 3\times x + 3\times 7$
$= x^2 + 7x + 3x + 21$
$= x^2 + 10x + 21$

b $(x-2)(x+4)$
$= x\times x + x\times 4 + (-2)\times x + (-2)\times 4$
$= x^2 + 4x - 2x - 8$
$= x^2 + 2x - 8$

The second line is often done mentally and not written down.

EXERCISE 7F

1 Expand and simplify:

a $(x+1)(x+2)$ b $(x+4)(x+2)$ c $(x+5)(x-1)$
d $(x+3)(x+1)$ e $(y+3)(y+2)$ f $(a+3)(a+7)$
g $(x+2)(x-2)$ h $(x-4)(x+2)$ i $(x+7)(x-3)$
j $(x-9)(x+2)$ k $(x-4)(x+3)$ l $(x+6)(x-2)$
m $(x-4)(x-3)$ n $(x-5)(x-8)$ o $(x-11)(x-4)$
p $(2x+3)(x-1)$ q $(x-4)(3x+2)$ r $(2x+3)(2x-4)$

Example 16 — Self Tutor

Expand and simplify:

a $(x+7)^2$ b $(3x-2)^2$

a $(x+7)^2$
$= (x+7)(x+7)$
$= x^2 + 7x + 7x + 49$
$= x^2 + 14x + 49$

b $(3x-2)^2$
$= (3x-2)(3x-2)$
$= 9x^2 - 6x - 6x + 4$
$= 9x^2 - 12x + 4$

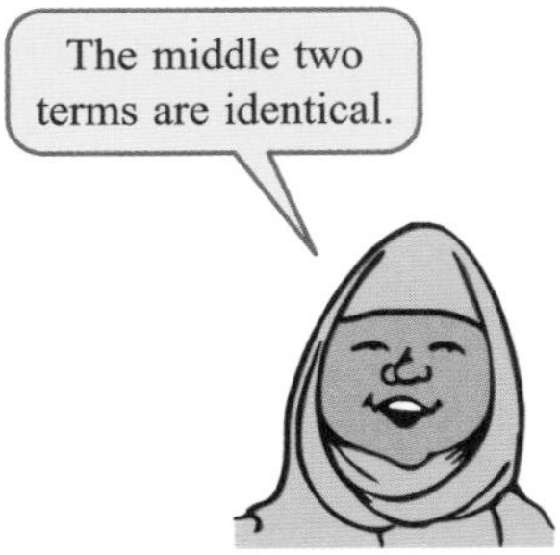

The middle two terms are identical.

2 Expand and simplify:

a $(x+1)^2$	**b** $(x+4)^2$	**c** $(x-2)^2$	**d** $(x-5)^2$
e $(3+y)^2$	**f** $(3-y)^2$	**g** $(2x+1)^2$	**h** $(2x-1)^2$
i $(1+4a)^2$	**j** $(1-4a)^2$	**k** $(a+b)^2$	**l** $(a-b)^2$

Example 17 — Self Tutor

Expand and simplify:

a $(x+3)(x-3)$ **b** $(2x-5)(2x+5)$

a $(x+3)(x-3)$
$= x^2 - 3x + 3x - 9$
$= x^2 - 9$

b $(2x-5)(2x+5)$
$= 4x^2 + 10x - 10x - 25$
$= 4x^2 - 25$

3 Expand and simplify:

a $(x+2)(x-2)$	**b** $(y-5)(y+5)$	**c** $(a+7)(a-7)$
d $(b-4)(b+4)$	**e** $(3+x)(3-x)$	**f** $(6-y)(6+y)$
g $(1+a)(1-a)$	**h** $(8-b)(8+b)$	**i** $(2x+1)(2x-1)$
j $(3a-2)(3a+2)$	**k** $(3+5b)(3-5b)$	**l** $(5-4y)(5+4y)$

G PERFECT SQUARE EXPANSION

An expression of the form $(a+b)^2$ is called a **perfect square**.

The large square alongside has area $(a+b)^2$.

We can also write the total area as

$$a^2 + ab + ab + b^2$$
$$= a^2 + 2ab + b^2$$

So, $\mathbf{(a+b)^2 = a^2 + 2ab + b^2}$

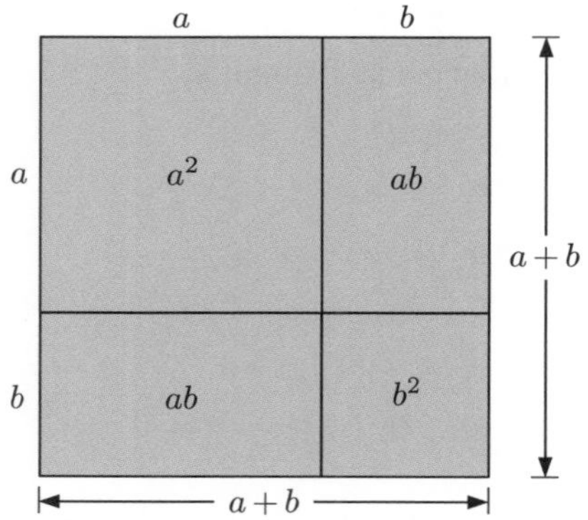

The following is a useful way of remembering the perfect square rules:

$$(a+b)^2 \quad = \quad a^2 \quad + \quad 2ab \quad + \quad b^2$$

- a: 1st term
- b: 2nd term
- a^2: square of first term
- $2ab$: twice the product of the two terms
- b^2: square of 2nd term

Example 18 **Self Tutor**

Expand and simplify:

a $(x+6)^2$ b $(2x+5)^2$

a $(x+6)^2$
$= x^2 + 2 \times x \times 6 + 6^2$
$= x^2 + 12x + 36$

b $(2x+5)^2$
$= (2x)^2 + 2 \times 2x \times 5 + 5^2$
$= 4x^2 + 20x + 25$

EXERCISE 7G

1 Expand and simplify:

a $(x+2)^2$ b $(a+3)^2$ c $(x+5)^2$ d $(x+11)^2$
e $(2x+1)^2$ f $(2x+4)^2$ g $(3x+2)^2$ h $(4x+3)^2$
i $(7x+1)^2$ j $(2x+y)^2$ k $(6+x)^2$ l $(3+5x)^2$

Example 19 **Self Tutor**

Expand and simplify:

a $(5-x)^2$ b $(3x-7)^2$

a $(5-x)^2$
$= (5+-x)^2$
$= 5^2 + 2 \times 5 \times (-x) + (-x)^2$
$= 25 - 10x + x^2$

b $(3x-7)^2$
$= (3x+-7)^2$
$= (3x)^2 + 2 \times 3x \times (-7) + (-7)^2$
$= 9x^2 - 42x + 49$

2 Expand and simplify:

a $(x-4)^2$ b $(x-1)^2$ c $(x-6)^2$ d $(d-3)^2$
e $(4-a)^2$ f $(7-x)^2$ g $(3x-1)^2$ h $(6-d)^2$
i $(2x-5)^2$ j $(3-4a)^2$ k $(3a-2b)^2$ l $(3-5x)^2$

H DIFFERENCE OF TWO SQUARES

An expression of the form $(a+b)(a-b)$ is called a **difference of two squares**.

Expanding this expression using the FOIL rule, $(a+b)(a-b) = a^2 + a(-b) + ba - b^2$
$= a^2 - \cancel{ab} + \cancel{ab} - b^2$
$= a^2 - b^2$

So, $\boldsymbol{(a+b)(a-b) = a^2 - b^2}$

Example 20 **Self Tutor**

Expand and simplify:

a $(x+3)(x-3)$ b $(2x-5)(2x+5)$

a $(x+3)(x-3)$
$= x^2 - 3^2$
$= x^2 - 9$

b $(2x-5)(2x+5)$
$= (2x)^2 - 5^2$
$= 4x^2 - 25$

EXERCISE 7H

1 Expand and simplify:

a $(y+4)(y-4)$ b $(b+1)(b-1)$ c $(x-9)(x+9)$

d $(a-8)(a+8)$ e $(5-b)(5+b)$ f $(2-x)(2+x)$

g $(10+a)(10-a)$ h $(7+y)(7-y)$ i $(3x-2)(3x+2)$

j $(4x+3)(4x-3)$ k $(1-2y)(1+2y)$ l $(5-3a)(5+3a)$

2 Use the difference of two squares expansion to find the value of 31×29.

Global context

click here

Representing algebra

Statement of inquiry:	The way that mathematicians write algebraic expressions has changed over time.
Global context:	Orientation in space and time
Key concept:	Form
Related concepts:	Equivalence, Representation
Objectives:	Knowing and understanding, Communicating
Approaches to learning:	Communication, Research

REVIEW SET 7A

1 Simplify using the index laws:

a $k^3 \times k^6$ b $(b^4)^3$ c $\frac{p^{13}}{p^5}$

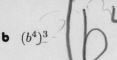

2 Express as a power of 5:

a $\frac{5^4 \times 5^3}{5^2}$ b $(5^4 \times 5^3)^2$ c 1

3 Simplify:

a 8^0 b 13×13^0 c $7 - 5^0$

4 Express in simplest form, without brackets:

a $(10xy^2)^2$ b $\left(\frac{m}{4n}\right)^3$ c $(2k^3)^2 \times k^{32}$

5 Simplify:

a 9^{-1} b 6^{-2} c 10^{-3}

6 Write as a power of 2, 3, or 5:

a $\frac{1}{8}$ **b** $\frac{1}{625}$ **c** $\frac{1}{(3^t)^5}$

7 Expand:

a $2(x+11)$ **b** $5x(7-x)$ **c** $-4(3-2x)$

8 Expand and simplify:

a $(x-6)(x+4)$ **b** $(x-9)(x-4)$ **c** $(2x+5)(x-2)$

9 Expand and simplify:

a $(x+8)^2$ **b** $(x-4)^2$ **c** $(7-2x)^2$

10 Expand and simplify:

a $(x+7)(x-7)$ **b** $(1+a)(1-a)$ **c** $(4x+5)(4x-5)$

REVIEW SET 7B

1 Simplify using the index laws:

a $x^3 \times x^3$ **b** $\frac{c^{12}}{c^7}$ **c** $(d^{11})^3$

2 Simplify using the index laws:

a $2ab \times 5a^2$ **b** $\frac{15x^3y}{3x^2y}$ **c** $\frac{t^4 \times t^2}{(t^2)^3}$

3 Simplify:

a $21^0 - 3$ **b** y^0 **c** $\left(\frac{3}{5}\right)^3$

4 Remove the brackets and simplify:

a $\left(\frac{c}{d}\right)^2$ **b** $\left(\frac{q}{4}\right)^3$ **c** $\left(\frac{ab}{8}\right)^2$

5 Simplify, giving answers in simplest rational form:

a $\left(\frac{4}{5}\right)^{-1}$ **b** $\left(\frac{2}{7}\right)^{-2}$ **c** $\left(3\frac{1}{3}\right)^{-2}$

6 Write without brackets or negative indices:

a $a^{-2}b^3$ **b** $(5a^{-2}b^3)^2$ **c** $(5p^{-3})^{-1}$

7 Expand and simplify:

a $3(x-8)$ **b** $-2(6-3x)$ **c** $2x^2(x^2-x+1)$

8 Expand and simplify:

a $(x+7)(x-1)$ **b** $(y-8)(y+3)$ **c** $(3x-1)(x+3)$

9 Expand and simplify:

a $4+5(x+2)$ **b** $13-3(x-4)$ **c** $5x+x(x-8)$

10 Expand and simplify:

a $(x+6)^2$ **b** $(2x-5)^2$ **c** $(3x+7)(3x-7)$

ACTIVITY — DIFFERENT BASE SYSTEMS

Our number system has a **base** of 10, probably because we have 10 fingers on our hands.

When we write a number in base 10, each digit corresponds to a multiple of a power of 10.

For example, the number 374 represents $3 \times 10^2 + 7 \times 10^1 + 4 \times 10^0$.

We can also write numbers in different bases. For example, we can write a number in base 5 by writing it in terms of powers of 5.

For example:

- $39 = 25 + 2 \times 5 + 4 \times 1 = 1 \times 5^2 + 2 \times 5^1 + 4 \times 5^0$, so we can write the number 39 in base 5 as 124. We write this as 124_5 so it is clear which base we are using.
- $53 = 2 \times 25 + 3 \times 1 = 2 \times 5^2 + 3 \times 5^0$, so $53 = 203_5$.

When numbers are written in base 2, it is called **binary notation**. Binary notation is used extensively in computing. When a number is written in binary notation, each digit is either a 0 or a 1.

For example, $41 = 32 + 8 + 1 = 2^5 + 2^3 + 2^0$, so $41 = 101\,001_2$.

What to do:

1 Write the following base 10 numbers in base 5:

a 17 **b** 21 **c** 42 **d** 77 **e** 133

2 Write the following base 10 numbers in binary notation:

a 5 **b** 11 **c** 20 **d** 38 **e** 45

3 Perform the following operations in base 5:

a $\begin{array}{r} 3_5 \\ +\ 4_5 \\ \hline \end{array}$ **b** $\begin{array}{r} 12_5 \\ +\ 24_5 \\ \hline \end{array}$ **c** $\begin{array}{r} 42_5 \\ -\ 30_5 \\ \hline \end{array}$

d $\begin{array}{r} 31_5 \\ -\ 14_5 \\ \hline \end{array}$ **e** $\begin{array}{r} 4_5 \\ \times\ 2_5 \\ \hline \end{array}$ **f** $\begin{array}{r} 22_5 \\ \times\ 3_5 \\ \hline \end{array}$

When performing these operations, think about how you would perform them in base 10.

4 Perform the following operations in base 2:

a $\begin{array}{r} 10_2 \\ +\ 101_2 \\ \hline \end{array}$ **b** $\begin{array}{r} 1010_2 \\ +\ 1101_2 \\ \hline \end{array}$ **c** $\begin{array}{r} 1011_2 \\ -\ 101_2 \\ \hline \end{array}$

d $\begin{array}{r} 1101_2 \\ -\ 110_2 \\ \hline \end{array}$ **e** $\begin{array}{r} 110_2 \\ \times\ 10_2 \\ \hline \end{array}$ **f** $\begin{array}{r} 1001_2 \\ \times\ 11_2 \\ \hline \end{array}$

Chapter 8

Equations

Contents:

OPENING PROBLEM

We are often faced with problems where we need to work out the value of an unknown quantity.

For example, consider the following questions:

i When 6 is added to a number, the result is 8. What is the number?
ii When 3 is subtracted from a number, the result is 11. What is the number?
iii When a number is multiplied by 4, the result is 28. What is the number?
iv When a number is divided by 5, the result is 3. What is the number?

Things to think about:

a Can you write each of the problems above as an *equation*?
b What techniques can you use to *solve* these problems? Use them to find the solutions.

Equations are a fundamental part of mathematics, and an important tool for problem solving. The use of equations dates back to Ancient Egypt, where the scribe **Ahmes** recorded a series of problems which were solved using equations.

An **equation** is a formal statement that one expression is equal to another.

The expressions are connected by an *equal* sign $=$.

The **left hand side** (LHS) of an equation is on the left of the $=$ sign.

The **right hand side** (RHS) of an equation is on the right of the $=$ sign.

For example: $\underbrace{5x-3}_{\text{LHS}} = \underbrace{2x+6}_{\text{RHS}}$

A SOLUTIONS OF AN EQUATION

A **solution** of an equation is a value of the variable which makes the equation true.

Consider the equation $5x - 3 = 2x + 6$.

When $x = 3$, LHS $= 5(3) - 3$ and RHS $= 2(3) + 6$
$= 15 - 3$ $= 6 + 6$
$= 12$ $= 12$ also.

So, $x = 3$ is a solution of the equation.

NUMBER OF SOLUTIONS

Some equations have exactly one solution. Others have no solution, two solutions, three solutions, and some have infinitely many solutions.

An **identity** is an equation which is always true no matter what value the variable takes.

For example:

- $x + 1 = x$ has no solutions
- $2x + 3 = 7$ has one solution: $x = 2$
- $x^2 = x$ has two solutions: $x = 0$ and $x = 1$

- $x^3 = 4x$ has three solutions: $x = 0$, $x = 2$, and $x = -2$
- $3x - x = 2x$ is true for all values of the variable x, so this equation is an identity.

EXERCISE 8A

1 For each of the following equations, state whether they are:

A true for *exactly one value* of x **B** true for *two values* of x
C true for *all values* of x **D** *never* true.

a $x + 2 = 6$ b $2x - 2x = 0$ c $\frac{x}{5} = 10$
d $x + 4 = 4 + x$ e $8 - x = 9$ f $x^2 = 4$
g $x^2 = 0$ h $x^2 = x$ i $9x - 7x = 2x$
j $x \times x = -9$ k $x \times -1 = x$ l $x + 2 = x - 2$

2 What integers, if any, make the following equations true?

a $z \times z = z$ b $3 - k = 0$ c $h - h = 5$
d $x \times x = -16$ e $4 - q = q - 4$ f $d + d = d$
g $t \times 1 = t$ h $10 + g = g + 10$ i $w - w = w$

3 Determine whether the following equations are identities:

a $x + 6 = 6 + x$ b $k + k = k^2$ c $m - m = 0$
d $y + 4y = 5y$ e $8 - t = t - 8$ f $p \div p = 1$

B LINEAR EQUATIONS

An equation is **linear** if the variable is raised only to the power 1.

For example: $5x - 3 = 2x + 6$ and $\frac{3}{4}x - 5 = -1$ are linear equations,
$x^2 + 4x + 3 = 0$, $x - \sqrt{x} = 2$, and $x^5 = 32$ are not linear equations.

In general, a linear equation will have only one solution.

SOLUTION BY INSPECTION

Some simple equations are easily solved by **inspection**.

For example, consider $x + 7 = 20$. We know that $13 + 7 = 20$, so $x = 13$ must be a solution.

SOLUTION BY GUESS, CHECK, AND IMPROVE

Another method for solving equations is to make some guesses. We substitute each guess into the equation to see if it makes the equation true. If it is not true, we *refine* our guess or make it better until we have found the actual solution. This method is known as **guess, check, and improve**.

For example, consider the equation $2x + 7 = 23$.

If we guess that $x = 2$, the LHS $= 2 \times 2 + 7 = 11$.

If we guess that $x = 6$, the LHS $= 2 \times 6 + 7 = 19$.
Although we do not yet have the solution, our guess is closer.

If we guess that $x = 8$, the LHS $= 2 \times 8 + 7 = 23$,
so $x = 8$ is the solution.

Guess x	$2x + 7$	
2	11	✗
6	19	✗
8	23	✓

EXERCISE 8B

1 Solve by inspection:

a $x+2=3$ **b** $x-7=2$

c $10+x=15$ **d** $3-x=-2$

e $x-4=-6$ **f** $2x=8$

g $-7x=28$ **h** $4x=52$

i $\frac{x}{8}=5$ **j** $\frac{x}{5}=-35$

k $\frac{10}{x}=-2$ **l** $\frac{-12}{x}=3$

2 One of the numbers in brackets is the correct solution to the given equation. Find the correct solution.

a $3x+8=14$ $\{0, 1, 2, 3\}$ **b** $5-3x=-4$ $\{0, 1, 2, 3\}$

c $7x+3=-11$ $\{-4, -3, -2, -1\}$ **d** $2x-5=x$ $\{-5, 0, 5, 10\}$

e $\frac{k}{4}=k+3$ $\{-8, -4, 4, 8\}$ **f** $7-2m=m+4$ $\{-2, -1, 0, 1, 2\}$

3 Solve using the method of guess, check, and improve:

a $3x+1=10$ **b** $5x-2=43$

c $52-7x=17$ **d** $25-3x=37$

4 Which of the following are identities?

a $x+3=3+x$ **b** $x-3=3-x$

c $6x-2x=4x$ **d** $x=4\times x$

e $2x-1=3$ **f** $x\times 1=x$

An identity is true for all values of x.

C MAINTAINING BALANCE

For any equation, the LHS must always equal the RHS. We can therefore think of an equation as a set of scales that must always be in **balance**.

The balance of an equation is maintained provided we perform the same operation on **both sides** of the equals sign.

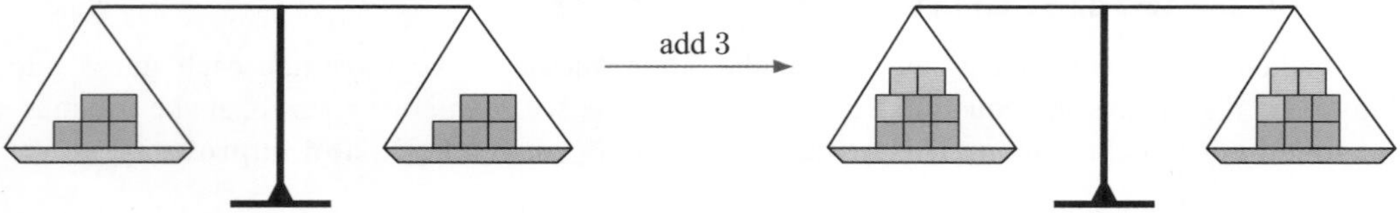

The balance of an equation will be maintained if we:

- add the same amount to both sides
- subtract the same amount from both sides
- multiply both sides by the same amount
- divide both sides by the same amount.

To maintain the balance, whatever operation we perform on one side of the equation, we must also perform on the other.

Example 1 **Self Tutor**

Write down the equation which results when:

a 3 is added to both sides of $x - 3 = 8$

b 4 is taken from both sides of $2x + 4 = 18$

c both sides of $5x = 15$ are divided by 5

d both sides of $\frac{x}{4} = -7$ are multiplied by 4.

a
$$x - 3 = 8$$
$$\therefore\ x - 3 + 3 = 8 + 3$$
$$\therefore\ x = 11$$

b
$$2x + 4 = 18$$
$$\therefore\ 2x + 4 - 4 = 18 - 4$$
$$\therefore\ 2x = 14$$

c
$$5x = 15$$
$$\therefore\ \frac{5x}{5} = \frac{15}{5}$$
$$\therefore\ x = 3$$

d
$$\frac{x}{4} = -7$$
$$\therefore\ \frac{x}{4} \times 4 = -7 \times 4$$
$$\therefore\ x = -28$$

EXERCISE 8C

1 Write down the equation which results when we add:

a 3 to both sides of $x - 3 = 2$

b 9 to both sides of $x - 9 = 0$

c 4 to both sides of $5x - 4 = 11$

d 5 to both sides of $7x - 5 = x + 1$.

2 Write down the equation which results when we subtract:

a 1 from both sides of $x + 1 = 5$

b 6 from both sides of $2x + 6 = 10$

c 5 from both sides of $3x + 5 = 2$

d 9 from both sides of $4x + 9 = 3x + 11$.

3 Write down the equation which results when we multiply both sides of:

a $\frac{x}{2} = 8$ by 2

b $\frac{x-1}{5} = 1$ by 5

c $\frac{3x}{7} = 2$ by 7

d $\frac{3x-4}{4} = -10$ by 4.

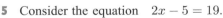

4 Write down the equation which results when we divide both sides of:

a $4x = -40$ by 4

b $-2x = 18$ by -2

c $3(2 - x) = 15$ by 3

d $-5(2x - 1) = -55$ by -5.

5 Consider the equation $2x - 5 = 19$.

a Use the method of guess, check, and improve to solve this equation.

b What equation results when 5 is added to both sides of the equation?

c Use inspection to solve the equation found in **b**.

d Did adding 5 to both sides of the equation change the solution to the equation?

6 Consider the equation $\frac{x+1}{2} = 3$.

a Use the method of guess, check, and improve to solve this equation.
b What equation results when both sides of the equation are multiplied by 2?
c What equation results when 1 is subtracted from both sides of the equation found in **b**?
d Did the operations in **b** and **c** change the solution to the equation?

D INVERSE OPERATIONS

When I woke up this morning there were 4 eggs in my refrigerator.

I found my chickens had already laid 2 eggs, so I then had $4 + 2 = 6$ eggs in total.

I fried 2 eggs to have with my breakfast, so I now have $6 - 2 = 4$ eggs left.

I now have the same number of eggs that I started with. Adding 2 eggs and subtracting 2 eggs cancel each other out.

Addition and subtraction are **inverse operations**.

Over the next week my chickens lay very well. The number of eggs in my fridge doubles, so I now have $4 \times 2 = 8$ eggs.

On the weekend I bake some cakes. Only half of the eggs now remain. This is $8 \div 2 = 4$ eggs, which is the same number that I started with.

The operations of multiplying by 2 and dividing by 2 cancel each other out.

Multiplication and division are **inverse operations**.

Example 2 **Self Tutor**

State the inverse of:

a $\times 4$ b $\div 7$ c $+ 6$ d $- 3$

a The inverse of $\times 4$ is $\div 4$.
b The inverse of $\div 7$ is $\times 7$.
c The inverse of $+ 6$ is $- 6$.
d The inverse of $- 3$ is $+ 3$.

We can use inverse operations to solve simple equations. To keep the equation balanced, we must perform the same operation on both sides of the equation.

Example 3 **Self Tutor**

Solve for x using a suitable inverse operation:

a $x + 6 = 13$ b $y - 4 = -1$ c $4g = 20$ d $\frac{h}{7} = -6$

a
$$x + 6 = 13$$
$$\therefore\ x + 6 - 6 = 13 - 6 \qquad \{\text{the inverse of } +6 \text{ is } -6\}$$
$$\therefore\ x = 7$$

b $y - 4 = -1$

$\therefore \ y - 4 + 4 = -1 + 4$ {the inverse of $-\ 4$ is $+\ 4$}

$\therefore \ y = 3$

c $4g = 20$

$\therefore \ \frac{4g}{4} = \frac{20}{4}$ {the inverse of $\times\ 4$ is $\div\ 4$}

$\therefore \ g = 5$

d $\frac{h}{7} = -6$

$\therefore \ \frac{h}{7} \times 7 = -6 \times 7$ {the inverse of $\div\ 7$ is $\times\ 7$}

$\therefore \ h = -42$

EXERCISE 8D

1 State the inverse of:

a $+\ 3$ **b** $-\ 8$ **c** $\times\ 2$ **d** $\div\ 5$

e $+\ 12$ **f** $\div\ 6$ **g** $-\ 5$ **h** $\times\ 9$

i $+\ \frac{2}{3}$ **j** $\div\ 13$ **k** $\times\ 15$ **l** $-\ \frac{4}{5}$

2 Simplify:

a $x - 3 + 3$ **b** $x + 5 - 5$ **c** $x \div 12 \times 12$ **d** $x \times 9 \div 9$

e $p + 4 - 4$ **f** $3q \div 3$ **g** $\frac{8r}{7} \times 7$ **h** $\frac{2s}{3} \div \frac{2}{3}$

3 Solve for x using a suitable inverse operation:

a $x + 4 = 10$ **b** $\frac{x}{10} = 1$ **c** $x - 9 = -2$ **d** $2x = 12$

e $x - 5 = 1$ **f** $x + 2 = 0$ **g** $\frac{x}{7} = -5$ **h** $5x = -55$

i $\frac{x}{8} = -4$ **j** $-20x = 60$ **k** $x + 5 = -2$ **l** $x - 7 = -16$

m $\frac{x}{-3} = 3$ **n** $x - 4 = 0$ **o** $-9x = -81$ **p** $x + 9 = -9$

4 Solve for x using a suitable inverse operation:

a $12x = -48$ **b** $x + 9 = -18$ **c** $x - 8 = -12$ **d** $\frac{x}{15} = -6$

e $x + 13 = 49$ **f** $13x = 0$ **g** $\frac{x}{-11} = -4$ **h** $x - 21 = -7$

5 Solve using a suitable inverse operation:

a $\frac{a}{5} = -2$ **b** $3b = 4$ **c** $-c = 9$ **d** $4 + d = 1$

e $e - 7 = 3$ **f** $\frac{1}{4}f = 15$ **g** $z - 7 = -9$ **h** $\frac{w}{6} = -12$

6 Solve using an inverse operation: $1 = \frac{3}{x}$

E ALGEBRAIC FLOWCHARTS

To solve harder equations, we need to know how algebraic expressions are built up. We can then use appropriate inverse operations to 'undo' the expression and isolate the variable. An **algebraic flowchart** is useful to help us do this.

For example, to build up the expression $3x + 2$, we start with x, multiply it by 3, then add on 2.

$$\boxed{x} \xrightarrow{\times 3} \boxed{3x} \xrightarrow{+ 2} \boxed{3x + 2}$$

We know that the inverse operation of $\times 3$ is $\div 3$, and the inverse operation of $+ 2$ is $- 2$.

To 'undo' the expression $3x + 2$, we perform **inverse operations** in the **reverse order**.

$$\boxed{3x + 2} \xrightarrow{- 2} \boxed{3x} \xrightarrow{\div 3} \boxed{x}$$

Example 4 Self Tutor

Use a flowchart to show how the expression $4x - 7$ is 'built up'.

Perform inverse operations in the reverse order to 'undo' the expression.

Building up: $\boxed{x} \xrightarrow{\times 4} \boxed{4x} \xrightarrow{- 7} \boxed{4x - 7}$

Undoing: $\boxed{4x - 7} \xrightarrow{+ 7} \boxed{4x} \xrightarrow{\div 4} \boxed{x}$

Example 5 Self Tutor

Use a flowchart to show how the expression $4(x - 7)$ is 'built up'.

Perform inverse operations in the reverse order to 'undo' the expression.

Building up: $\boxed{x} \xrightarrow{- 7} \boxed{x - 7} \xrightarrow{\times 4} \boxed{4(x - 7)}$

Undoing: $\boxed{4(x - 7)} \xrightarrow{\div 4} \boxed{x - 7} \xrightarrow{+ 7} \boxed{x}$

EXERCISE 8E

1 Use flowcharts to show how to 'build up' and 'undo':

a $7x + 3$ **b** $7(x + 3)$ **c** $5(x - 2)$

d $5x - 2$ **e** $\dfrac{x}{3} + 1$ **f** $\dfrac{x + 1}{3}$

g $\dfrac{x}{8} - 5$ **h** $\dfrac{x - 5}{8}$ **i** $2x - 6$

j $\dfrac{x}{-3} + 10$ **k** $8(x - 7)$ **l** $\dfrac{x - 3}{4}$

The order of operations is very important!

Example 6 **Self Tutor**

Use flowcharts to show how to 'build up' and 'undo':

a $\dfrac{3x+4}{7}$ **b** $1-\dfrac{x}{2}$

a *Building up*: $\boxed{x} \xrightarrow{\times 3} \boxed{3x} \xrightarrow{+4} \boxed{3x+4} \xrightarrow{\div 7} \boxed{\dfrac{3x+4}{7}}$

Undoing: $\boxed{\dfrac{3x+4}{7}} \xrightarrow{\times 7} \boxed{3x+4} \xrightarrow{-4} \boxed{3x} \xrightarrow{\div 3} \boxed{x}$

b *Building up*: $\boxed{x} \xrightarrow{\div -2} \boxed{-\dfrac{x}{2}} \xrightarrow{+1} \boxed{1-\dfrac{x}{2}}$

Undoing: $\boxed{1-\dfrac{x}{2}} \xrightarrow{-1} \boxed{-\dfrac{x}{2}} \xrightarrow{\times -2} \boxed{x}$

2 Use flowcharts to show how to 'build up' and 'undo':

a $\dfrac{3x+2}{5}$ **b** $\dfrac{3x}{5}+2$ **c** $\dfrac{3(x+2)}{5}$

d $\dfrac{7x-1}{6}$ **e** $\dfrac{7x}{6}-1$ **f** $\dfrac{7(x-1)}{6}$

g $\dfrac{5x}{6}-3$ **h** $\dfrac{5(x-3)}{6}$ **i** $\dfrac{5x-3}{6}$

j $1-\dfrac{2x}{3}$ **k** $\dfrac{1-2x}{3}$ **l** $\dfrac{2(1-x)}{3}$

ACTIVITY 1 EXPRESSION INVADERS

Click on the icon to play a game where you can practise building and undoing expressions.

EXPRESSION INVADERS

F SOLVING EQUATIONS

To solve equations like $4x-5=25$, we first consider how the expression on the LHS has been built up. We then isolate the unknown by using **inverse operations** in the **reverse order**.

ACTIVITY 2 SOLVING BY SCALES

Click on the icon to solve equations using a set of scales.

PRACTICE

Example 7 **Self Tutor**

Solve for x: $4x - 5 = 25$

$4x - 5 = 25$

$\therefore\ 4x - 5 + 5 = 25 + 5$ {adding 5 to both sides}

$\therefore\ 4x = 30$ {simplifying}

$\therefore\ \frac{4x}{4} = \frac{30}{4}$ {dividing both sides by 4}

$\therefore\ x = 7\frac{1}{2}$ {simplifying}

Check: LHS $= 4(7\frac{1}{2}) - 5 = 30 - 5 = 25 =$ RHS ✓

Check your answer by substituting back into the original equation.

EXERCISE 8F

1 Solve for x:

- **a** $2x + 1 = 5$
- **b** $4x + 7 = 27$
- **c** $3x + 7 = 19$
- **d** $3x + 1 = -23$
- **e** $5x - 9 = 11$
- **f** $8x - 3 = 0$
- **g** $2x - 7 = -4$
- **h** $2x - 11 = 23$
- **i** $7 + 8x = -9$
- **j** $6 - 3x = 0$
- **k** $8 + 13x = 34$
- **l** $11 + 4x = -6$

Example 8 **Self Tutor**

Solve for x: $\frac{x}{4} + 5 = -8$

$\frac{x}{4} + 5 = -8$

$\therefore\ \frac{x}{4} + 5 - 5 = -8 - 5$ {subtracting 5 from both sides}

$\therefore\ \frac{x}{4} = -13$ {simplifying}

$\therefore\ \frac{x}{4} \times 4 = -13 \times 4$ {multiplying both sides by 4}

$\therefore\ x = -52$ {simplifying}

Check: LHS $= \frac{-52}{4} + 5 = -13 + 5 = -8 =$ RHS ✓

2 Solve for x:

- **a** $\frac{x}{2} + 1 = 3$
- **b** $\frac{x}{2} - 5 = 6$
- **c** $\frac{x}{8} + 3 = 5$
- **d** $\frac{x}{3} - 4 = -1$
- **e** $\frac{x}{3} - 4 = -11$
- **f** $\frac{x}{6} + 2 = -2$
- **g** $\frac{x}{9} - 7 = 0$
- **h** $\frac{x}{7} + 5 = -3$
- **i** $\frac{x}{11} + 31 = 33$

Example 9 **Self Tutor**

Solve for x: $32 - 5x = 8$

$$32 - 5x = 8$$
$$\therefore\ 32 - 5x - 32 = 8 - 32 \quad \{\text{subtracting 32 from both sides}\}$$
$$\therefore\ -5x = -24$$
$$\therefore\ \frac{-5x}{-5} = \frac{-24}{-5} \quad \{\text{dividing both sides by } -5\}$$
$$\therefore\ x = 4\tfrac{4}{5}$$

Check: LHS $= 32 - 5(4\frac{4}{5}) = 32 - 5(\frac{24}{5}) = 32 - 24 = 8 =$ RHS ✓

3 Solve for x:

a $15 - 2x = 7$
b $2 - 3x = 8$
c $1 - 4x = -15$
d $4 - 5x = -21$
e $16 - 8x = 0$
f $22 - 3x = 1$
g $14 - x = -1$
h $19 - 4x = -9$
i $-5x + 12 = -8$

Example 10 **Self Tutor**

Solve the equation: $\dfrac{2x-3}{3} = -2$

$$\frac{2x-3}{3} = -2$$
$$\therefore\ \frac{2x-3}{3} \times 3 = -2 \times 3 \quad \{\text{multiplying both sides by 3}\}$$
$$\therefore\ 2x - 3 = -6$$
$$\therefore\ 2x - 3 + 3 = -6 + 3 \quad \{\text{adding 3 to both sides}\}$$
$$\therefore\ 2x = -3$$
$$\therefore\ \frac{2x}{2} = \frac{-3}{2} \quad \{\text{dividing both sides by 2}\}$$
$$\therefore\ x = -\tfrac{3}{2}$$

Check: LHS $= \dfrac{2(-\frac{3}{2}) - 3}{3} = \dfrac{-6}{3} = -2 =$ RHS ✓

4 Solve for x:

a $\dfrac{x+1}{3} = 4$
b $\dfrac{4x-1}{5} = 7$
c $\dfrac{2x-5}{2} = 1$
d $\dfrac{3x+1}{4} = -5$
e $\dfrac{5x+6}{-2} = 7$
f $\dfrac{2x+1}{-5} = 11$
g $\dfrac{11x-1}{8} = -7$
h $\dfrac{6x-2}{-5} = -2$
i $\dfrac{11+4x}{3} = -11$

Example 11 — Self Tutor

Solve the equation: $3(2x-1)=-21$

$$3(2x-1)=-21$$
$$\therefore \frac{3(2x-1)}{3}=\frac{-21}{3} \quad \{\text{dividing both sides by 3}\}$$
$$\therefore 2x-1=-7$$
$$\therefore 2x-1+1=-7+1 \quad \{\text{adding 1 to both sides}\}$$
$$\therefore 2x=-6$$
$$\therefore \frac{2x}{2}=\frac{-6}{2} \quad \{\text{dividing both sides by 2}\}$$
$$\therefore x=-3$$

Check: LHS $=3(2(-3)-1)=3(-7)=-21=$ RHS ✓

5 Solve for x:

- **a** $2(x-1)=18$
- **b** $3(2x+1)=15$
- **c** $5(2x-7)=10$
- **d** $4(3x-5)=-28$
- **e** $-4(3x-2)=44$
- **f** $7(3x-7)=-49$
- **g** $6(3x-2)=12$
- **h** $-5(4x+1)=-15$
- **i** $-6(3+8x)=-18$

6 Solve the following equations:

- **a** $3a+5=14$
- **b** $\frac{x}{8}-1=55$
- **c** $\frac{3x-1}{2}=7$
- **d** $4(x+5)=24$
- **e** $6(n-2)=12$
- **f** $5a+9=-31$
- **g** $\frac{2x-5}{4}=0$
- **h** $\frac{x}{5}-3=12$
- **i** $\frac{x+15}{3}=6$
- **j** $5(2n-1)=-35$
- **k** $\frac{3k+5}{2}=13$
- **l** $-8(5z+1)=24$

ACTIVITY 3 — REAL WORLD PROBLEMS

We are often faced with real world problems where we need to work out the value of an unknown quantity.

For example, consider these problems:

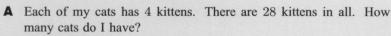

A Each of my cats has 4 kittens. There are 28 kittens in all. How many cats do I have?

B My training course runs for 6 hours. It finishes at 8 pm. What time does it start?

C This morning I bought some plants from the nursery. When I divided them equally into 5 large pots, I found I had 3 plants in each. How many plants did I buy this morning?

D Bernadette tells me that 3 years ago she was 11 years old. How old is she now?

What to do:

1 Answer the **Opening Problem** on page **150**.

2 Match each of the real world problems above to the corresponding "find the number" question in the **Opening Problem**. Hence solve the real world problems.

ACTIVITY 4 — SOLVING EQUATIONS

Click on the icon to practise solving linear equations.

PRACTICE

G EQUATIONS WITH A REPEATED UNKNOWN

DEMO

If the unknown or variable appears more than once in the equation, we need to take extra steps in its solution.

For example, consider the equation $3x + 1 = x + 7$.

In this case the unknown appears twice, once on each side of the equation.

We can represent the equation using the set of scales shown.

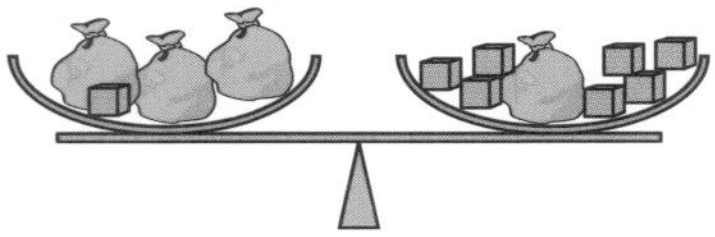

The unknown x is the number of blocks in each bag.

We can add or subtract bags or blocks on both sides of the scales to maintain the balance.

Removing a bag is like taking x from both sides. This gives us the equation $2x + 1 = 7$.

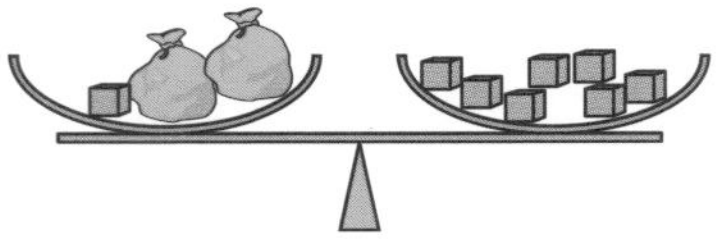

We can then use inverse operations to solve for x.

In general, we follow these steps to solve equations:

Step 1: If necessary, expand any brackets and collect like terms.

Step 2: If necessary, remove the unknown from one side of the equation. Remember to balance the other side.

Step 3: Use inverse operations to isolate the unknown and solve the equation.

Example 12 — Self Tutor

Solve for d: $2d + 3(d - 1) = 7$

$$\begin{aligned}
2d + 3(d-1) &= 7 \\
\therefore\ 2d + 3d - 3 &= 7 && \{\text{expanding brackets}\} \\
\therefore\ 5d - 3 &= 7 && \{\text{collecting like terms}\} \\
\therefore\ 5d - 3 + 3 &= 7 + 3 && \{\text{adding 3 to both sides}\} \\
\therefore\ 5d &= 10 \\
\therefore\ \frac{5d}{5} &= \frac{10}{5} && \{\text{dividing both sides by 5}\} \\
\therefore\ d &= 2
\end{aligned}$$

Check: LHS $= 2(2) + 3(2 - 1) = 4 + 3 = 7 =$ RHS ✓

EXERCISE 8G

1 Solve the following equations:

- **a** $2x + 3x = 10$
- **b** $5x + 4 + 3x = -36$
- **c** $3x - 6 - 2x + 7 = 16$
- **d** $4y - 9 + 3y - 5 = -14$
- **e** $5x + 3(x + 2) = 30$
- **f** $2m + 4(m - 3) = 3$
- **g** $7x + 2(x + 1) = 28$
- **h** $-3(p + 2) + 4(p - 2) = 1$
- **i** $t + \frac{t}{3} = 8$
- **j** $d - \frac{d}{5} = -8$
- **k** $2x + \frac{x}{3} = -14$
- **l** $\frac{x}{2} - \frac{x}{3} = 2$

Example 13 **Self Tutor**

Solve for x: $3x + 2 = x + 14$

$$3x + 2 = x + 14$$
$\therefore\ 3x + 2 - x = x + 14 - x$ {subtracting x from both sides}
$\therefore\ 2x + 2 = 14$
$\therefore\ 2x + 2 - 2 = 14 - 2$ {subtracting 2 from both sides}
$\therefore\ 2x = 12$
$\therefore\ x = 6$ {dividing both sides by 2}

Check: LHS $= 3(6) + 2 = 18 + 2 = 20$
RHS $= 6 + 14 = 20$ ✓

2 Solve the following equations:

- **a** $2x - 1 = 5 + x$
- **b** $3x + 1 = x + 5$
- **c** $2x - 6 = 7x + 14$
- **d** $4x - 5 = 2x + 1$
- **e** $7x + 7 = 3x + 23$
- **f** $x - 6 = 5x + 4$

Example 14 **Self Tutor**

Solve for x: $4x + 3 = 23 - x$

$$4x + 3 = 23 - x$$
$\therefore\ 4x + 3 + x = 23 - x + x$ {adding x to both sides}
$\therefore\ 5x + 3 = 23$
$\therefore\ 5x + 3 - 3 = 23 - 3$ {subtracting 3 from both sides}
$\therefore\ 5x = 20$
$\therefore\ x = 4$ {dividing both sides by 5}

Check: LHS $= 4(4) + 3 = 16 + 3 = 19$
RHS $= 23 - 4 = 19$ ✓

3 Solve the following equations:

- **a** $x + 2 = 4 - x$
- **b** $2x + 5 = 10 - 3x$
- **c** $2 + 7x = 3 - 3x$
- **d** $3x - 11 = 9 - 2x$
- **e** $8 - 9x = 3 - 4x$
- **f** $9 - 3x = 5 - 6x$

Ce05

Example 15 **Self Tutor**

Solve for x: $3(x+2) = x - 1$

$$3(x+2) = x - 1$$
$\therefore\ 3x + 6 = x - 1$ {expanding the brackets}
$\therefore\ 3x + 6 - x = x - 1 - x$ {subtracting x from both sides}
$\therefore\ 2x + 6 = -1$
$\therefore\ 2x = -7$ {subtracting 6 from both sides}
$\therefore\ x = -\frac{7}{2}$ {dividing both sides by 2}

Check: LHS $= 3((-\frac{7}{2}) + 2) = 3(-\frac{3}{2}) = -\frac{9}{2}$
RHS $= (-\frac{7}{2}) - 1 = -\frac{9}{2}$ ✓

4 Solve the following equations:
- **a** $2(x+1) = x + 5$
- **b** $3(t-2) = t + 4$
- **c** $6(2x-3) = x - 7$
- **d** $4(3y-1) = 2y + 1$
- **e** $2(a-5) = 5 - 3a$
- **f** $8(p+2) = 1 + 3p$

5 **a** Try to solve $7(a+3) = 21 + 7a$. What do you notice?
- **b** How many values of a satisfy the equation?
- **c** What name do we give to an equation like this?

6 **a** Try to solve $3(a+1) = 4 + 3a$. What do you notice?
- **b** How many values of a satisfy the equation?

7 Leigh's teacher asks him to expand $5(2+3x)$ using the distributive law. He incorrectly writes $5(2+3x) = 10x + 15$.
- **a** By substituting $x = 4$, can you show that Leigh's expansion is incorrect?
- **b** Are there any values of x for which Leigh's statement is true?

8 Solve the following equations:
- **a** $4 - x = 2(x+1) + 1$
- **b** $3x + 1 = 2(1-3x) + 19$
- **c** $10 - x = 5(x-3) + 7$
- **d** $7 + 6p = 3 + 2(1-p)$

9 Solve for x:
- **a** $3(x-5) = 5x + 1$
- **b** $2x + 7 + 4(2x+3) = -1$
- **c** $x - 2 + 4(x-1) = 2$
- **d** $5(x+1) + 5(x-1) = 30$
- **e** $4 - 3x - (x+5) = 3$
- **f** $7(1-x) - 6(2-x) = 8$
- **g** $3x - 2(x+3) - 4x = 0$
- **h** $8(2x-1) - 5(2x+3) = -5$

10 Solve the following equations:
- **a** $3(x-6) = 2(2-x) + 3$
- **b** $2(x-8) = 3(x-5)$
- **c** $4(2x+3) - 10 = 5(3-x)$
- **d** $5(1-2x) + 3(x+5) = 2(1+x) - 9$
- **e** $x - 7 - (3x+2) = 8x + 11$
- **f** $7 - 6x = 8(1+x) - (1-x)$
- **g** $5x + 2(3-x) = 4 - (2-5x)$
- **h** $7 - (2-3x) = 12 - (5-4x)$
- **i** $4x = 4(3x-1) - 2(3-x)$
- **j** $3(x-1) - 4(5+x) = 4(2x+1)$

INVESTIGATION — RECURRING DECIMALS

In **Chapter 3** we encountered **recurring decimals** such as $0.\overline{5} = 0.5555....$.

We can now use our skills with equations to convert recurring decimals such as $0.\overline{5}$ to fractions.

What to do:

1 Let $x = 0.\overline{5}$, so $x = 0.5555....$.

- **a** Multiply both sides of this equation by 10 and hence explain why $10x = 5 + x$.
- **b** Solve this equation to find the value of $0.\overline{5}$ as a fraction.

2 Follow similar steps to convert the following recurring decimals to fractions:

a 0.777.... **b** 0.888.... **c** 0.333.... **d** 0.444....

3 Convert the following recurring decimals to fractions:

a 0.262626.... **b** 0.5151.... **c** 1.0909.... **d** 2.0909....

Hint: In **a**, multiply both sides of $x = 0.262626....$ by 100.

ACTIVITY 5 — ARITHMAGONS

The diagram opposite is an **arithmagon**. The number in each square is equal to the sum of the numbers in the two circles connected to it.

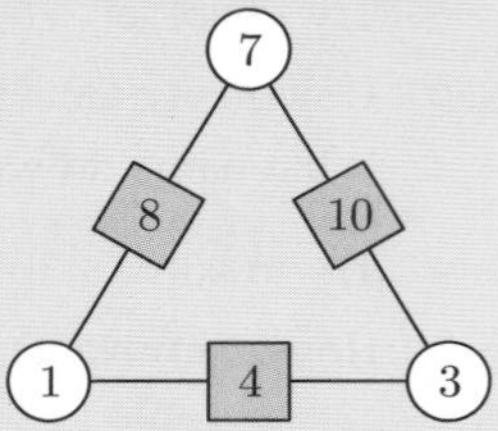

What to do:

1 Copy and complete these arithmagons:

a

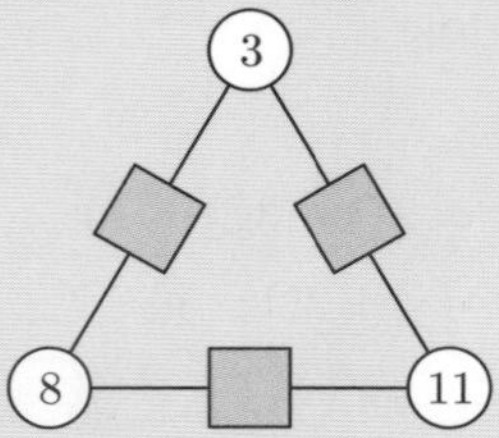

b

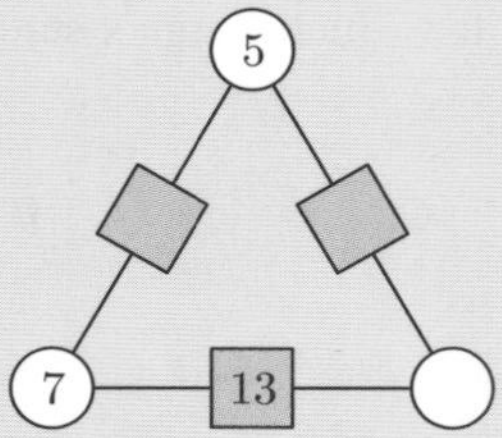

c

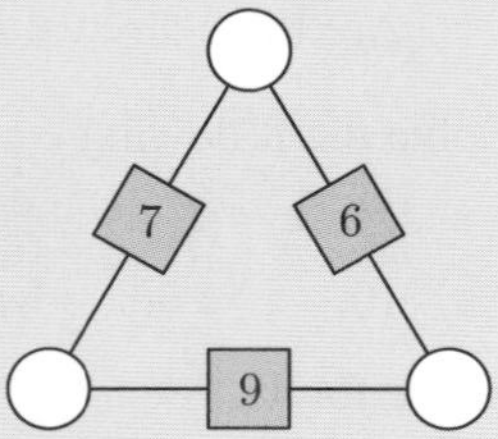

You will probably find that **1 c** is the hardest, because completing an arithmagon is harder if you are only given the values in each square.

2 Consider the following approach for **1 c**:

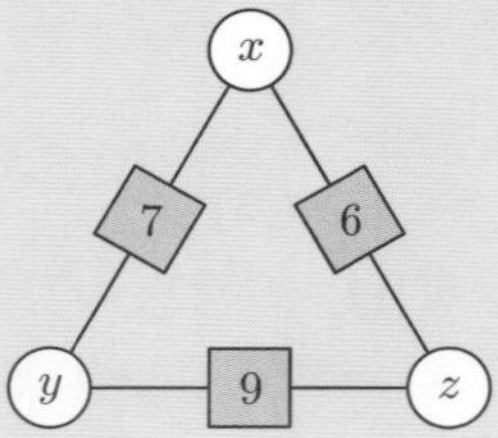

Let the numbers in the circles be x, y, and z.

$\therefore\ x + y = 7$

$y + z = 9$

$x + z = 6$

Adding these three equations gives

$2x + 2y + 2z = 22$

$\therefore\ x + y + z = 11$

We know that $y+z=9$, so $x=2$

$\therefore$ $y=5$ and $z=4$.

Use this approach to complete these arithmagons:

a

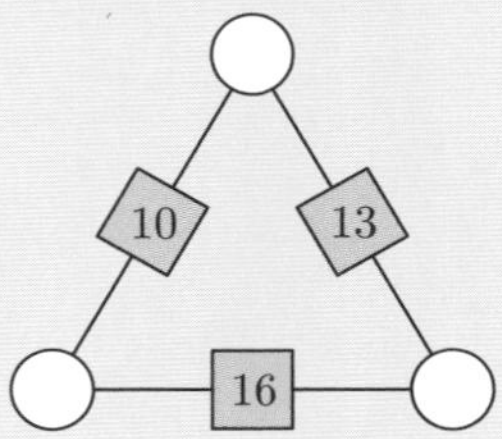

b

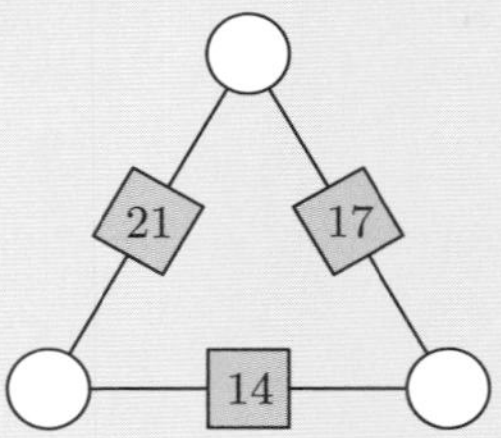

c

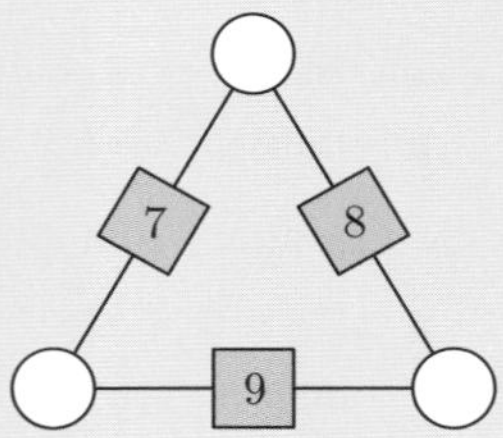

REVIEW SET 8A

1 For each of the following equations, state whether they are:

A true for *exactly one value* of x **B** true for *two values* of x

C true for *all values* of x **D** *never* true.

a $x+3=x$ **b** $x-4=1$ **c** $x^2=1$ **d** $2x-x=x$

2 State the inverse of $\div 6$.

3 Find the equation which results when:

a 2 is added to both sides of $3x-2=-11$

b 9 is subtracted from both sides of $4x+9=-1$.

4 Solve $x+5=2$ by inspection.

5 One of the numbers 6, 10, -6, or -4 is the solution to the equation $8x+3=3(x-9)$. Find the solution.

6 Solve using a suitable inverse operation:

a $x-11=4$ **b** $6x=42$ **c** $a+4=-9$ **d** $\frac{t}{-3}=7$

7 Use a flowchart to show how the following expressions are built up from x:

a $\frac{x}{6}+1$ **b** $4(3x-4)$ **c** $\frac{2-4x}{3}$

8 Use a flowchart to show how to isolate x from the following expressions:

a $\frac{x}{7}-3$ **b** $4(x+1)$ **c** $1+3x$

9 Solve for x:

a $10x-7=13$ **b** $5+4x=29$ **c** $4x-5=5x-6$

10 Solve for x:

a $7x-6=6x-1$ **b** $4(5x+1)=14$

c $3x+2(3-x)=-3$ **d** $4x-2(3x-1)=5-7x$

e $3(x+6)-4(4-2x)=7x+6$ **f** $9-5(x-1)=2(x+4)$

REVIEW SET 8B

1 Determine whether the following equations are identities:

a $x - 5 = 5 - x$ **b** $8 \times m = m \times 8$ **c** $2t + 2t = 4t^2$

2 State the inverse of:

a multiplying by 5 **b** subtracting 7.

3 Solve using a suitable inverse operation:

a $a - 3 = 4$ **b** $-5b = 45$ **c** $c + 17 = 7$ **d** $\frac{d}{8} = -12$

4 Use a flowchart to show how the following expressions are built up from x:

a $\frac{x+3}{2}$ **b** $5x - 9$ **c** $\frac{x}{7} - 2$

5 Use a flowchart to show how to isolate x from the following expressions:

a $3x - 1$ **b** $\frac{8x+10}{3}$ **c** $5 - \frac{2x}{3}$

6 Solve for x:

a $3x + 5 = 17$ **b** $\frac{x}{4} + 1 = -11$ **c** $5 + 2x = 3$

7 Solve for x:

a $\frac{1+2x}{3} = 1$ **b** $\frac{1+2x}{3} = 0$ **c** $\frac{1+2x}{3} = -1$

8 Solve for x:

a $2x + 1 = x + 8$ **b** $x - 4 = 5x - 1$ **c** $3(x - 3) = 8 - x$

9 Solve for x:

a $3(4 - x) - 2x = -13$ **b** $3x - 5 = 3 - x$

c $2(4x - 3) + x = 3(2x - 1) + 2$ **d** $2(x - 3) - 3(4 - x) = 4(2x - 5)$

10 Ms Maxwell wrote the equation $\frac{x}{3} + 2 = 7$ on the board. She told her class there were *two* good ways to solve the equation.

a The first method is to first multiply *each* term in the equation by 3.

i Find the equation that results when *each* term is multiplied by 3.

ii Hence solve the equation.

b The second method is to first subtract 2 from each side of the equation.

i Find the equation that results when 2 is subtracted from both sides of $\frac{x}{3} + 2 = 7$.

ii Hence solve the equation.

c Do the two methods give the same answer?

Chapter 9

The geometry of polygons

Contents:

OPENING PROBLEM

The figure alongside contains two pairs of parallel lines.

Things to think about:

- **a** What name is given to this shape?
- **b** Which angles in the figure are equal?
- **c** What is the sum of the sizes of:
  - **i** the red angles
  - **ii** the green angles?
- **d** What is the total sum of the angles of this figure?

POLYGONS

A **polygon** is a closed 2-dimensional shape with straight line edges that do not cross.

For example:

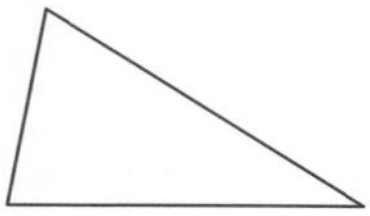 and 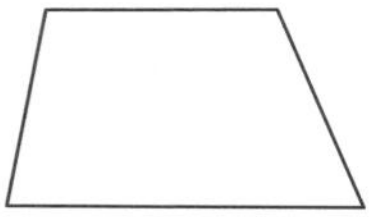 are polygons.

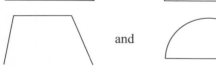

 and 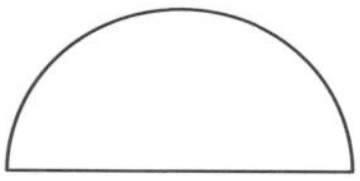 are not polygons.

In this chapter we will first revise some geometrical facts about angles and lines. We will then look at the properties of some particular polygons.

A REVIEW OF GEOMETRICAL FACTS

You should be familiar with the following facts about angles and lines.

ANGLES

Whenever two lines meet, an **angle** is formed between them.

The shaded angle is written as $A\widehat{B}C$.

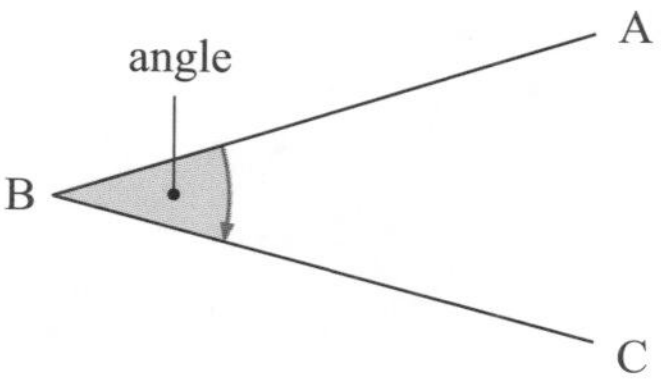

We can classify angles according to their **size**.

Revolution	Straight Angle	Right Angle
 One complete turn 1 revolution $= 360°$.	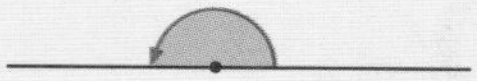 $\frac{1}{2}$ turn 1 straight angle $= 180°$.	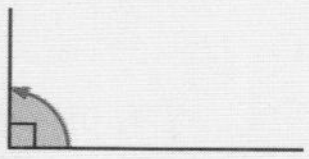 $\frac{1}{4}$ turn 1 right angle $= 90°$.

Acute Angle	Obtuse Angle	Reflex Angle
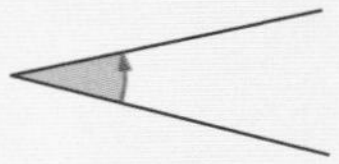		
Less than a $\frac{1}{4}$ turn. An acute angle has size between 0° and 90°.	Between $\frac{1}{4}$ turn and $\frac{1}{2}$ turn. An obtuse angle has size between 90° and 180°.	Between $\frac{1}{2}$ turn and 1 turn. A reflex angle has size between 180° and 360°.

ANGLE PAIRS

- Two angles with sizes that add to 90° are called **complementary angles**.
- Two angles with sizes that add to 180° are called **supplementary angles**.
- **Vertically opposite angles** occur whenever two lines intersect.

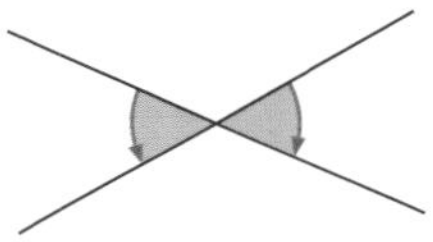

LINE TERMINOLOGY

- **Line (AB)** is the endless straight line passing through the points A and B.

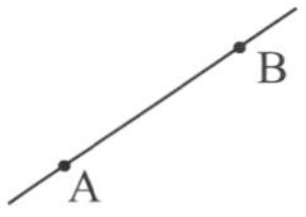

- **Line segment [AB]** is the part of the straight line (AB) which connects A to B.
  The length of [AB] is written as AB.

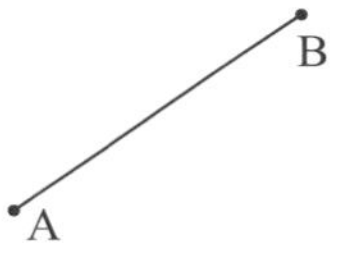

- **Concurrent lines** are three or more lines all passing through a common point.

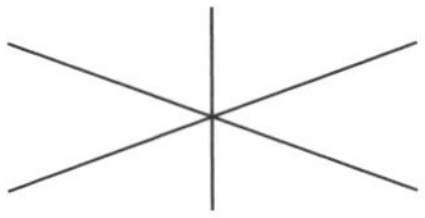

- **Collinear points** are points which lie in a straight line.

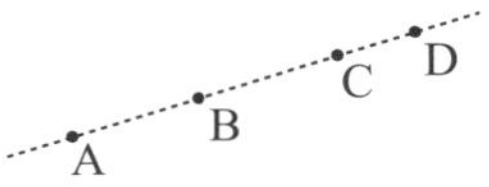

- **Perpendicular lines** intersect at right angles. We indicate this with a small square.

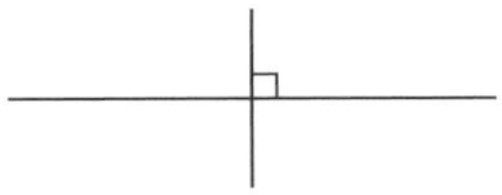

- **Parallel lines** are lines which never intersect. We use arrowheads to indicate parallelism.

GEOMETRIC THEOREMS

Title	Theorem	Figure
Angles at a point	The sum of the sizes of the angles at a point is 360°.	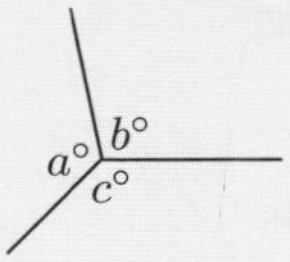 $a+b+c=360$
Angles on a straight line	The sum of the sizes of the angles on a line is 180°.	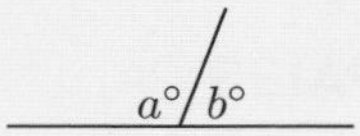 $a+b=180$
Vertically opposite angles	Vertically opposite angles are equal in size.	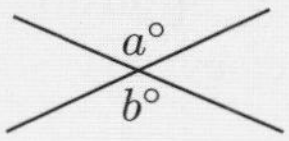 $a=b$
Corresponding angles	When two *parallel* lines are cut by a third line, angles in corresponding positions are equal in size.	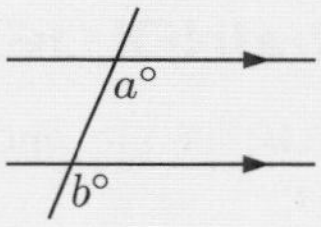 $a=b$
Alternate angles	When two *parallel* lines are cut by a third line, angles in alternate positions are equal in size.	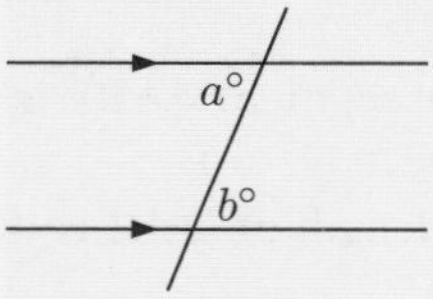 $a=b$
Co-interior or allied angles	When two *parallel* lines are cut by a third line, co-interior angles are supplementary.	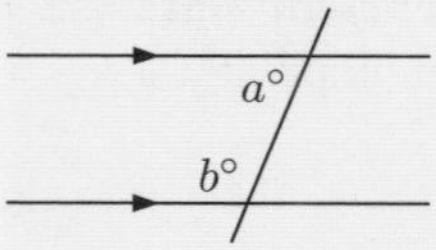 $a+b=180$

EXERCISE 9A

1 State whether the following are true or false:

- **a** An angle measuring 88° is an acute angle.
- **b** An angle measuring 92° is an obtuse angle.
- **c** The size of an angle depends on the lengths of its arms.
- **d** When a vertical line crosses a horizontal line, the angle formed is a straight angle.
- **e** $\frac{2}{3}$ of a straight angle is an acute angle.
- **f** A right angle is neither an acute angle nor an obtuse angle.

2 $\widehat{AOB}$ is a right angle, and [OP] can rotate about O between [OA] and [OB].

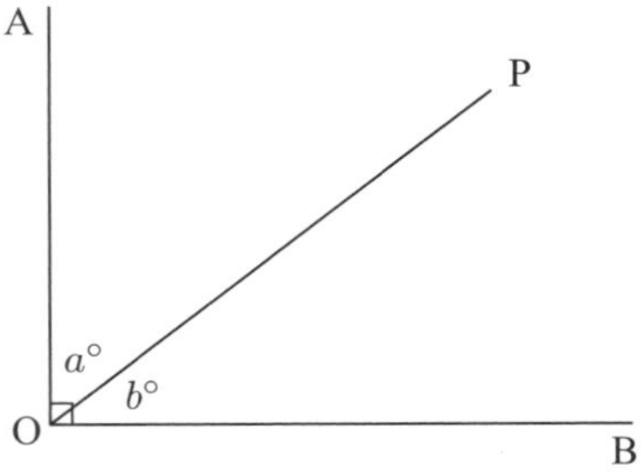

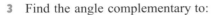

- **a** If $a = 76$, find b.
- **b** If $b = 55$, find a.
- **c** Find the value of b if a is 0.
- **d** Find the value of a if b is 89.
- **e** If $a = b$, what is the value of each?

3 Find the angle complementary to:

a 28° **b** 77° **c** $y°$ **d** $(90 - x)°$

4 Find the angle supplementary to:

a 85° **b** 127° **c** $q°$ **d** $(180 - n)°$ **e** $(x + 90)°$

5 Find the values of the variables, giving brief reasons for your answers:

a

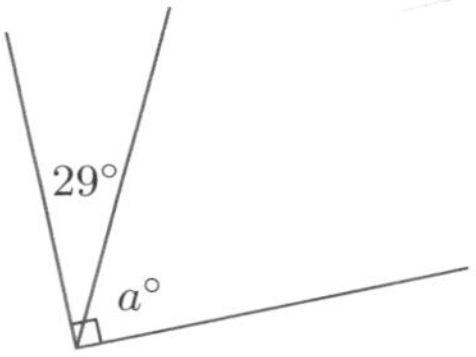

b

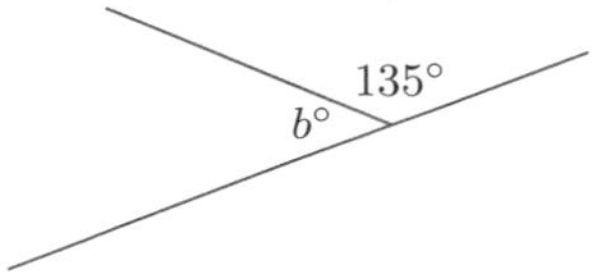

c

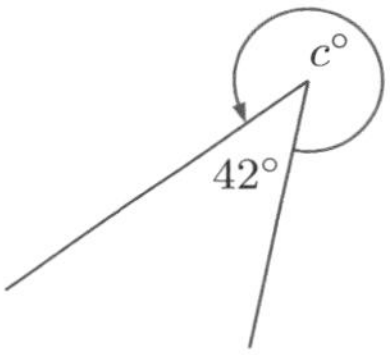

d

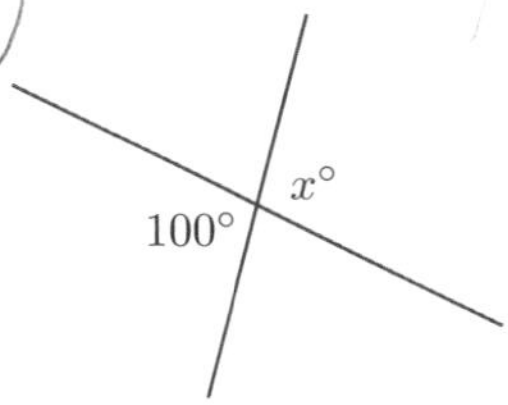

e

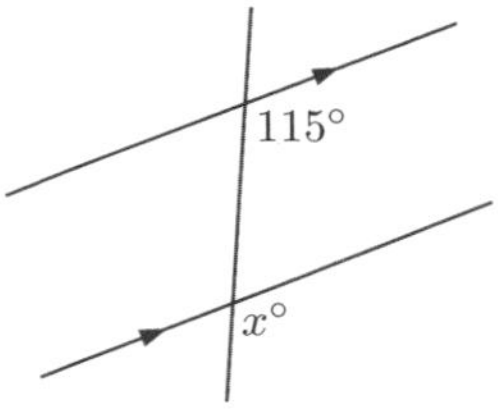

f

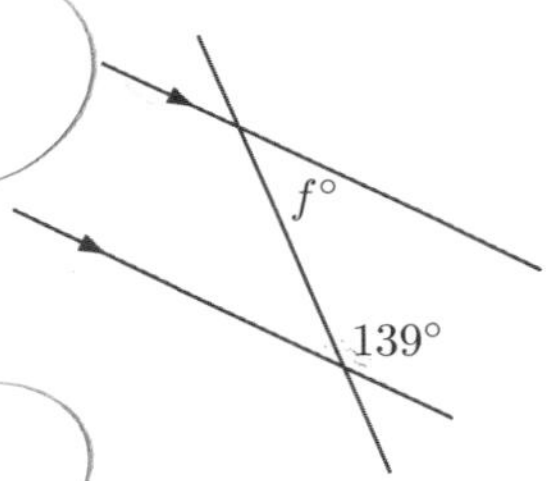

g

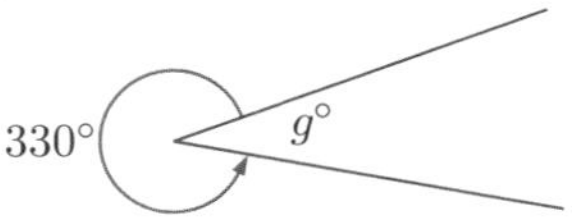

h

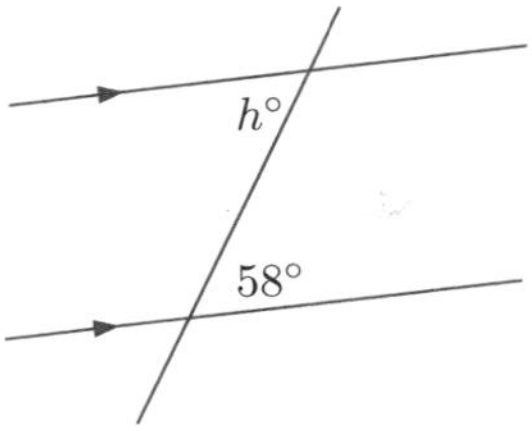

i

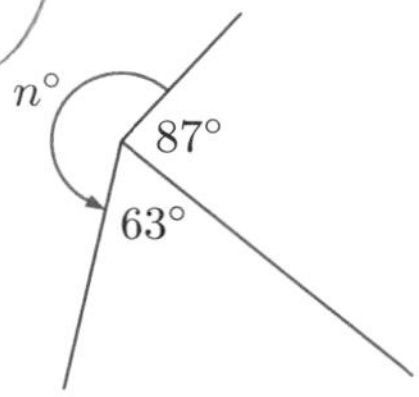

j

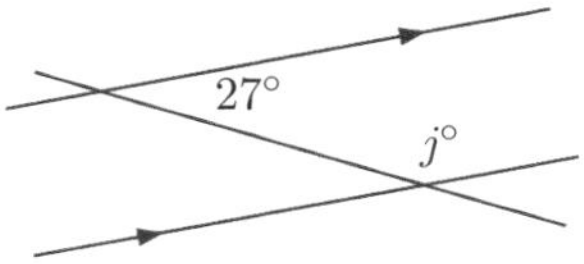

k

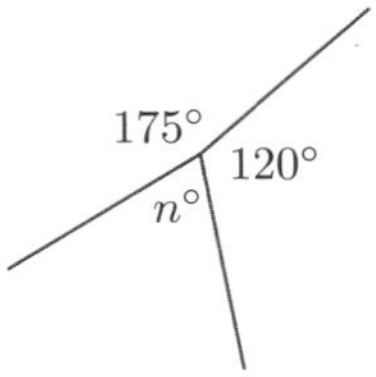

l

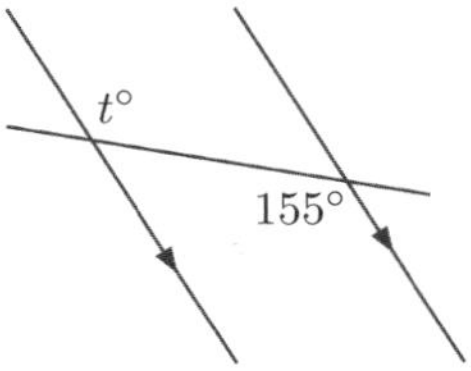

m

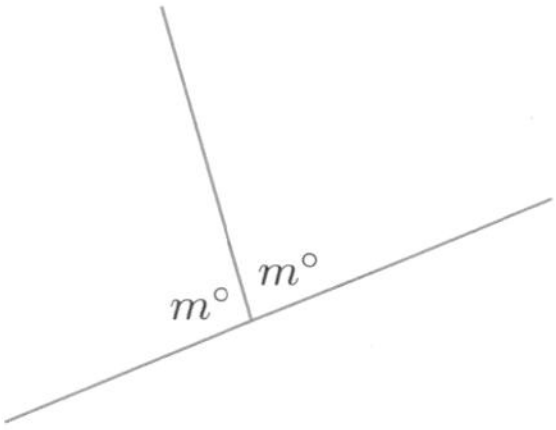

n

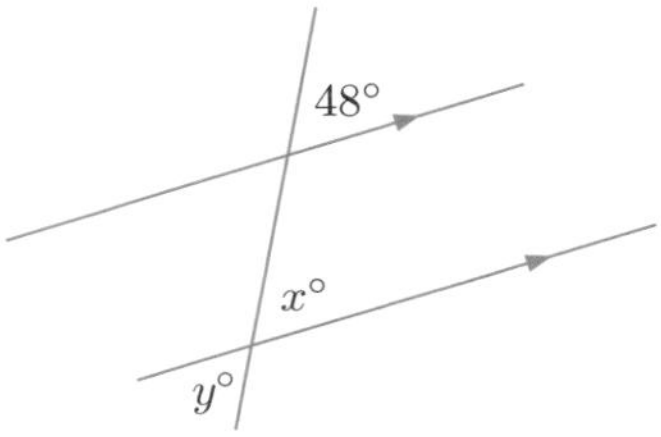

o

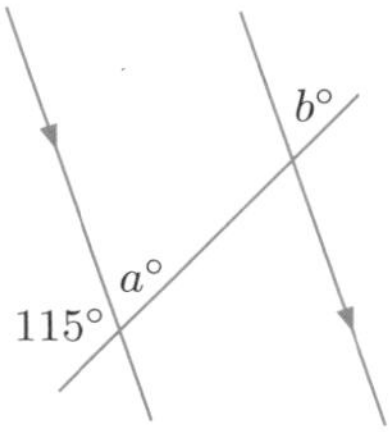

Example 1 **Self Tutor**

Find, giving brief reasons, the value of x:

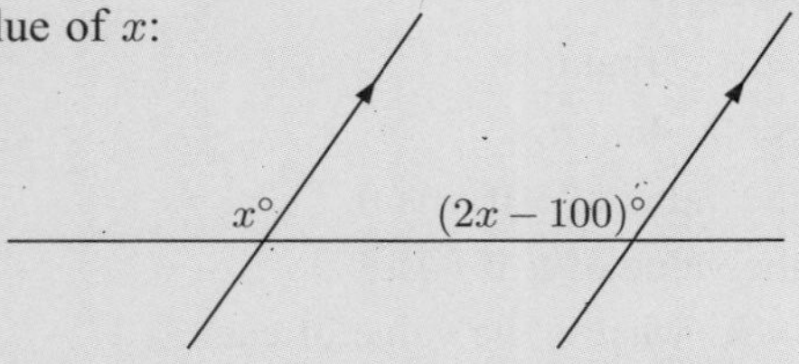

$$2x - 100 = x \quad \{\text{equal corresponding angles}\}$$
$$\therefore\ 2x - 100 - x = x - x \quad \{\text{subtracting } x \text{ from both sides}\}$$
$$\therefore\ x - 100 = 0$$
$$\therefore\ x = 100$$

6 Find, giving brief reasons, the values of the unknowns:

a

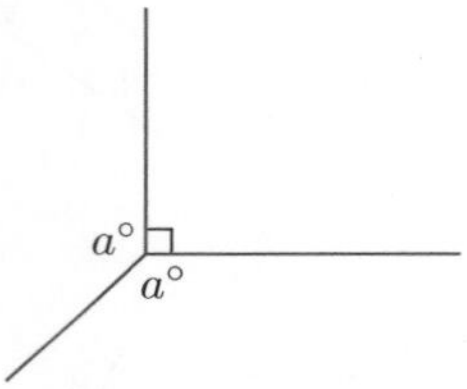

b

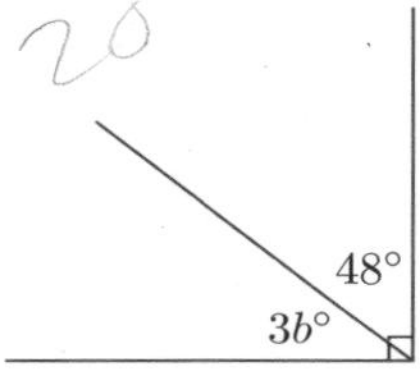

c

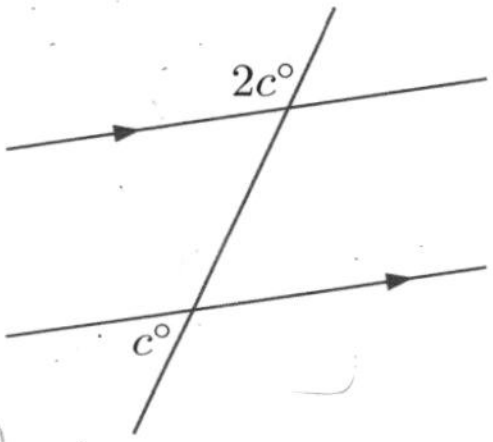

d

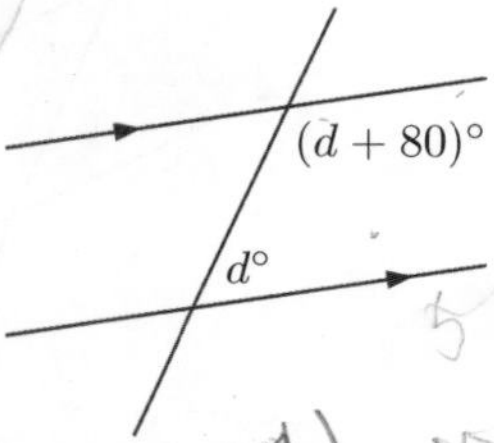

e

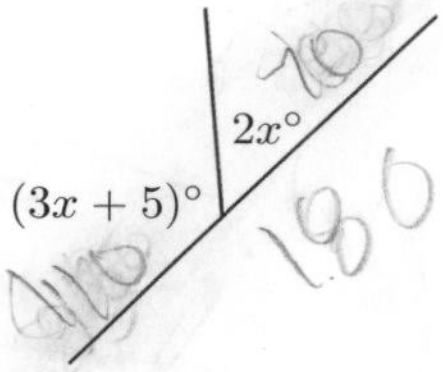

f

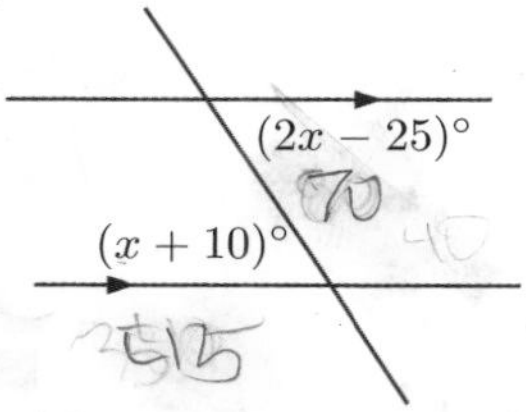

g

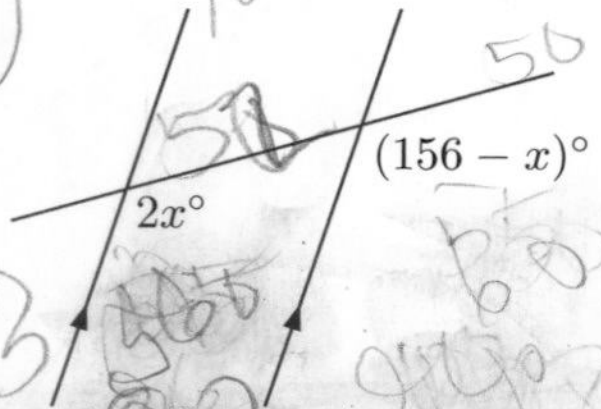

h

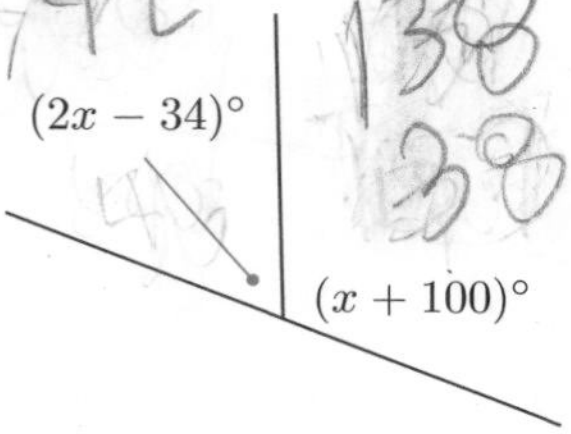

i

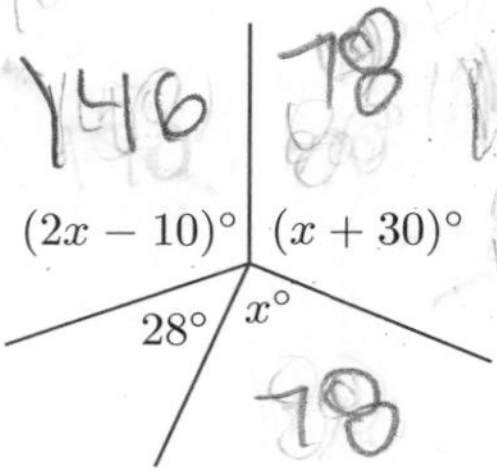

7 These diagrams are not drawn to scale, but the information on them is correct. State whether [AB] is parallel to [CD], giving a brief reason for your answer.

a

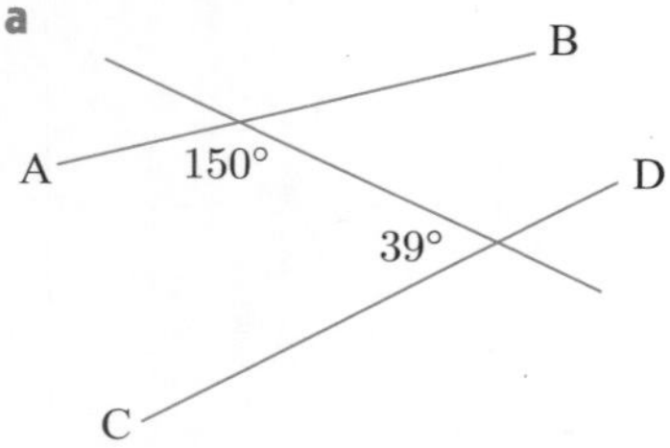

b

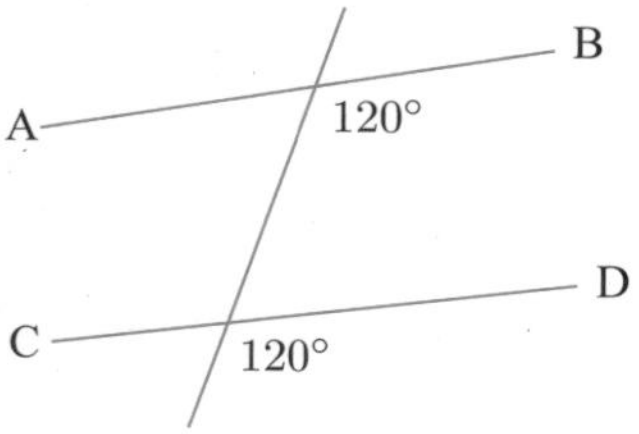

c

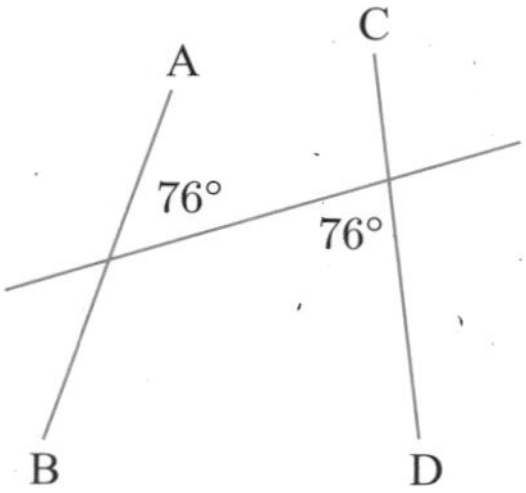

B TRIANGLES

A **triangle** is a polygon which has three sides.

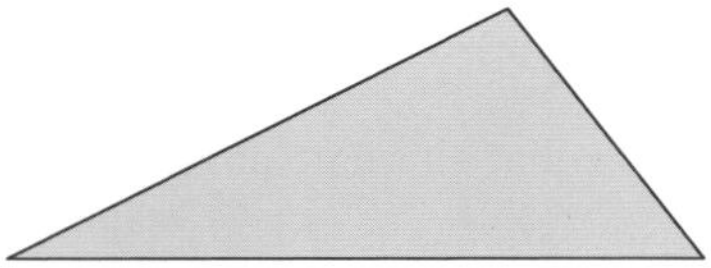

CLASSIFICATION BY SIDES

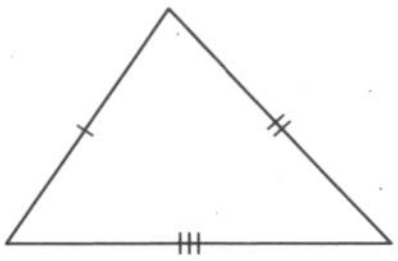

Scalene triangle
no equal sides

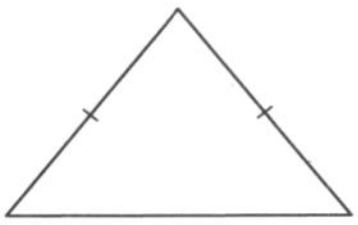

Isosceles triangle
two equal sides

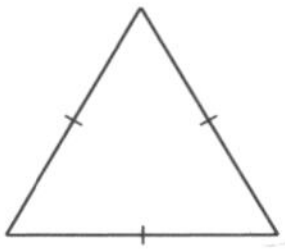

Equilateral triangle
three equal sides

CLASSIFICATION BY ANGLES

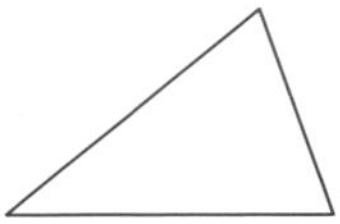

Acute angled triangle
all acute angles

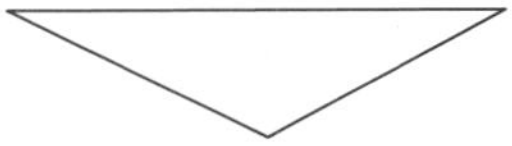

Obtuse angled triangle
one obtuse angle

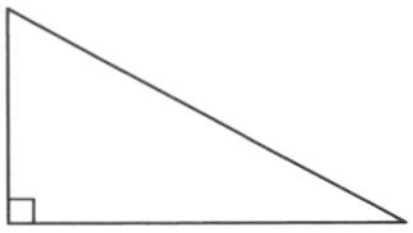

Right angled triangle
one right angle

PROPERTIES OF TRIANGLES

All triangles have the following properties:

- The sum of the interior angles of a triangle is 180°.

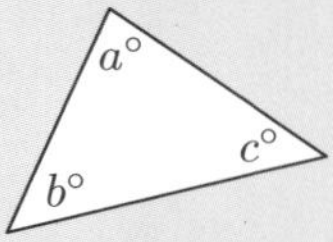

$a + b + c = 180$

GEOMETRY PACKAGE

- Any exterior angle is equal to the sum of the interior opposite angles.

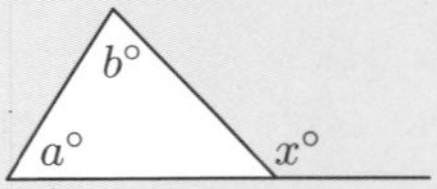

$x = a + b$

GEOMETRY PACKAGE

- The longest side is opposite the largest angle.

Proof that the sum of the angles of a triangle is 180°:

Draw a triangle ABC with angles $a°$, $b°$, and $c°$.

Draw a line segment [DE] through B which is parallel to [AC].

Using equal alternate angles,

$\widehat{ABD} = a°$ and $\widehat{CBE} = c°$.

But $a + b + c = 180$ {angles on a line}

$\therefore$ $a + b + c = 180$

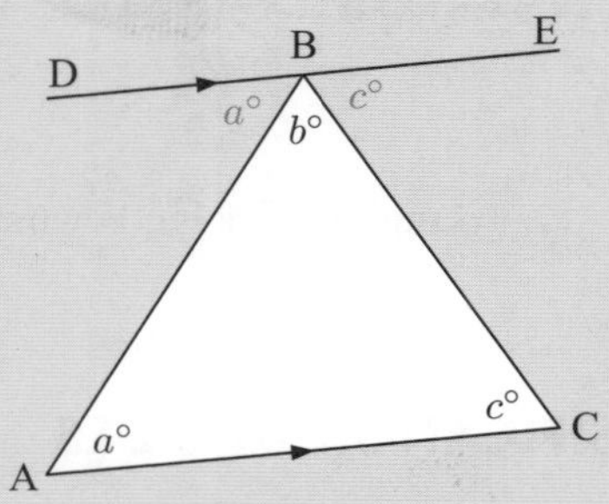

Example 2 **Self Tutor**

Find the value of the unknown:

a

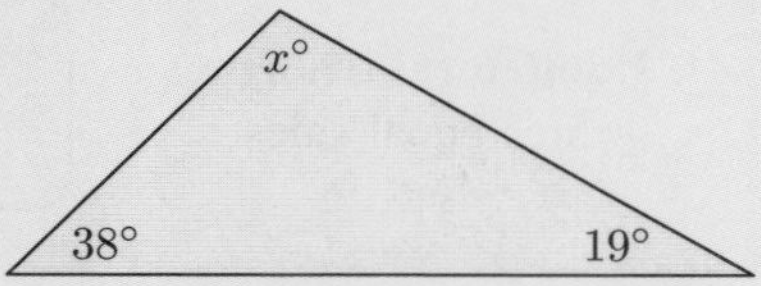

b

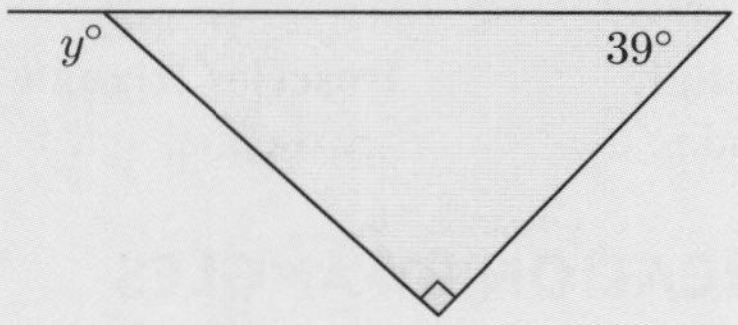

a $x + 38 + 19 = 180$ {angle sum of a triangle}

$\therefore$ $x + 57 = 180$

$\therefore$ $x + 57 - 57 = 180 - 57$ {subtracting 57 from both sides}

$\therefore$ $x = 123$

b $y = 39 + 90$ {exterior angle of a triangle}

$\therefore$ $y = 129$

EXERCISE 9B

1 Classify the following triangles as scalene, isosceles, or equilateral:

a

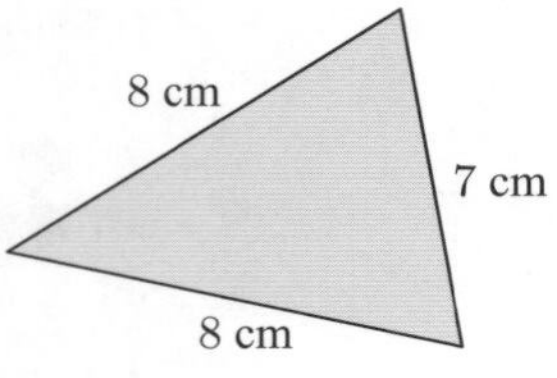

b

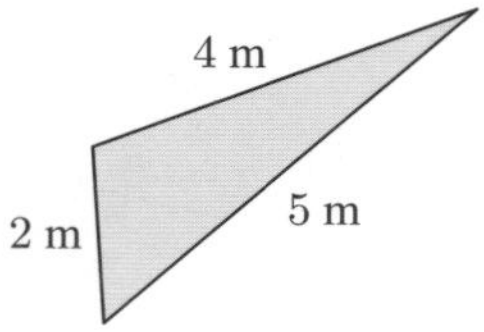

c

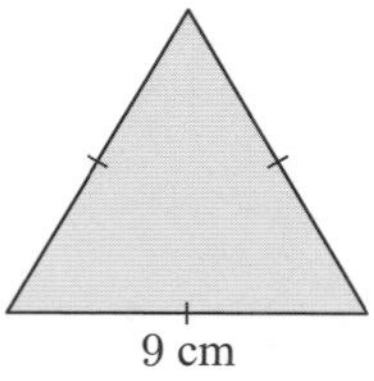

2 Classify the following triangles as acute angled, obtuse angled, or right angled:

a

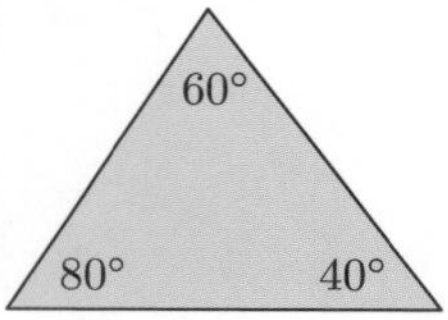

b

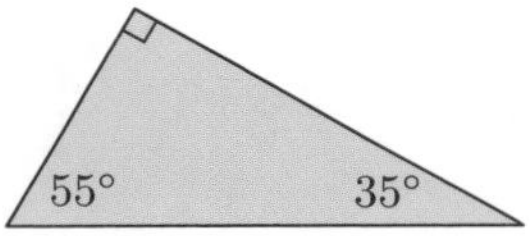

c

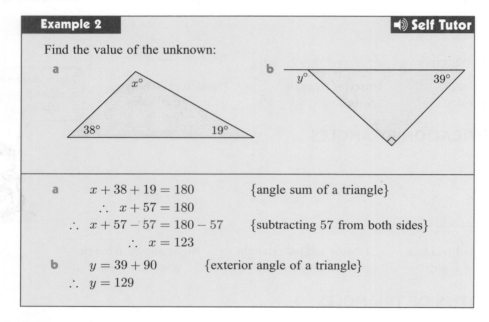

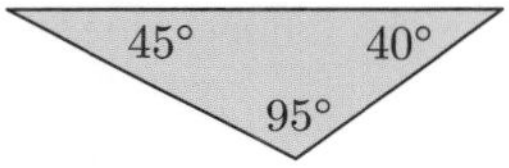

3 These diagrams are not drawn to scale, but the information on them is correct. Find the values of the unknowns:

a

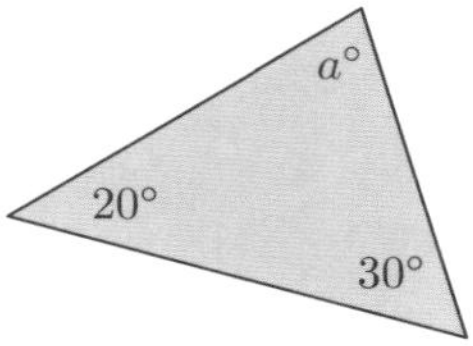

b

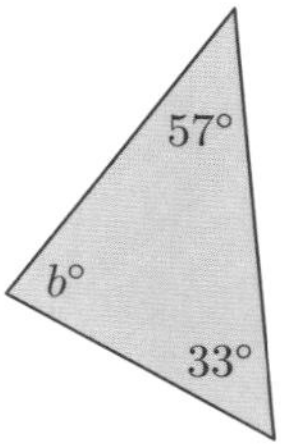

c

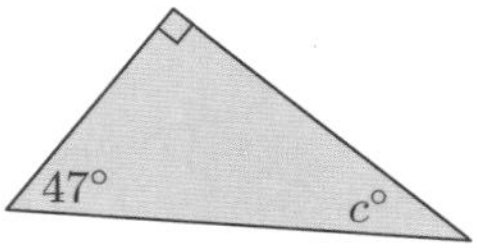

d

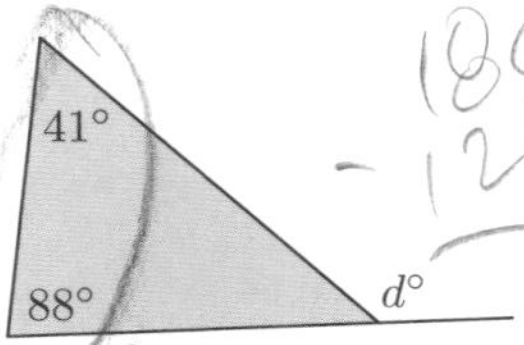

e

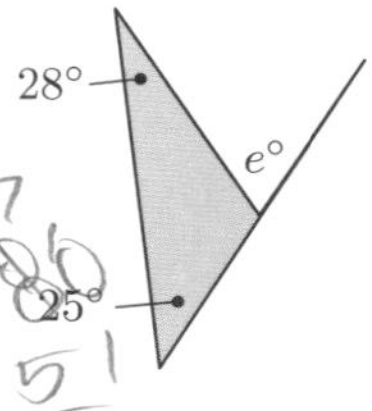

f

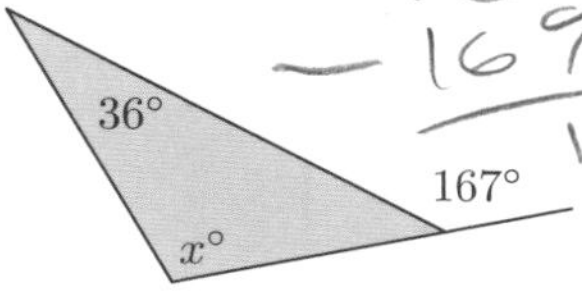

4 Two of the angles in Nancy's triangular pizza slice are 72° and 58°. Find the measure of the third angle.

5 State whether the following statements are *true* or *false*:

- **a** The sum of the angles of a triangle is equal to two right angles.
- **b** A right angled triangle can contain an obtuse angle.
- **c** The sum of two angles of a triangle is always greater than the third angle.
- **d** The two smaller angles of a right angled triangle are supplementary.

6 The following triangles are *not* drawn to scale.
State the longest side of each triangle.

a

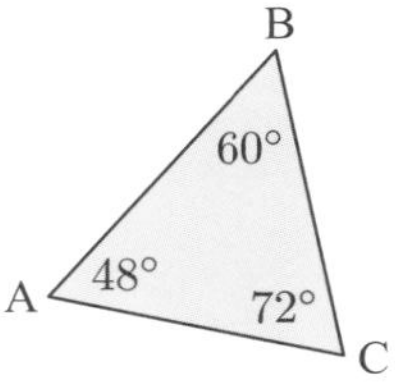

b

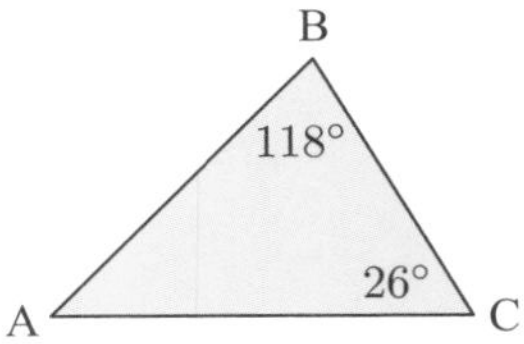

c

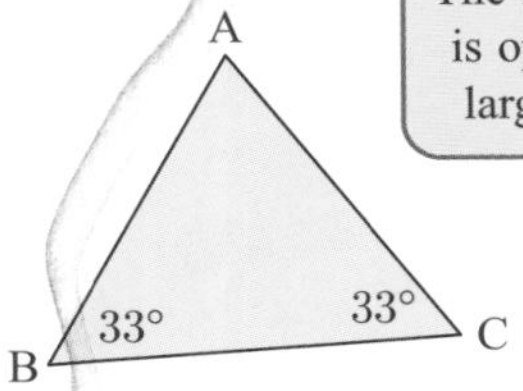

d

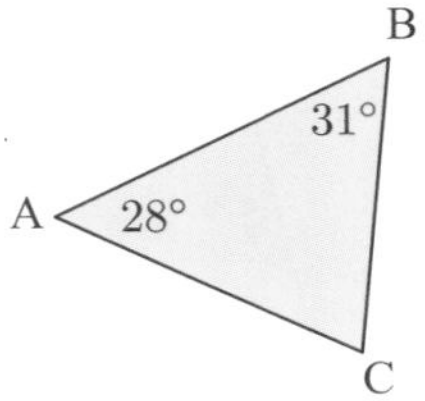

e

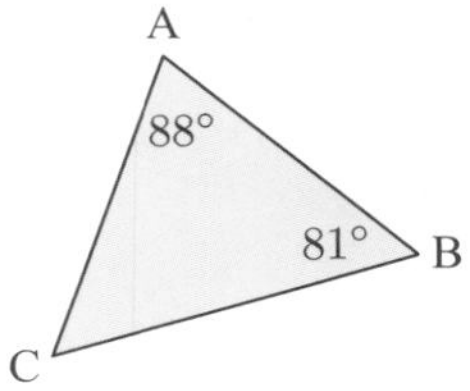

f

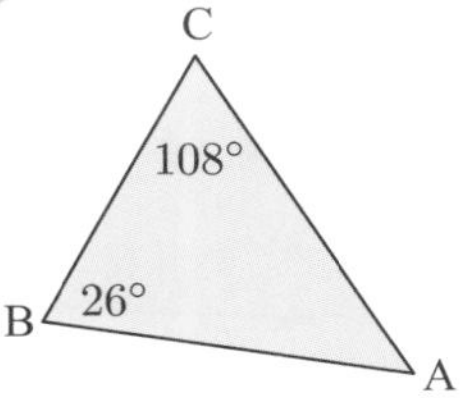

g

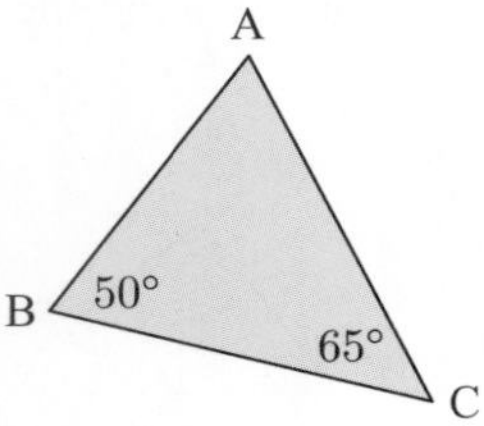

h

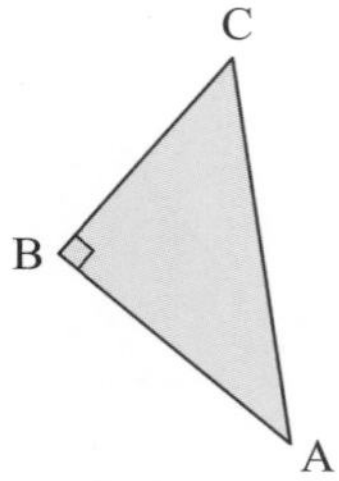

i

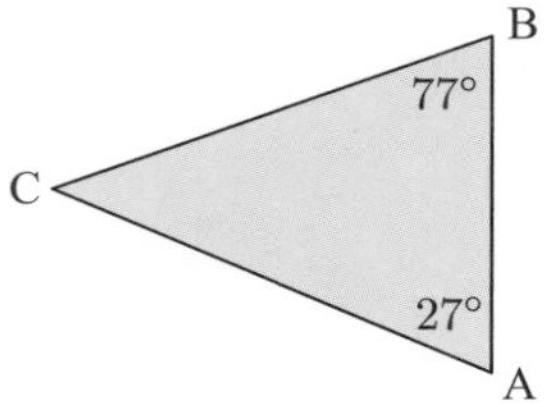

Example 3 **Self Tutor**

Find the values of the variables:

a

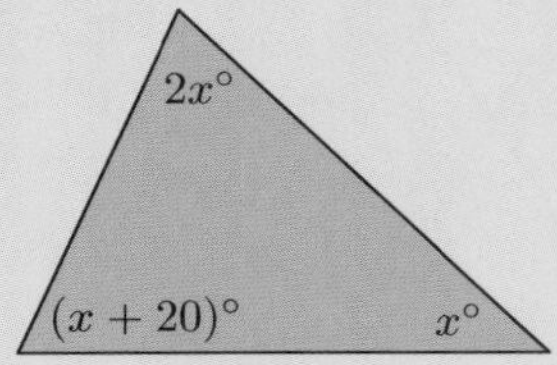

b

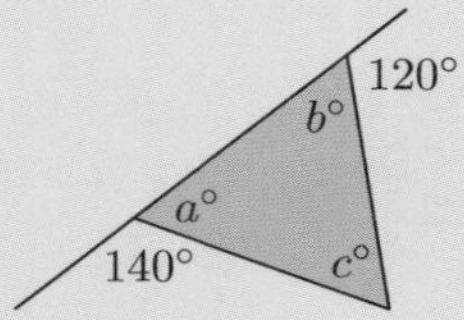

a $2x + x + (x + 20) = 180$ {angle sum of a triangle}

$\therefore\ 4x + 20 = 180$ {collecting like terms}

$\therefore\ 4x = 160$ {subtracting 20 from both sides}

$\therefore\ x = 40$

b $a = 180 - 140 = 40$ {angles on a line}

Likewise $b = 180 - 120 = 60$

But $a + b + c = 180$ {angle sum of a triangle}

$\therefore\ 40 + 60 + c = 180$

$\therefore\ 100 + c = 180$

$\therefore\ c = 80$

7 Find the values of the variables:

a

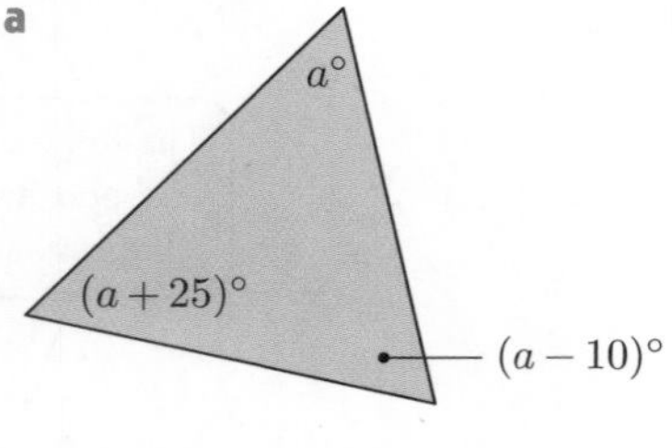

b

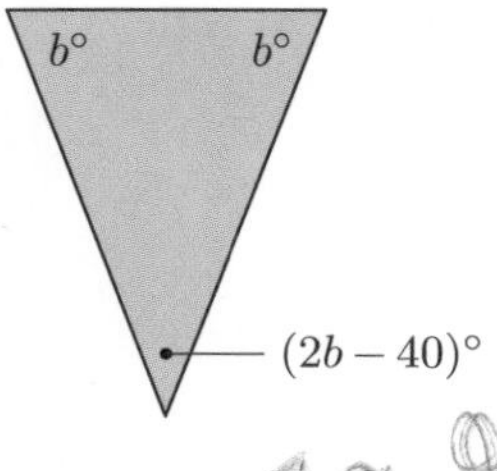

c

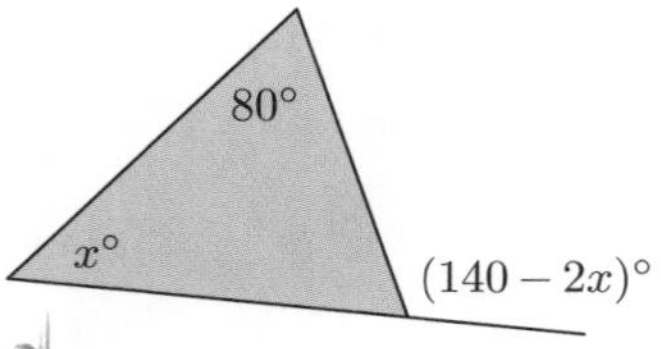

d

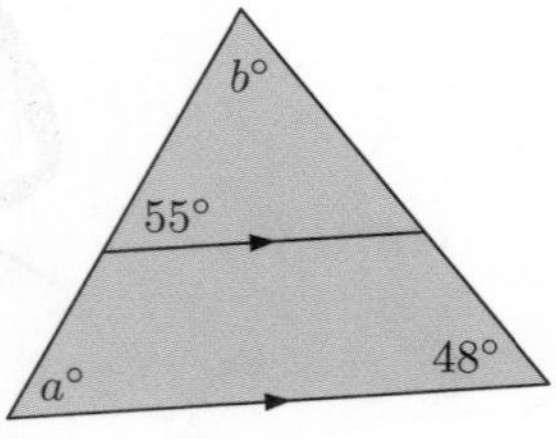

e

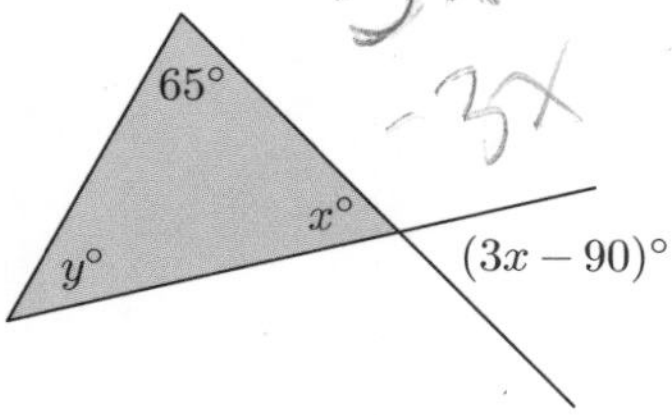

f

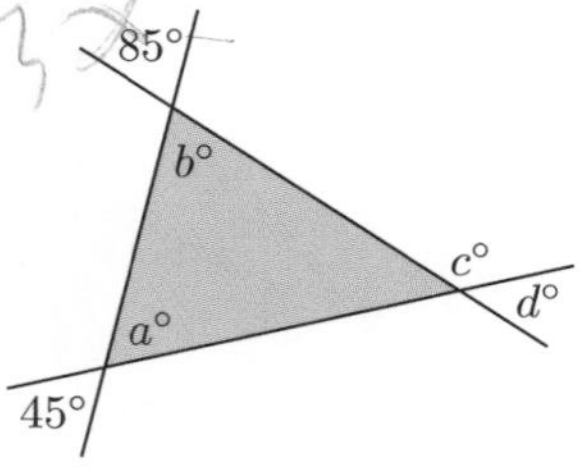

RESEARCH

Research the use of triangles in the construction of bridges.

Explain what is meant by the statement "*the triangle is the only rigid polygon*" and how this helps the bridge structure.

©iStockphoto - Jan Ribak

C ISOSCELES TRIANGLES

An **isosceles triangle** is a triangle in which two sides are equal in length.

The angles opposite the two equal sides are called the **base angles**.

The vertex where the two equal sides meet is called the **apex**.

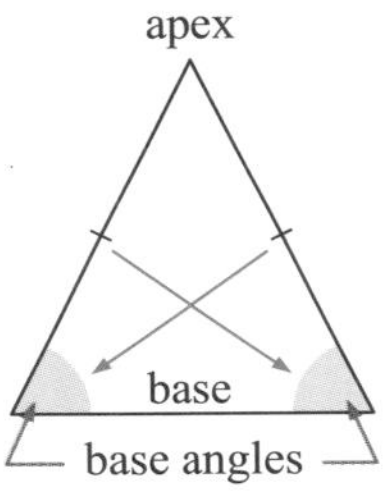

GEOMETRY PACKAGE

THE ISOSCELES TRIANGLE THEOREM

In any isosceles triangle:

- the base angles are equal
- the line joining the apex to the midpoint of the base bisects the vertical angle and meets the base at right angles.

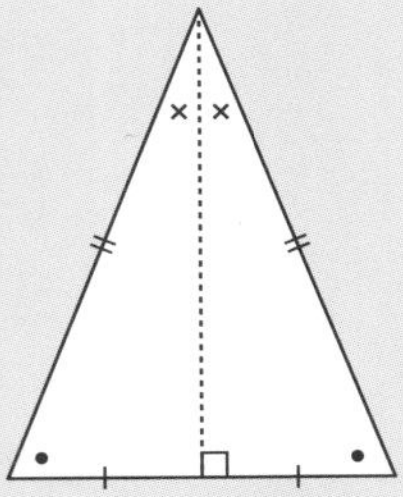

CONVERSES

With many theorems there are *converses* which we can use in problem solving.

Converse 1: If a triangle has two equal angles, then it is isosceles.

Converse 2: The angle bisector of the apex of an isosceles triangle bisects the base at right angles.

DISCUSSION

What does the word *converse* mean?

Which of the following are also converses of the isosceles triangle theorem?

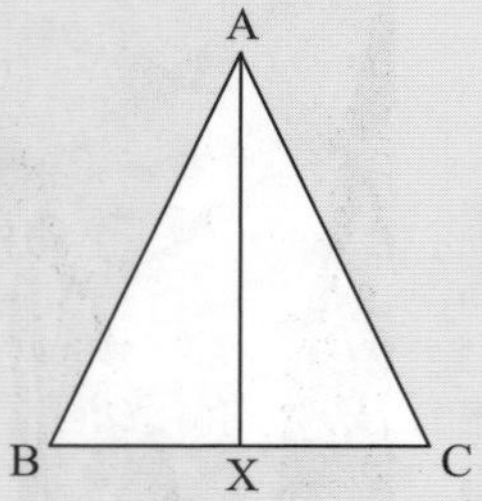

1. If the line joining one vertex to the midpoint of the opposite side is perpendicular to that side, then the triangle is isosceles.
2. If the line joining one vertex to the midpoint of the opposite side bisects the angle at the vertex, then the triangle is isosceles.
3. If a perpendicular to one side of the triangle passes through a vertex and bisects the angle at that vertex, then the triangle is isosceles.

Example 4 — Self Tutor

Find x:

a

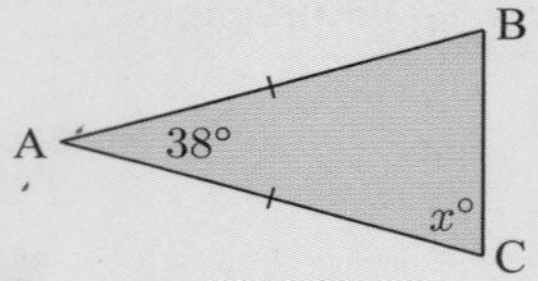

b

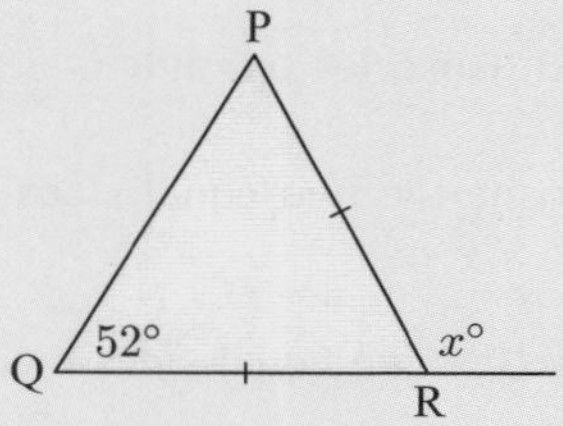

a

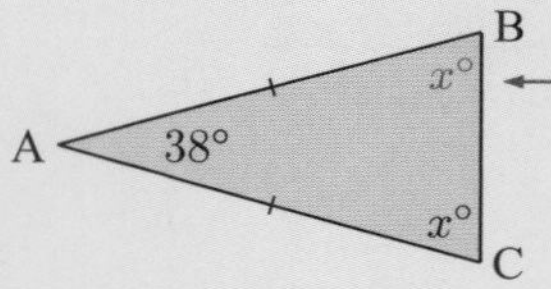

Since AB = AC, the triangle is isosceles.

$\therefore$ $A\widehat{B}C = x°$ {isosceles triangle theorem}

Now $x + x + 38 = 180$ {angle sum of a triangle}

$\therefore$ $2x + 38 = 180$

$\therefore$ $2x = 142$ {subtracting 38 from both sides}

$\therefore$ $x = 71$

b

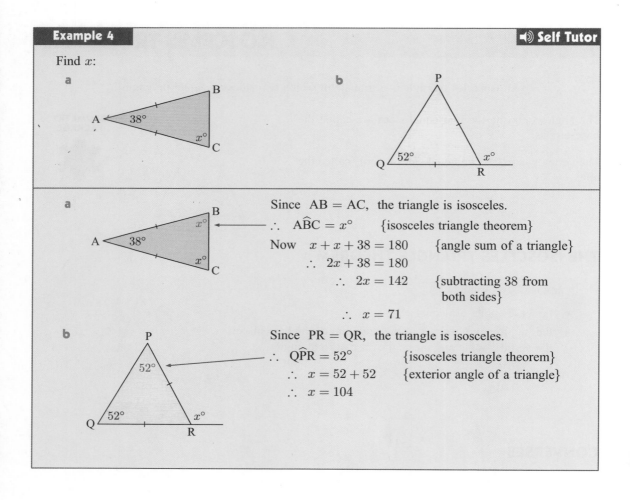

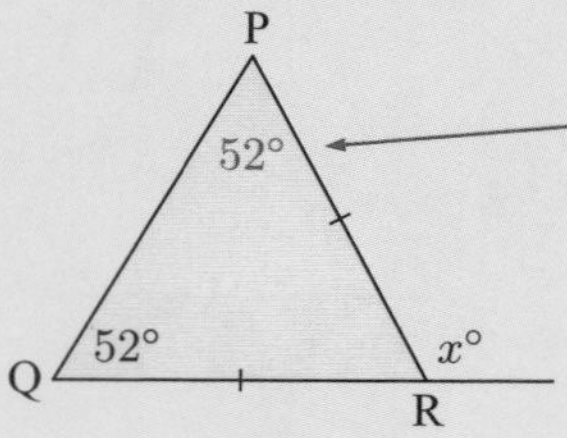

Since PR = QR, the triangle is isosceles.

$\therefore$ $Q\widehat{P}R = 52°$ {isosceles triangle theorem}

$\therefore$ $x = 52 + 52$ {exterior angle of a triangle}

$\therefore$ $x = 104$

EXERCISE 9C

1 Find x:

a

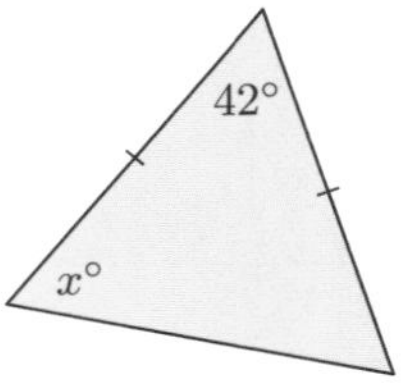

b

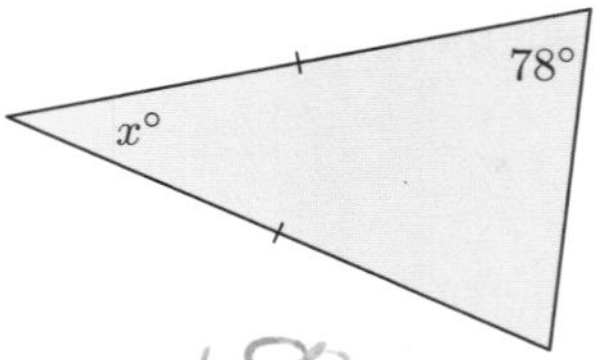

c

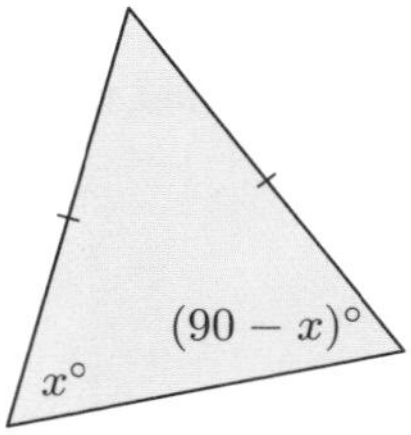

d

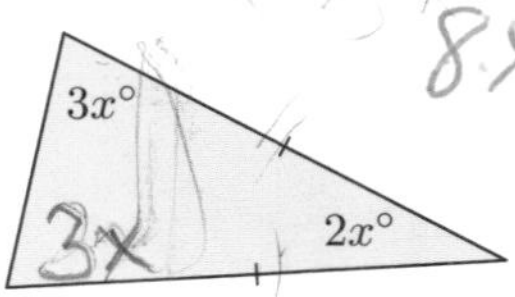

e

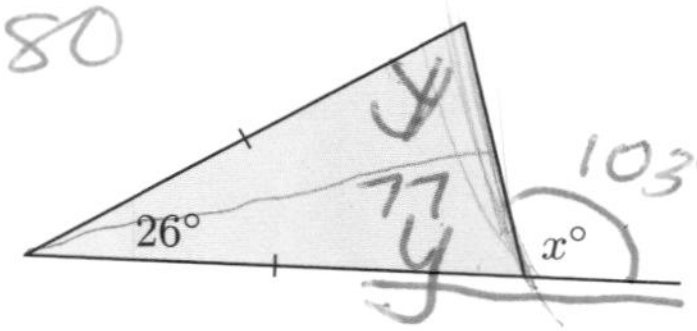

f

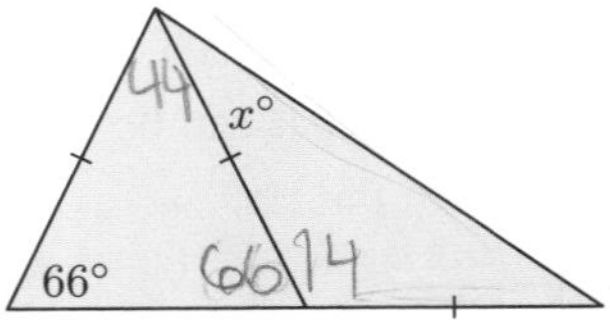

2 Find x, giving brief reasons:

a

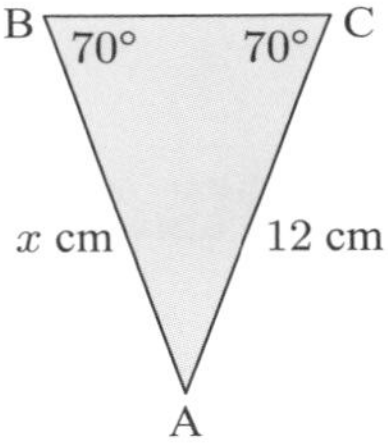

b

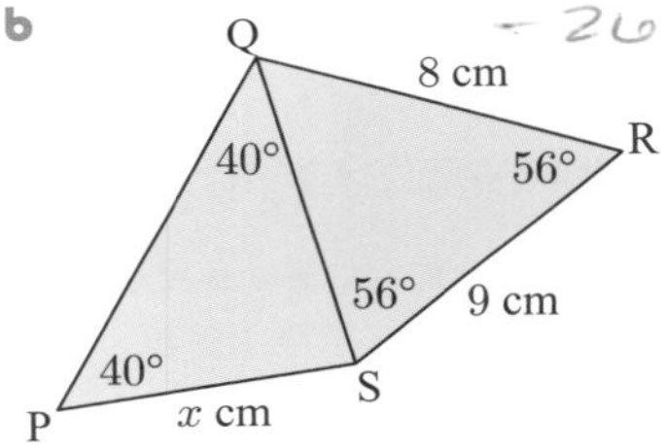

c

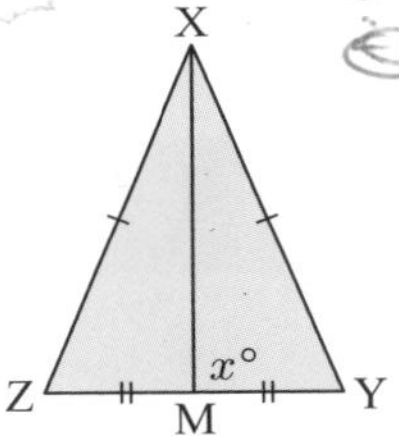

d

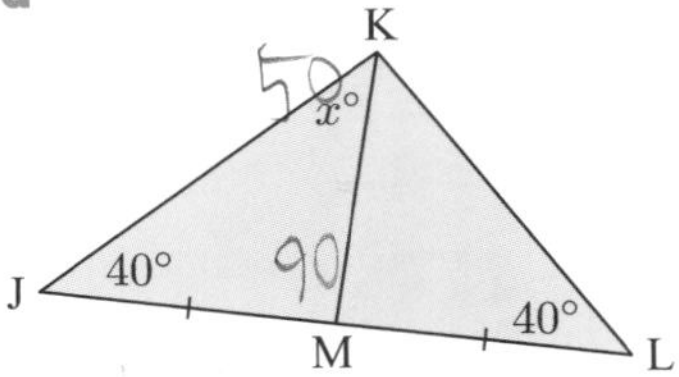

e

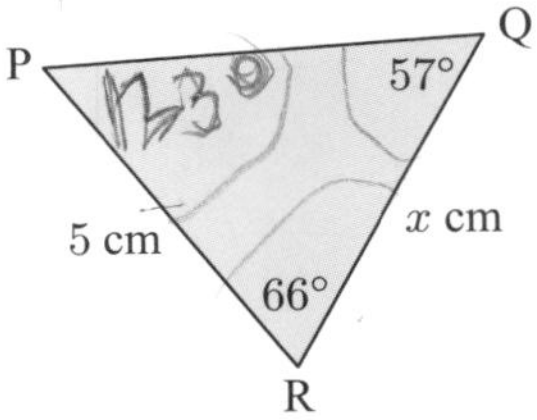

f

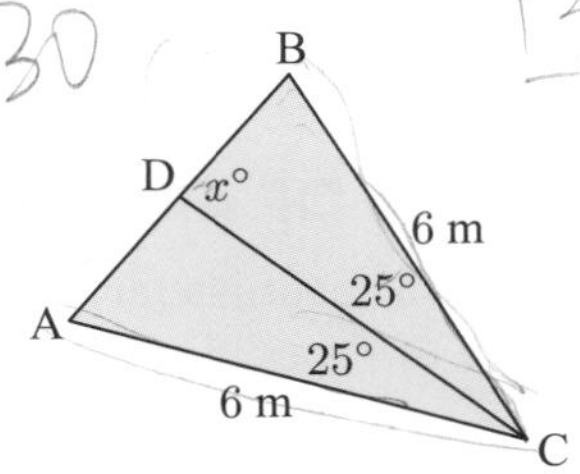

g

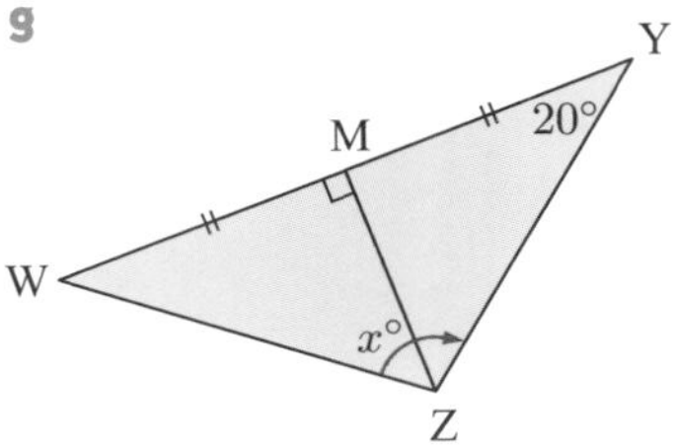

h

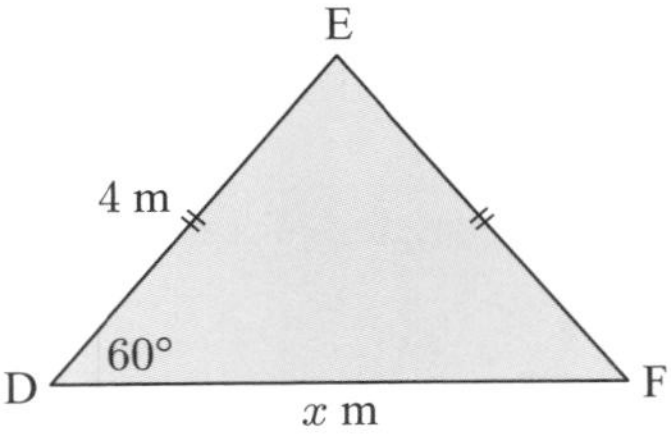

i

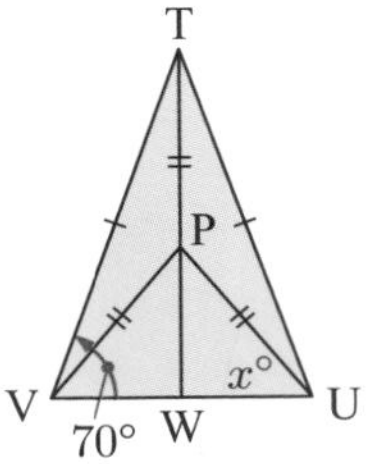

3 The triangular control frame of a hang glider has an angle of 46° between the two equal sides. Find the measure of the other two angles.

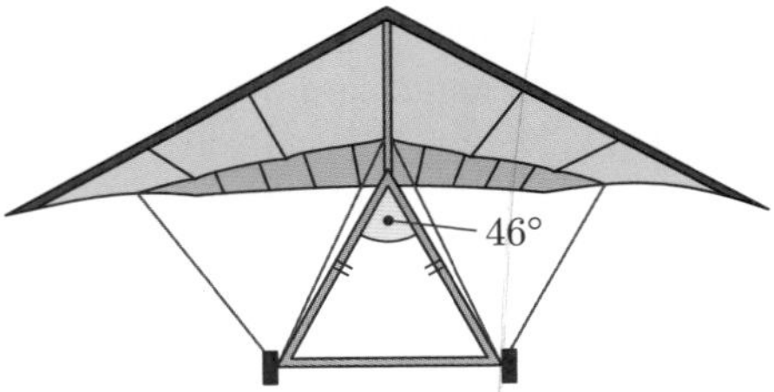

4 The figure alongside has not been drawn to scale, but the information given is correct.

- **a** Find x.
- **b** What can be deduced about the triangle?

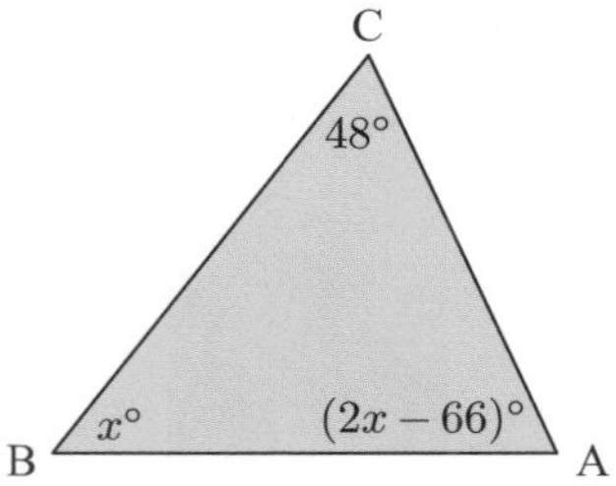

5 The figure alongside has not been drawn to scale, but the information given is correct.

- **a** Find $\widehat{ABD}$.
- **b** What can be deduced about triangle ABD?
- **c** Find x.

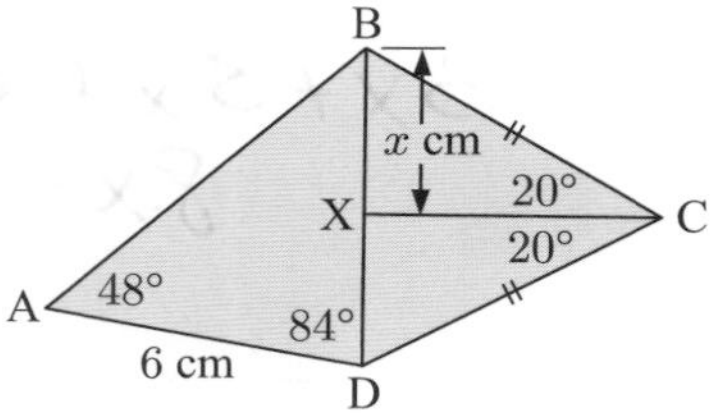

6 The base angles of an isosceles triangle each measure $(5x - 12)°$, and the angle at the apex measures $(4x + 8)°$. What are the sizes of these angles?

D QUADRILATERALS

A **quadrilateral** is a polygon which has four sides.

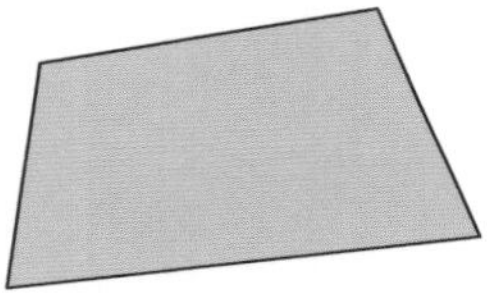

ANGLES OF A QUADRILATERAL

Suppose a quadrilateral is drawn on a piece of paper.

If the four angles are torn off and reassembled at a point, we notice that the angle sum is always 360°.

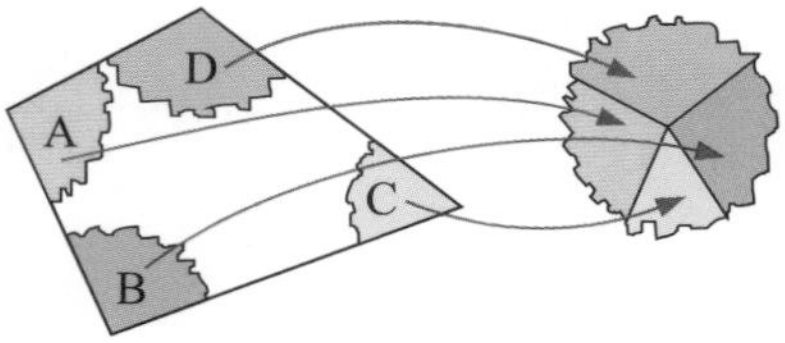

DEMO

The sum of the interior angles of a quadrilateral is 360°.

GEOMETRY PACKAGE

Proof:

Suppose we divide the quadrilateral into two triangles. Each triangle has an angle sum of 180°, so the angle sum of the quadrilateral $= 2 \times 180° = 360°$.

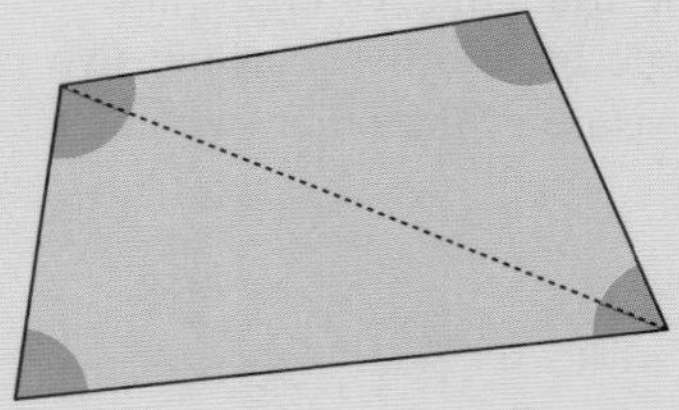

Example 5 | **Self Tutor**

Find the value of x:

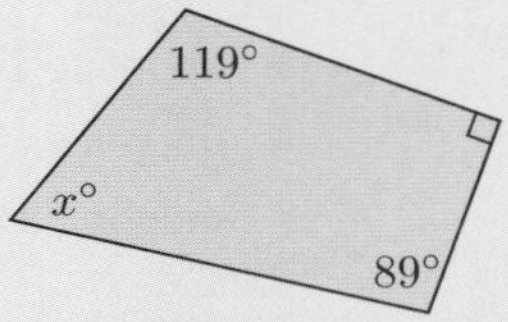

$$x + 89 + 90 + 119 = 360 \quad \{\text{angle sum of a quadrilateral}\}$$
$$\therefore \; x + 298 = 360$$
$$\therefore \; x = 62 \quad \{\text{subtracting 298 from both sides}\}$$

EXERCISE 9D.1

1 Find the value of x:

a

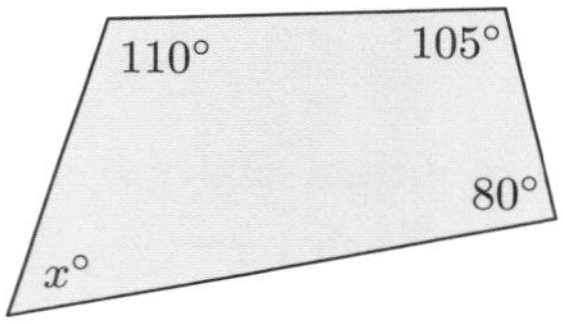

b

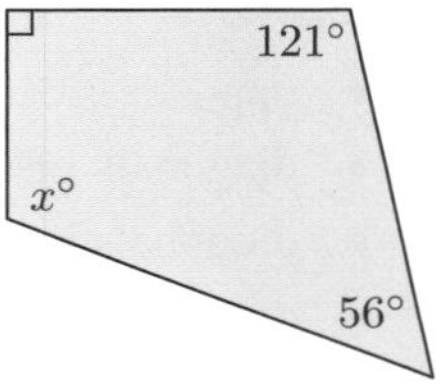

c

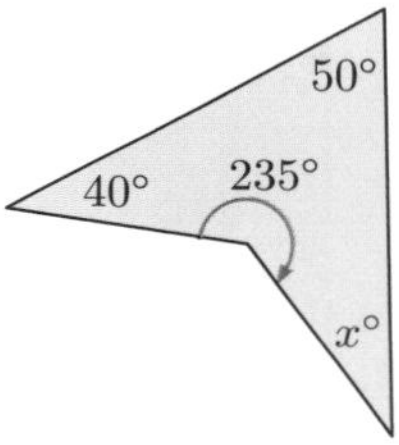

d

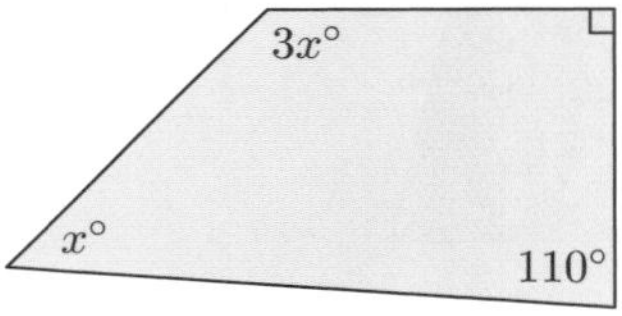

e

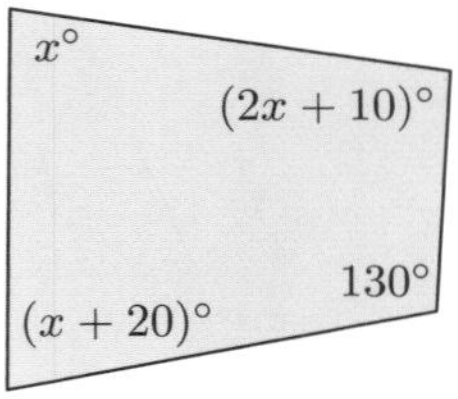

f

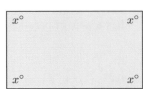

2 Find the values of the unknowns:

a

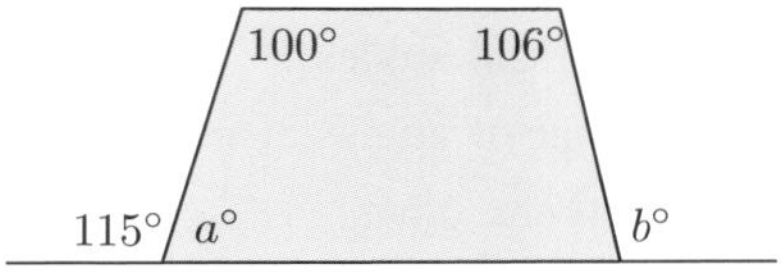

b

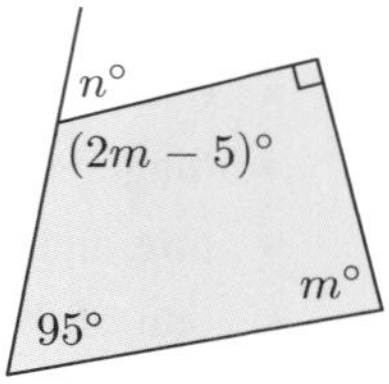

c

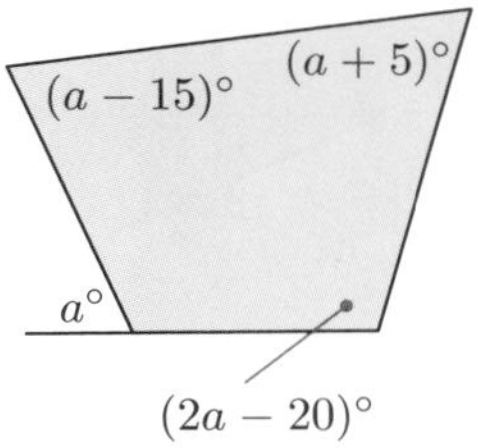

SPECIAL QUADRILATERALS

There are six special quadrilaterals.

1 A **parallelogram** is a quadrilateral which has opposite sides parallel.

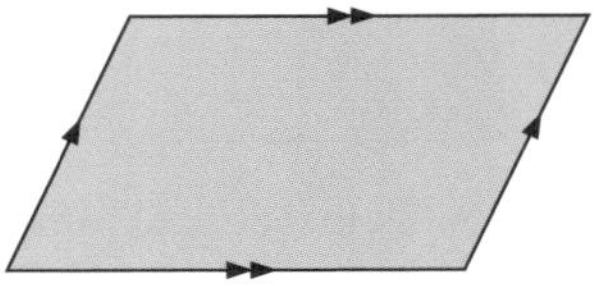

Properties:

- opposite sides are equal in length
- opposite angles are equal in size
- diagonals bisect each other.

GEOMETRY PACKAGE

2 A **rectangle** is a parallelogram with four equal angles of 90°.

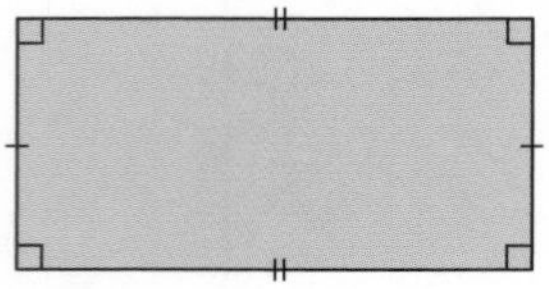

Properties:

- opposite sides are parallel and equal
- diagonals bisect each other
- diagonals are equal in length.

GEOMETRY PACKAGE

3 A **rhombus** is a quadrilateral in which all sides are equal in length.

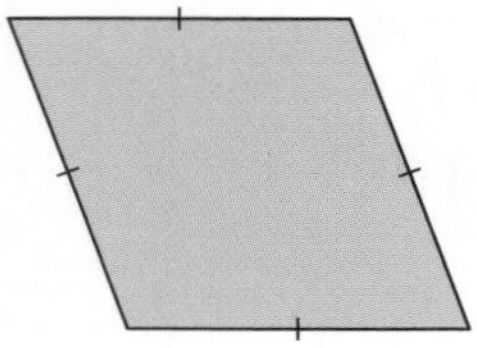

Properties:

- opposite sides are parallel
- opposite angles are equal in size
- diagonals bisect each other at right angles
- diagonals bisect the angles at each vertex.

GEOMETRY PACKAGE

4 A **square** is a rhombus with four equal angles of 90°.

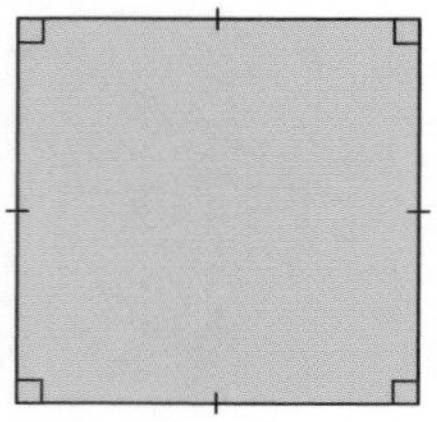

Properties:

- opposite sides are parallel
- diagonals bisect each other at right angles
- diagonals bisect the angles at each vertex
- diagonals are equal in length.

GEOMETRY PACKAGE

5 A **trapezium** is a quadrilateral which has a pair of parallel opposite sides.

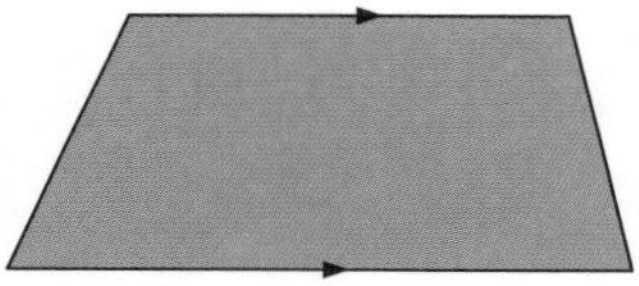

6 A **kite** is a quadrilateral which has two pairs of adjacent sides equal in length.

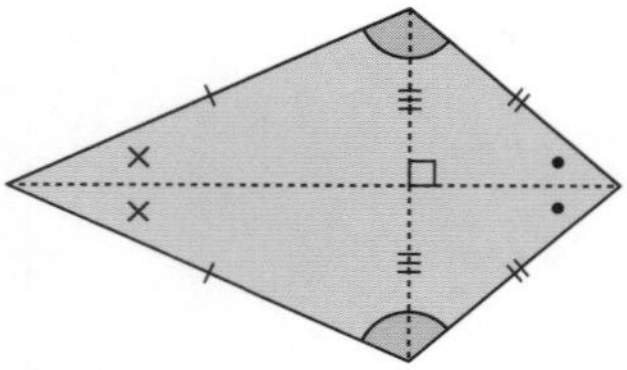

Properties:

- one diagonal is a line of symmetry
- one pair of opposite angles are equal
- diagonals cut each other at right angles
- **one** diagonal bisects **one** pair of angles at the vertices
- one of the diagonals bisects the other.

Example 6 Self Tutor

Draw three diagrams to show all the properties of a parallelogram.

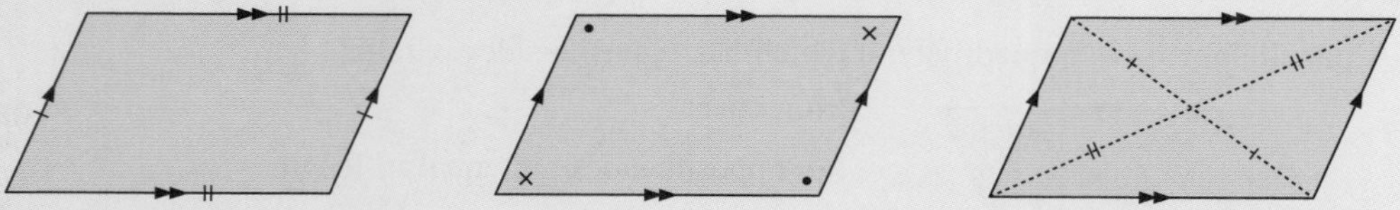

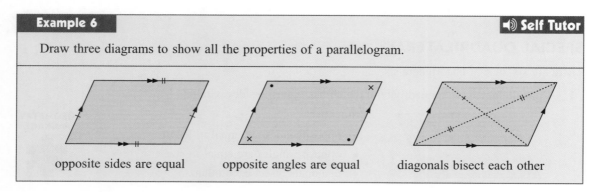

opposite sides are equal | opposite angles are equal | diagonals bisect each other

Example 7 **Self Tutor**

Find x, giving brief reasons for your answer:

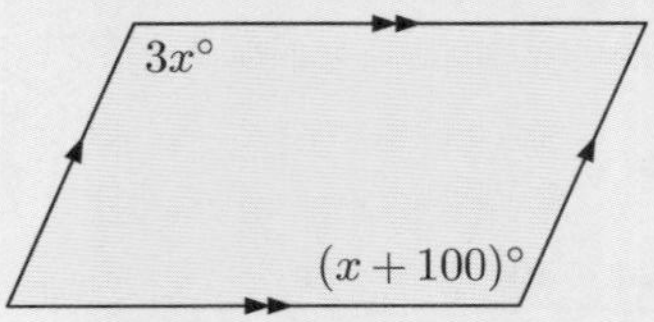

The figure is a parallelogram.

$\therefore\ 3x = x + 100$ {opposite angles of a parallelogram}

$\therefore\ 2x = 100$ {subtracting x from both sides}

$\therefore\ x = 50$

EXERCISE 9D.2

1 Draw four or more diagrams which show all the properties of:

a a square **b** a kite **c** a rhombus.

2 Find the values of the variables:

a

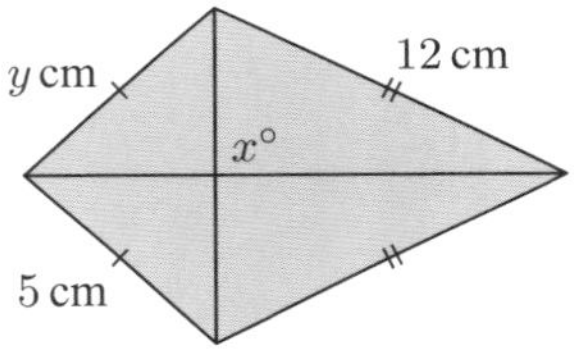

b

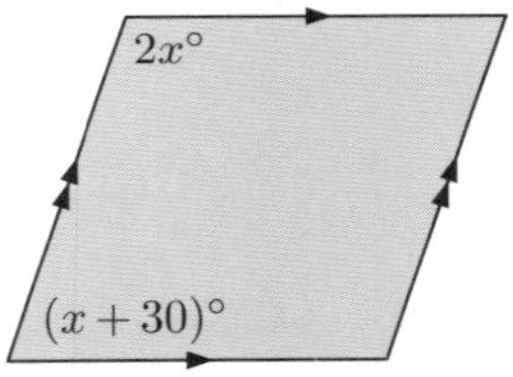

c

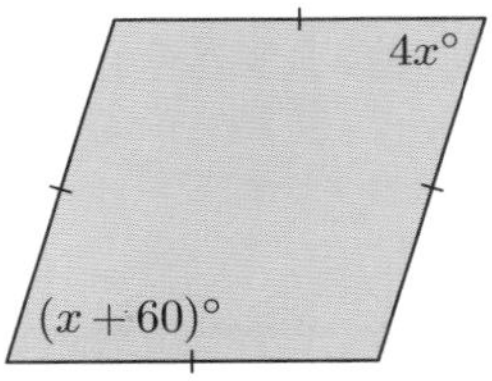

d

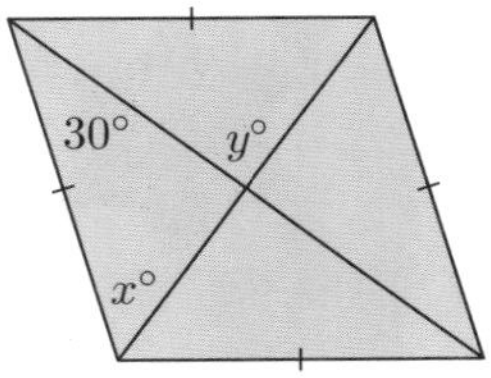

e

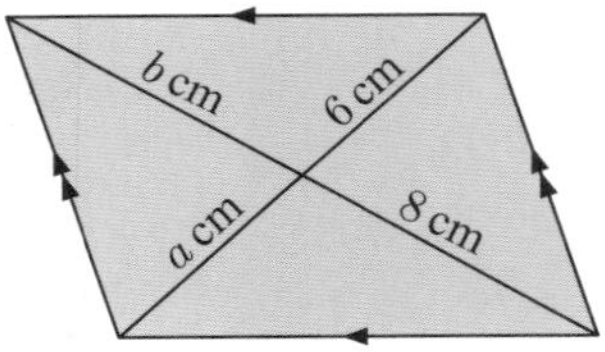

f

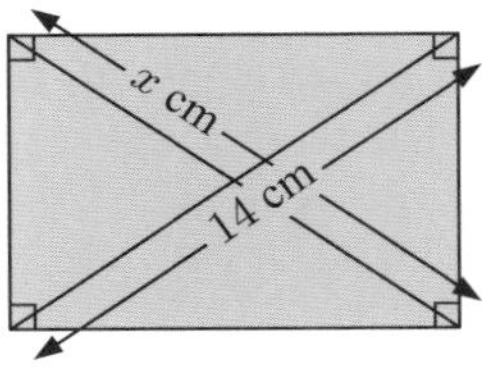

3 True or false?

a A square is a quadrilateral in which all sides are equal.

b A quadrilateral in which all sides are equal is a square.

c The diagonals of a parallelogram are equal in length.

d The diagonals of a kite intersect at right angles.

4 Jarrod draws a quadrilateral ABCD and its diagonals [AC] and [BD]. He notices that [AC] and [BD] intersect at right angles.

a What types of quadrilateral could ABCD be? Explain your answer.

b Jarrod measures the diagonals, and notices that one diagonal is twice the length of the other. He also notices that the diagonals bisect each other. What type of quadrilateral must ABCD be? Explain your answer.

c If the shorter diagonal [AC] is 4 cm long, sketch and label quadrilateral ABCD.

5 Find the values of the unknowns:

a

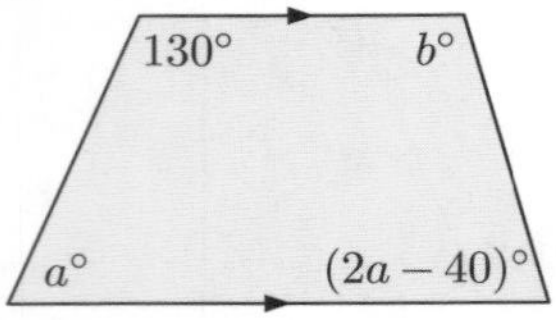

b

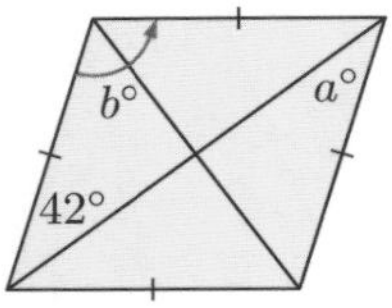

c

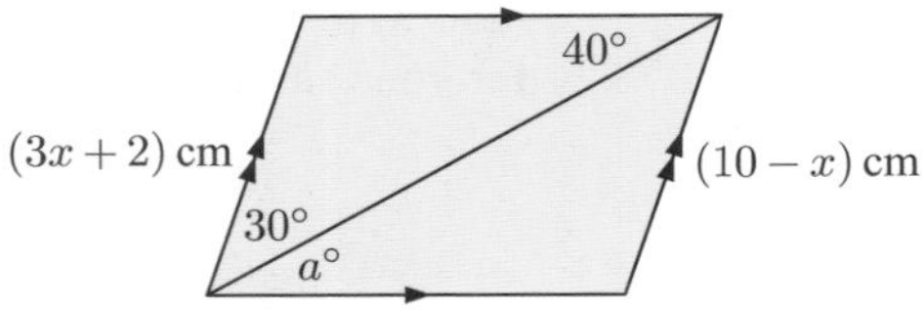

6 The figure alongside is not drawn to scale, but the information on it is correct. What can be deduced about quadrilateral ABCD?

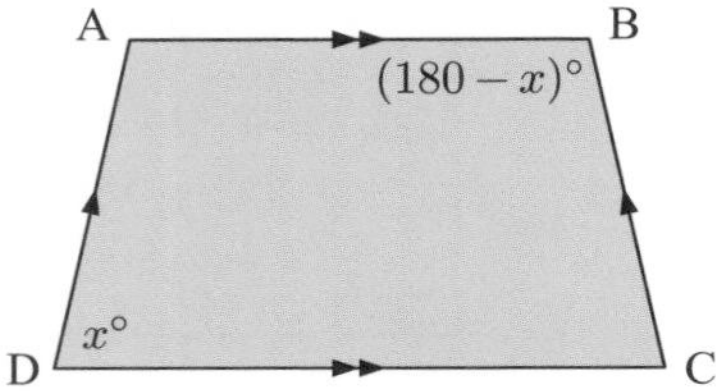

7 True or false? "A square is a special case of both a parallelogram and a rhombus."

8

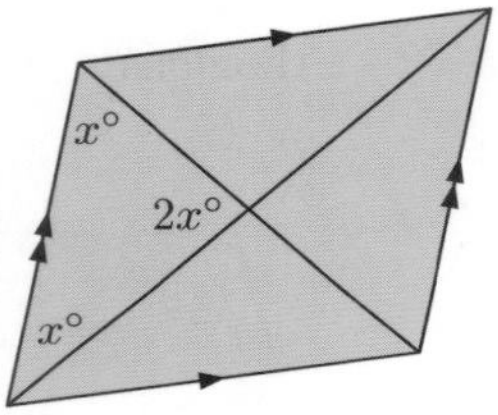

This figure is not drawn accurately, but the information given is correct. What is the special name for this quadrilateral?

RESEARCH

Research the use of rhombuses, parallelograms, and kites in art and architecture.

Moorish tiles at La Alhambra, Granada.

INVESTIGATION 1 THE MIDPOINTS OF A QUADRILATERAL

When the midpoints of adjacent sides of a rectangle are joined, the resulting figure appears to be a parallelogram.

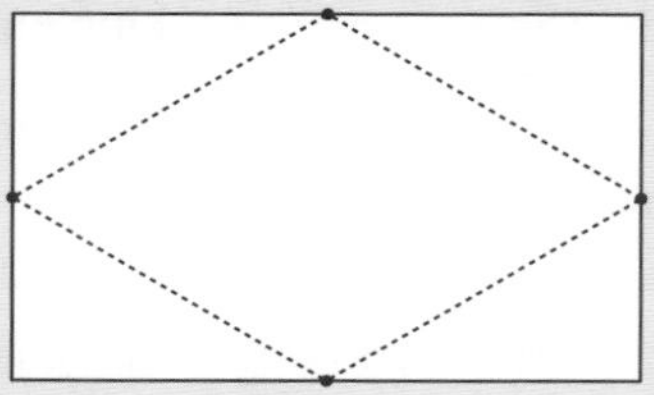

What to do:

1 Draw your own rectangle. Find the midpoints of the sides, and join them.

2 Repeat **1** with:

a a parallelogram **b** a rhombus **c** a kite **d** a trapezium.

3 Repeat with a few quadrilaterals of your own choosing, including non-convex ones such as this:

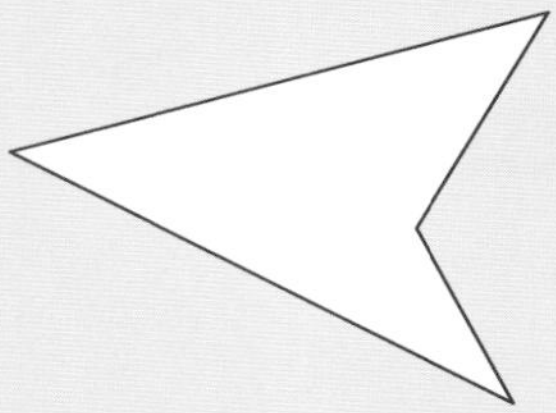

4 Copy and complete: "When the midpoints of adjacent sides of a quadrilateral are joined, the resulting figure is always a ......".

E ANGLES OF AN n-SIDED POLYGON

We have seen that a quadrilateral can be divided into 2 triangles, each with an angle sum of 180°, so the sum of the angles in a quadrilateral is $2 \times 180° = 360°$.

We can likewise find the sum of the angles of *any* polygon by dividing it into triangles.

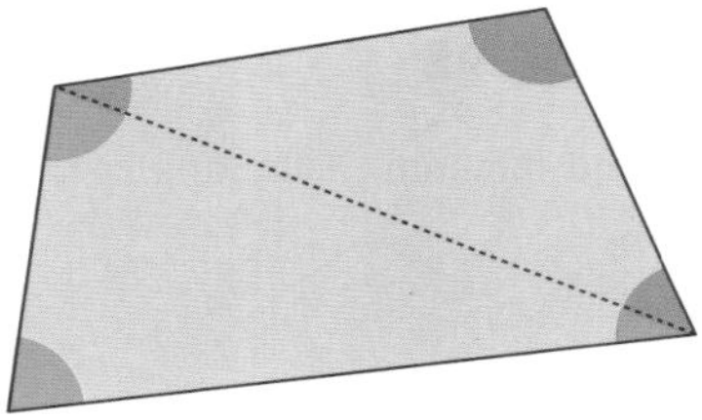

INVESTIGATION 2 ANGLES OF AN n-SIDED POLYGON

What to do:

1 Draw any pentagon, and label one of its vertices A. Draw in all of the diagonals from A. Notice that 3 triangles are formed.

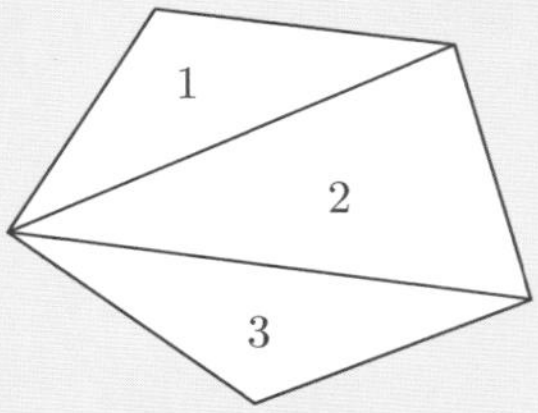

2 Repeat with a hexagon, a heptagon (7-gon), and an octagon, drawing diagonals from one vertex only.

3 Copy and complete the following table:

Polygon	*Number of sides*	*Number of triangles*	*Angle sum of polygon*
quadrilateral	4	2	$2 \times 180° = 360°$
pentagon	5	3	
hexagon			
heptagon			
octagon			
20-gon			

4 Copy and complete:
"The sum of the sizes of the interior angles of any n-sided polygon is ...... $\times$ 180°."

From the **Investigation** you should have discovered that:

The sum of the sizes of the interior angles of any n-sided polygon is $(n-2) \times 180°$.

Example 8 — Self Tutor

Find x:

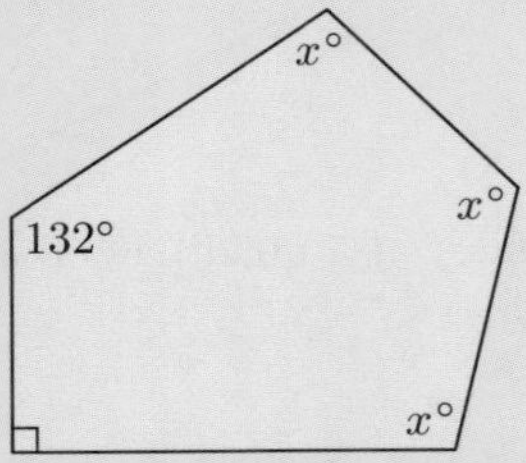

The figure has 5 sides.

$\therefore$ the sum of its interior angles is $3 \times 180° = 540°$

$$\therefore\ x + x + x + 132 + 90 = 540$$
$$\therefore\ 3x + 222 = 540$$
$$\therefore\ 3x = 318$$
$$\therefore\ x = 106$$

EXERCISE 9E

1 Find the sum of the angles of:

a

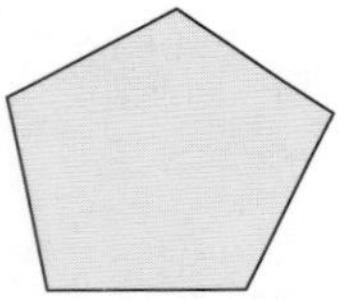

b

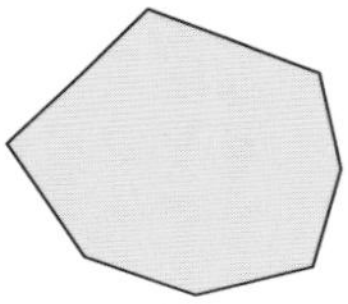

c

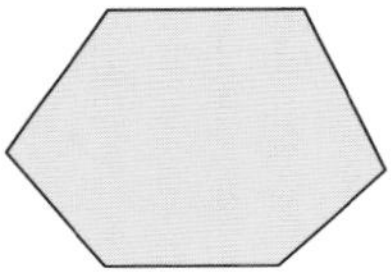

d a polygon with 12 sides **e** a 15-gon.

2 Find x:

a

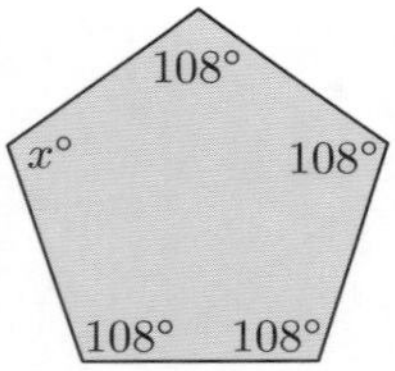

b

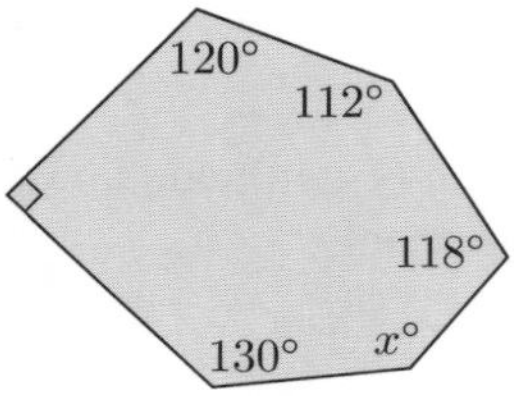

c

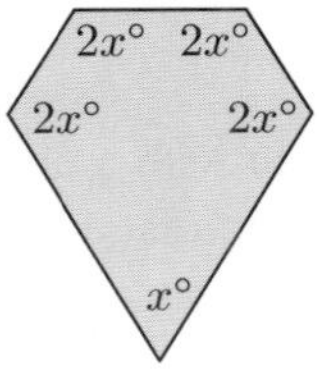

d

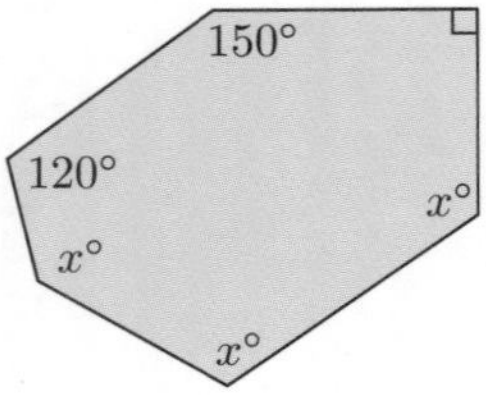

e

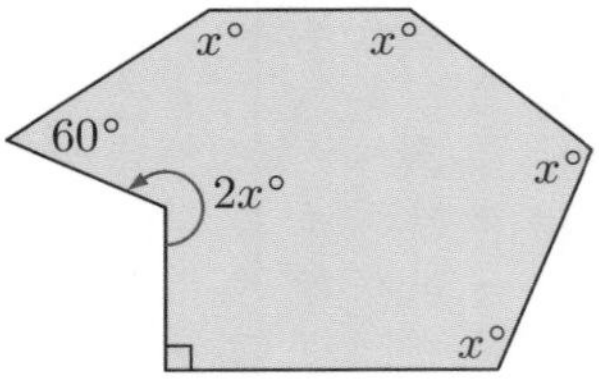

f

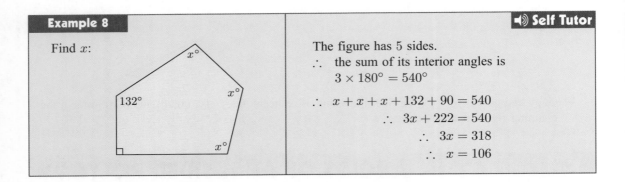

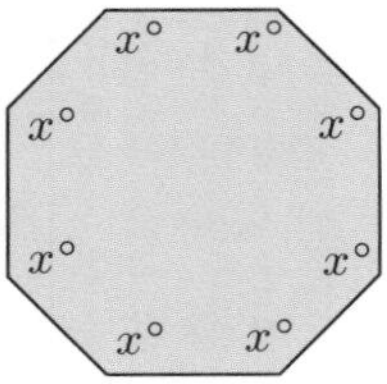

3 A pentagon has three right angles and two other equal angles. What is the size of each of the two equal angles?

4 The sum of the angles of a polygon is 1980°. How many sides has the polygon?

5 A **regular** polygon has all sides of equal length and all angles of equal size.

a Copy and complete the following table:

Regular polygon	*Number of sides*	*Sum of angles*	*Size of each angle*
triangle			
quadrilateral			
pentagon			
hexagon			
octagon			
decagon			

b Copy and complete:

i the sum of the angles of an n-sided polygon is ......

ii the size of each angle of a regular n-sided polygon is ......

c Find the size of each angle of a regular 12-sided polygon.

6 **a** What is the maximum number of reflex angles that a hexagon can have?

b Draw a hexagon with this number of reflex angles.

7 Find the sum of the shaded angles.

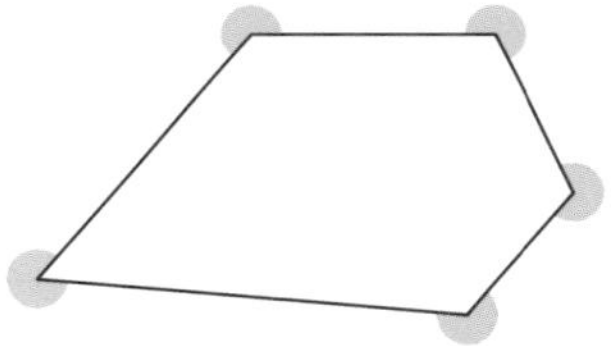

8 **a** How many sides does this figure have?

b Hence find the sum of the interior angles of the figure.

c Find the size of each angle in the figure, and check that their sum agrees with your answer to **b**.

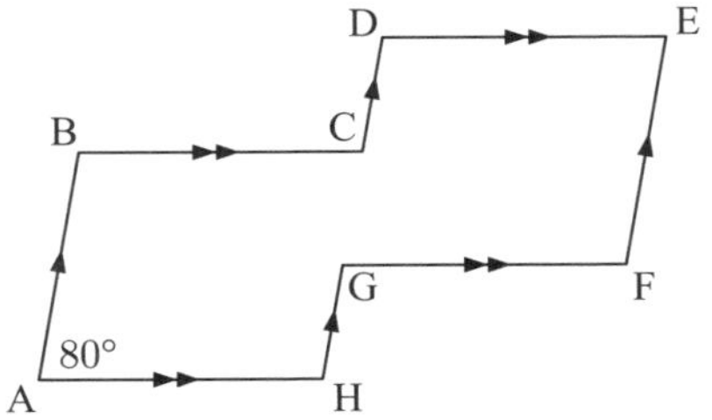

REVIEW SET 9A

1 Find the value of each variable, giving reasons for your answers:

a

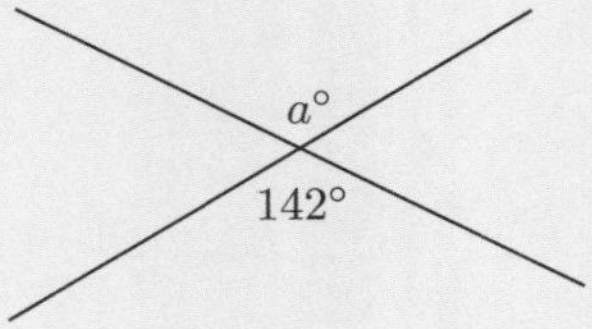

b

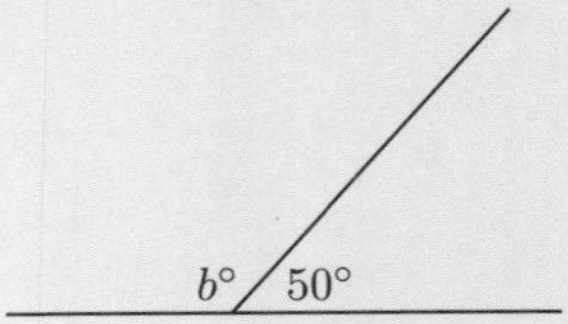

c

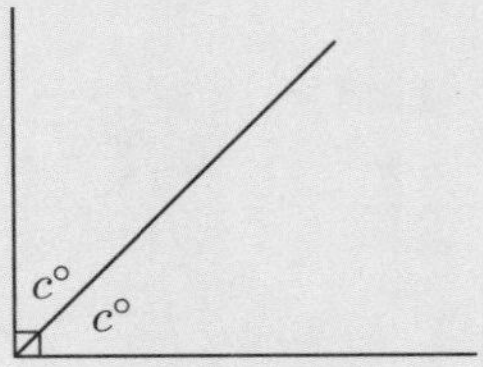

2 Find the angle:

a complementary to 63°

b supplementary to 26°.

3 Find the value of each variable, giving reasons for your answers:

a

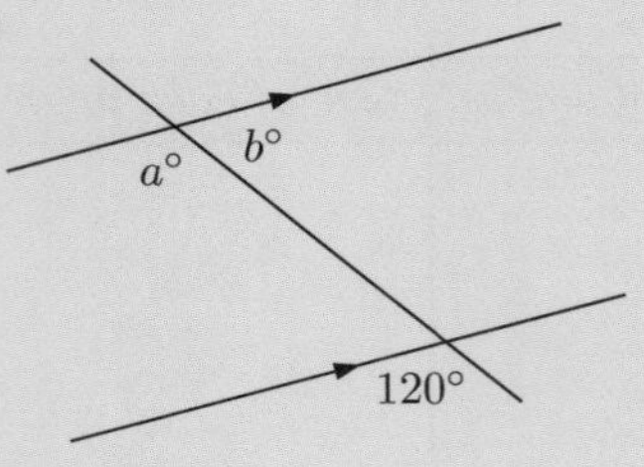

b

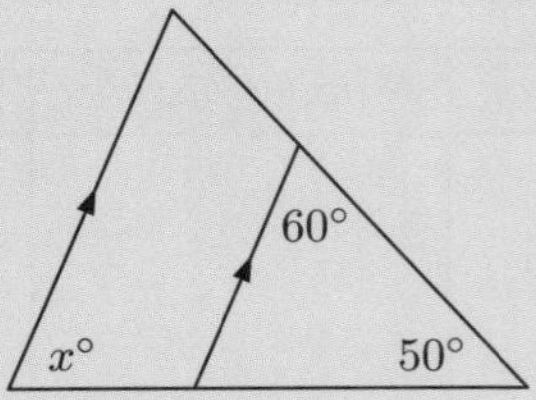

c

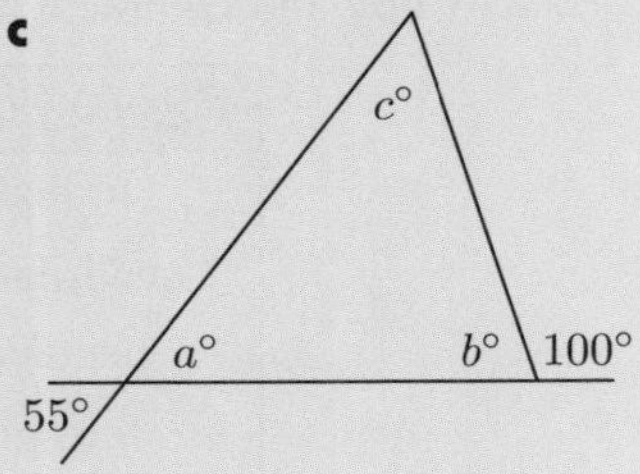

4 Classify each triangle by side lengths and by angles:

a

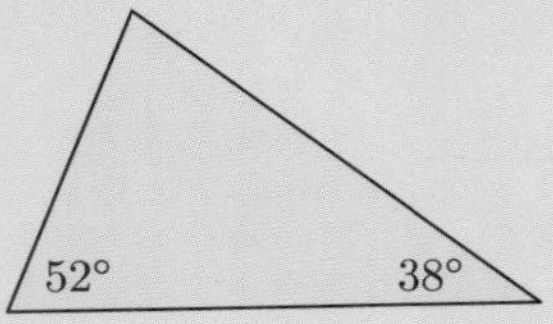

b

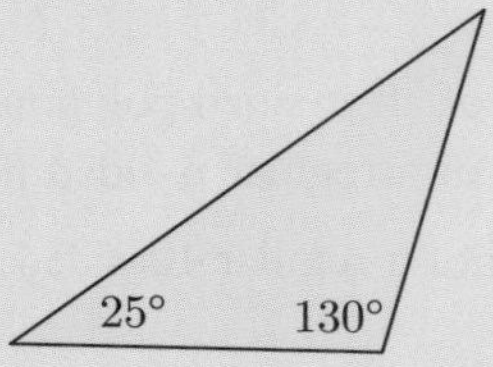

c

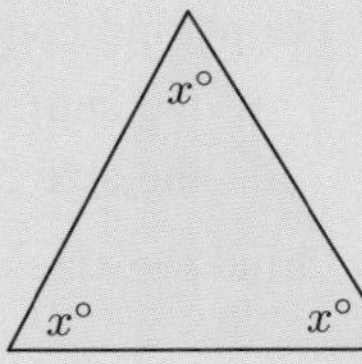

5 Find the values of the variables, giving brief reasons for your answers:

a

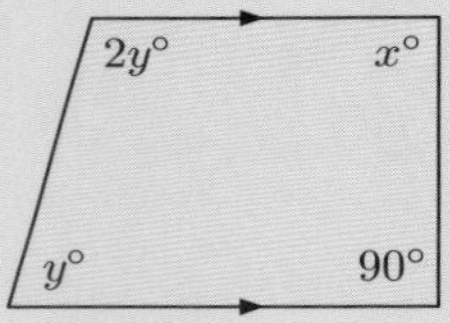

b

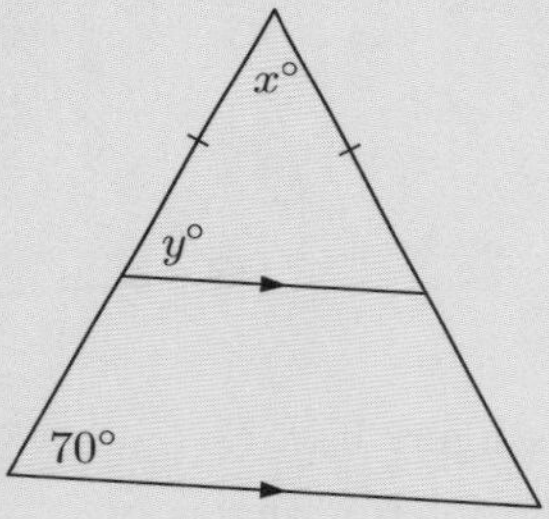

c

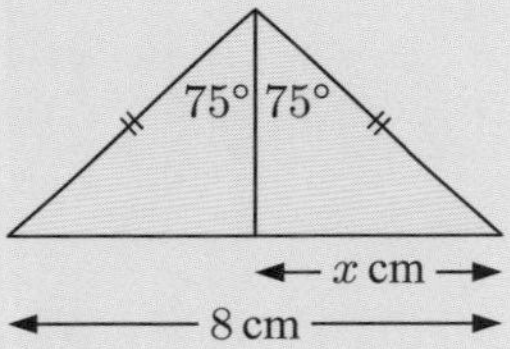

6 The quadrilaterals below are not drawn to scale, but the information on them is correct. Classify each quadrilateral.

a

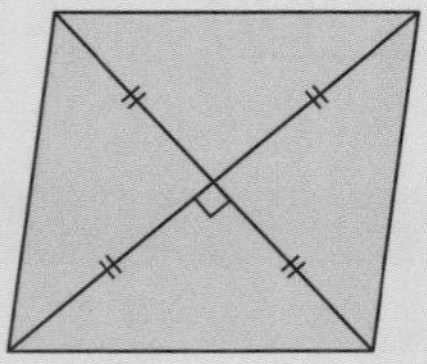

b

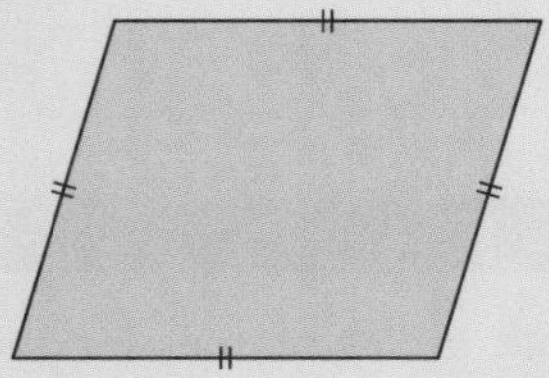

c

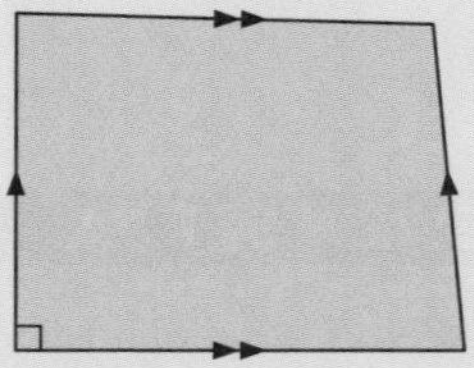

7 Find x:

a

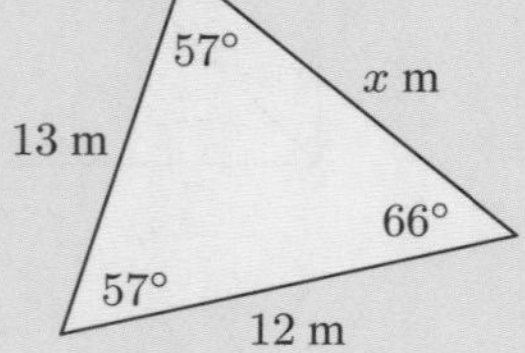

b

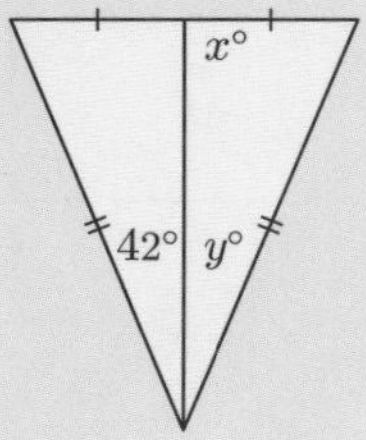

c

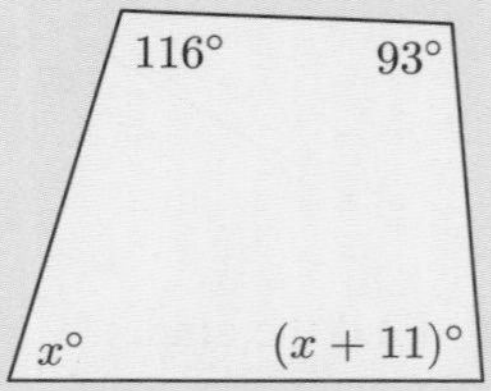

8 Find the values of the variables in the figure alongside:

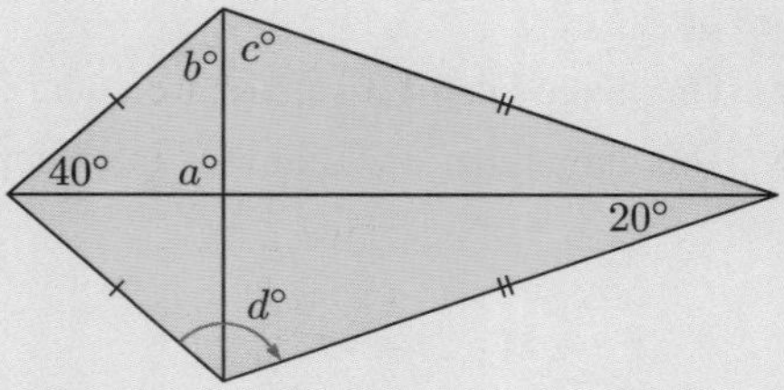

9 Find the sum of the angles of a polygon with 11 sides.

10 Find x:

a

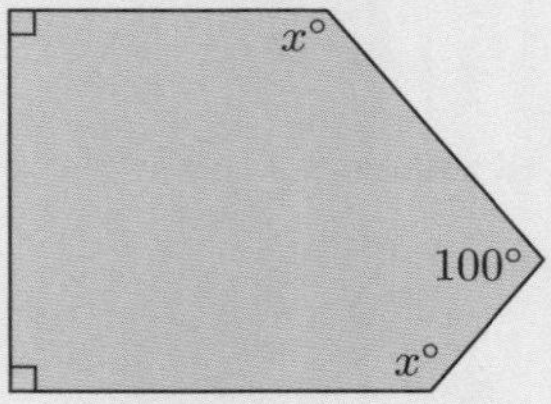

b

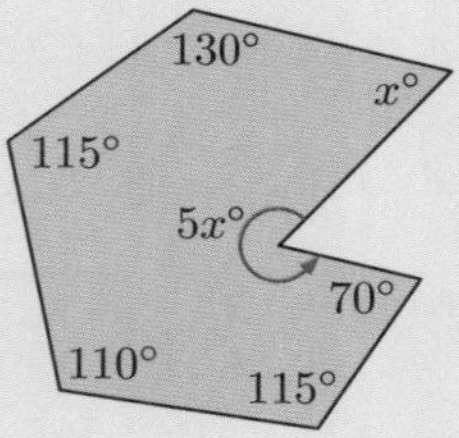

REVIEW SET 9B

1 Classify this triangle as:

a scalene, isosceles, or equilateral

b acute angled, obtuse angled, or right angled.

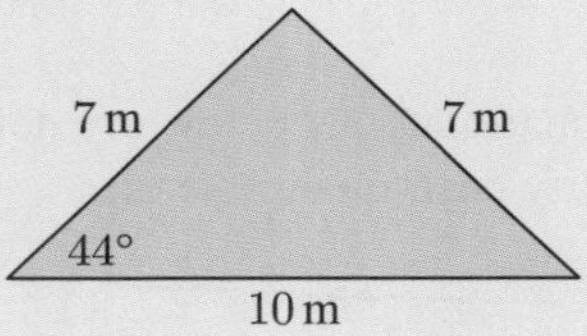

2 Find the value of x, giving reasons for your answer:

a

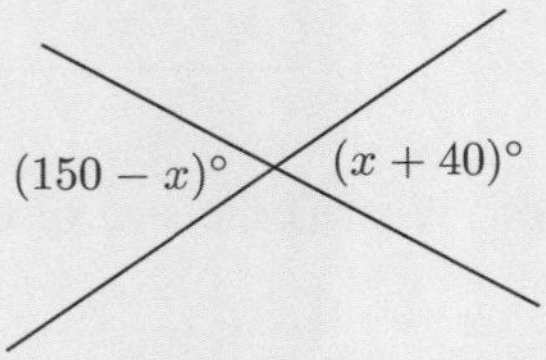

b

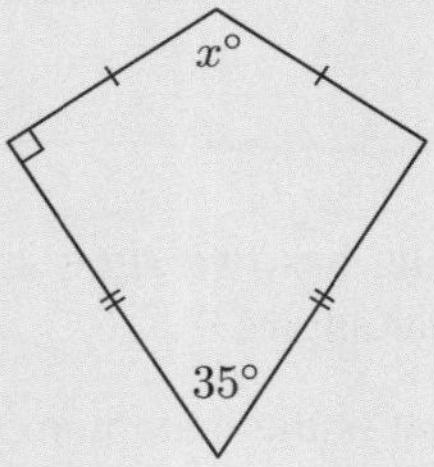

3 Draw two diagrams to illustrate the properties of a rectangle.

4 Find the values of the variables:

a

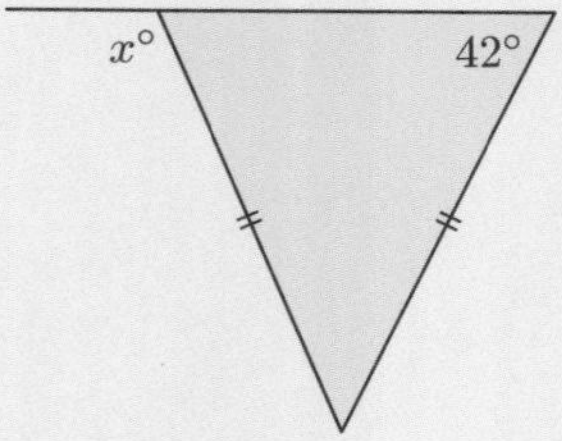

b

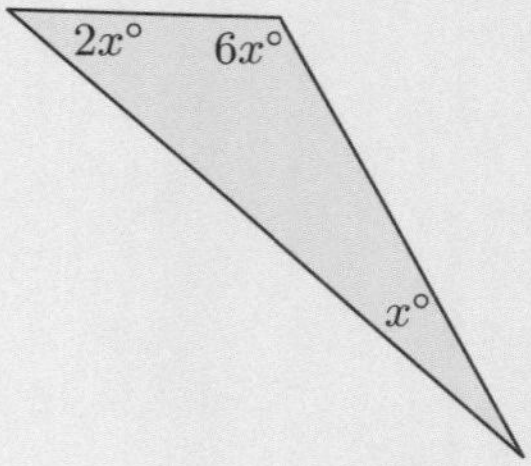

c

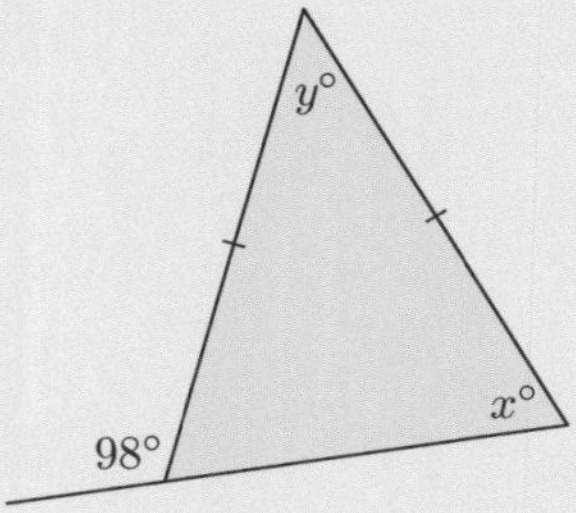

5 True or false?

a The diagonals of a square are equal in length.

b The diagonals of a rhombus intersect at right angles.

6

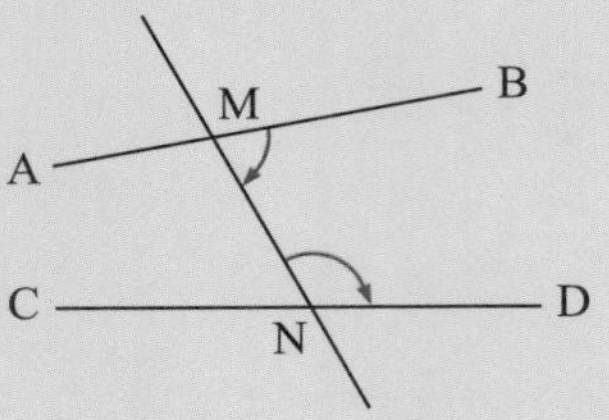

The given figure is not drawn to scale.

a What name describes the two marked angles?

b If the marked angles are supplementary, what does this say about [AB] and [CD]?

c If $B\widehat{M}N$ is acute, what can we say about $A\widehat{M}N$?

7 Find the values of the variables, giving brief reasons for your answers.

a

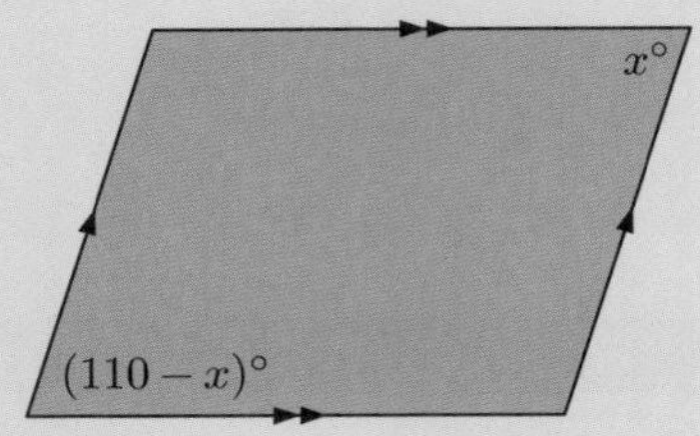

b

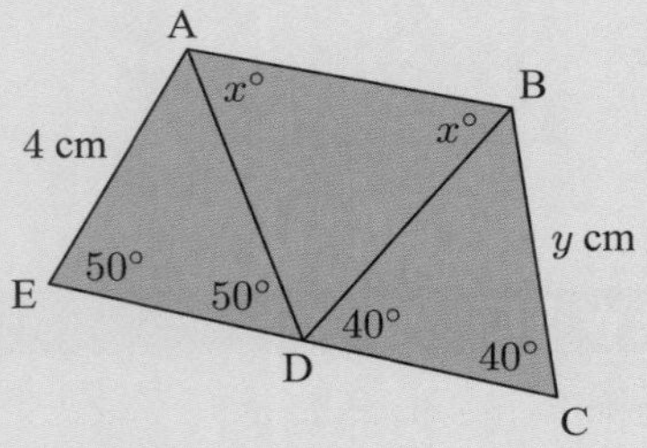

8 The quadrilaterals below are not drawn to scale, but the information on them is correct. Classify each quadrilateral.

a

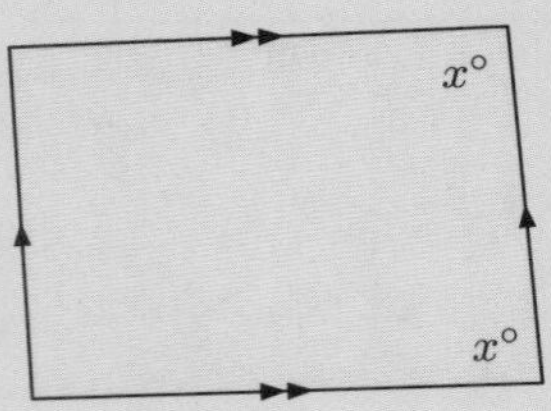

b

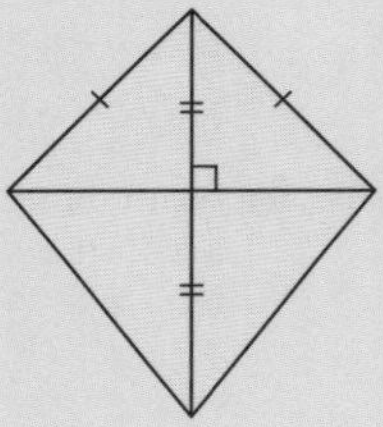

c

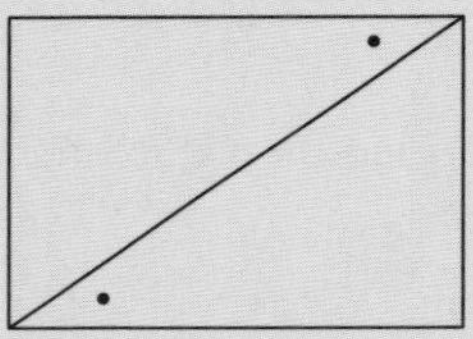

9 A hexagon has two right angles and four other equal angles. What is the size of each of the four equal angles?

10 **a** What is the maximum number of reflex angles a pentagon can have?

b Draw a pentagon with this number of reflex angles.

Chapter 10

Radicals and Pythagoras

Contents:

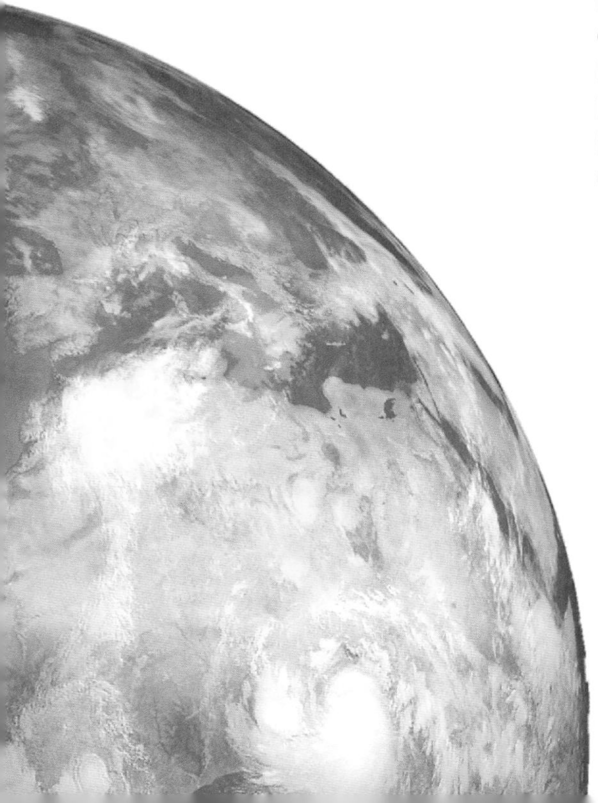

OPENING PROBLEM

Phil is concerned that the street lamp outside his house is not quite at right angles to the ground.

He marks a point A on the lamp 1.5 m from its base, and a point B on the ground 2 m from the lamp's base. Using a tape measure, he finds that the distance between A and B is 2.40 m.

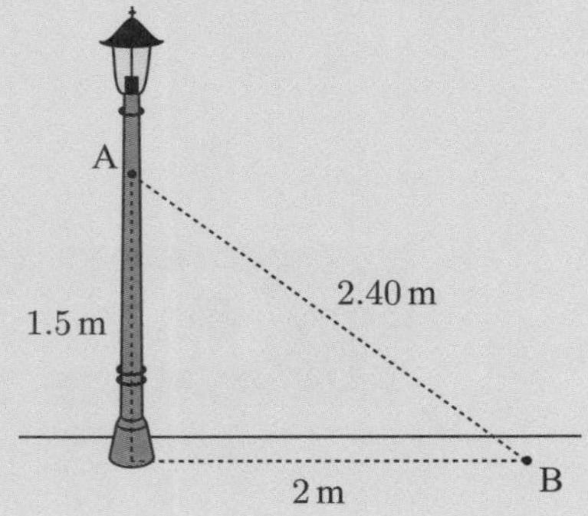

Things to think about:

a What assumptions has Phil made?

b Is the street lamp at right angles to the ground?

HISTORICAL NOTE

For many centuries people have used right angled corners to construct buildings and to divide land into rectangular fields. They have done this quite accurately by relatively simple means.

Over 3000 years ago the Egyptians knew that a triangle with sides in the ratio $3:4:5$ was right angled. They used a loop of rope with 12 knots equally spaced along it to make corners in their building construction.

Around 500 BC, the Greek mathematician **Pythagoras of Samos** proved a rule which connects the sides of a right angled triangle. According to legend, he discovered the rule while studying the tiled palace floor as he waited for an audience with the ruler Polycrates.

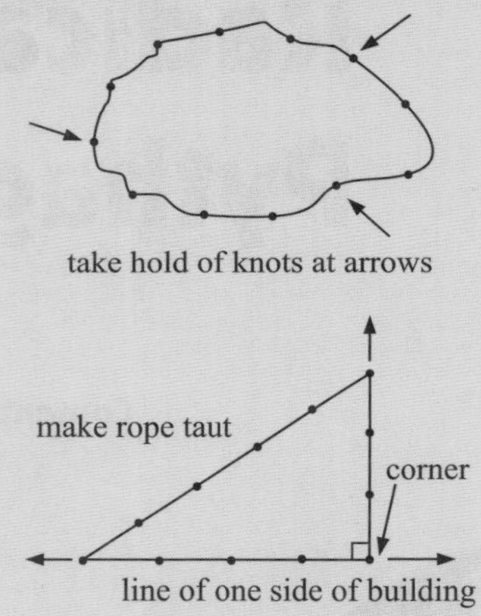

The discovery of **Pythagoras' theorem** led to the classification of a different type of number which does not have a terminating or recurring decimal value, but which does have a distinct place on the number line. These are called **surds** and are **irrational numbers**.

A SQUARE ROOTS

The **square root** of a number a is the non-negative number which, when squared, gives a.

$\sqrt{a}$ is always either positive or zero, so $\sqrt{a} \geqslant 0$.

$\sqrt{\ }$ is called the **radical** or **square root sign**.

RADICALS AND SURDS

Any number written with the radical sign $\sqrt{}$ is called a **radical**.
An irrational radical is called a **surd**.

The radicals $\sqrt{7}$ and $\sqrt{8}$ are examples of surds.

$\sqrt{9}$ is a radical but it is not a surd. This is because $\sqrt{9}=3$, which is a rational number.

RULES FOR SQUARE ROOTS

Since $0\times 0=0$, $\boldsymbol{\sqrt{0}=0}$

The square root of 5 is the positive number which, when multiplied by itself, gives 5.

So, $(\sqrt{5})^2=\sqrt{5}\times\sqrt{5}=5$.

$$\boldsymbol{(\sqrt{a})^2=\sqrt{a}\sqrt{a}=a} \quad \text{for all positive numbers } a.$$

Example 1 — Self Tutor

Simplify:

a $(\sqrt{11})^2$

b $(2\sqrt{3})^2$

a $(\sqrt{11})^2=\sqrt{11}\times\sqrt{11}$
$=11$

b $(2\sqrt{3})^2=2\sqrt{3}\times2\sqrt{3}$
$=2\times2\times\sqrt{3}\times\sqrt{3}$
$=4\times3$
$=12$

In the following **Investigation** we discover other properties of square roots.

INVESTIGATION 1 — PROPERTIES OF RADICALS

Notice that $(\sqrt{2}\sqrt{3})^2=(\sqrt{2})^2\times(\sqrt{3})^2$ {using $(ab)^n=a^nb^n$}
$=2\times3$
$=6$
$\therefore\ \sqrt{2}\sqrt{3}=\sqrt{6}$

What to do:

1 Use the technique above to show that:

a $\sqrt{2}\sqrt{7}=\sqrt{14}$ **b** $\sqrt{3}\sqrt{7}=\sqrt{21}$ **c** $\sqrt{5}\sqrt{6}=\sqrt{30}$

2 If a and b are positive numbers, what do you think $\sqrt{a}\sqrt{b}$ simplifies to? Can you prove your result?

3 By rearranging $\sqrt{2}\sqrt{3}=\sqrt{6}$, we find that $\dfrac{\sqrt{6}}{\sqrt{2}}=\sqrt{3}$ and $\dfrac{\sqrt{6}}{\sqrt{3}}=\sqrt{2}$.

Use your results from **1** to find:

a $\dfrac{\sqrt{14}}{\sqrt{2}}$ **b** $\dfrac{\sqrt{14}}{\sqrt{7}}$ **c** $\dfrac{\sqrt{21}}{\sqrt{3}}$ **d** $\dfrac{\sqrt{21}}{\sqrt{7}}$ **e** $\dfrac{\sqrt{30}}{\sqrt{5}}$ **f** $\dfrac{\sqrt{30}}{\sqrt{6}}$

Give reasons for your answers.

4 If a and b are positive numbers, what do you think $\dfrac{\sqrt{a}}{\sqrt{b}}$ simplifies to? Can you prove your result?

From the **Investigation** above you should have discovered that:

For positive numbers a and b, $\sqrt{a}\sqrt{b} = \sqrt{ab}$ and $\dfrac{\sqrt{a}}{\sqrt{b}} = \sqrt{\dfrac{a}{b}}$.

Example 2 **Self Tutor**

Simplify:

a $\sqrt{3}\sqrt{5}$ **b** $\dfrac{\sqrt{18}}{\sqrt{3}}$ **c** $\sqrt{\dfrac{4}{9}}$

a $\sqrt{3}\sqrt{5}$
$= \sqrt{3 \times 5}$
$= \sqrt{15}$

b $\dfrac{\sqrt{18}}{\sqrt{3}}$
$= \sqrt{\dfrac{18}{3}}$
$= \sqrt{6}$

c $\sqrt{\dfrac{4}{9}}$
$= \dfrac{\sqrt{4}}{\sqrt{9}}$
$= \dfrac{2}{3}$

RADICALS IN SIMPLEST FORM

Some radicals can be rewritten in a form so the number under the square root sign is made smaller.

For example, $\sqrt{12} = \sqrt{4 \times 3} = \sqrt{4}\sqrt{3} = 2\sqrt{3}$.

If a radical is written so the number under the square root sign is the smallest integer possible, we say it is in **simplest radical form.**

To write a radical in simplest form, look for the highest perfect square factor under the radical sign. Write the square root of this factor as a whole number in front of the radical of the remaining factor.

Example 3 **Self Tutor**

Write in simplest form:

a $\sqrt{20}$ **b** $\sqrt{98}$

a $\sqrt{20}$
$= \sqrt{4 \times 5}$ {4 is the highest square factor of 20}
$= \sqrt{4}\sqrt{5}$
$= 2\sqrt{5}$

b $\sqrt{98}$
$= \sqrt{49 \times 2}$ {49 is the highest square factor of 98}
$= \sqrt{49}\sqrt{2}$
$= 7\sqrt{2}$

EXERCISE 10A

1 Simplify:

a $(\sqrt{5})^2$ **b** $(\sqrt{13})^2$ **c** $(\sqrt{19})^2$ **d** $(\sqrt{20})^2$

e $(3\sqrt{3})^2$ **f** $(4\sqrt{5})^2$ **g** $(6\sqrt{2})^2$ **h** $(2\sqrt{6})^2$

2 Simplify:

a $\sqrt{5}\times\sqrt{7}$ **b** $\dfrac{\sqrt{20}}{\sqrt{10}}$ **c** $\sqrt{6}\times\sqrt{11}$ **d** $\dfrac{\sqrt{39}}{\sqrt{3}}$

e $\sqrt{\dfrac{1}{49}}$ **f** $\sqrt{10}\times\sqrt{23}$ **g** $\sqrt{17}\times\sqrt{3}$ **h** $\dfrac{\sqrt{68}}{\sqrt{2}}$

i $\dfrac{\sqrt{91}}{\sqrt{13}}$ **j** $\sqrt{\dfrac{81}{25}}$ **k** $\dfrac{\sqrt{7}\times\sqrt{6}}{\sqrt{2}}$ **l** $\sqrt{5}\times\sqrt{6}\times\sqrt{7}$

3 State whether the following radicals are surds. If the radical is a surd, find its value correct to 2 decimal places. If the radical is not a surd, find its exact value.

a $\sqrt{10}$ **b** $\sqrt{100}$ **c** $\sqrt{65}$ **d** $\sqrt{6}$

e $\sqrt{\dfrac{1}{4}}$ **f** $\sqrt{27}$ **g** $\sqrt{\dfrac{9}{16}}$ **h** $\sqrt{2\frac{7}{9}}$

4 Write in simplest form:

a $\sqrt{8}$ **b** $\sqrt{20}$ **c** $\sqrt{18}$

d $\sqrt{32}$ **e** $\sqrt{27}$ **f** $\sqrt{52}$

g $\sqrt{48}$ **h** $\sqrt{50}$ **i** $\sqrt{108}$

j $\sqrt{75}$ **k** $\sqrt{45}$ **l** $\sqrt{99}$

m $\sqrt{300}$ **n** $\sqrt{60}$ **o** $\sqrt{88}$

p $\sqrt{140}$

Look for the highest perfect square factor under the radical sign.

5 Show that $\dfrac{\sqrt{96}}{\sqrt{6}} = 4$:

a by using the rule $\dfrac{\sqrt{a}}{\sqrt{b}} = \sqrt{\dfrac{a}{b}}$

b by first writing $\sqrt{96}$ in simplest form.

B SOLVING $x^2 = k$

In the previous Section we dealt with surds like $\sqrt{7}$.

Notice that $\sqrt{7}\times\sqrt{7} = 7$ and $(-\sqrt{7})\times(-\sqrt{7}) = 7$ {as negative × negative = positive}.

So, if we were asked to solve the equation $x^2 = 7$, it is clear that x could equal $\sqrt{7}$ or $-\sqrt{7}$. The squares of both of these numbers are 7.

We write the solutions as $x = \pm\sqrt{7}$, which reads "plus or minus the square root of 7".

Consider $x^2 = k$.
If $k > 0$, then $x = \pm\sqrt{k}$.
If $k = 0$, then $x = 0$ is the only solution.
If $k < 0$, then there are **no real solutions**.

A **real** number is a number which can be placed on the number line.

Example 4 — Self Tutor

Solve for x:

a $x^2 = 4$ **b** $x^2 = 11$ **c** $x^2 = -5$

a $x^2 = 4$
$\therefore\ x = \pm\sqrt{4}$
$\therefore\ x = \pm 2$ $\{x = 2$ or $x = -2\}$

b $x^2 = 11$
$\therefore\ x = \pm\sqrt{11}$ $\{x = \sqrt{11}$ or $x = -\sqrt{11}\}$

c $x^2 = -5$ has no real solutions, since x^2 cannot be negative.

Example 5 — Self Tutor

Solve for x:

a $x^2 + 4 = 9$ **b** $10 + x^2 = 26$

a $x^2 + 4 = 9$
$\therefore\ x^2 = 5$ {subtracting 4 from both sides}
$\therefore\ x = \pm\sqrt{5}$

b $10 + x^2 = 26$
$\therefore\ x^2 = 16$ {subtracting 10 from both sides}
$\therefore\ x = \pm\sqrt{16}$
$\therefore\ x = \pm 4$

EXERCISE 10B

1 Solve for x:

a $x^2 = 9$ **b** $x^2 = 49$ **c** $x^2 = 36$ **d** $x^2 = 0$
e $x^2 = 1$ **f** $x^2 = 17$ **g** $x^2 = 23$ **h** $x^2 = 100$
i $x^2 = -4$ **j** $x^2 = -7$ **k** $x^2 = 27$ **l** $x^2 = -27$

2 Solve for x:

a $x^2 + 5 = 9$ **b** $x^2 + 16 = 25$ **c** $x^2 + 2 = 27$
d $x^2 + 7 = 23$ **e** $8 + x^2 = 44$ **f** $x^2 + 14 = 39$
g $10 + x^2 = 60$ **h** $x^2 + 5 = 49$ **i** $6 + x^2 = 18$

Example 6 **Self Tutor**

Solve for x:

a $2x^2 = 24$ **b** $x^2 + (2x)^2 = 20$

a
$$2x^2 = 24$$
$$\therefore\ x^2 = 12 \quad \{\text{dividing both sides by } 2\}$$
$$\therefore\ x = \pm\sqrt{12}$$
$$\therefore\ x = \pm\sqrt{4}\sqrt{3}$$
$$\therefore\ x = \pm 2\sqrt{3}$$

b
$$x^2 + (2x)^2 = 20$$
$$\therefore\ x^2 + 4x^2 = 20 \quad \{\text{index law}\}$$
$$\therefore\ 5x^2 = 20$$
$$\therefore\ x^2 = 4 \quad \{\text{dividing both sides by } 5\}$$
$$\therefore\ x = \pm\sqrt{4}$$
$$\therefore\ x = \pm 2$$

3 Solve for x:

a $2x^2 = 18$ **b** $3x^2 = 48$ **c** $5x^2 = 20$
d $x^2 + x^2 = 32$ **e** $x^2 + 2x^2 = 90$ **f** $x^2 + 5x^2 = 120$
g $x^2 + (2x)^2 = 45$ **h** $x^2 + (3x)^2 = 70$ **i** $x^2 + (2x)^2 = 1$

C PYTHAGORAS' THEOREM

A **right angled triangle** is a triangle which has a right angle as one of its angles.

The side **opposite** the right angle is called the **hypotenuse**. It is the **longest** side of the triangle.

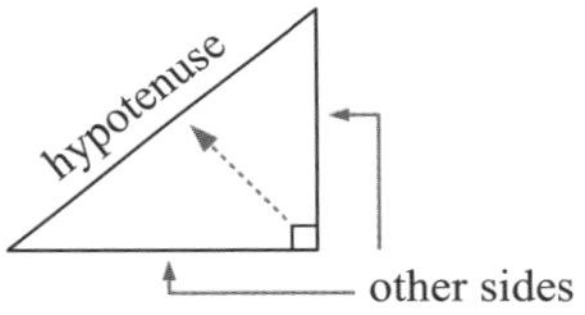

Right angled triangles are frequently observed in real world situations. For example:

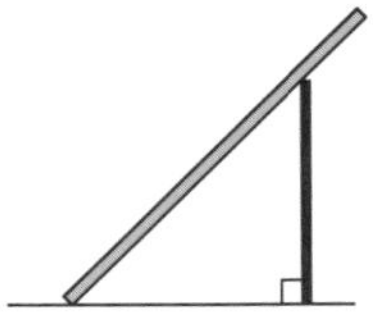

ladder leaning against a wall

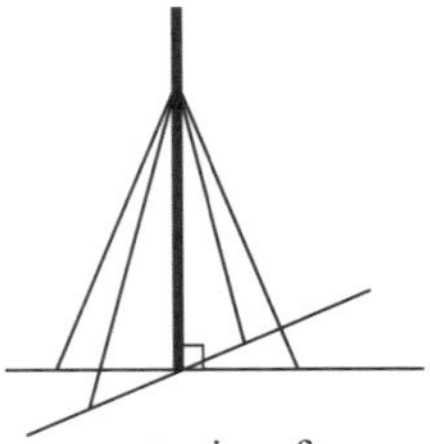

support wires for a mast or antenna

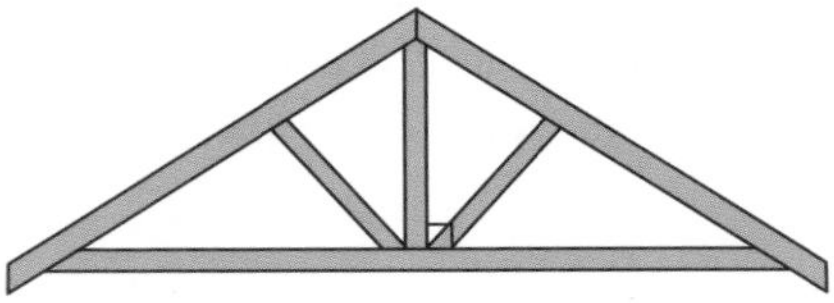

in trusses for roof structures

If a triangle is right angled, the special relationship connecting the lengths of its sides is called **Pythagoras' theorem**.

INVESTIGATION 2 DISCOVERING PYTHAGORAS' THEOREM

Consider a right angled triangle which has a hypotenuse of length c cm, and the other two sides have lengths a cm and b cm.

We are looking for an equation which connects a, b, and c.

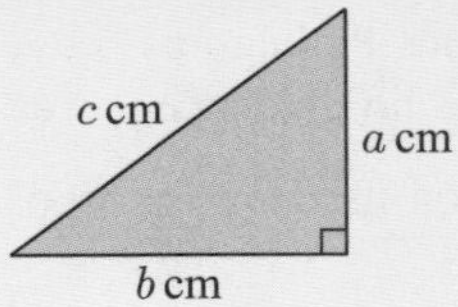

What to do:

1 Draw a horizontal line of length 4 cm. At one end, draw a vertical line of length 3 cm. The lines you have drawn form a right angle.

2 Complete a right angled triangle by drawing in the hypotenuse. In this case $a = 3$ and $b = 4$. Find c by measuring this hypotenuse.

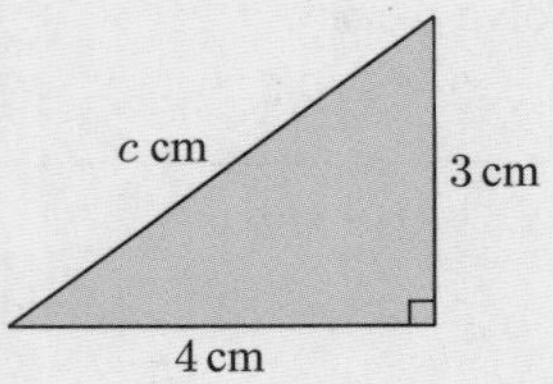

3 **a** Copy the table and complete the second row using the information from **2**.

b Complete the rest of the table using three more right angled triangles for which a and b are specified.

a	b	c	a^2	b^2	c^2	a^2+b^2
3	4		9			
6	8					
5	12					
4	7					

4 State any conclusions you draw from the information in this table.

5 Construct two more right angled triangles with lengths a and b of your choosing. Does your conclusion hold for these triangles?

6 Click on the icon to further explore the side lengths of right angled triangles.

PYTHAGORAS SIMULATION

PYTHAGORAS' THEOREM

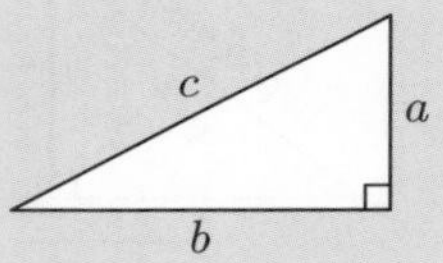

In a right angled triangle with hypotenuse of length c, and other sides of length a and b,

$$c^2 = a^2 + b^2.$$

In geometric form, Pythagoras' theorem states:

In any right angled triangle, the area of the square on the hypotenuse is equal to the sum of the areas of the squares on the other two sides.

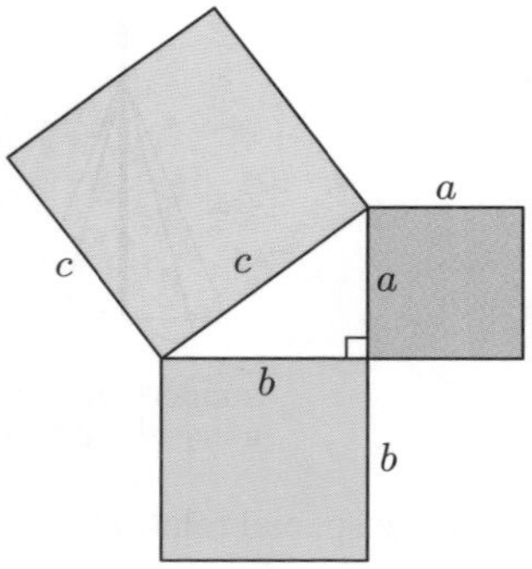

Look back at the tile pattern on page **192**. Can you see this figure in the pattern?

WORKSHEET

DISCUSSION PYTHAGORAS' THEOREM

How did Pythagoras prove his theorem? He probably did not use algebra, since there is no evidence it was invented until well after his lifetime.

Click on the icon for a possible answer.

PYTHAGORAS' PROOF

There are over 400 different proofs of Pythagoras' theorem. One of them is presented below.

Proof:

On a square we draw 4 identical right angled triangles, as illustrated. A smaller square is formed in the centre.

Suppose the hypotenuse of each triangle has length c, and the other two side lengths are a and b.

The total area of the large square
$= 4 \times$ area of one triangle $+$ area of smaller square

$$\therefore \quad (a+b)^2 = 4 \times \frac{1}{2}ab + c^2$$
$$\therefore \quad a^2 + 2ab + b^2 = 2ab + c^2$$
$$\therefore \quad a^2 + b^2 = c^2$$

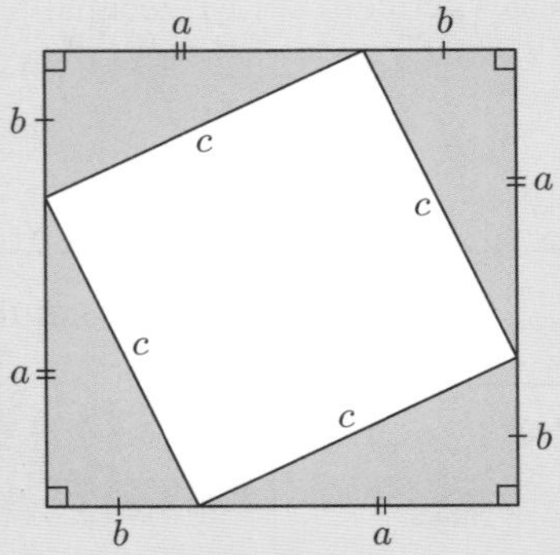

We can use Pythagoras' theorem to find side lengths in right angled triangles.

Example 7 Self Tutor

Find the length of the hypotenuse in the given right angled triangle:

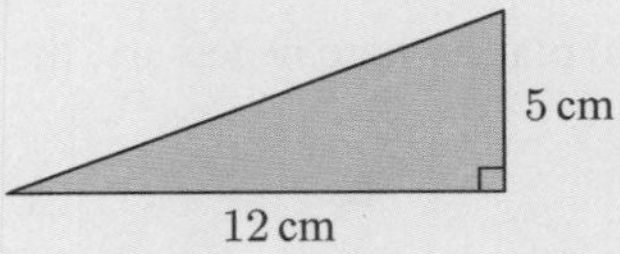

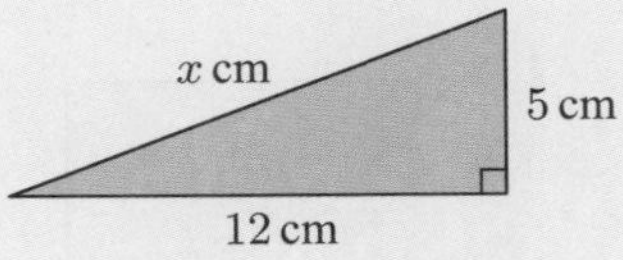

Let the hypotenuse have length x cm.

$\therefore \quad x^2 = 12^2 + 5^2 \qquad$ {Pythagoras}

$\therefore \quad x^2 = 144 + 25$

$\therefore \quad x^2 = 169$

$\therefore \quad x = \pm\sqrt{169}$

$\therefore \quad x = 13 \qquad$ {as $x > 0$}

The hypotenuse has length 13 cm.

We reject the negative answer as the length of a side must be positive!

EXERCISE 10C

1 Find the length of the hypotenuse in each right angled triangle. Leave your answer in simplest radical form.

a
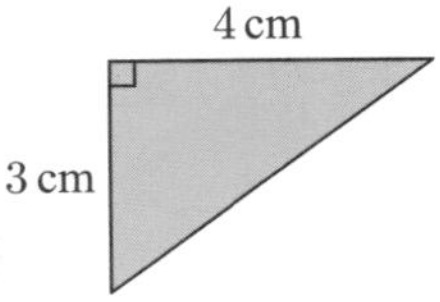

b
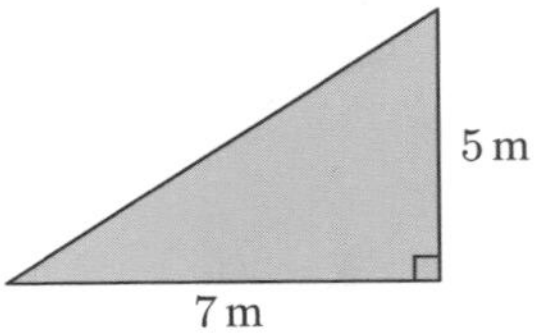

c
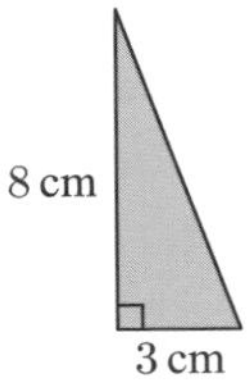

d
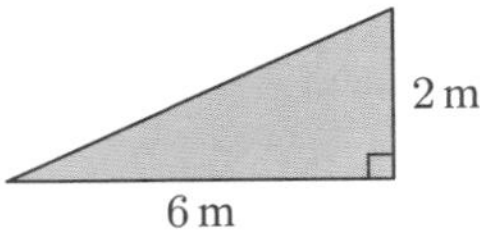

e
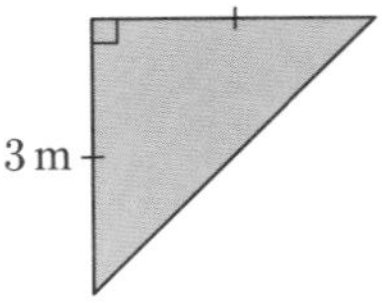

f
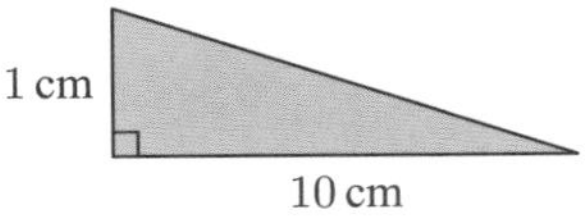

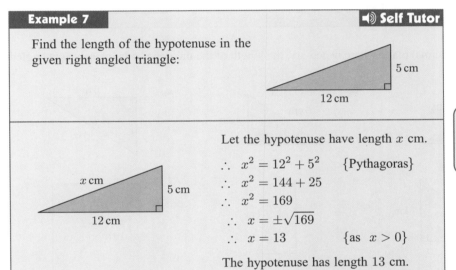

Example 8 **Self Tutor**

Find the length of the unknown side, giving your answer correct to 1 decimal place.

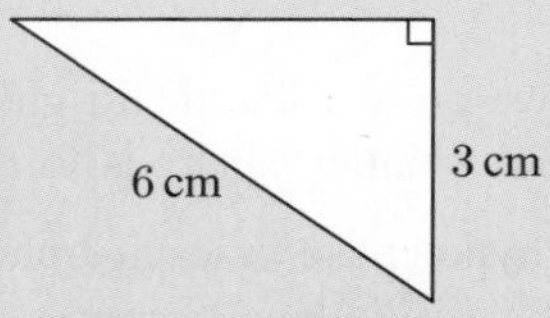

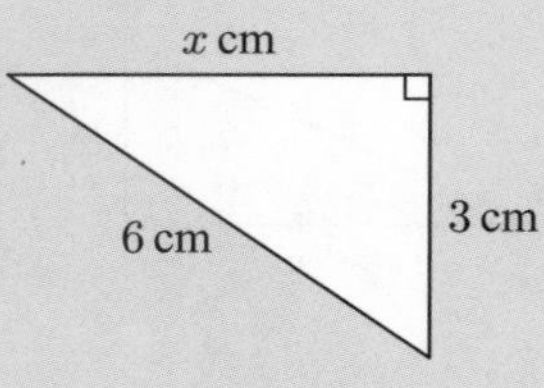

Let the third side have length x cm.

$\therefore\ x^2 + 3^2 = 6^2$ {Pythagoras}

$\therefore\ x^2 + 9 = 36$

$\therefore\ x^2 = 27$

$\therefore\ x = \pm\sqrt{27}$

$\therefore\ x = \sqrt{27}$ {as $x > 0$}

The third side has length ≈ 5.2 cm.

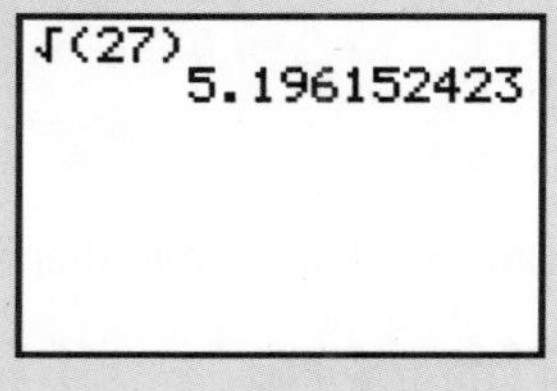

2 Find, correct to 1 decimal place where necessary, the length of the unknown side in each right angled triangle.

a
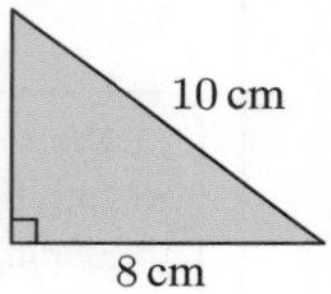

b
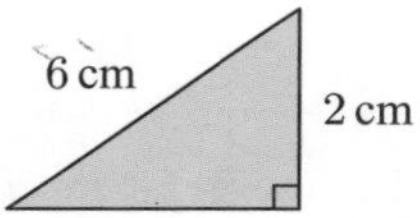

c
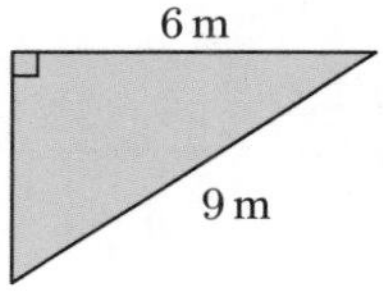

d
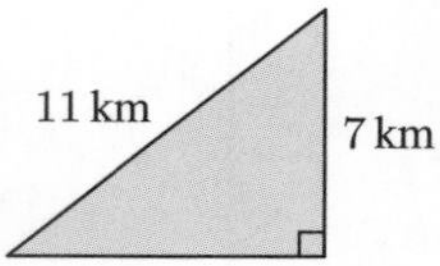

e
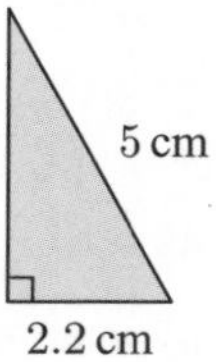

f
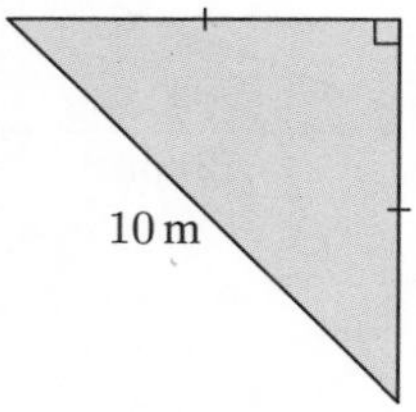

3 Find the length of the unknown side in each right angled triangle. Leave your answer in simplest radical form.

a
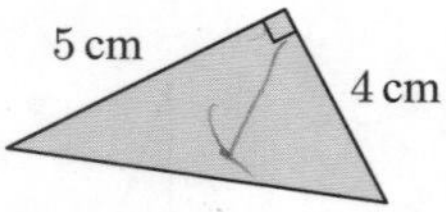

b
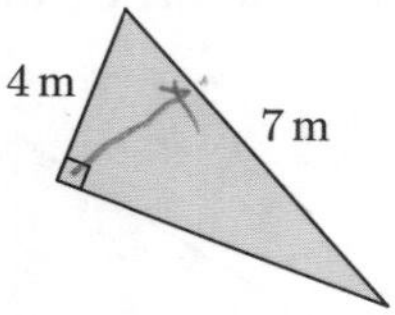

c
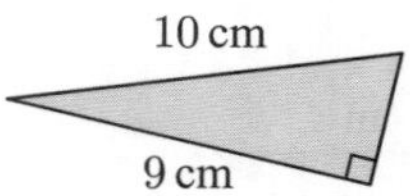

d
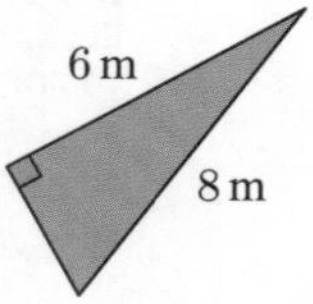

e
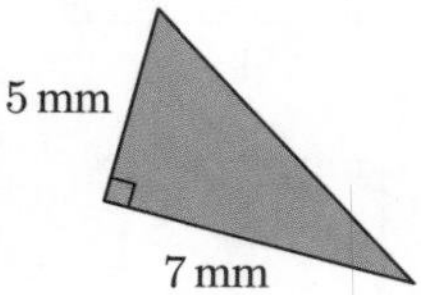

f
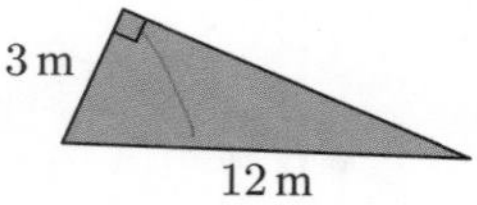

Example 9 **Self Tutor**

Find the value of y:

a

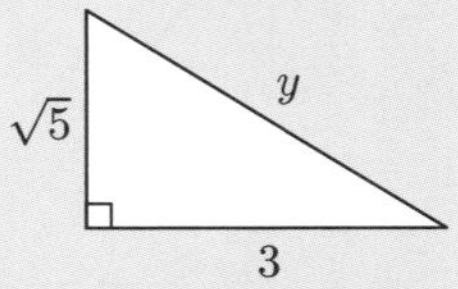

b

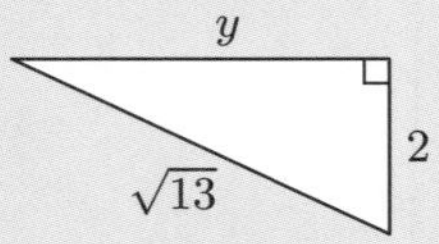

a $y^2 = 3^2 + (\sqrt{5})^2$ {Pythagoras}

$\therefore\ y^2 = 9 + 5$

$\therefore\ y^2 = 14$

$\therefore\ y = \pm\sqrt{14}$

$\therefore\ y = \sqrt{14}$ {as $y > 0$}

b $y^2 + 2^2 = (\sqrt{13})^2$ {Pythagoras}

$\therefore\ y^2 + 4 = 13$

$\therefore\ y^2 = 9$

$\therefore\ y = \pm\sqrt{9}$

$\therefore\ y = 3$ {as $y > 0$}

4 Find the value of y:

a

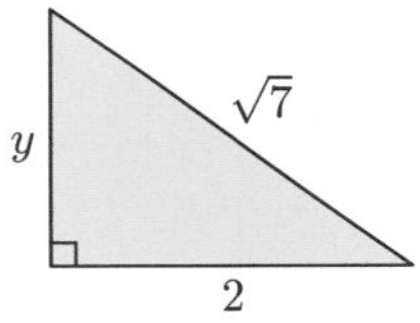

b

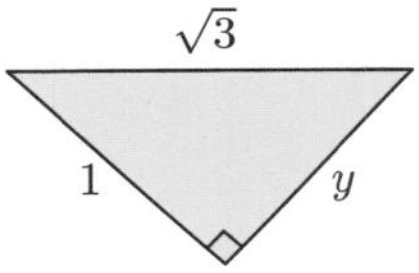

c

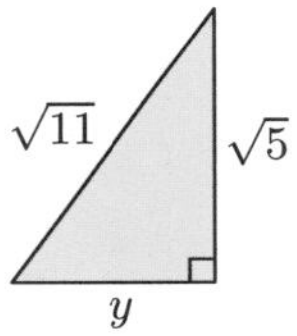

d

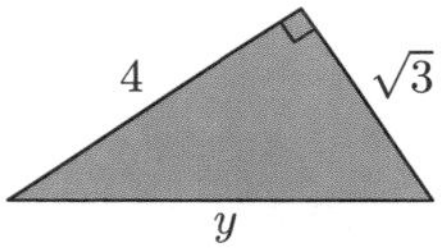

e

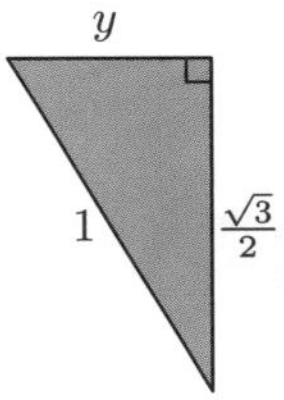

f

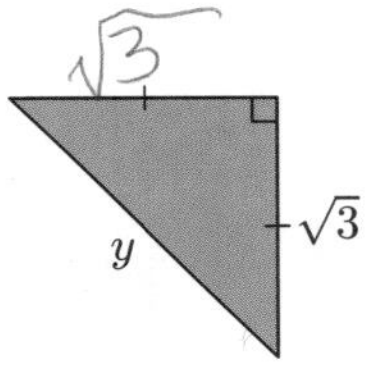

Example 10 **Self Tutor**

Find the unknown lengths:

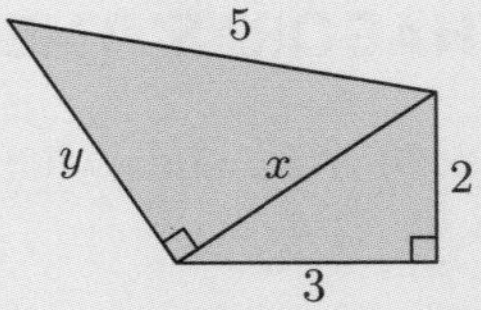

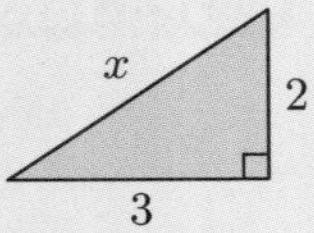

$x^2 = 3^2 + 2^2$ {Pythagoras}

$\therefore\ x^2 = 9 + 4$

$\therefore\ x^2 = 13$

$\therefore\ x = \sqrt{13}$ {as $x > 0$}

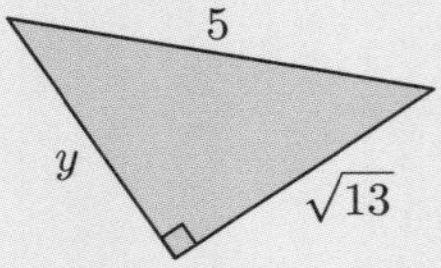

$y^2 + (\sqrt{13})^2 = 5^2$ {Pythagoras}

$\therefore\ y^2 + 13 = 25$

$\therefore\ y^2 = 12$

$\therefore\ y = \sqrt{12}$ {as $y > 0$}

$\therefore\ y = 2\sqrt{3}$

5 Find the unknown lengths:

a

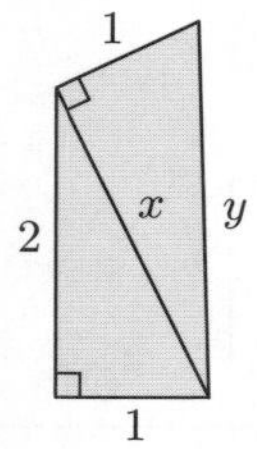

b

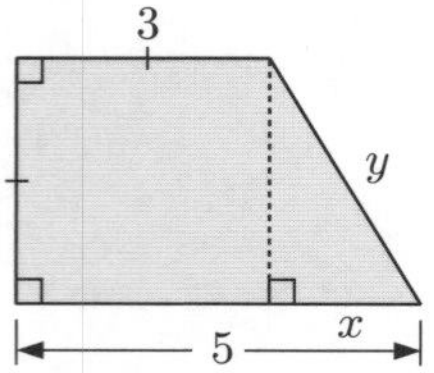

c

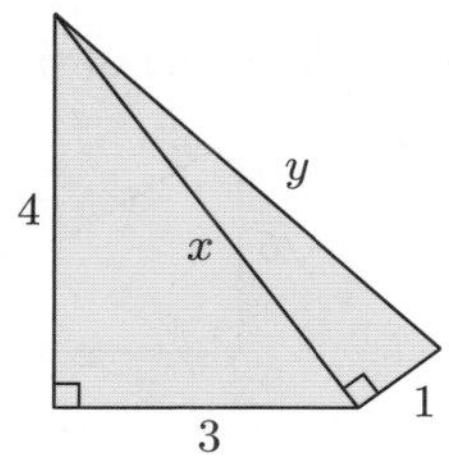

d

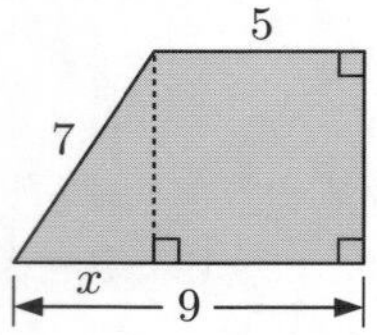

e

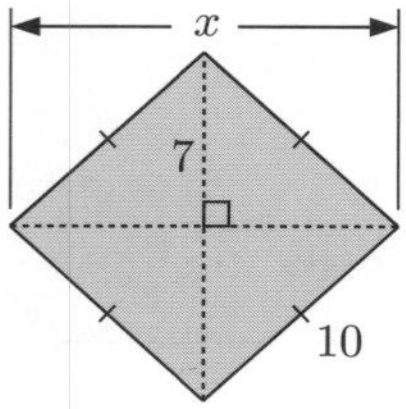

f

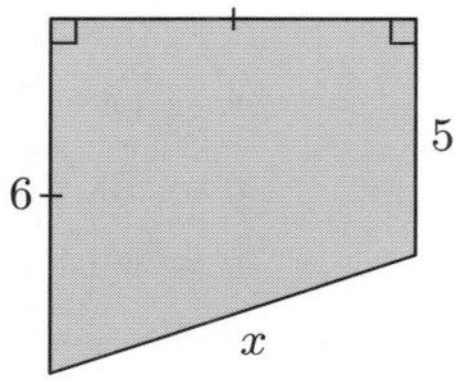

g

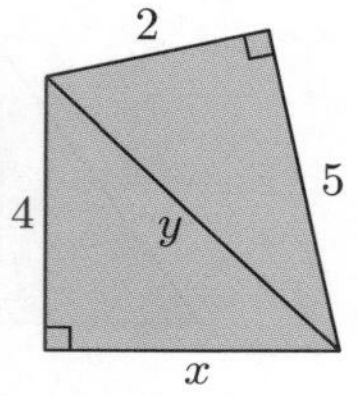

h

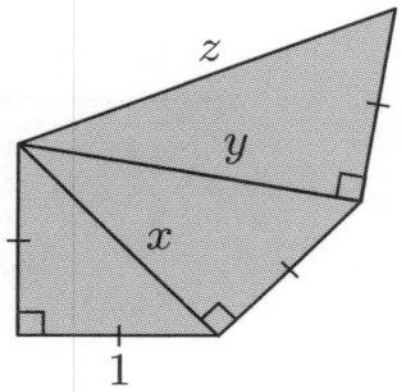

i

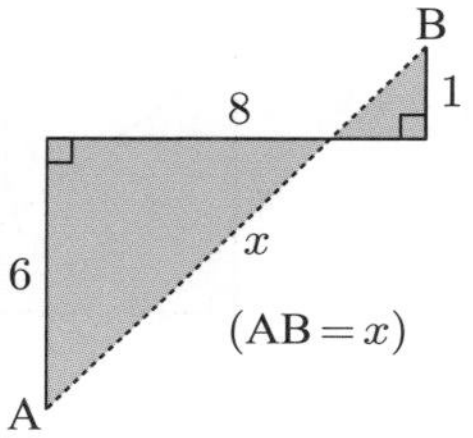

D THE CONVERSE OF PYTHAGORAS' THEOREM

If we are given the lengths of three sides of a triangle, the **converse of Pythagoras' theorem** gives us a simple **test** to determine whether the triangle is right angled.

THE CONVERSE OF PYTHAGORAS' THEOREM

If a triangle has sides of length a, b, and c units where $a^2 + b^2 = c^2$, then the triangle is right angled.

PYTHAGORAS SIMULATION

Example 11 — Self Tutor

Is the triangle with sides 8 cm, 9 cm, and 12 cm right angled?

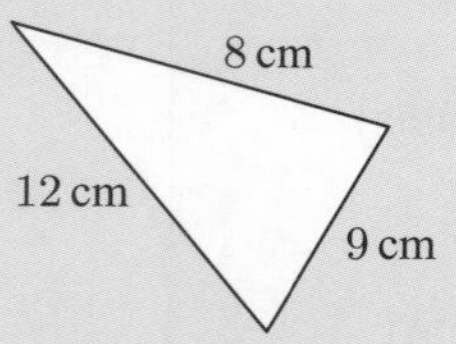

The two shorter sides have lengths 8 cm and 9 cm.

Now $8^2 + 9^2 = 64 + 81 = 145$

whereas $12^2 = 144$

$\therefore \ 8^2 + 9^2 \neq 12^2$

$\therefore$ the triangle is not right angled.

The hypotenuse would be the longest side!

EXERCISE 10D

1. The following figures are not drawn to scale. Which of the triangles are right angled?

a
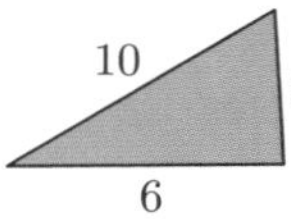

b
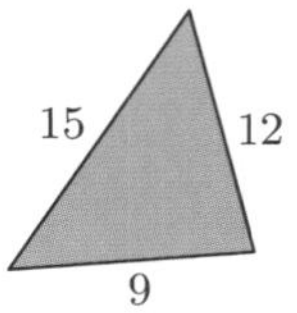

c
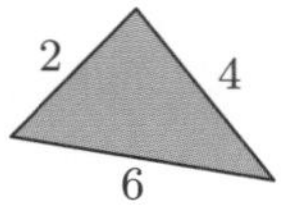

The right angle would be opposite the hypotenuse or longest side.

d
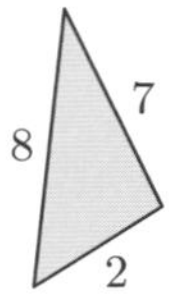

e
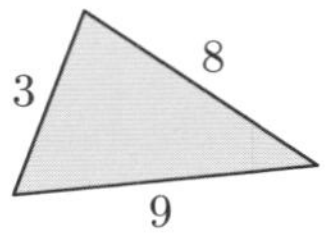

f
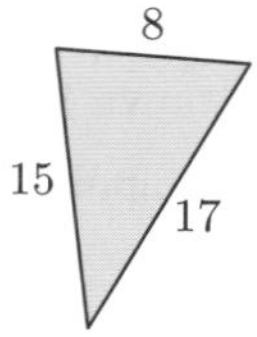

2. The following figures are not drawn to scale. Which of the triangles are right angled? For those triangles that are, indicate which angle is the right angle.

a
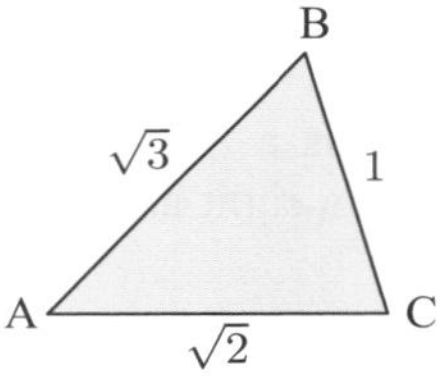

b
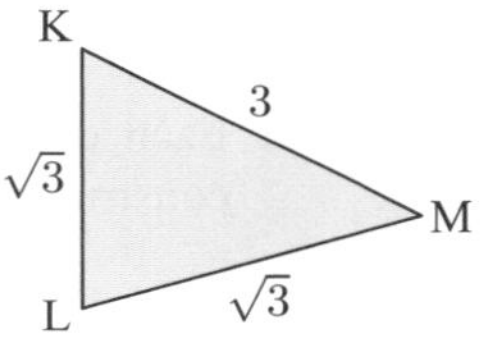

c
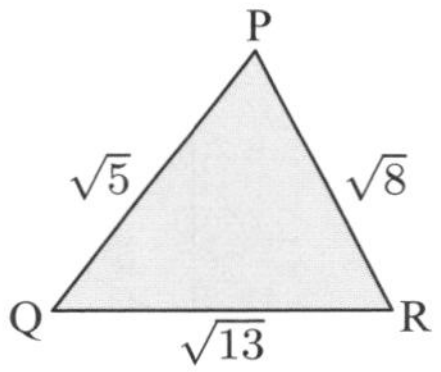

d
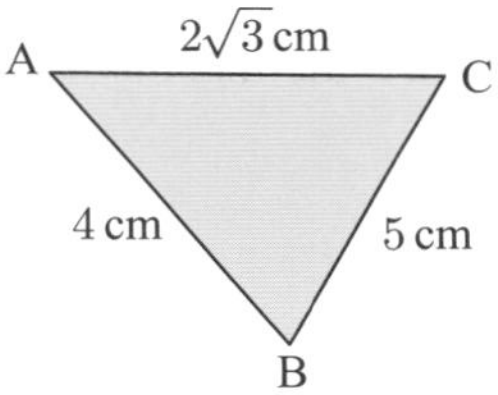

e
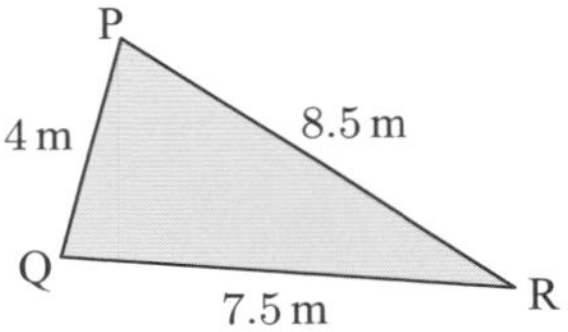

f
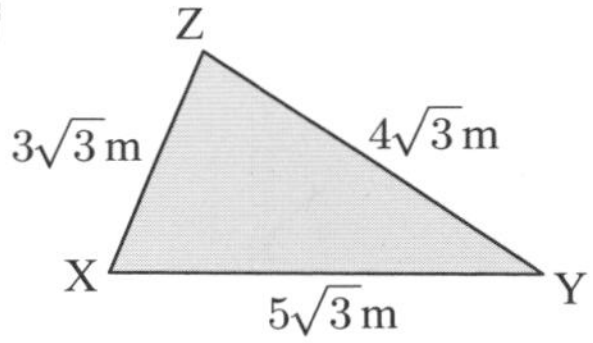

3. Meredith is trying to make a scarf by cutting some cloth into a right angled triangle. The triangle she makes has side lengths 40 cm, 42 cm, and 58 cm. Is Meredith's triangle right angled?

4. Answer the **Opening Problem** on page **192**.

ACTIVITY — TESTING FOR RIGHT ANGLES

What to do:

1. Select an object around your school which appears to be at right angles to the ground. It could be a telegraph pole, a table leg, or a wall.
2. Mark a point on your object, and measure its height a above the ground.
3. Mark a point on the ground, and measure its distance b from the base of the object.
4. Measure the distance c between the two points. Make sure that your tape measure is taut.

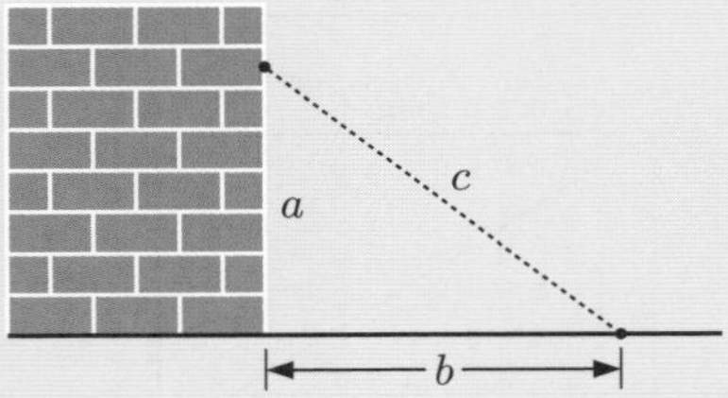

5. Use the converse of Pythagoras' theorem to determine whether the object is at right angles to the ground.

E PROBLEM SOLVING USING PYTHAGORAS

Right angled triangles occur in many practical problems. In these situations we can apply Pythagoras' theorem to help find unknown side lengths.

The problem solving approach involves the following steps:

Step 1: Draw a neat, clear diagram of the situation.
Step 2: Mark known lengths and right angles on the diagram.
Step 3: Use a symbol such as x to represent the unknown length.
Step 4: Write down Pythagoras' theorem for the given information.
Step 5: Solve the equation.
Step 6: Where necessary, write your answer in sentence form.

The following special geometrical figures contain right angled triangles:

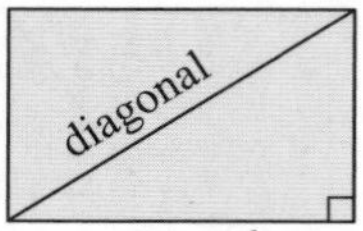

rectangle

Each corner of a **rectangle** is a right angle. We can construct a diagonal to form a right angled triangle.

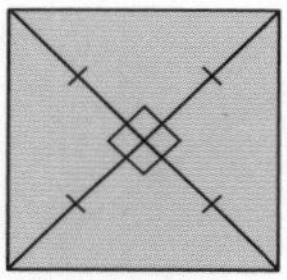
square

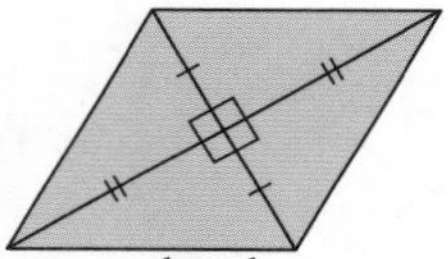
rhombus

In a **square** and a **rhombus**, the diagonals bisect each other at right angles.

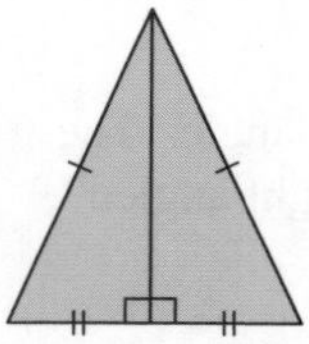
isosceles triangle

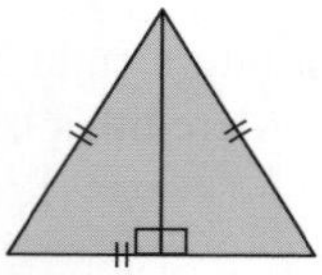
equilateral triangle

In an **isosceles triangle** and an **equilateral triangle**, the altitude bisects the base at right angles.

Example 12 — Self Tutor

The rectangular frame of a gate is 3 m by 5 m.
Find, to the nearest centimetre, the length of the diagonal support across the frame.

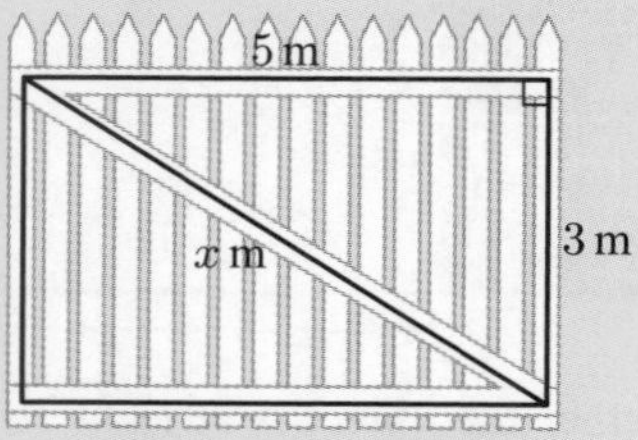

Let the diagonal support have length x m.

Now $x^2 = 3^2 + 5^2$ {Pythagoras}

$\therefore\ x^2 = 9 + 25$

$\therefore\ x^2 = 34$

$\therefore\ x = \sqrt{34}$ {as $x > 0$}

$\therefore$ the support is $\sqrt{34} \approx 5.83$ m long.

EXERCISE 10E

1. Consider the diagonal of a 5 cm by 8 cm rectangle. Find the diagonal's length:
   a. in radical form
   b. to the nearest mm.

2. Find the length of the diagonal of a square with side length 6.8 cm. Give your answer in radical form, and also as a decimal to the nearest mm.

3. What is the longest iron rod which can be placed flat across the diagonal of a 4 m by 2.5 m garden shed floor?

4. A rhombus has diagonals 6 cm and 10 cm. Find the length of one side of the rhombus.

5. Three roads [AB], [BC], and [CA] form a right angled triangle. AC is 9 km and BC is 5 km. Liam rides his bicycle from A to B to C. What extra distance does he travel compared with going directly from A to C?

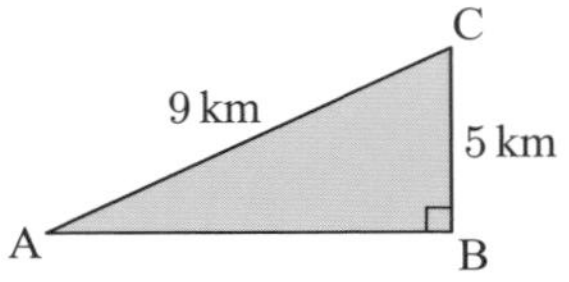

6. 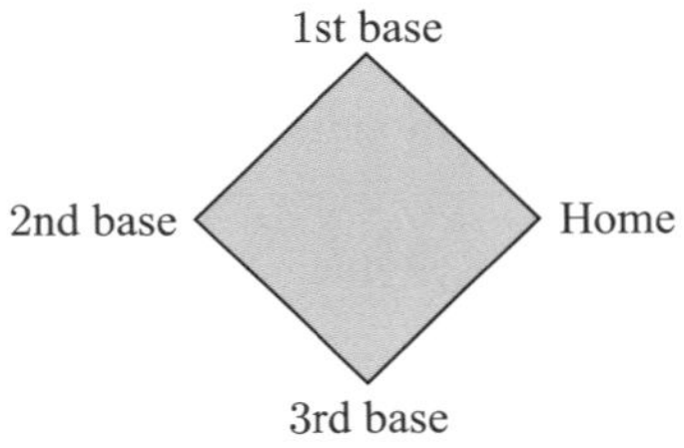

A baseball 'diamond' is a square whose sides are 27 m long. Find, to the nearest $\frac{1}{10}$ metre, the distance from the home plate to second base.

Example 13 — Self Tutor

An 8 m long ladder has its feet placed 3 m out from a vertical wall. How far up the wall will the ladder reach, to the nearest cm?

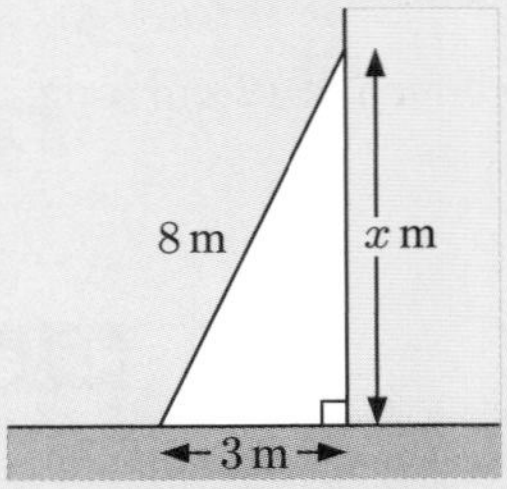

Suppose the ladder reaches x m up the wall.

Now $x^2 + 3^2 = 8^2$ {Pythagoras}

$\therefore\ x^2 + 9 = 64$

$\therefore\ x^2 = 55$

$\therefore\ x = \sqrt{55}$ {as $x > 0$}

$\therefore$ the ladder reaches $\sqrt{55} \approx 7.42$ m up the wall.

7. When the feet of a ladder are placed 2.5 m from a wall, the ladder just reaches an 8 m high window. How long is the ladder?

8. A car travels 9 km due north and then 12 km due west. How far is the car from its starting point?

9. A cyclist is 32 km east and 18 km south of her starting point. She wants to return to her starting point in a direct line.
   a. How far is the cyclist in a direct line from her starting point?
   b. How long will it take her to return to her starting point if she can ride at 36 km per hour?

10 Two trains A and B leave the station at the same time. Train A travels north at a constant speed of 45 km per hour. Train B travels east at a constant speed of 70 km per hour.

a How far will each train have travelled after 3 hours?

b Find the distance between A and B after 3 hours.

11 A large flagpole is held to the ground by six cables, as illustrated. If the cables have to be replaced, what length of cabling must be purchased?

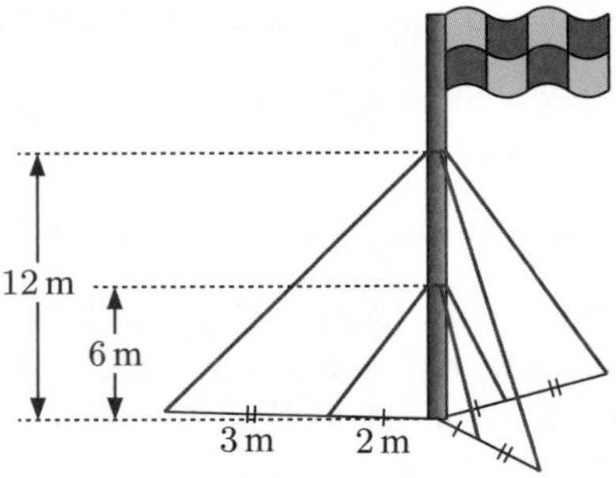

Example 14 Self Tutor

An equilateral triangle has sides of length 8 cm. Find the height of the triangle, to the nearest mm.

We draw an altitude which *bisects* the base.

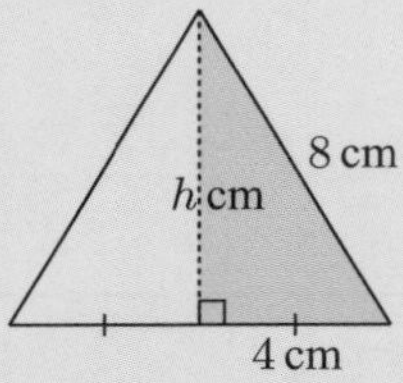

$h^2 + 4^2 = 8^2$ {Pythagoras}

$\therefore h^2 + 16 = 64$

$\therefore h^2 = 48$

$\therefore h = \sqrt{48}$ {as $h > 0$}

$\therefore$ the height of the triangle ≈ 6.9 cm.

12 Find the height of an equilateral triangle with sides of length 10 cm.

13 An isosceles triangle has equal sides measuring 10 cm, and a base which is 12 cm long. Find the length of the altitude of the triangle from the apex to the base.

Example 15 Self Tutor

A square has diagonals of length 10 cm. Find the length of a side, to the nearest mm.

Let the sides have length x cm.

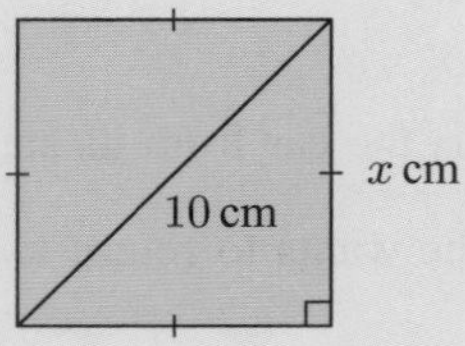

$\therefore x^2 + x^2 = 10^2$ {Pythagoras}

$\therefore 2x^2 = 100$

$\therefore x^2 = 50$

$\therefore x = \sqrt{50}$ {as $x > 0$}

$\therefore$ the sides have length $\sqrt{50} \approx 7.1$ cm.

14 A square has diagonals of length 15 cm. Find the length of a side, to the nearest mm.

15 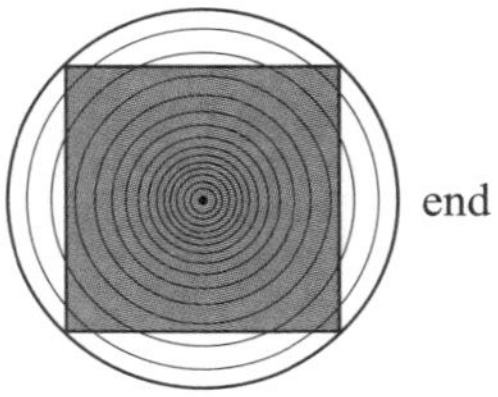

A log is 60 cm in diameter. Find the dimensions of the largest square section beam which can be cut from the log.

16 The longer side of a rectangle is three times the length of the shorter side. Each diagonal of the rectangle is 22 cm long. Find the dimensions of the rectangle.

17 An equilateral triangle has an altitude of length 16 cm. Find the length of each side.

18 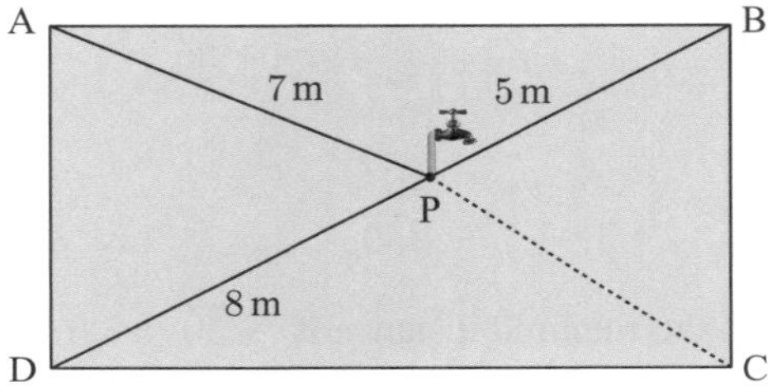

ABCD is a rectangular garden plot.
P is a water tap.
Find the distance from the tap to corner C.

19 In the given rectangle, find the distance from A to B.

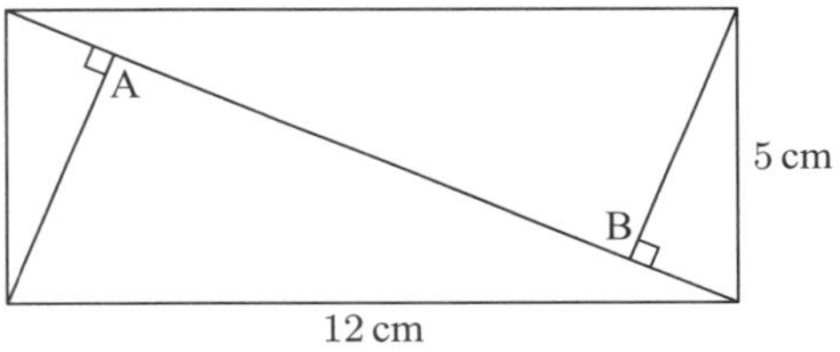

F 3-DIMENSIONAL PROBLEMS

Pythagoras' theorem is often used to find lengths in **3-dimensional** problems.

Example 16 Self Tutor

A cone is 7 cm high and has a base radius of 3 cm.
Find the slant height of the cone.

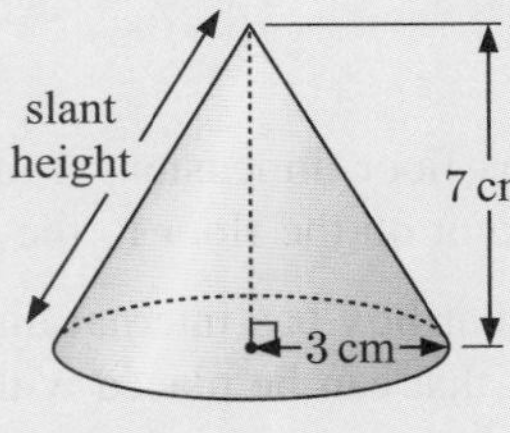

Let the slant height be s cm.

$\therefore \; s^2 = 7^2 + 3^2$ {Pythagoras}

$\therefore \; s^2 = 49 + 9$

$\therefore \; s^2 = 58$

$\therefore \; s = \sqrt{58}$ {as $s > 0$}

$\therefore$ the slant height is $\sqrt{58} \approx 7.62$ cm.

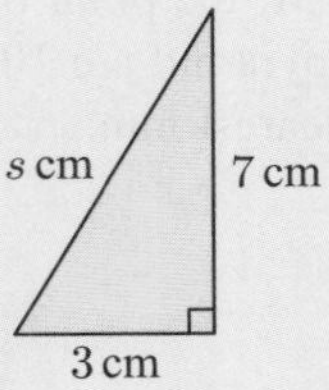

Sometimes we need to apply Pythagoras' theorem *twice.*

Example 17 **Self Tutor**

A room has floor dimensions 5 m by 4 m. The height of the room is 3 m. Find the distance from a corner point on the floor to the opposite corner point on the ceiling.

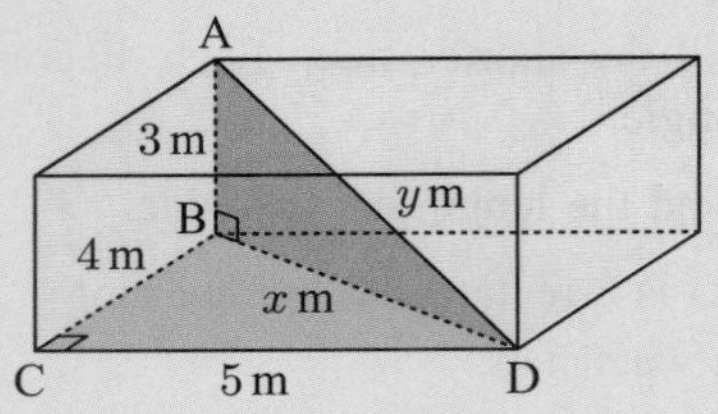

We join [BD] and [AD].
Let BD $= x$ m and AD $= y$ m.

In $\triangle$BCD, $x^2 = 4^2 + 5^2$ {Pythagoras}
In $\triangle$ABD, $y^2 = x^2 + 3^2$ {Pythagoras}

$\therefore \; y^2 = (4^2 + 5^2) + 3^2$
$\therefore \; y^2 = 16 + 25 + 9$
$\therefore \; y^2 = 50$
$\therefore \; y = \sqrt{50}$ {as $y > 0$}

$\therefore$ the required distance is $\sqrt{50} \approx 7.07$ m.

EXERCISE 10F

1 A cylindrical barrel is 100 cm high, and has a base diameter of 75 cm. Find the length of the longest iron rod that can fit inside the barrel.

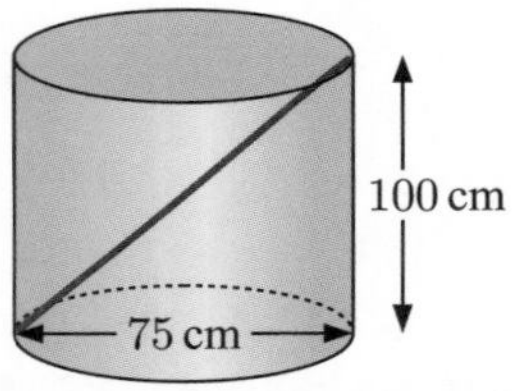

2 A cone has a slant height of 9 cm, and a base radius of 5 cm. Find the height of the cone.

3 A cube has sides of length 1 cm.
Find the length of a diagonal of the cube.

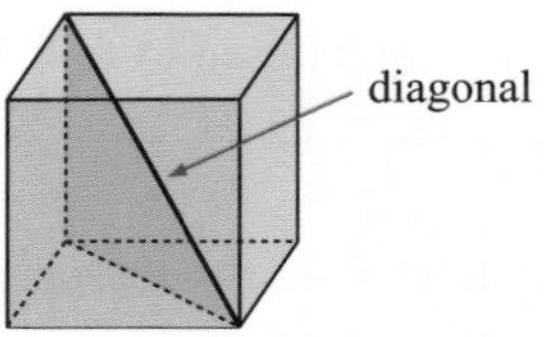

4 A room has floor dimensions 4 m by 3 m. The height of the room is 3 m. Find the distance from a corner point on the floor to the opposite corner point of the ceiling.

5 A rectangular box has internal dimensions 5 cm by 3 cm by 1 cm. Find the length of the longest matchstick that can be placed within the box.

6 ABCDE is a square-based pyramid. The apex of the pyramid E is directly above M, the point of intersection of [AC] and [BD]. All edges of the pyramid are 10 cm long. Find the height of the pyramid, to the nearest mm.

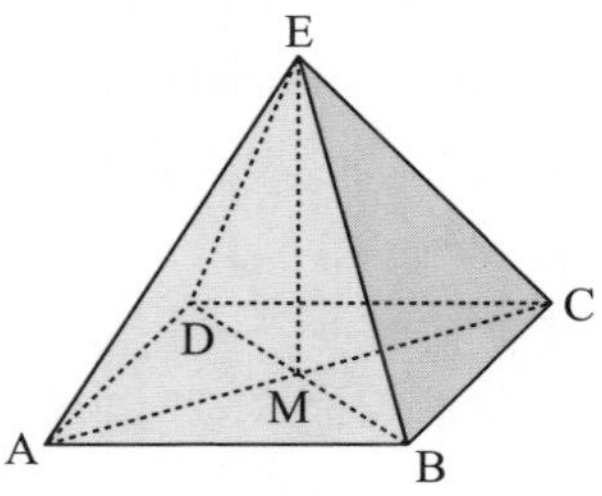

G CUBE ROOTS

We have seen previously that $2 \times 2 \times 2$ can be written as 2^3, which we read as '2 cubed'.
We know that $2^3 = 8$.

The **cube root** of a number a is the number which, when cubed, gives a.

We say that the *cube root* of 8 is 2, and write $\sqrt[3]{8} = 2$.

Finding the cube root of a number is the opposite of cubing the number.

To find the cube root of 27, we need to find the number which, when multiplied by itself twice, gives 27.

Since $3 \times 3 \times 3 = 27$, the number is 3. So, $\sqrt[3]{27} = 3$.

We notice that $(-3) \times (-3) \times (-3) = -27$,

so $\sqrt[3]{-27} = -3$.

$\sqrt[3]{\ }$ is called the **cube root sign**. It reads "the cube root of".

So, we can find the cube root of both positive and negative numbers.

Finding the cube roots of cubes such as 1, 8, 27, 64, and 125 is easy, but for other cube roots we use a calculator. Click on the icon for instructions.

Just as $\sqrt{\dfrac{a}{b}} = \dfrac{\sqrt{a}}{\sqrt{b}}$, $\sqrt[3]{\dfrac{a}{b}} = \dfrac{\sqrt[3]{a}}{\sqrt[3]{b}}$

Example 18 Self Tutor

Evaluate, giving a reason:

a $\sqrt[3]{216}$ **b** $\sqrt[3]{-64}$

a Since $6 \times 6 \times 6 = 216$,
$\sqrt[3]{216} = 6$

b Since $(-4) \times (-4) \times (-4) = -64$,
$\sqrt[3]{-64} = -4$

Example 19 Self Tutor

Use a calculator to find, rounded to 3 decimal places:

a $\sqrt[3]{21}$ **b** $\sqrt[3]{-85}$

Casio fx-CG20

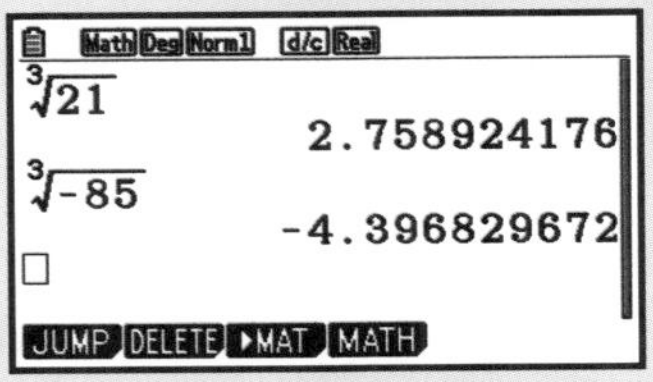

TI-84 Plus

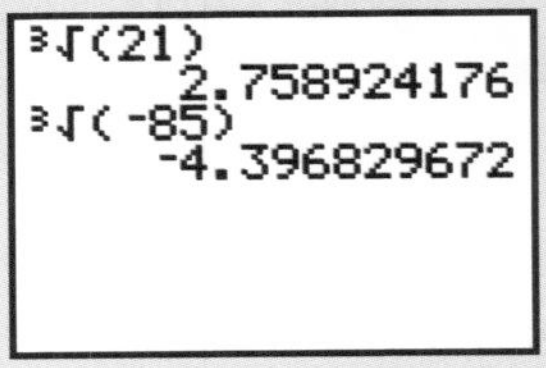

TI-*n*spire

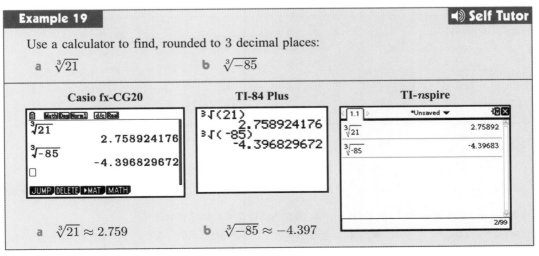

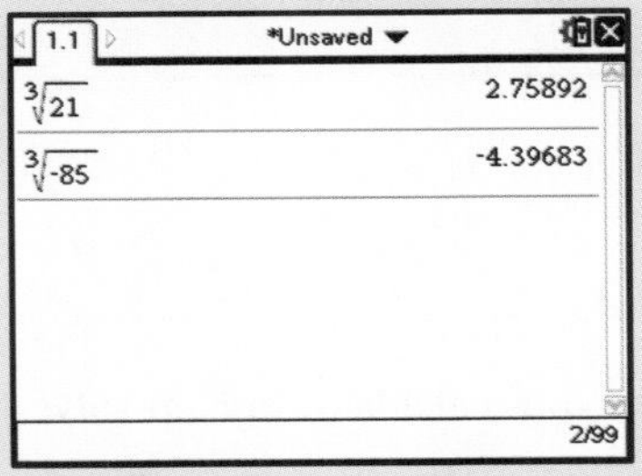

a $\sqrt[3]{21} \approx 2.759$ **b** $\sqrt[3]{-85} \approx -4.397$

EXERCISE 10G

1 Evaluate:

a $\sqrt[3]{1}$ **b** $\sqrt[3]{-1}$ **c** $\sqrt[3]{-27}$ **d** $\sqrt[3]{8}$ **e** $\sqrt[3]{-8}$

f $\sqrt[3]{64}$ **g** $\sqrt[3]{125}$ **h** $\sqrt[3]{-216}$ **i** $\sqrt[3]{-1000}$ **j** $\sqrt[3]{343}$

2 Use your calculator to find, rounded to 2 decimal places:

a $\sqrt[3]{4}$ **b** $\sqrt[3]{-15}$ **c** $\sqrt[3]{100}$ **d** $\sqrt[3]{450}$ **e** $\sqrt[3]{-3000}$

Example 20 **Self Tutor**

Evaluate: **a** $\sqrt[3]{\frac{1}{64}}$ **b** $\sqrt[3]{3\frac{3}{8}}$

a $\sqrt[3]{\frac{1}{64}}$

$= \frac{\sqrt[3]{1}}{\sqrt[3]{64}}$

$= \frac{1}{4}$

b $\sqrt[3]{3\frac{3}{8}}$

$= \sqrt[3]{\frac{27}{8}}$

$= \frac{\sqrt[3]{27}}{\sqrt[3]{8}}$

$= \frac{3}{2}$

3 Evaluate:

a $\sqrt[3]{\frac{1}{125}}$ **b** $\sqrt[3]{\frac{-8}{27}}$ **c** $\sqrt[3]{\frac{343}{64}}$ **d** $\sqrt[3]{-1\frac{91}{125}}$

Example 21 **Self Tutor**

Solve for x:

a $x^3 = 512$ **b** $x^3 + 1 = 0$ **c** $x^3 = 45$

a $x^3 = 512$

$\therefore\ x = \sqrt[3]{512}$

$\therefore\ x = 8$

$\{\text{as } 8^3 = 512\}$

b $x^3 + 1 = 0$

$\therefore\ x^3 = -1$

$\therefore\ x = \sqrt[3]{-1}$

$\therefore\ x = -1$

$\{\text{as } (-1)^3 = -1\}$

c $x^3 = 45$

$\therefore\ x = \sqrt[3]{45}$

$\therefore\ x \approx 3.56$

{using a calculator}

4 Solve for x:

a $x^3 = 64$ **b** $x^3 - 27 = 0$ **c** $x^3 + 216 = 0$ **d** $x^3 = 0$

e $x^3 = -125$ **f** $x^3 + 8 = 0$ **g** $x^3 - 1 = 0$ **h** $x^3 = -1\,000\,000$

5 Use your calculator to help solve for x, rounded to 2 decimal places:

a $x^3 = 60$ **b** $x^3 = 200$ **c** $x^3 + 36 = 0$ **d** $x^3 - 800 = 0$

REVIEW SET 10A

1 Solve for x:

a $x^2 = 81$ **b** $x^2 + 5 = 30$ **c** $3x^2 = -12$

2 Simplify:

a $\left(\sqrt{7}\right)^2$ **b** $\sqrt{3} \times \sqrt{5}$ **c** $\dfrac{\sqrt{6}}{\sqrt{2}}$

d $\sqrt{\dfrac{9}{64}}$ **e** $\sqrt[3]{-216}$ **f** $\sqrt[3]{\dfrac{27}{125}}$

3 Find x, in simplest radical form:

a

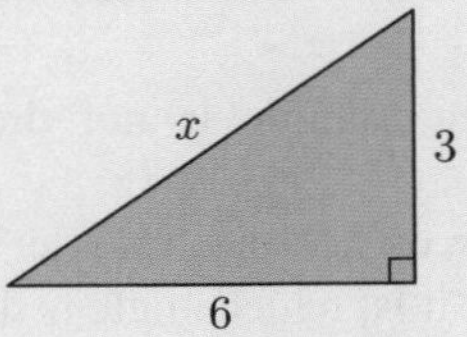

b

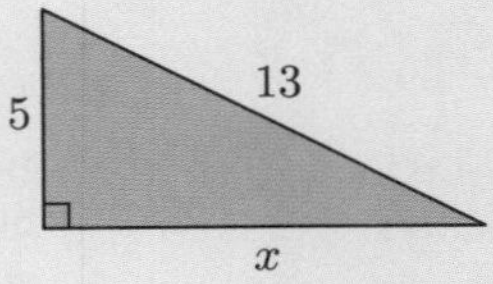

c

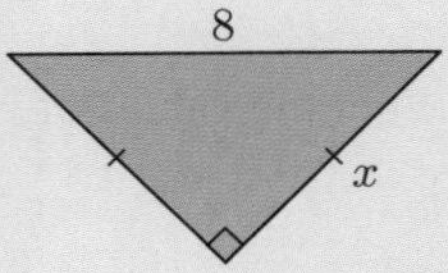

4 A rectangle has sides of length 6 cm and 7 cm. Find the length of the diagonal, to the nearest mm.

5 The given triangles are not drawn to scale. Is either of the triangles right angled? Explain your answers.

a

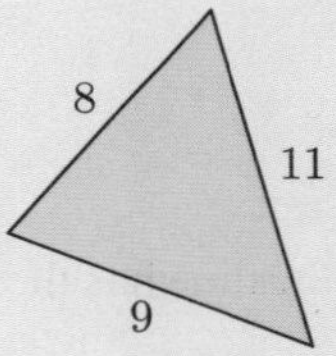

b

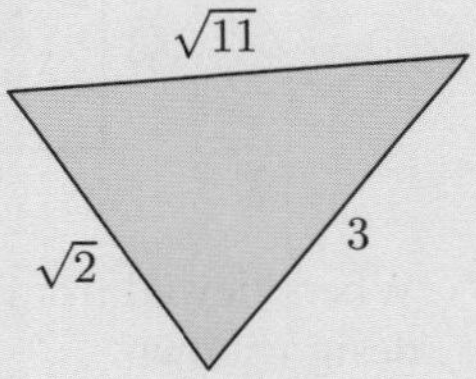

6 Find the unknown lengths:

a

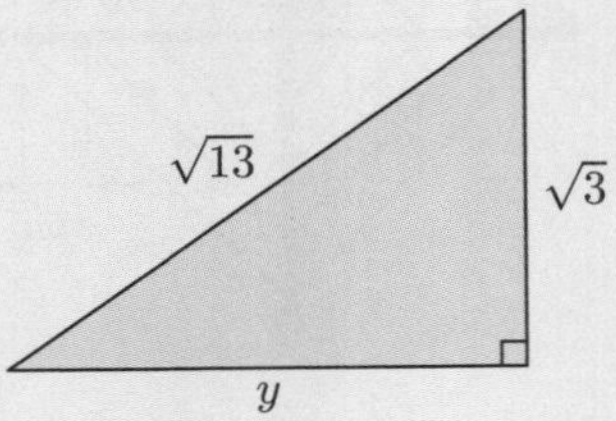

b

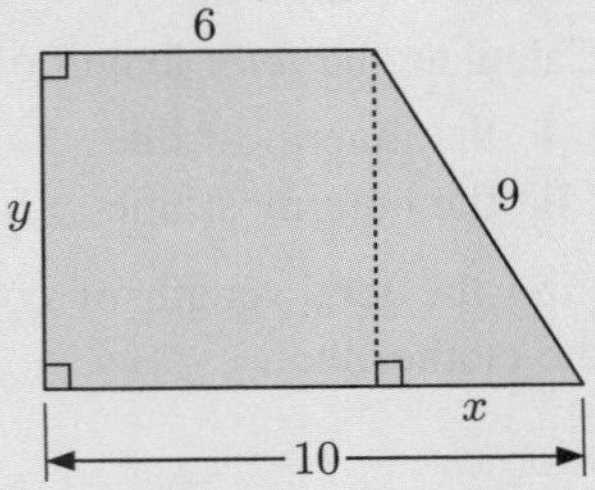

7 An 8 m long ladder leans against a vertical wall, with its feet 2.5 m away from the wall. Find how far up the wall the ladder reaches, to the nearest cm.

8 Two brothers leave their house at the same time. Alex runs due east at a constant speed of 10 km per hour, and Boris walks due south at a constant speed of 4 km per hour.

a How far has each brother travelled after 30 minutes?

b Find the distance between the two brothers after 30 minutes.

9 A 15 cm nail just fits inside a cylindrical can which is 12 cm tall. Find the base radius of the cylinder.

10 Use your calculator to find, rounded to 3 decimal places:

a $\sqrt[3]{7}$ **b** $\sqrt[3]{-200}$ **c** $\sqrt[3]{800}$

REVIEW SET 10B

1 Simplify:

a $\left(3\sqrt{7}\right)^2$ **b** $\sqrt{\dfrac{1}{16}}$ **c** $\dfrac{\sqrt{8}\times\sqrt{3}}{\sqrt{6}}$ **d** $\sqrt[3]{-\dfrac{343}{1000}}$

2 Solve for x:

a $6x^2 = -30$ **b** $2x^2 + 2x^2 = 48$ **c** $x^2 + (2x)^2 = 65$

3 Write in simplest radical form:

a $\sqrt{125}$ **b** $\sqrt{98}$

4 A rectangle measures 4 m by 5 m. Find the length of its diagonals, to 1 decimal place.

5 Find the values of x and y:

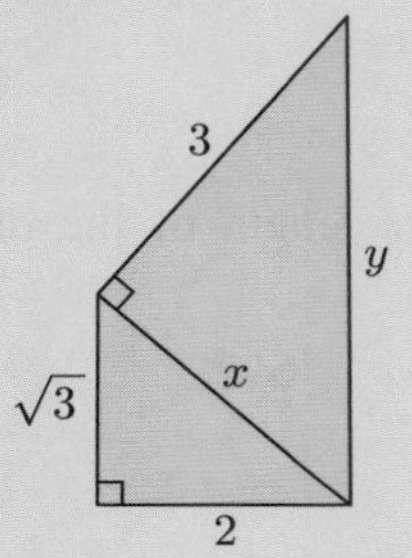

6 The following triangle is not drawn to scale.
State whether or not the triangle is right angled, and if it is, which angle is the right angle.

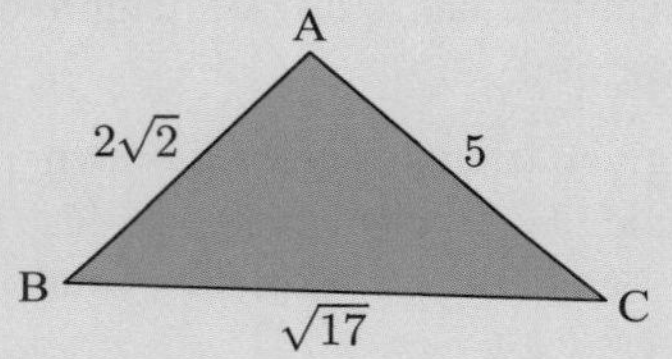

7 When viewed from above, a clothesline has the design shown.
Each of the arms is 1.6 m long.

a Find the value of x.

b Calculate the *total* length of:

i the innermost line

ii the outermost line.

c Find the total length of cord needed for the clothesline.

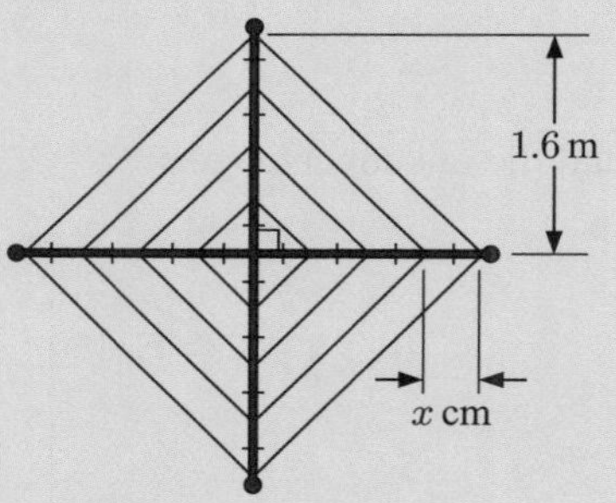

8 Solve for x:

a $x^3 = -125$ **b** $x^3 = 729$ **c** $x^3 + 7 = 34$

9 Marty is constructing a cage for his sister's pet mouse. The cage is to have the dimensions shown, and the shaded surface will be a window.

a Find the value of x.

b Find, to 1 decimal place, the value of y.

c Find the area of the window.

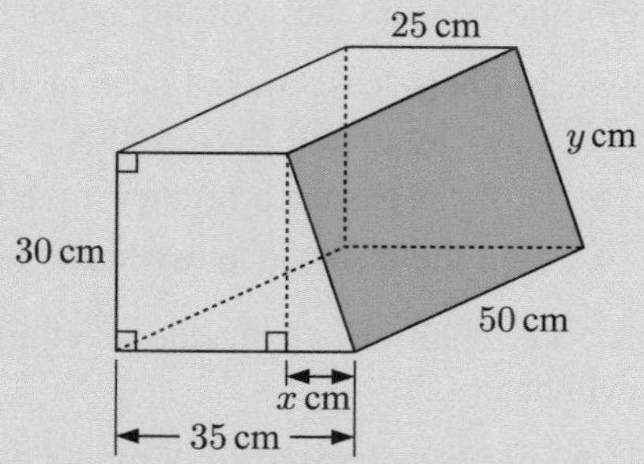

10 What is the longest knitting needle that will fit in a 10 cm by 24 cm by 35 cm box?

Chapter 11

Length and area

Contents:

OPENING PROBLEM

A 5.0 m by 6.0 m apartment consists of 6 rooms as shown.

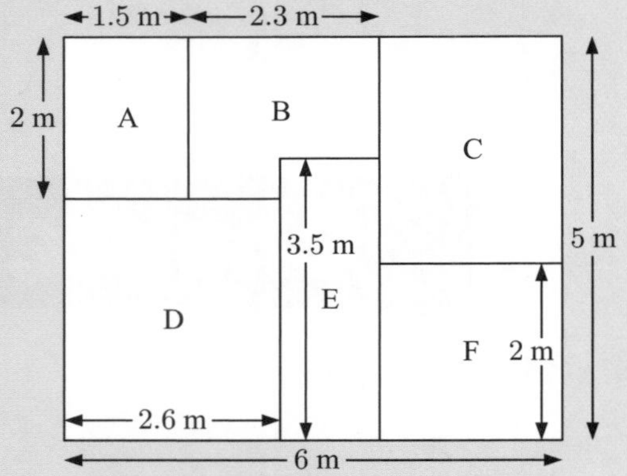

Things to think about:

a What is the total length of walls in the apartment?

b What is the floor area of room A?

c The dimensions of room C are not given. How can we find the area of room C?

d Room B is not a simple rectangle. How can we find the area of room B?

Many people such as builders, engineers, architects, landscapers, and surveyors rely on accurate measurements of **lengths** and **areas** to carry out their jobs.

A LENGTH

A **length** is a measure of the distance between two points.

The **metre** (m) is the base unit for length in the metric system.

When the metric system was being developed in 18th century France, the metre was defined as one ten-millionth of the distance from the North Pole to the equator through Paris.

Since 1983, the metre has been defined as the distance light travels in a vacuum in $\frac{1}{299\,792\,458}$ of a second.

From the metre, other units of length have been devised to handle smaller or larger distances. Millimetres (mm), centimetres (cm), and kilometres (km) are commonly used.

1 kilometre (km) = 1000 metres (m)
1 metre (m) = 100 centimetres (cm)
1 centimetre (cm) = 10 millimetres (mm)

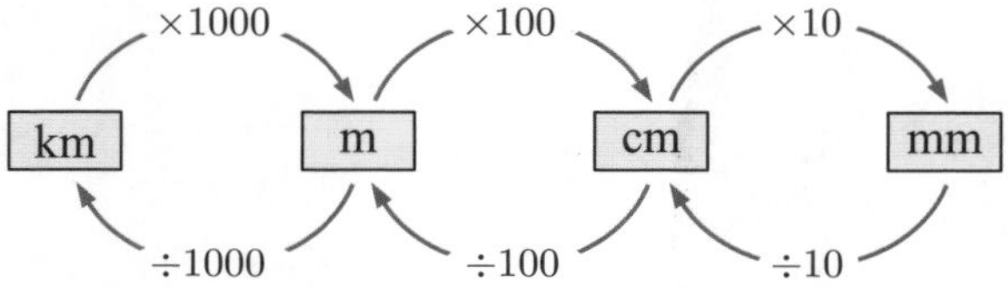

To convert from smaller units to larger units we **divide** by the conversion factor.

Example 1 — Self Tutor

Convert:

a 200 cm to m **b** 25 km to m

a 200 cm
$= 200 \div 100$ m
$= 2$ m

b 25 km
$= 25 \times 1000$ m
$= 25\,000$ m

To convert from larger units to smaller units we **multiply** by the conversion factor.

EXERCISE 11A

1 Estimate the following lengths in the units given, then check your estimates by measuring:

- **a** the length of your pen (mm)
- **b** the width of your exercise book (mm)
- **c** the height of your desk (cm)
- **d** the length of the whiteboard (m)
- **e** the height of your teacher (m)
- **f** the length of your classroom (m)
- **g** the width of the school soccer field (m)

2 Convert:

- **a** 70 mm to cm
- **b** 12 km to m
- **c** 120 cm to m
- **d** 3.2 m to mm
- **e** 1250 m to km
- **f** 350 cm to km

3 A submarine dived to a depth of 635 600 cm. Write this depth in:

- **a** metres
- **b** kilometres.

4 Find the sum of:

- **a** 7 m + 35 cm + 21 mm in centimetres
- **b** 4.3 km + 520 m + 860 cm in metres.

5 The world records for the triple jump are:

Mens	Jonathan Edwards (GBR)	18.29 m
Womens	Inessa Kravets (UKR)	15.50 m

- **a** Write each of the records in cm.
- **b** How much further, in cm, did Jonathan Edwards jump than Inessa Kravets?

6 How many 12 mm thick biscuits can be cut from a 54 cm roll of biscuit dough?

7 A snail and a caterpillar are 2.7 m apart. The snail moves 33 mm towards the caterpillar, and the caterpillar moves 19.2 cm towards the snail. Find the new distance between them, in centimetres.

8 An office building has 12 floors above ground level. There are 18 steps between each floor, and each step is 17.8 cm high. How many metres does a worker climb if he walks up to the top floor?

B PERIMETER

The **perimeter** of a closed figure is the total length around its **boundary**.

PERIMETER FORMULAE

The following are perimeter formulae for commonly occurring shapes:

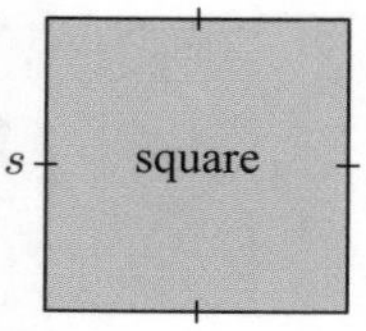

$P = 4s$

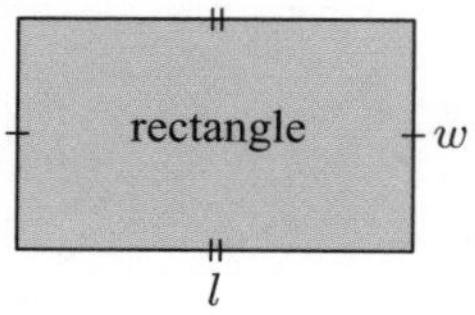

$P = 2(l + w)$

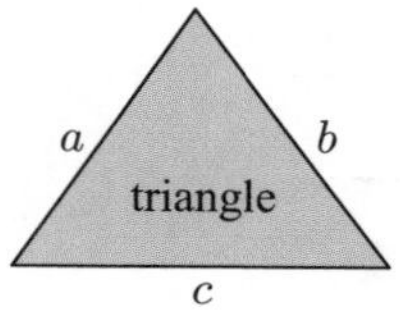

$P = a + b + c$

Example 2 Self Tutor

Find the perimeter of the following figures:

a

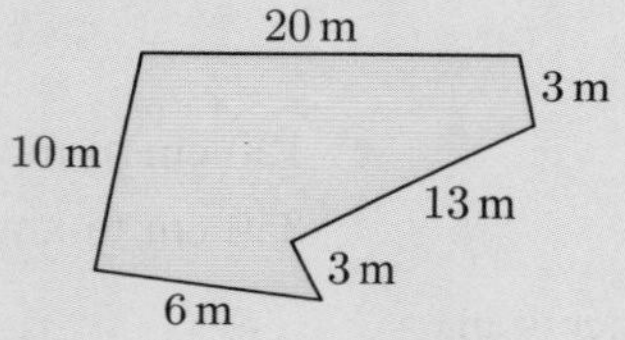

b

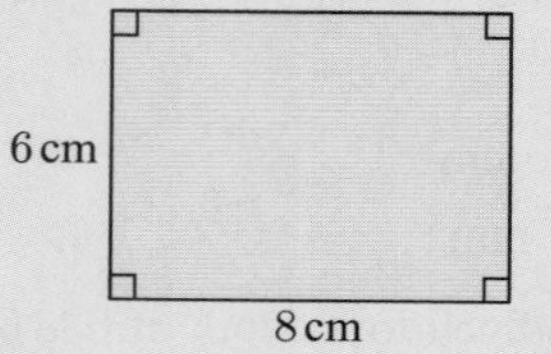

a Perimeter
$= (10 + 20 + 3 + 13 + 3 + 6)$ m
$= 55$ m

b Perimeter
$= 2(8 + 6)$ cm
$= 2 \times 14$ cm
$= 28$ cm

EXERCISE 11B

1 Find the perimeter of each figure:

a

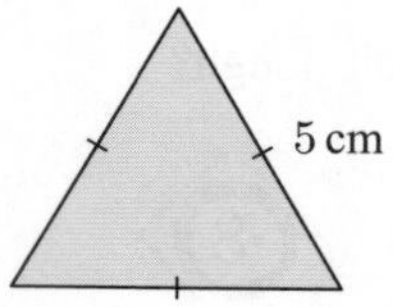

b

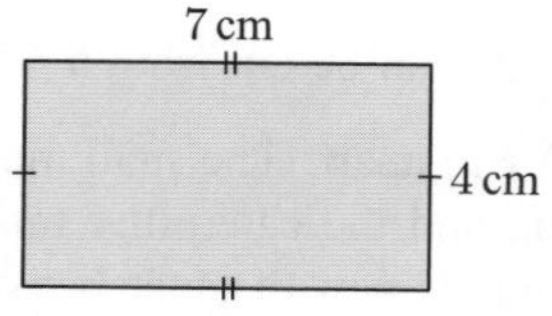

c

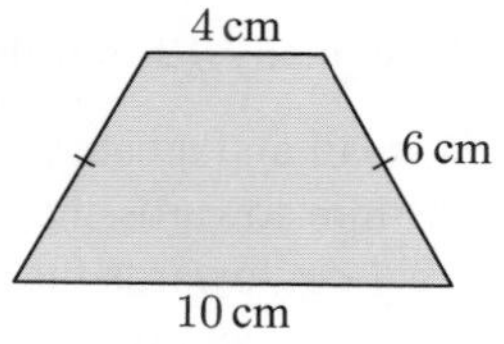

d

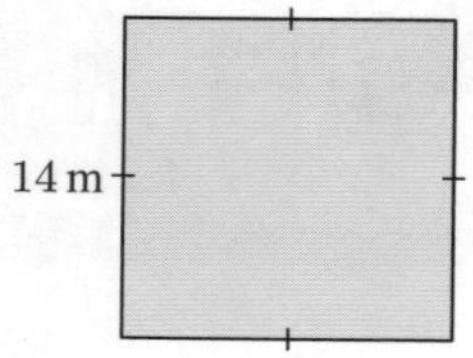

e

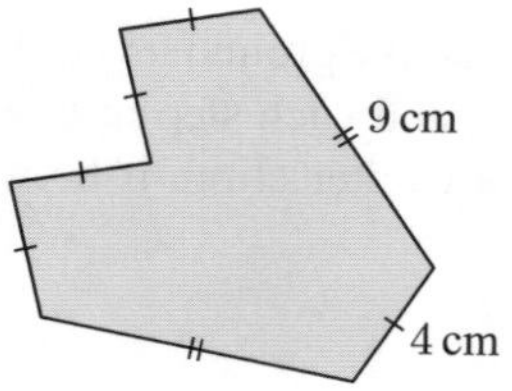

2 A farmer fences a 400 m by 350 m field with a 4-strand wire fence. Find:

- **a** the perimeter of the field
- **b** the total length of wire required
- **c** the total cost of wire required given that a single strand of wire costs 12.4 cents per metre.

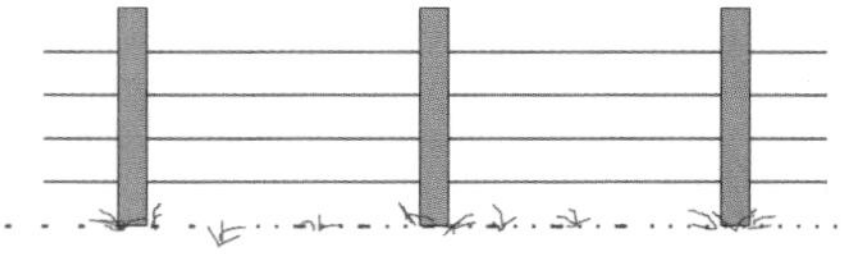

3

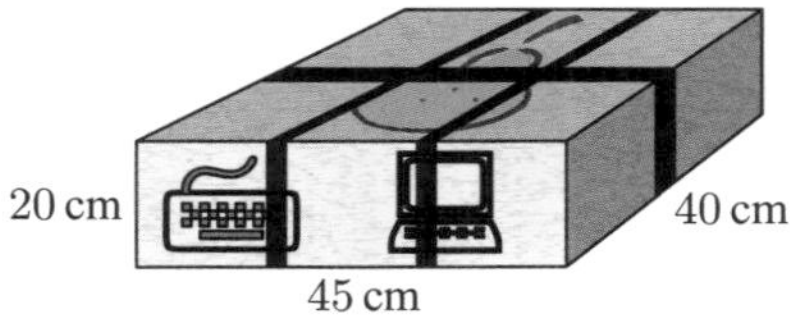

Boxes containing computers are fastened with three pieces of tape, as shown.
Each piece of tape is overlapped 5 cm at the join.
Calculate the total length of tape required for 20 boxes.

4 Find the perimeter of each figure:

a

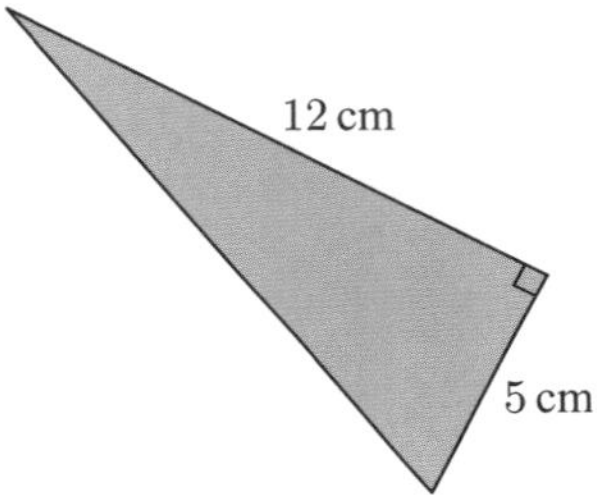

b

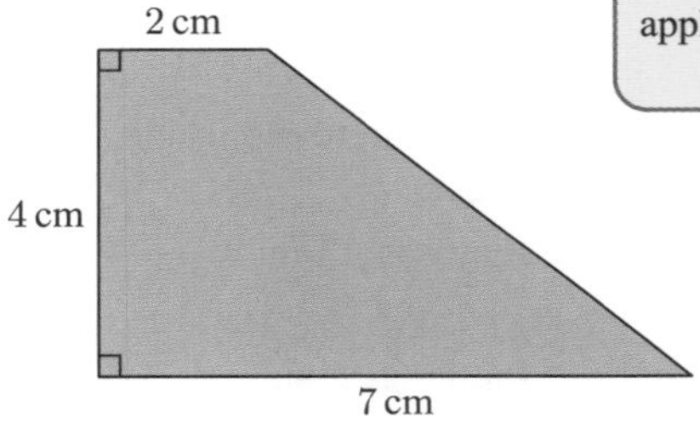

You will need to apply Pythagoras' theorem.

5 Kim decides to get fit by running laps of a nearby shopping complex. Its dimensions are shown in the diagram alongside.
How many laps does he have to complete to run 13 km in total?

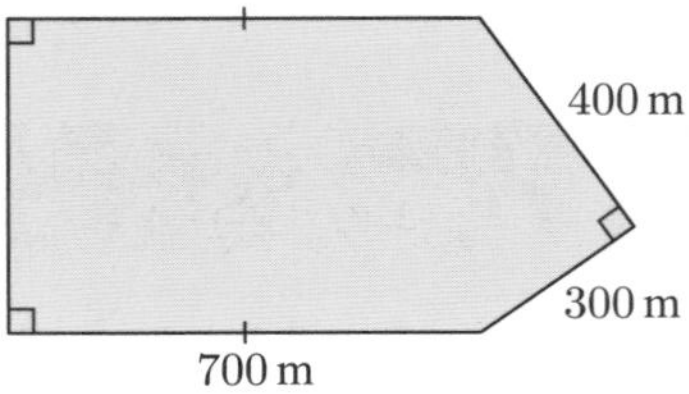

Example 3 **Self Tutor**

Find the perimeter P of each figure, giving your answer in simplest form:

a

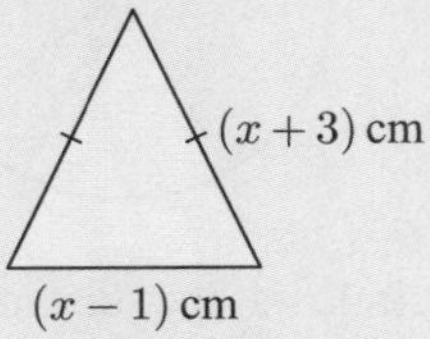

b

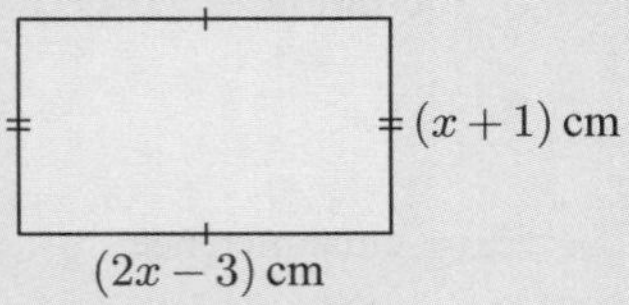

a
$P =$ two lots of $(x+3)$ cm $+$ one lot of $(x-1)$ cm
$P = 2(x+3)$ cm $+$ $(x-1)$ cm
$P = (2x+6+x-1)$ cm
$\therefore\ P = (3x+5)$ cm

b
$P =$ two lots of $(x+1)$ cm $+$ two lots of $(2x-3)$ cm
$P = 2(x+1)$ cm $+$ $2(2x-3)$ cm
$P = (2x+2+4x-6)$ cm
$\therefore\ P = (6x-4)$ cm

6 Find the perimeter P of each figure, giving your answer in simplest form.

a

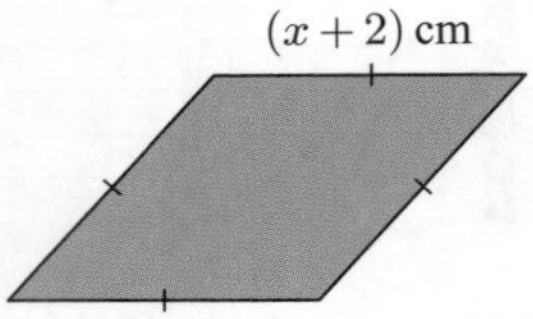

b

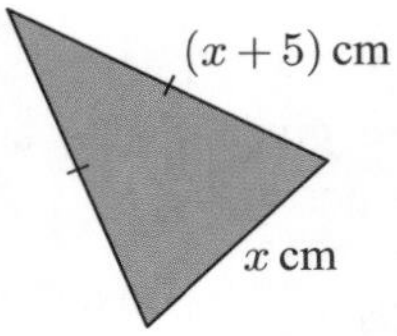

c

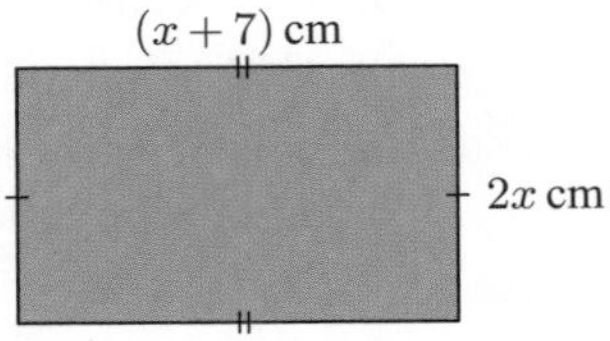

d

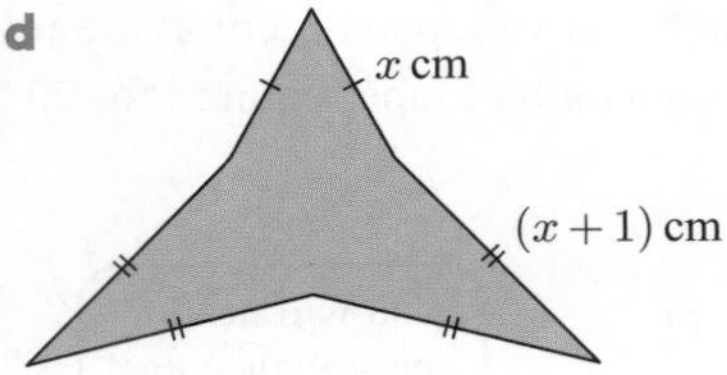

e

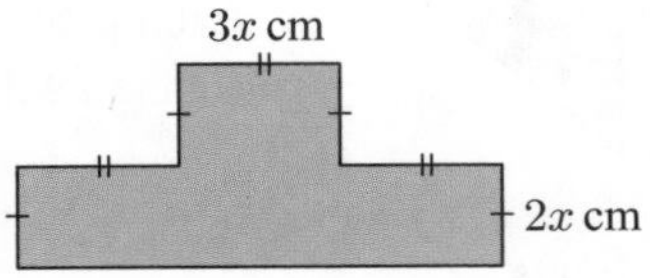

f

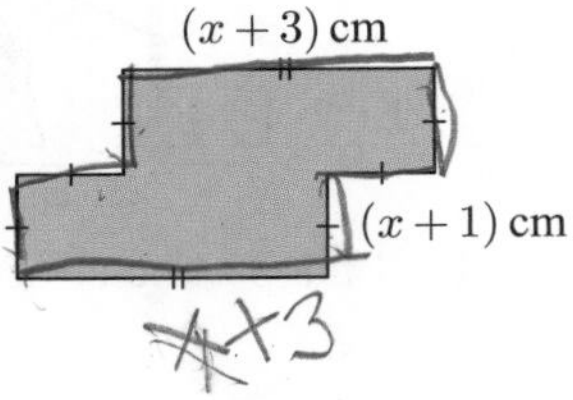

7 **a** Find the perimeter P of the figure alongside, giving your answer in simplest form.

b If the perimeter of the figure is 43 m:

i find x

ii find the length of the longest side.

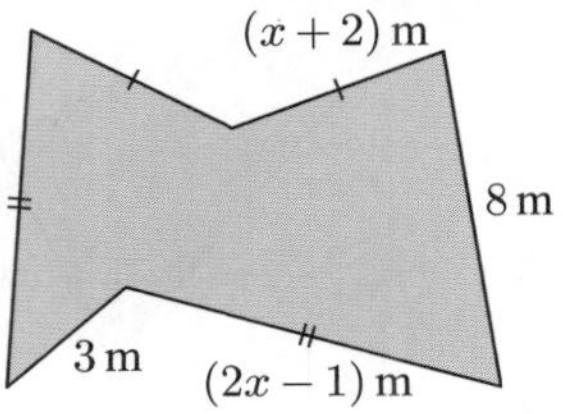

C CIRCUMFERENCE

So far we have found the perimeters of shapes with straight edges. We will now look at finding the perimeter of a **circle**.

A **circle** is a 2-dimensional shape. It is the set of all points which are a constant distance from a fixed point called the **centre** of the circle.

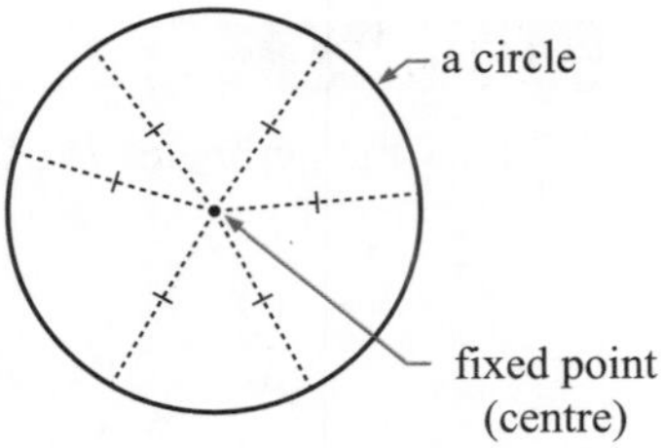

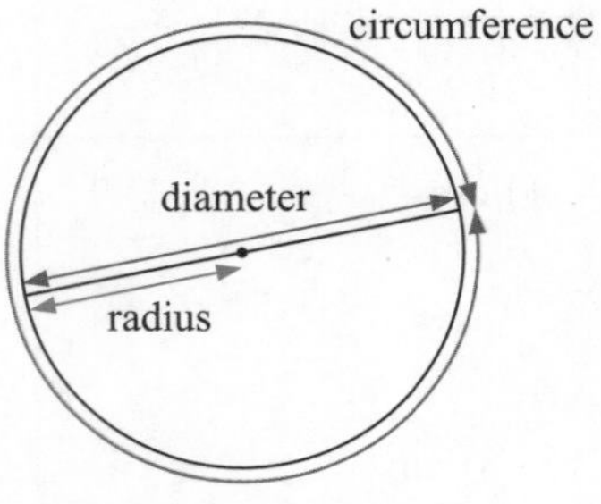

The **diameter** of a circle is the distance across the circle measured through its centre.

The **radius** of a circle is the distance between any point on the circle and the centre. The radius is half the length of the diameter.

The **circumference** of a circle is the perimeter or length around its boundary.

In the following **Investigation** we explore the relationship between the circumference and diameter of any circle.

INVESTIGATION 1 — CIRCUMFERENCE

You will need:

- a ruler
- a pencil
- some cylinders such as a soft drink can, a toilet roll, and a coin

DEMO

What to do:

1. Use a ruler to measure the diameter of one of your objects.
2. Mark a point on the circumference of your object, and then roll it along a flat surface for one complete revolution, as shown. The distance between the two marks is the circumference of your object.

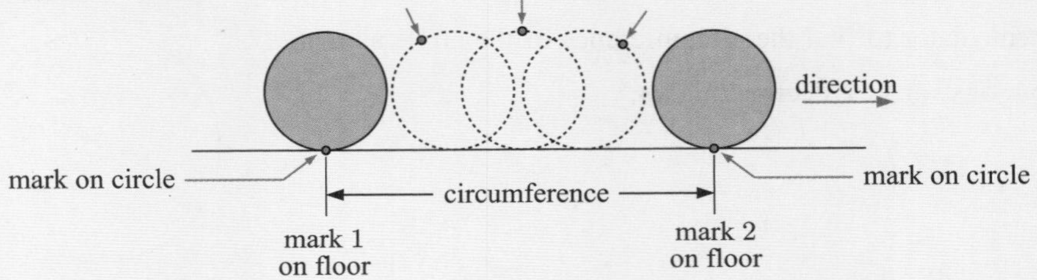

   It may be more accurate to roll the object 10 times, then divide the total distance by 10 to get the circumference.

3. Copy the table below, and complete it with measurements from your objects.

Circular object	*Circumference*	*Diameter*	$\frac{\textit{Circumference}}{\textit{Diameter}}$
⋮	⋮	⋮	⋮

4. Compare your results with those of other students. What do you notice?

Whenever the circumference of a circle is divided by its diameter, the answer is always the same. You should have found this in the **Investigation** above, allowing for slight inaccuracies in measurements.

The ratio $\frac{\text{circumference}}{\text{diameter}}$ is symbolised by the Greek letter π known as 'pi'.

For any circle, circumference $= \pi \times$ diameter

or $C = \pi \times d$.

The **circumference** of a circle $C = \pi d$ where d is the **diameter** of the circle
or $C = 2\pi r$ where r is the **radius** of the circle.

The value of π correct to 30 decimal places is
$\pi \approx 3.141\,592\,653\,589\,793\,238\,462\,643\,383\,279$.

In practice we use $\pi \approx 3.14$, which is rounded to 3 significant figures, or else use the appropriate keys on our calculator. When using a calculator, we round off the **final answer** only.

Example 4 — Self Tutor

Use $\pi \approx 3.14$ to find the circumference of a circle with:

a diameter 20 cm

b radius 3.6 cm

a $C = \pi d$
$\approx 3.14 \times 20$ cm
≈ 62.8 cm
The circumference is about 62.8 cm.

b $C = 2\pi r$
$\approx 2 \times 3.14 \times 3.6$ cm
≈ 22.6 cm
The circumference is about 22.6 cm.

Example 5 — Self Tutor

Use your calculator to find the circumference of the circle shown.

Round your answer to 2 decimal places.

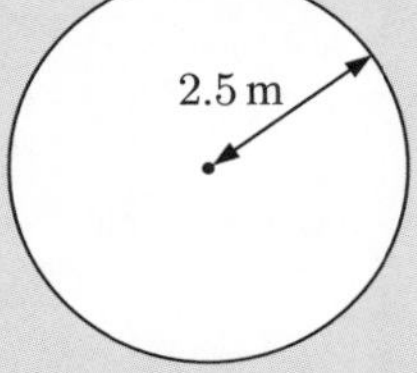

The radius of the circle is 2.5 metres.

$C = 2\pi r$
$= 2 \times \pi \times 2.5$ m
≈ 15.71 m

GRAPHICS CALCULATOR INSTRUCTIONS

Casio fx-CG20

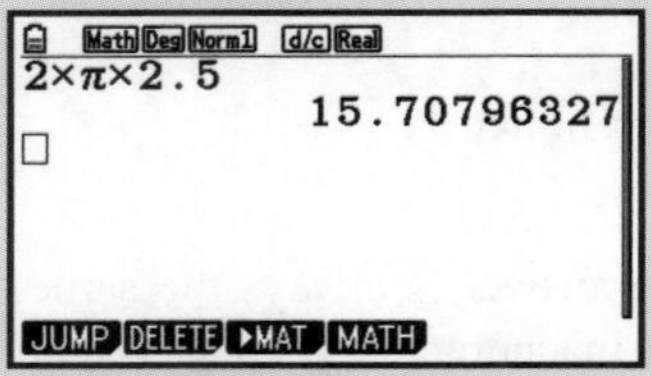

TI-84 Plus

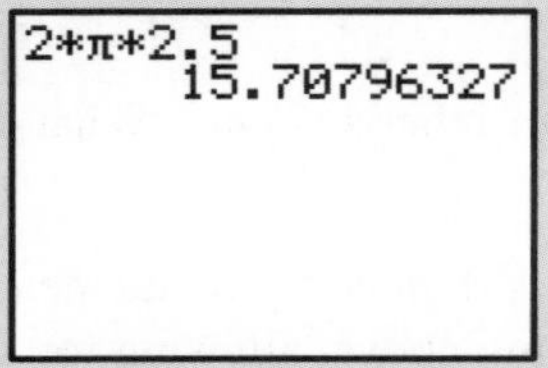

TI-*n*spire

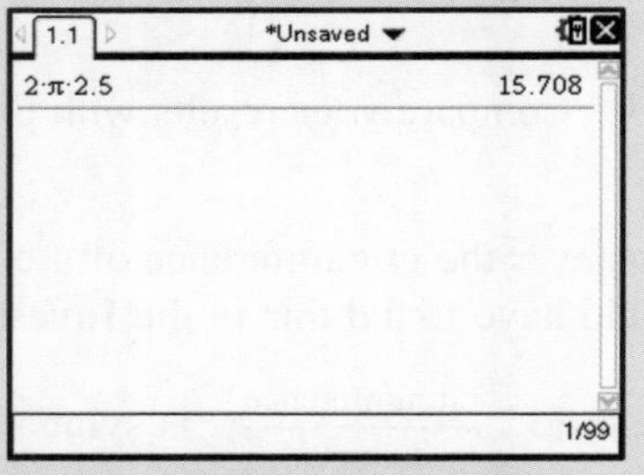

The circumference is approximately 15.71 m.

EXERCISE 11C

In this **Exercise**, round your answers to 3 significant figures unless stated otherwise.

1 Use $\pi \approx 3.14$ to find the circumference of:

a
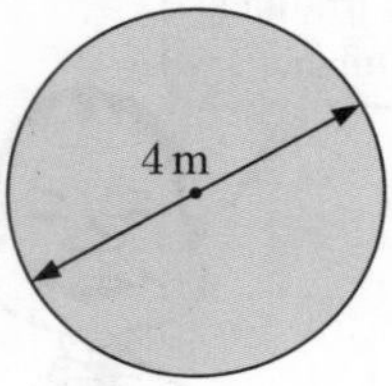

b
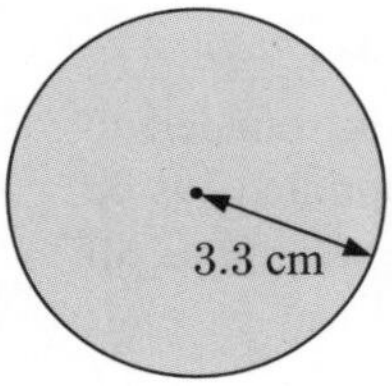

c
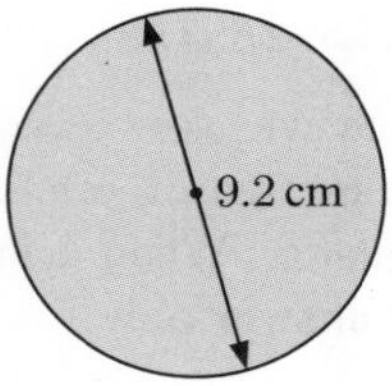

2 Using your calculator, find the circumference of a circle with:

a radius 9 m **b** diameter 16 cm **c** radius 6.8 km

3 Find the circumference of a cylindrical deodorant can with base diameter 4 cm.

4 A circular pond has radius 1.5 m. Find the perimeter of the pond.

5 Natalie is sewing a fringe on a circular rug with the dimensions shown.
How many metres of fringing will Natalie need?

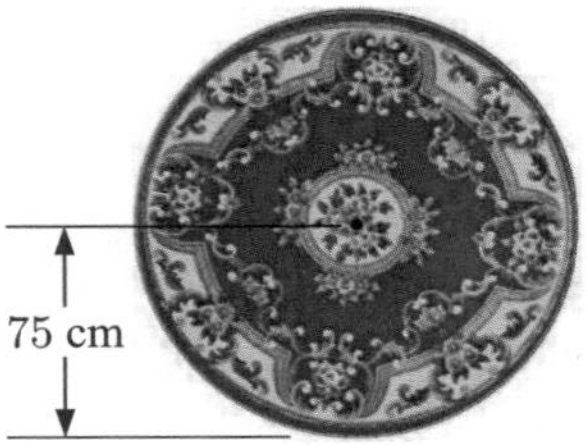

6 The minute hand of a clock is 6 cm long. How far does the tip travel between noon and 1:30 pm?

7 A car tyre has a diameter of 70 cm.

a Find the circumference of the tyre.

b How many kilometres would be travelled if the tyre rotates 20 000 times?

c How many times will the tyre rotate if the car travels 45 km?

8 A circle has the same perimeter as a square with side length 8 cm. What is the circle's radius?

9 Which is the shorter path from A to B: around the 2 smaller semi-circles or around the large semi-circle?

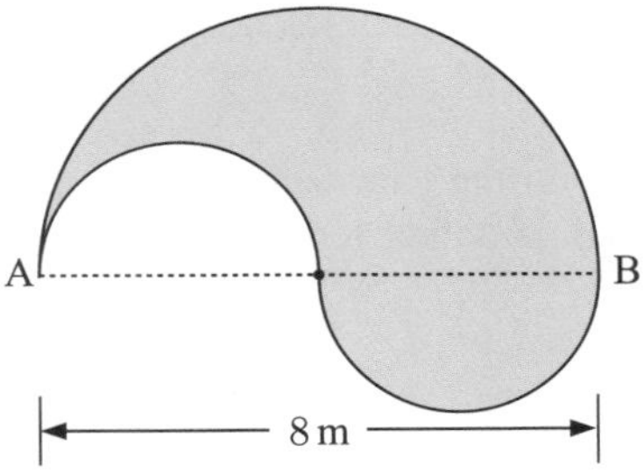

10

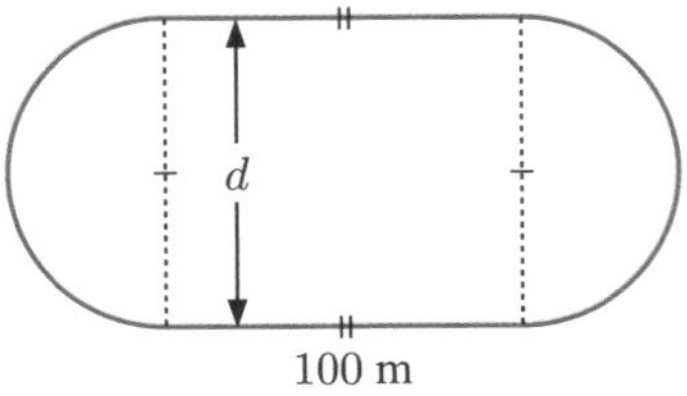

An athletics track has two 'straights' measuring 100 m, and two identical semi-circular sections of 100 m each. What is the distance d between the two straight sections of track?

ACTIVITY — TRUNDLE WHEEL

A trundle wheel is an instrument used for measuring distances. It consists of a wheel on a handle, and a device which counts the number of revolutions of the wheel.

What to do:

1 Obtain a trundle wheel with circumference 1 metre.
The wheel has circumference $C = 2\pi r = 100$ cm.

2 Solve $2\pi r = 100$ cm to find the radius of the wheel.
Check your answer using a ruler or tape measure.

3 Use your trundle wheel to make measurements around your school, such as the distance around the oval, the length of a school building, the length of a tennis court, the perimeter of a tennis court, or the length of the fence around the school.

4 What would the error in the measurement of a kilometre be, if your trundle wheel had a radius which was too small by:

a 1 cm **b** 1 mm **c** 0.1 mm?

INVESTIGATION 2 LENGTHS OF CURVES

Finding the length of a curve accurately can be quite difficult. However, the length of a curve can be *estimated* by placing pins along the curve and using them to guide a piece of string. The length of string required can then be measured with your ruler.

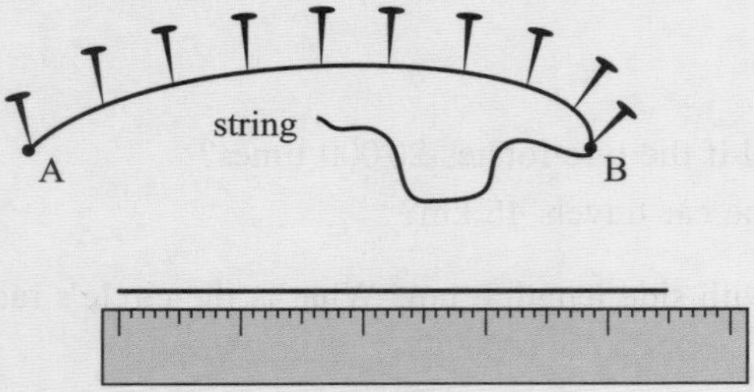

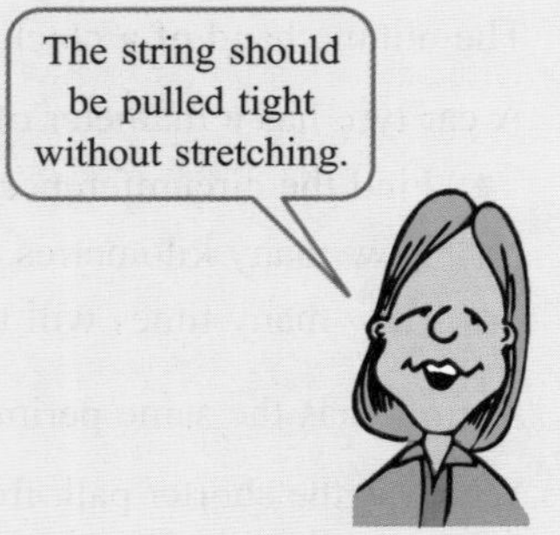

The string should be pulled tight without stretching.

What to do:

1 Click on the icon and print the two curves. Use the method described above to estimate their lengths, placing the pins in the positions shown.

PRINTABLE WORKSHEET

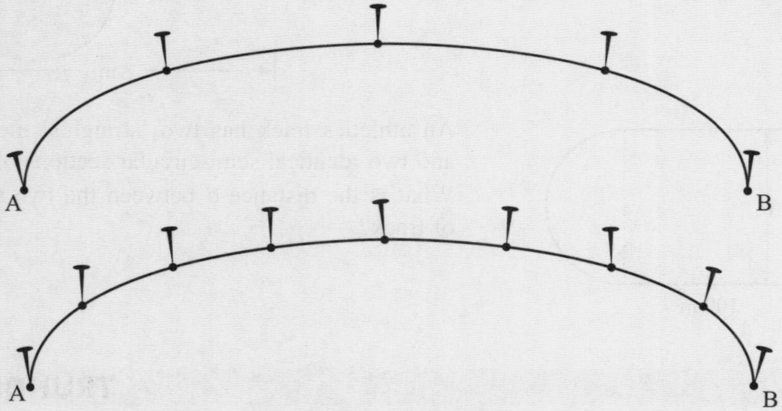

2 Write up your findings by considering the following questions:

a Which estimate do you think is more accurate?

b Do the pins have to be equally spaced?

c Where is it most important to have the pins?

d How could you improve your estimate of the length of this curve?

3 Draw a curved figure of your own choosing. Use the method above to obtain a good estimate of its length.

D AREA

An **area** is the amount of *surface* inside a 2-dimensional shape.

We can measure area using **square millimetres** (mm^2), **square centimetres** (cm^2), **square metres** (m^2), **hectares** (ha), or **square kilometres** (km^2).

1 square millimetre is the area enclosed by a square of side length 1 mm.
1 square centimetre is the area enclosed by a square of side length 1 cm.
1 square metre is the area enclosed by a square of side length 1 m.
1 hectare is the area enclosed by a square of side length 100 m.
1 square kilometre is the area enclosed by a square of side length 1 km.

CONVERTING AREA UNITS

The square alongside has area $1\ cm^2$.

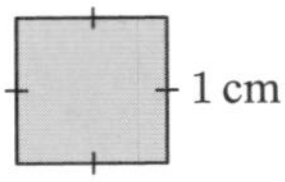

We can write $1\ cm^2 = 1\ cm \times 1\ cm$.

Since $1\ cm = 10\ mm$, we can also write
$1\ cm^2 = 10\ mm \times 10\ mm = 100\ mm^2$.

We can repeat this process to convert between other units of area:

$$1\ cm^2 = 10\ mm \times 10\ mm = 100\ mm^2$$
$$1\ m^2 = 100\ cm \times 100\ cm = 10\,000\ cm^2$$
$$1\ ha = 100\ m \times 100\ m = 10\,000\ m^2$$
$$1\ km^2 = 1000\ m \times 1000\ m = 1\,000\,000\ m^2 \text{ or } 100\ ha$$

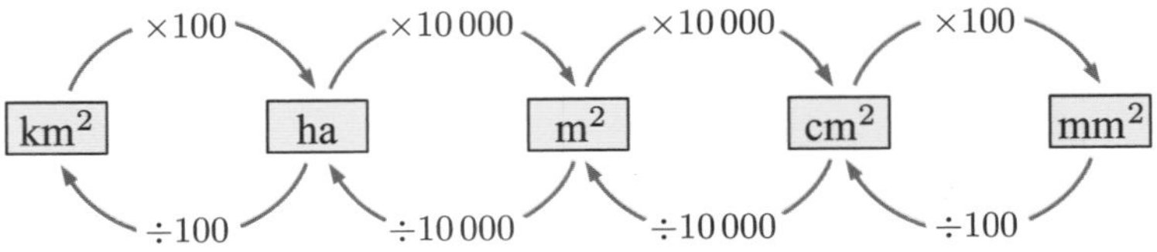

Example 6 — Self Tutor

Convert:

a $250\ mm^2$ to cm^2
b $8\ m^2$ to cm^2
c 3.5 ha to m^2

a $250\ mm^2$
$= 250 \div 100\ cm^2$
$= 2.5\ cm^2$

b $8\ m^2$
$= 8 \times 10\,000\ cm^2$
$= 80\,000\ cm^2$

c 3.5 ha
$= 3.5 \times 10\,000\ m^2$
$= 35\,000\ m^2$

EXERCISE 11D

1 A postage stamp is most likely to have an area of:

A 10 mm^2 **B** 10 cm^2 **C** 10 m^2 **D** 10 ha

2 The floor of an elevator is most likely to have an area of:

A 3 mm^2 **B** 3 cm^2 **C** 3 m^2 **D** 3 ha

3 A school playground is most likely to have an area of:

A 2 cm^2 **B** 2 m^2 **C** 2 ha **D** 2 km^2

4 State the units that you would most likely use to measure the area of:

a a DVD **b** a cricket ground **c** a 5 cent coin **d** Spain.

5 Convert:

a 2 m^2 to cm^2 **b** 36.5 ha to m^2 **c** 3280 mm^2 to cm^2
d 3 654 200 cm^2 to m^2 **e** 782 000 m^2 to ha **f** 8.8 cm^2 to mm^2
g 5 km^2 to ha **h** 3000 ha to km^2 **i** 50 km^2 to m^2

6 25 gym mats, each with an area of 24 000 cm^2, fit perfectly onto a classroom floor. Find the area of the room in: **a** cm^2 **b** m^2.

E AREA FORMULAE

In previous years we have seen the following area formulae:

RECTANGLES

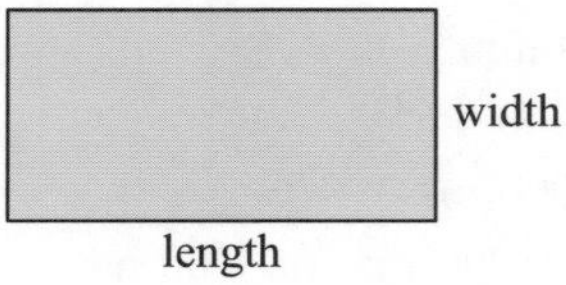

Area = length × width

TRIANGLES

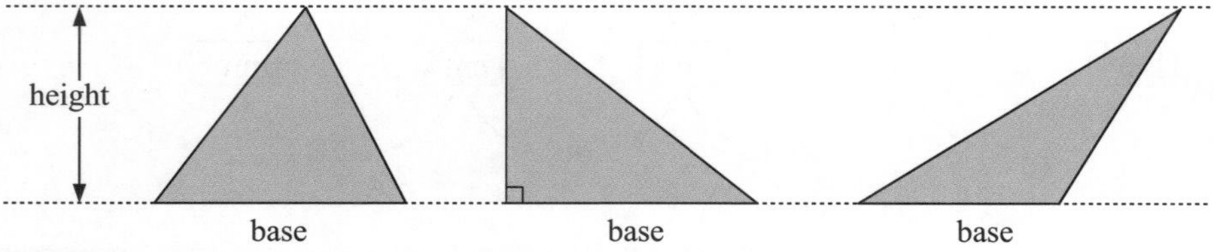

DEMO

$$\textbf{Area} = \frac{1}{2}(\textbf{base} \times \textbf{height})$$

PARALLELOGRAMS

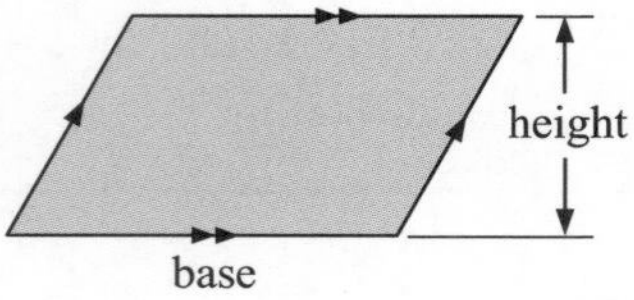

Area = base × height

DEMO

TRAPEZIA

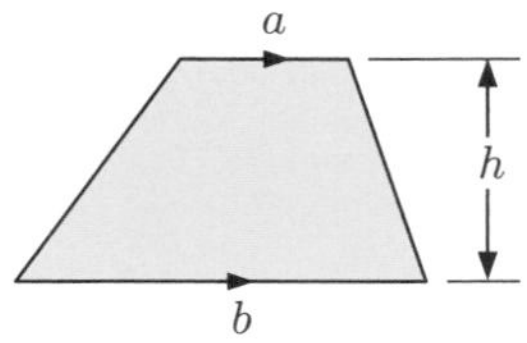

$$\text{Area} = \left[\begin{array}{c}\textbf{The average}\\ \textbf{length of the}\\ \textbf{parallel sides}\end{array}\right] \times \left[\begin{array}{c}\textbf{the distance}\\ \textbf{between the}\\ \textbf{parallel sides}\end{array}\right]$$

$$= \left(\frac{a+b}{2}\right) \times h$$

DEMO

Example 7 — Self Tutor

Find the area of:

a

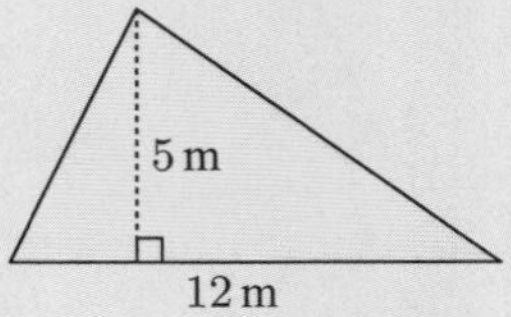

b

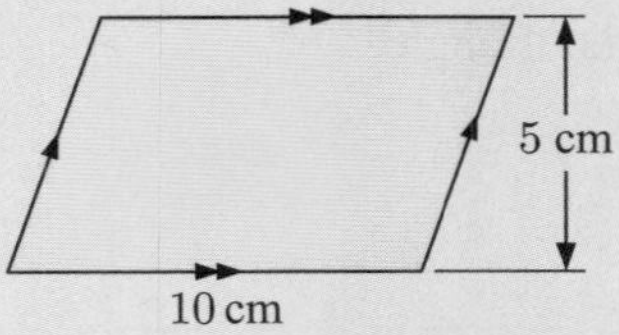

c

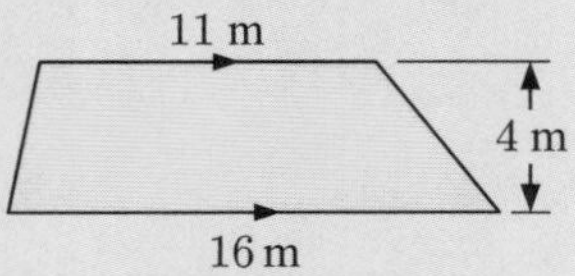

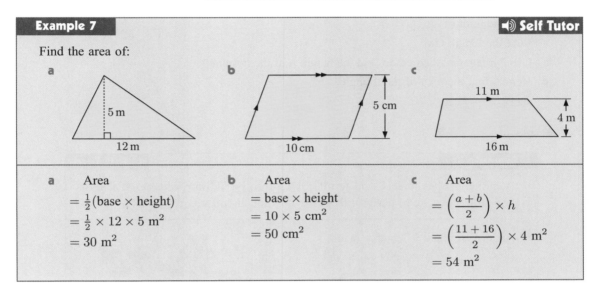

a Area
$= \frac{1}{2}(\text{base} \times \text{height})$
$= \frac{1}{2} \times 12 \times 5 \text{ m}^2$
$= 30 \text{ m}^2$

b Area
$= \text{base} \times \text{height}$
$= 10 \times 5 \text{ cm}^2$
$= 50 \text{ cm}^2$

c Area
$= \left(\frac{a+b}{2}\right) \times h$
$= \left(\frac{11+16}{2}\right) \times 4 \text{ m}^2$
$= 54 \text{ m}^2$

EXERCISE 11E

1 Find the area of the shaded region:

a

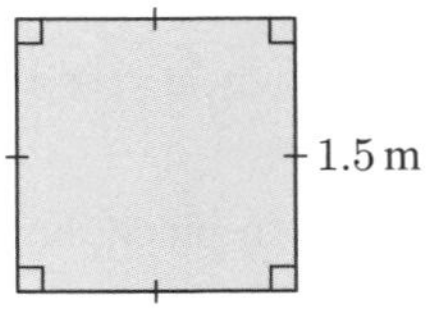

b

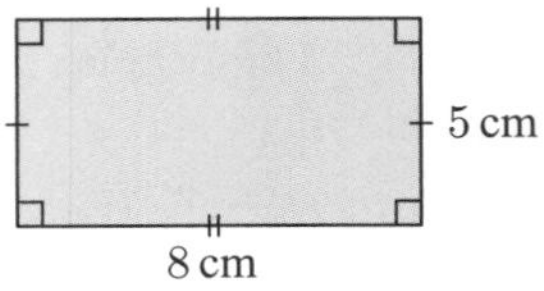

c

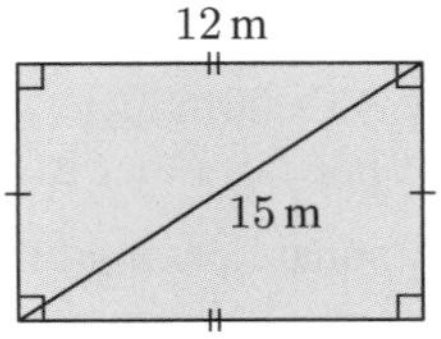

d

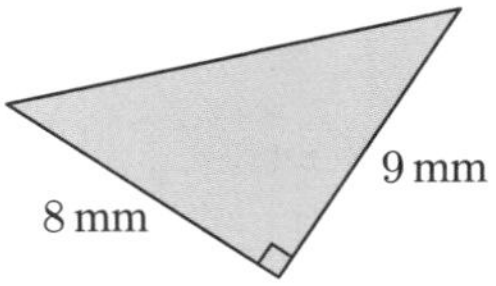

e

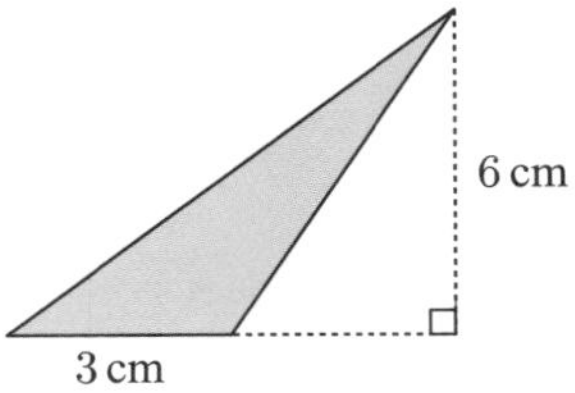

f

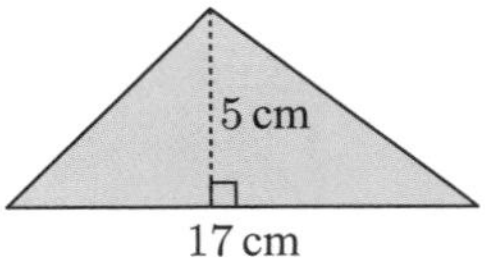

g

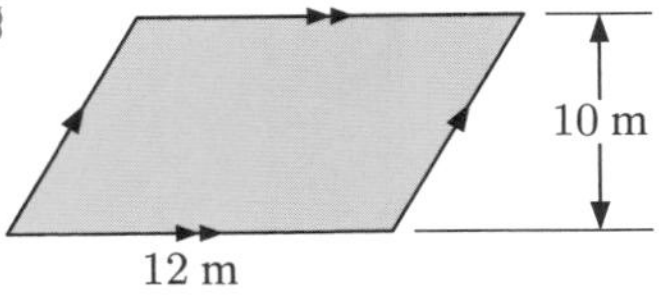

h

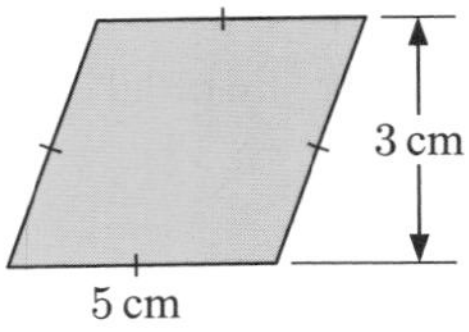

i

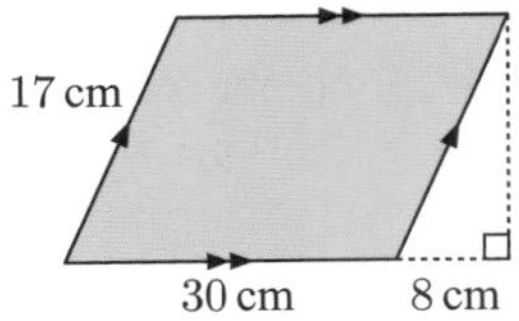

j

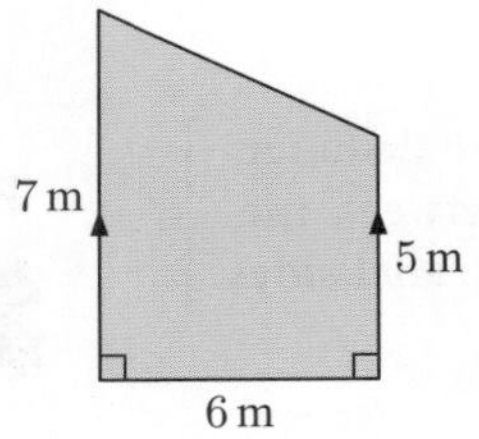

k

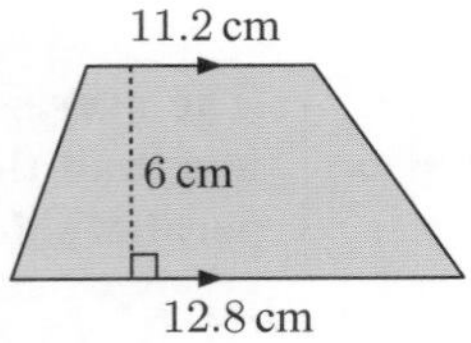

l

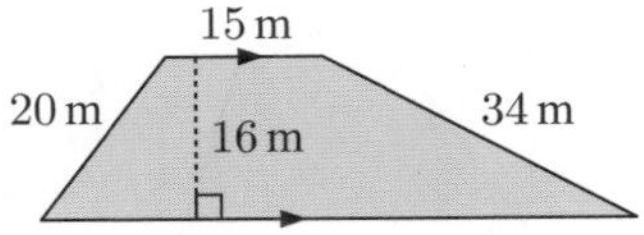

2 Consider the isosceles triangle shown.
M is the midpoint of [BC].

a Find the length CM.

b Use Pythagoras' theorem to find the height h of the triangle.

c Hence, find the area of the triangle.

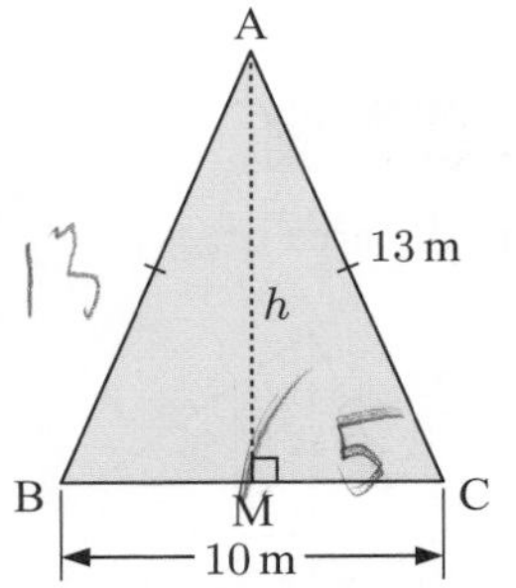

Example 8 **Self Tutor**

A farmer wishes to seed and fertilise a 1200 m by 750 m paddock. If it costs \$85.80 per hectare to perform this task, how much will it cost in total?

$$\begin{aligned}\text{Area of paddock} &= \text{length} \times \text{width}\\ &= 1200 \times 750 \text{ m}^2\\ &= \frac{1200 \times 750}{10\,000} \text{ ha}\\ &= 90 \text{ ha}\\ \therefore\ \text{total cost} &= 90 \times \$85.80\\ &= \$7722\end{aligned}$$

3 Anya's farm measures 800 metres by 1.2 km. 36 hectares are sown with wheat. Find the percentage of her farm that is sown with wheat.

4 A square paving brick has an area of 225 cm^2. If each brick fits tightly in place, how many bricks are needed to pave a path 1.2 m by 12 m?

5 A standard double bed sheet is 254 cm long and 228 cm wide. A queen bed sheet is 274 cm long and 245 cm wide.

a Find the area of:

  i a double bed sheet **ii** a queen bed sheet.

b Copy and complete: "A queen bed sheet is ...... % larger than a double bed sheet."

6 **a** Find the amount of material required to make the sail shown.

b Find the cost of the sail if the material costs \$19.50 per square metre.

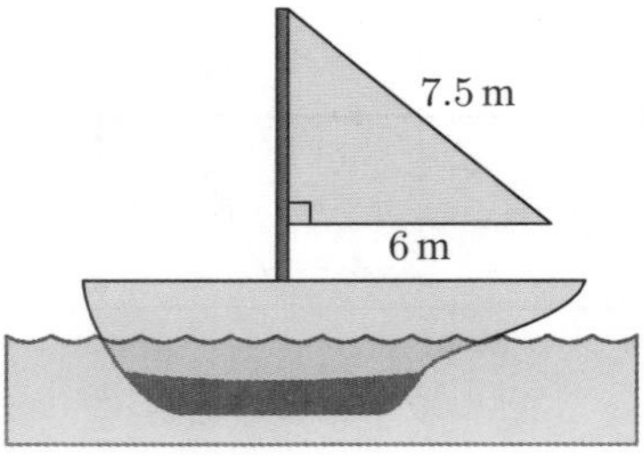

7 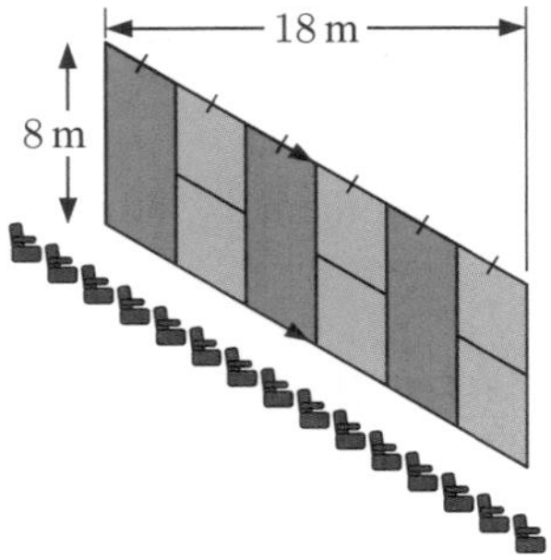

A feature wall at a movie theatre is made from green and red panels, as shown.

- **a** Find the area of the feature wall.
- **b** Find the area of:
  - **i** each red panel
  - **ii** each green panel.

8

- **a** Find the area of the top of this desk.
- **b** A classroom has 25 of these desks. The top surface of each desk is to be repainted. Find the total area to be painted, in m^2.

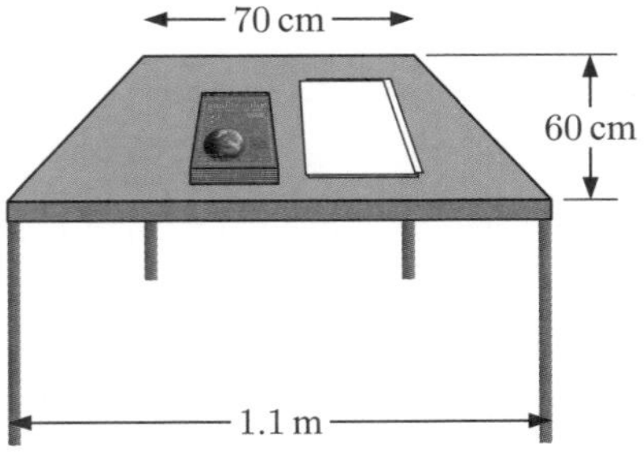

9 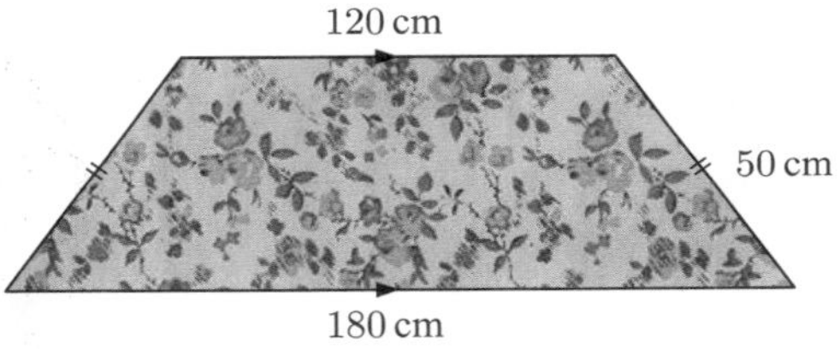

Vanessa is using the material alongside to make a skirt.
Find the area of the material.

10 Find the area A of the following shaded regions, giving your answers in simplest form:

a 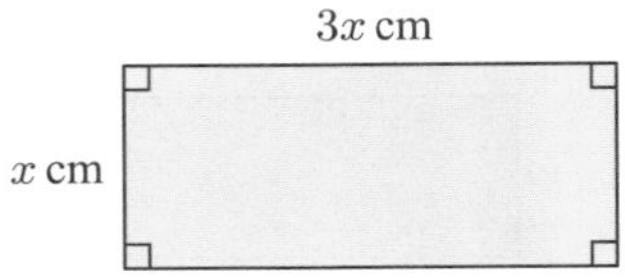

b 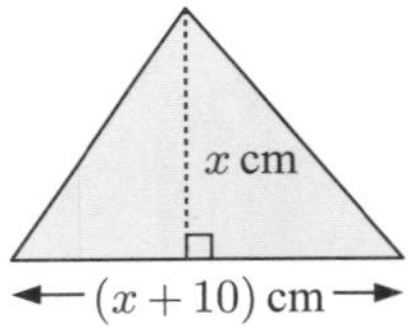

c 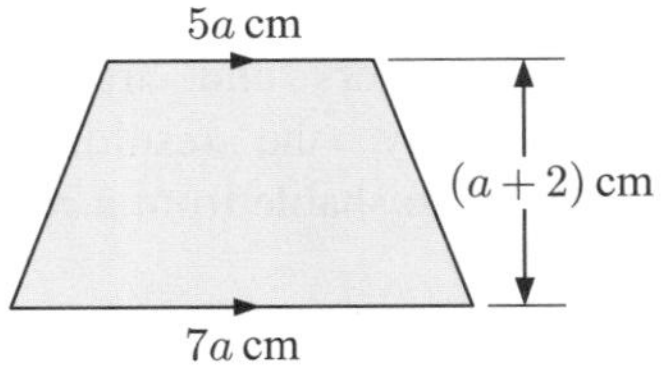

11 The trapezium alongside has area 57 cm^2. Find the length of [AD].

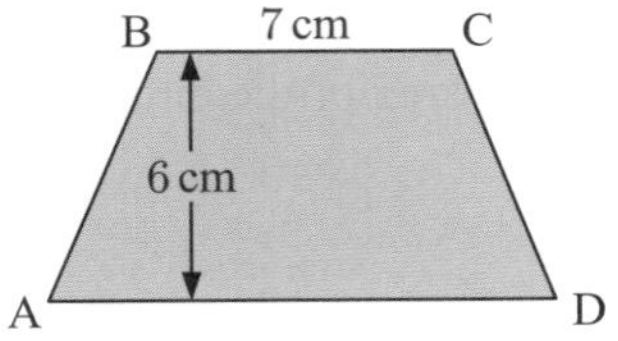

12 Show that the shortest distance from B to [AC] is $\dfrac{ac}{\sqrt{a^2+c^2}}$.

Hint: Find the area of $\triangle$ABC in two different forms.

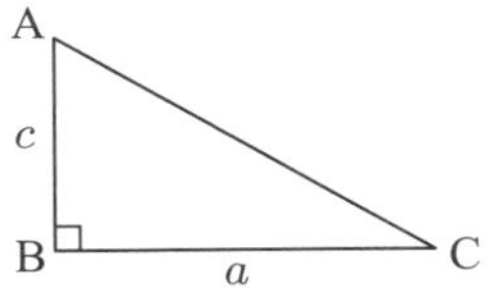

13 Find the area of the shaded region.

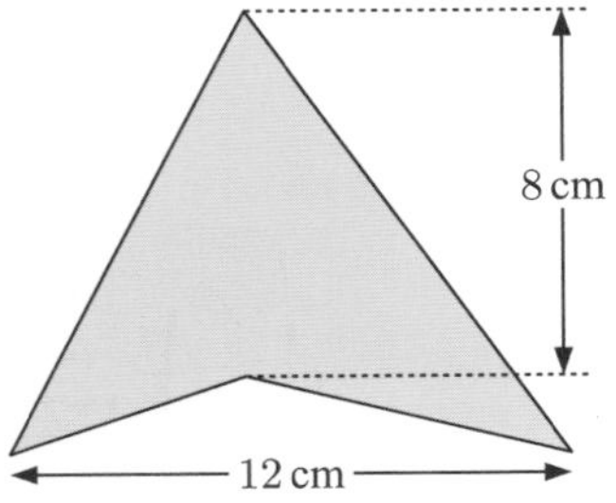

F AREAS OF CIRCLES AND ELLIPSES

Consider cutting a circle of radius r into 16 equal sectors and arranging them as shown:

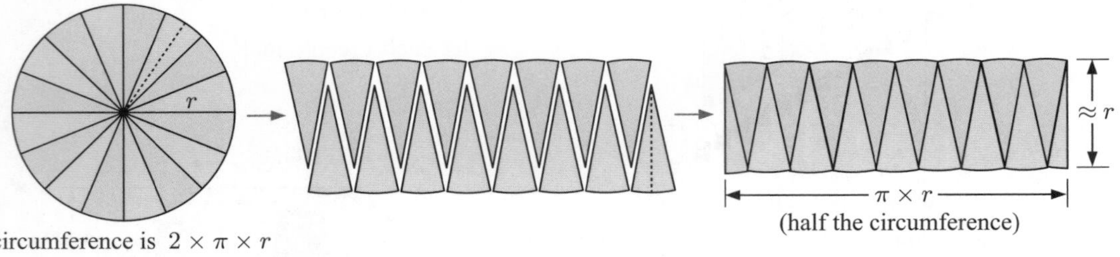

The figure obtained closely resembles a rectangle. The height of the rectangle is the radius of the circle.

The top "edge" is the sum of all the arc lengths of the blue sectors. This is half the circumference of the circle, which is

$$\tfrac{1}{2} \times 2\pi r = \pi \times r.$$

The bottom "edge" is made up from the arcs of the yellow sectors in a similar way.

DEMO

PROTRACTOR

Perform this demonstration for yourself. Click on the icon, then print the protractor and cut it into equal sectors.

If the original circle is cut into 1000 equal sectors and arranged in the same way, the resulting figure is indistinguishable from a rectangle.

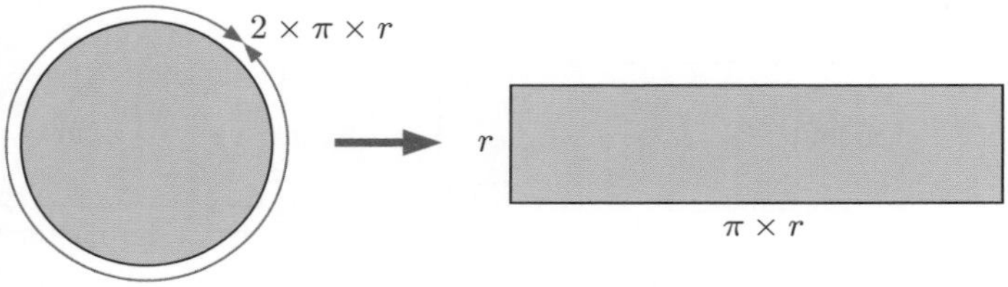

So, the area of the circle $A = \text{length} \times \text{width}$ of the rectangle

$$\therefore \quad A = \pi \times r \times r$$

$$\therefore \quad A = \pi r^2$$

The area of a circle of radius r is given by **Area** $= \boldsymbol{\pi r^2}$.

Example 9 — Self Tutor

Find the area of the circle, rounding your answer to 1 decimal place.

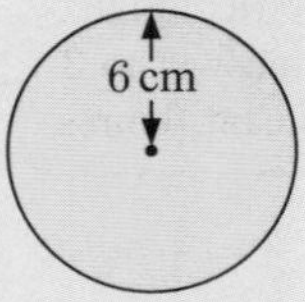

$A = \pi r^2$

$\therefore\ A = \pi \times 6^2\ \text{cm}^2$ {the radius is 6 cm}

$\therefore\ A \approx 113.1\ \text{cm}^2$

ELLIPSES

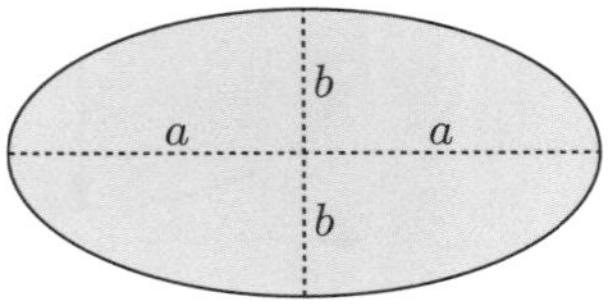

The area of an ellipse with **semi-axes** a and b is given by

Area $\boldsymbol{A = \pi ab}$

Notice that when $a = b$, the ellipse becomes a circle with radius a, and its area is πa^2.

Example 10 — Self Tutor

Find the area of the ellipse, rounding your answer to 1 decimal place.

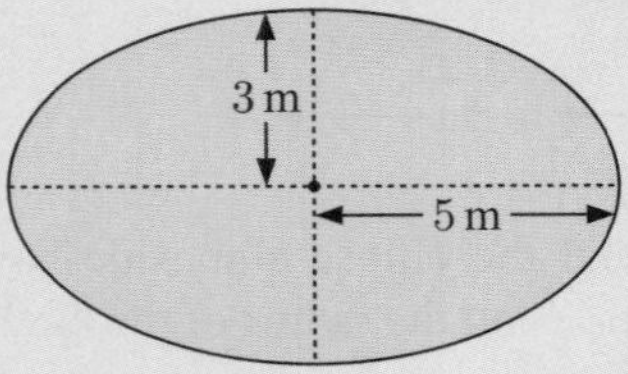

$A = \pi ab$

$\therefore\ A = \pi \times 5 \times 3\ \text{m}^2$

$\therefore\ A \approx 47.1\ \text{m}^2$

EXERCISE 11F

1 Find the area of each figure, rounding your answer to 2 decimal places:

a

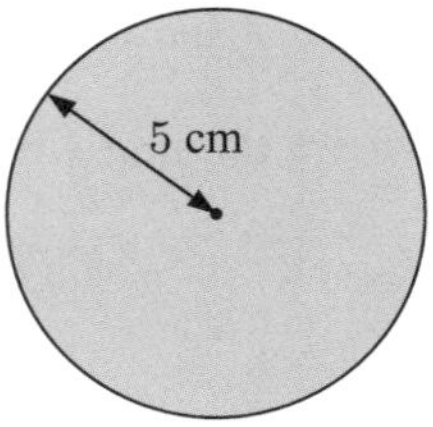

b

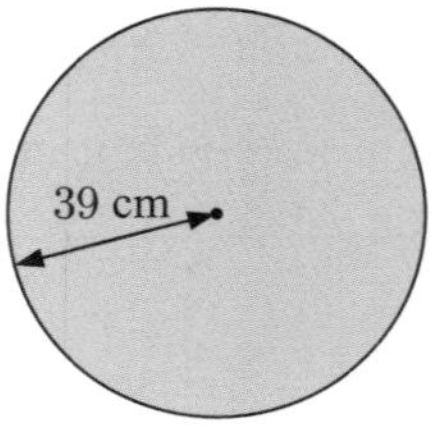

c

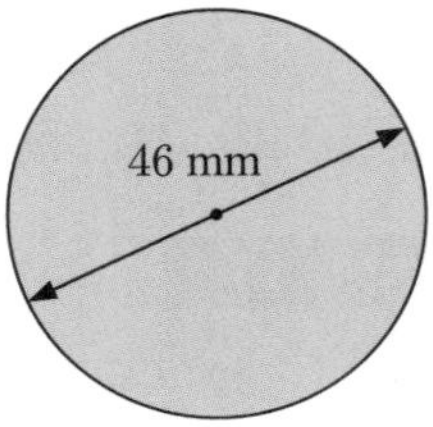

d

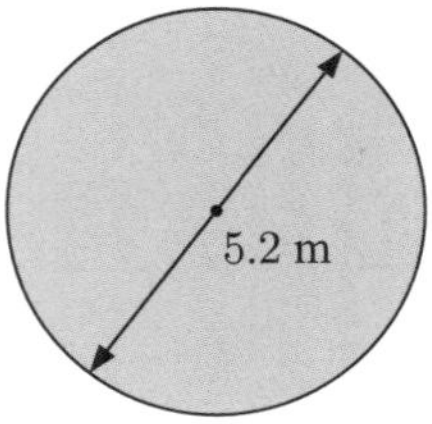

e

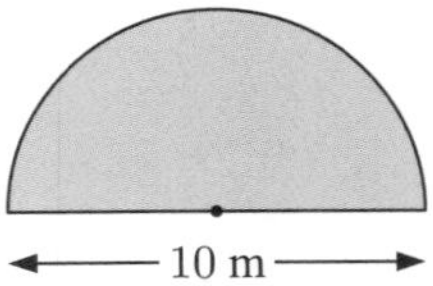

f

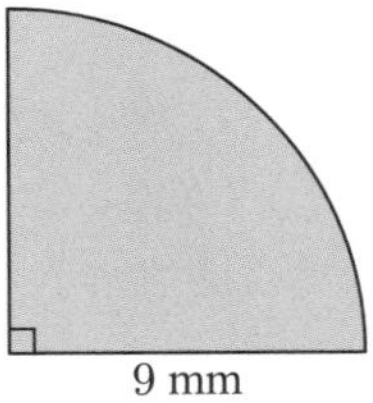

2 A circle has diameter 4.8 cm. Find, rounded to 2 decimal places, its:

a perimeter **b** area.

3 When a water balloon bursts on the ground, it makes a rough circle of water with diameter 26 cm. Find the approximate area of ground that is wet.

Unless otherwise specified, give your answer to 3 significant figures.

4 A donkey is tethered to a post by a 3.6 m long rope. Over what area can the donkey roam?

5 Find the area of each figure:

a

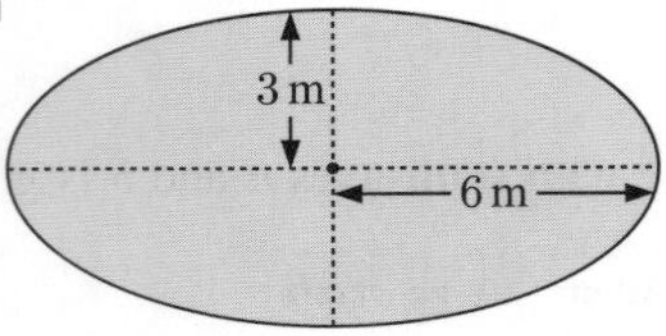

b

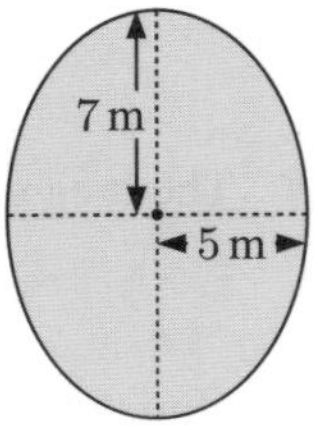

c

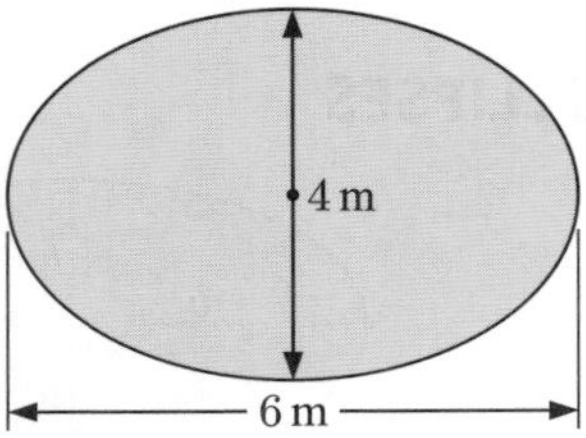

d

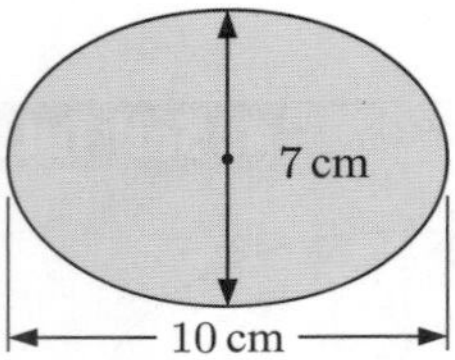

e

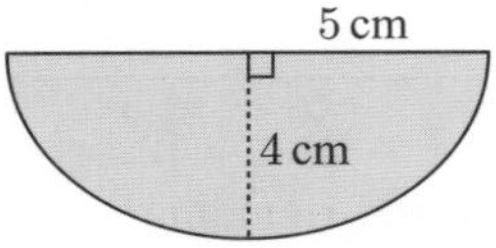

half ellipse

f

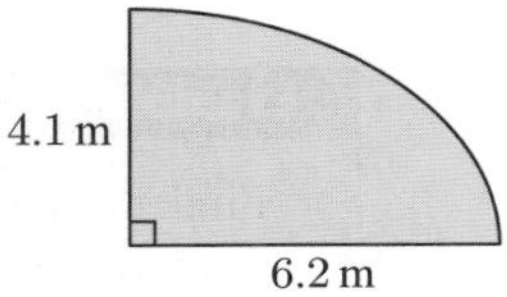

quarter ellipse

6 The circle and the ellipse alongside have the same area. Find the radius of the circle.

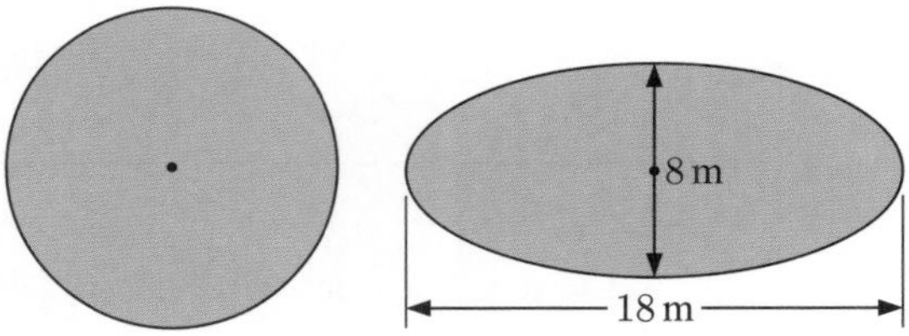

G AREAS OF COMPOSITE FIGURES

Composite figures are figures made up from two or more basic shapes.

To calculate the area of a composite figure, we divide it into shapes that we are familiar with.

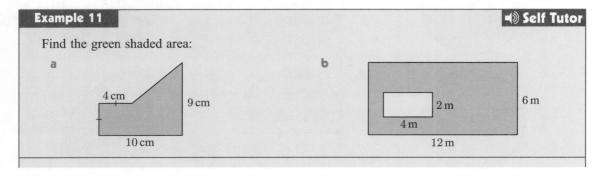

Example 11 Self Tutor

Find the green shaded area:

a

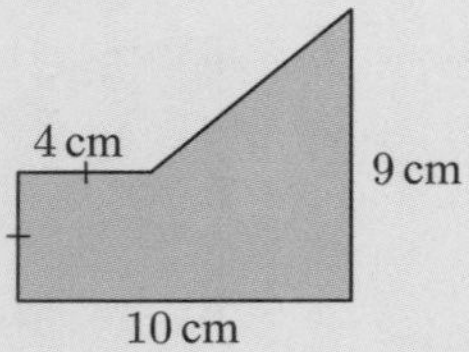

b

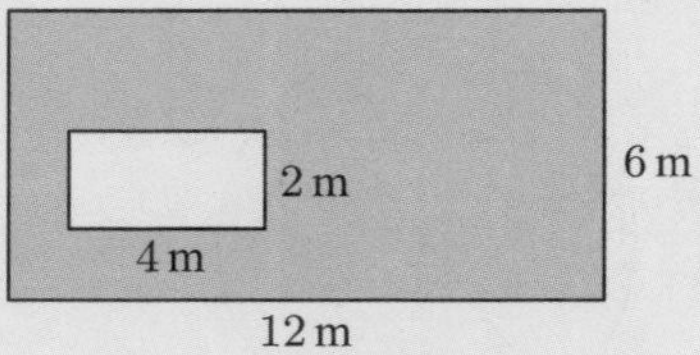

a We divide the figure into a rectangle and a triangle as shown.

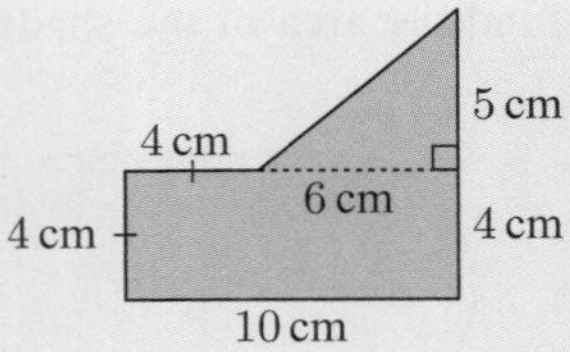

Area = area of rectangle + area of triangle
$= 10 \times 4 \text{ cm}^2 + \frac{1}{2} \times 6 \times 5 \text{ cm}^2$
$= (40 + 15) \text{ cm}^2$
$= 55 \text{ cm}^2$

b Area = area of large rectangle − area of small rectangle
$= 12 \times 6 \text{ m}^2 - 4 \times 2 \text{ m}^2$
$= (72 - 8) \text{ m}^2$
$= 64 \text{ m}^2$

EXERCISE 11G

1 Find the shaded area:

a
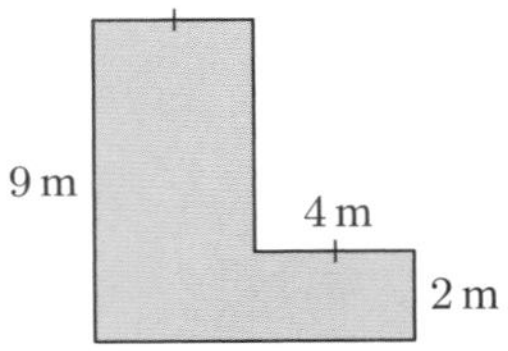

b
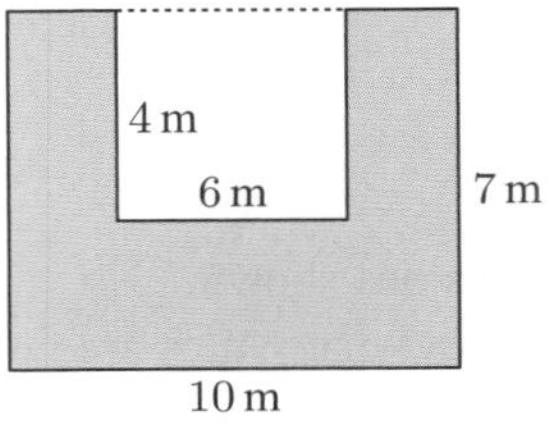

c
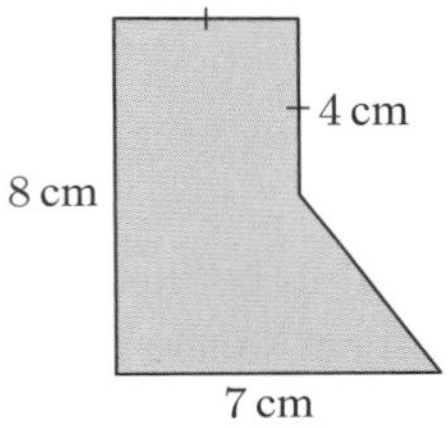

d
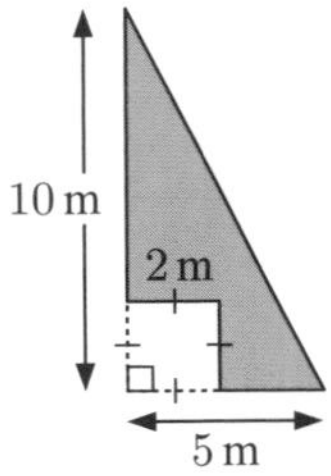

e
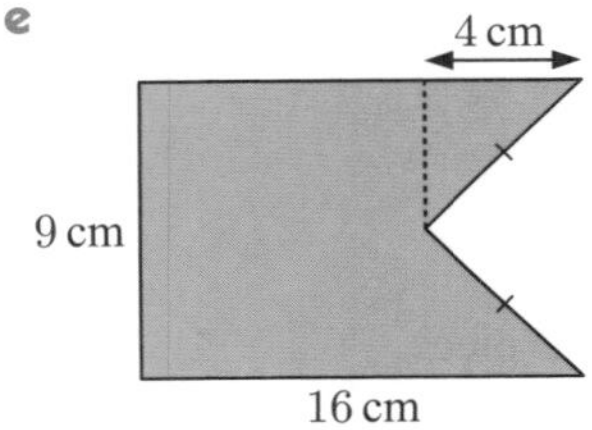

f
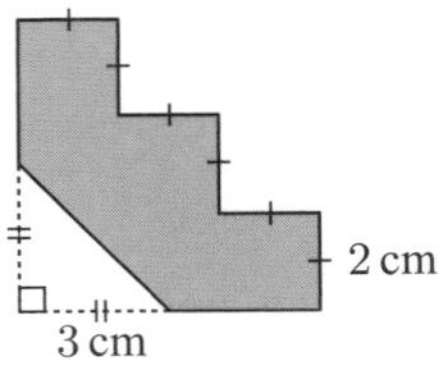

Example 12 **Self Tutor**

Find, rounded to 1 decimal place, the pink shaded area:

a
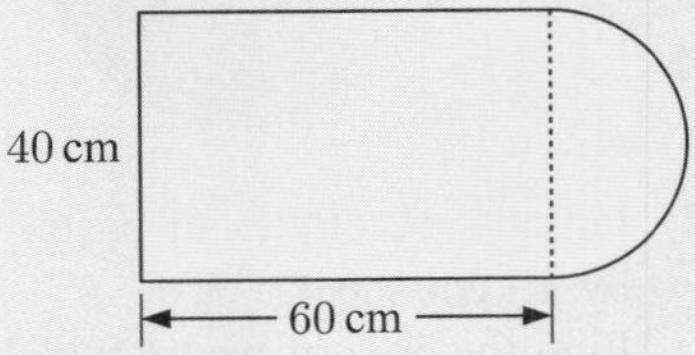

b
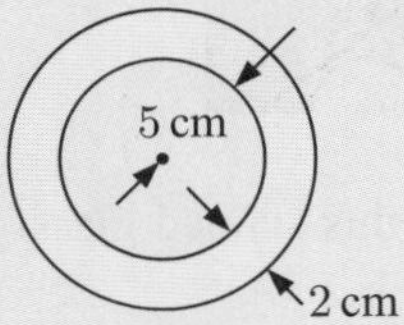

a Area = area of rectangle + area of semi-circle
$= 40 \times 60 \text{ cm}^2 + \frac{1}{2} \times (\pi \times 20^2) \text{ cm}^2$ {area of circle $= \pi r^2$}
$\approx 3028.3 \text{ cm}^2$

b Area = area of large circle − area of small circle
$= \pi \times 7^2 \text{ cm}^2 - \pi \times 5^2 \text{ cm}^2$
$\approx 75.4 \text{ cm}^2$

2 Find the area of the shaded region, rounding your answer to 2 decimal places:

a

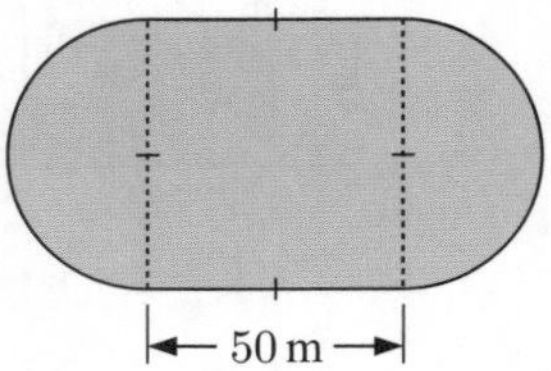

b

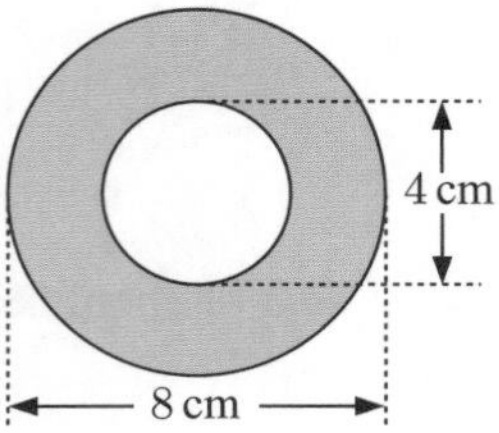

c

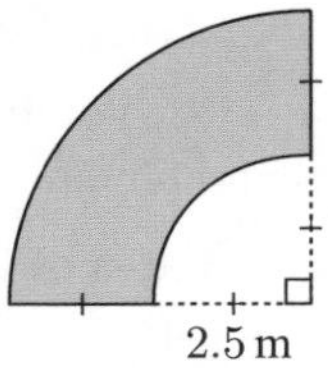

d

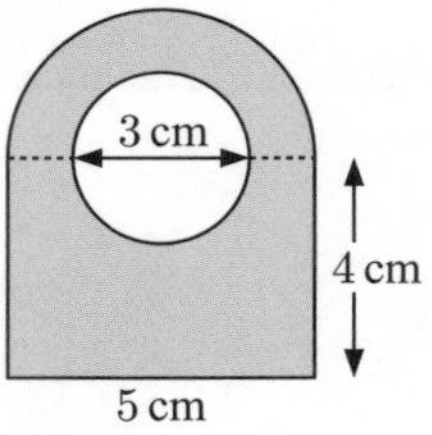

e

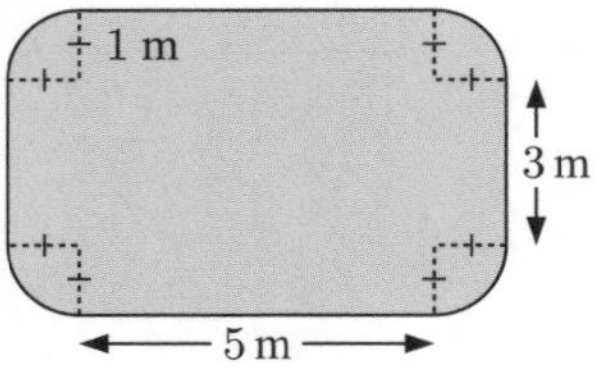

f

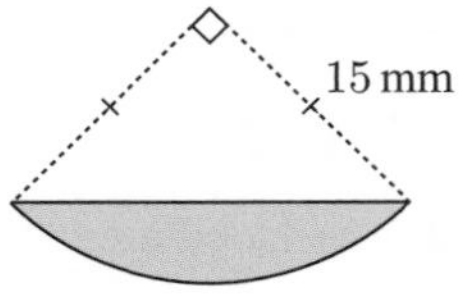

3 A wall to be tiled has the dimensions shown.
If 30 cm square tiles are used, how many tiles are needed?

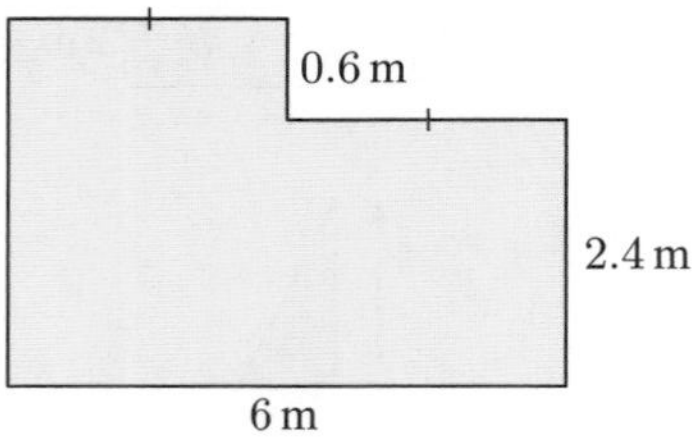

4 Find the area of the jigsaw puzzle piece shown.
Give your answer to the nearest mm^2.

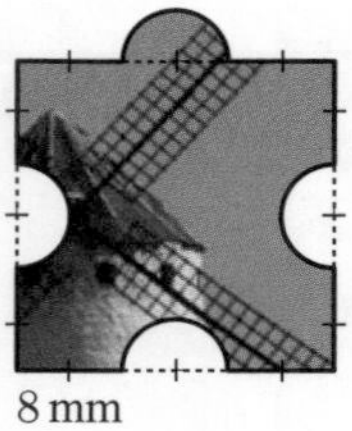

5 A plain metal washer is shown below.
Find the area of the top surface.

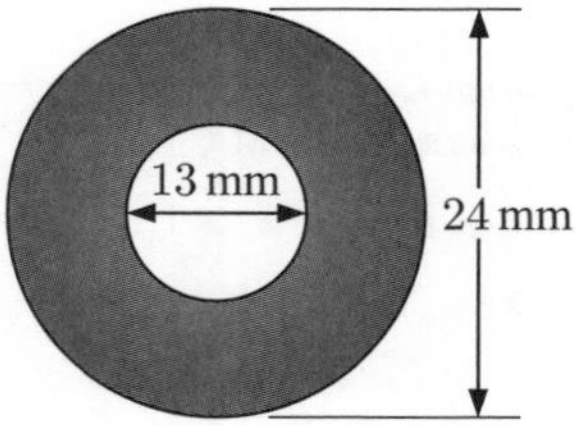

6 Find the area of this stained glass window.

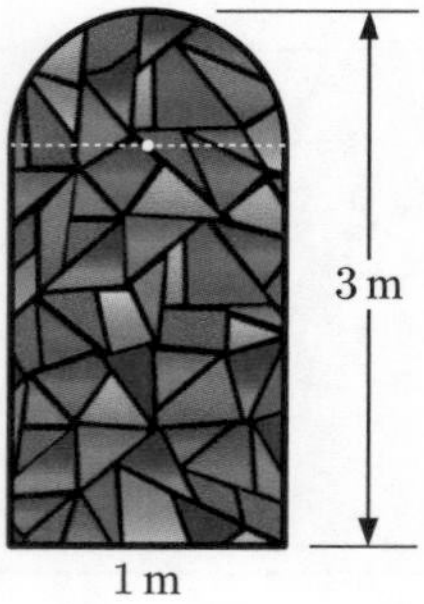

7 Ian cuts 12 circles of pastry from a 30 cm by 40 cm sheet.
Find the area of pastry which remains.

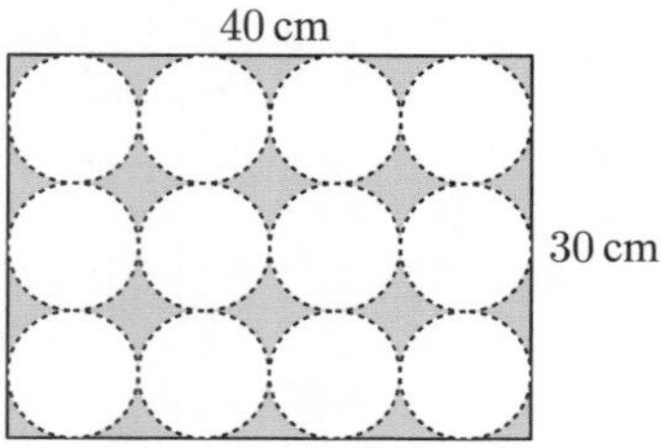

8 Find the area A of the following shaded regions. Give your answers in simplest form.

a

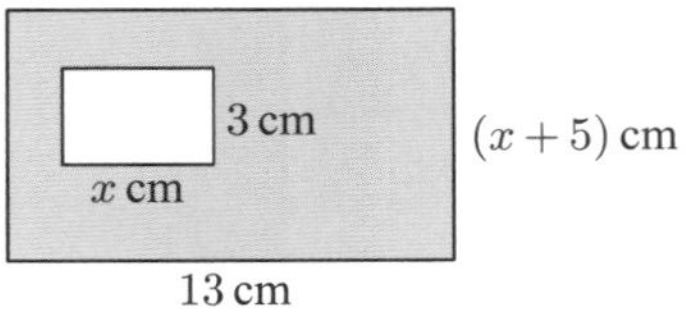

b

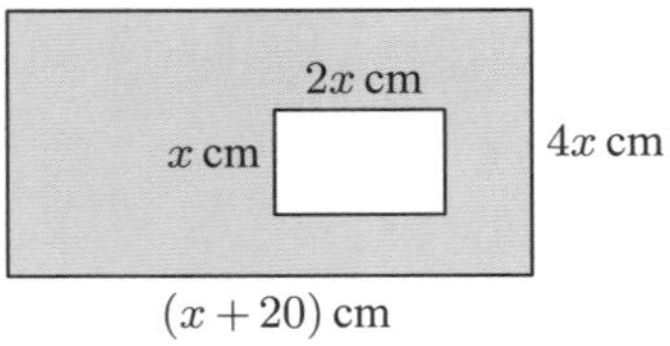

c

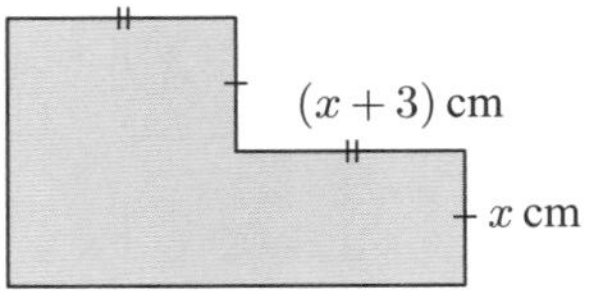

d

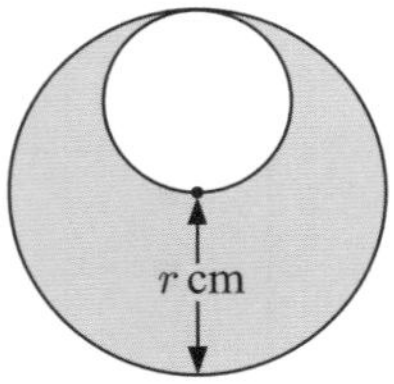

9 Show that the blue area enclosed by the two arcs is equal to the area of the isosceles right angled triangle ABC.

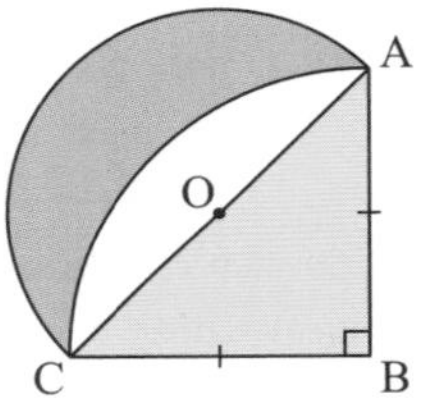

10

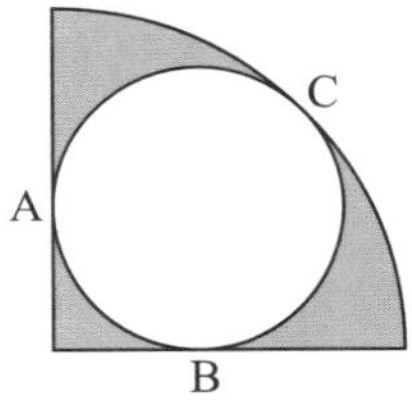

A circle with radius r is inscribed in a quarter circle with radius R, touching it at A, B, and C.

a Find the relationship between R and r.

b Find the ratio of the shaded area to the area of the small circle.

INVESTIGATION 3 — PICK'S RULE FOR AREAS

Below is a diagram of a polygon whose **vertices** or corner points lie on **lattice points**.

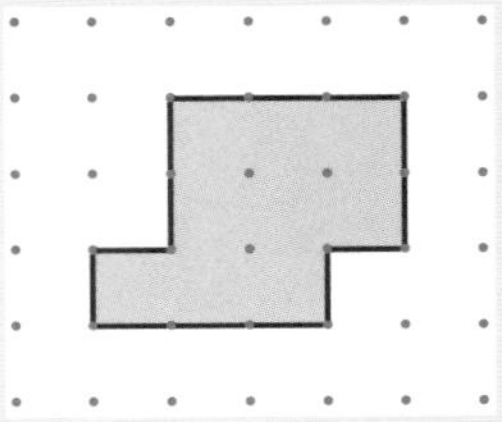

The lattice points which lie on the figure are referred to as **boundary points**.

The lattice points which lie inside the figure are referred to as **interior points**.

The figure shown has 14 boundary points and 3 interior points.

Suppose $B =$ the number of boundary points,
and $I =$ the number of interior points.

What to do:

1 For the figures below, copy and complete the table which follows:

a

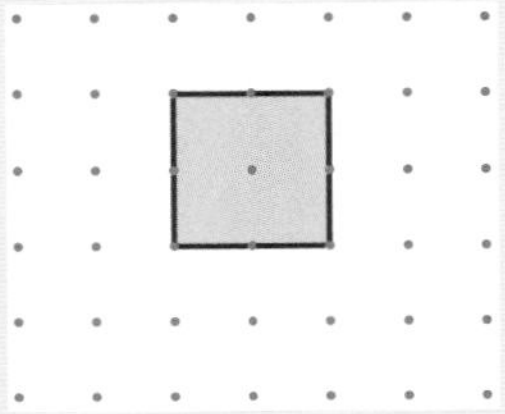

b

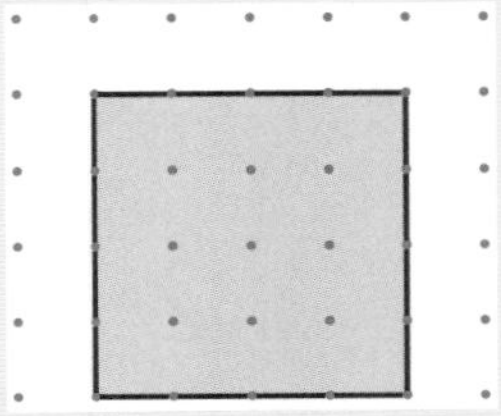

c

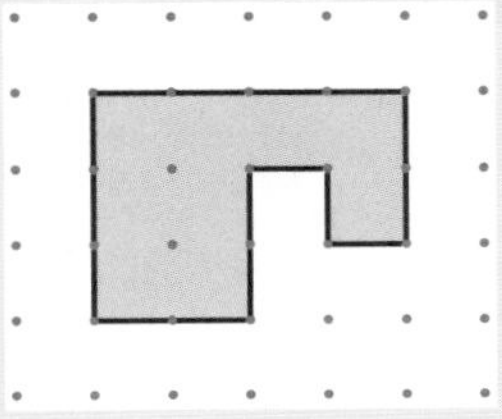

d

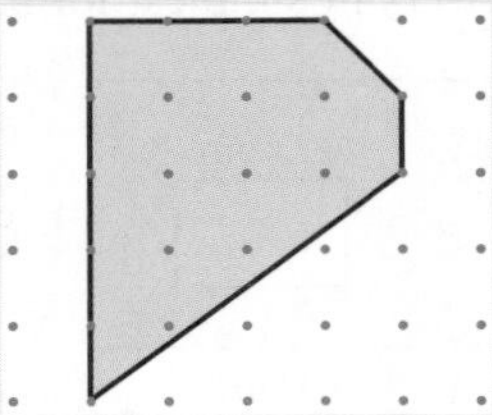

e

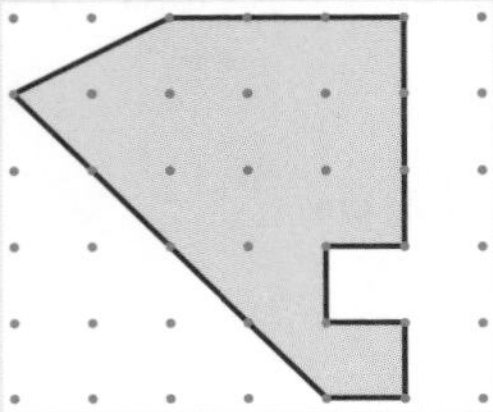

f

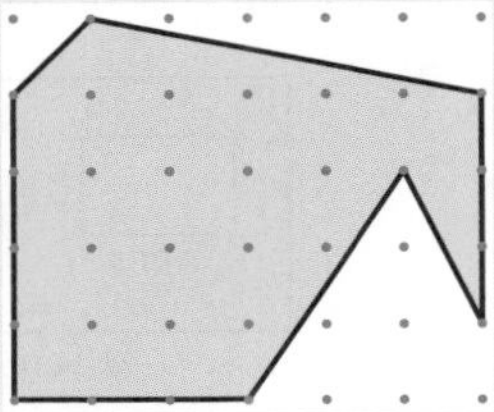

Figure	B	$\frac{B}{2}$	I	$\frac{B}{2}+I$	*Area* A
a					
b					
c					
d					
e					
f					

2 Look at the last two columns of your table. Suggest a rule connecting A, B, and I. This result is called **Pick's Rule**.

3 Draw several polygons of your own on grid paper, and check that your rule is correct.

REVIEW SET 11A

1 Convert:

a 95 mm to cm **b** 4.8 km to m **c** 3.15 ha to m^2

d 55 000 cm^2 to m^2 **e** 3.4 m^2 to cm^2 **f** 18 500 m^2 to ha

2 Find the perimeter of:

a

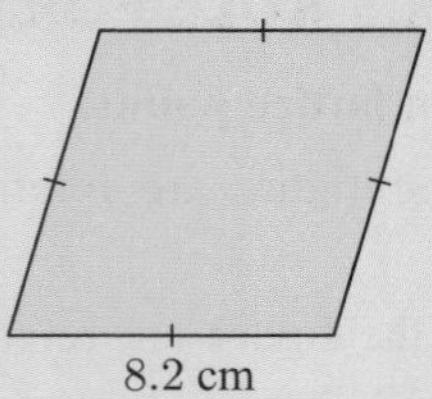

b

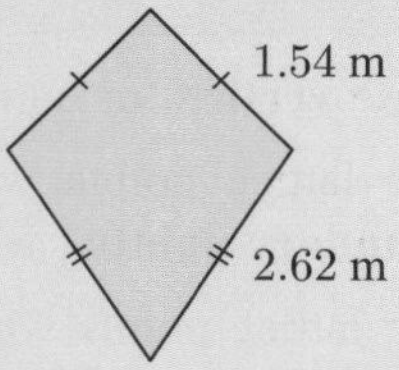

c

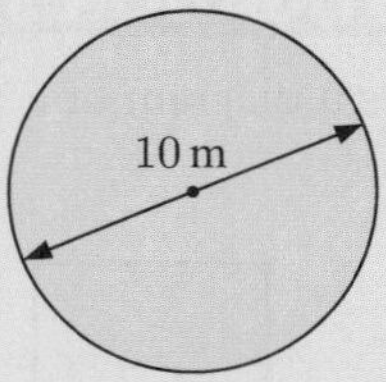

3 A circle has radius 5.6 cm. Find, rounded to 1 decimal place, its:

a circumference **b** area.

4 Find the area of a right angled triangle with base 10 cm and hypotenuse 26 cm.

5 The floor of a classroom is most likely to have an area of:

A 50 cm^2 **B** 5 m^2 **C** 0.5 km^2 **D** 50 m^2 **E** 50 ha

6 Find the pink shaded area:

a

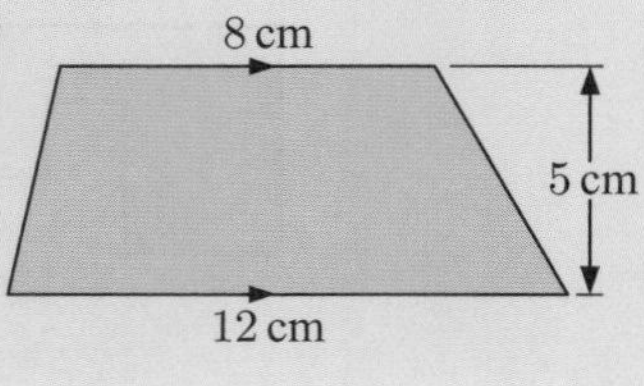

b

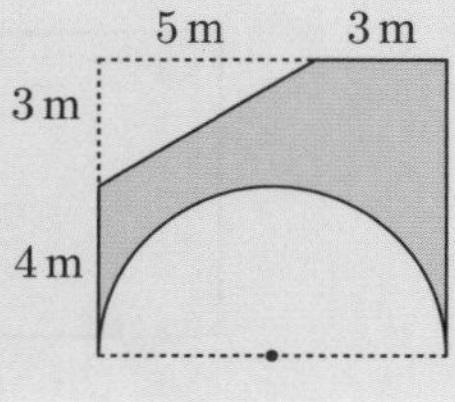

c

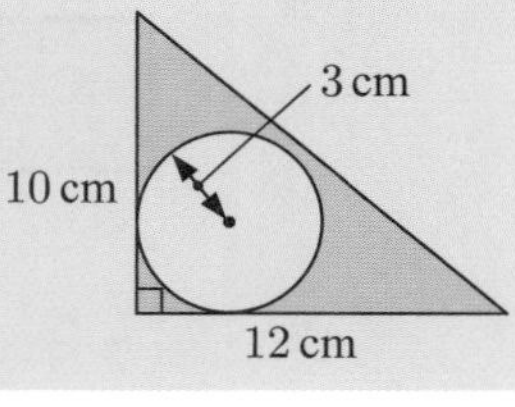

7 A hockey pitch is 55 m by 91 m.

a Find the total area of the pitch.

b Find the cost of preparing the pitch with "instant lawn" at a cost of €6.40 per square metre.

8 The door illustrated is fitted into a metal door frame. Find:

a the length of metal required for the frame

b the area of the door.

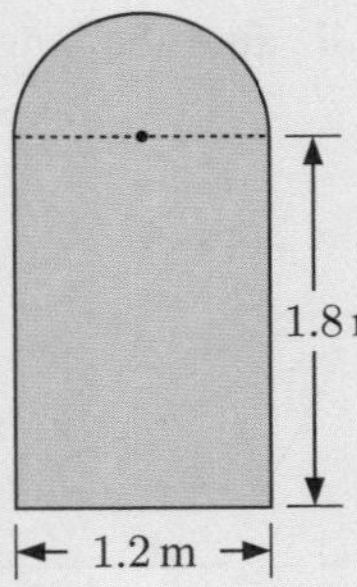

9 Find the area of:

a

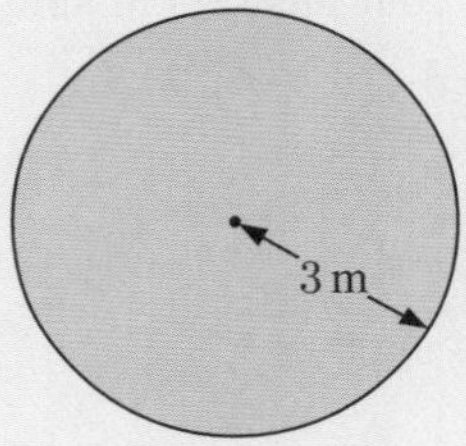

b

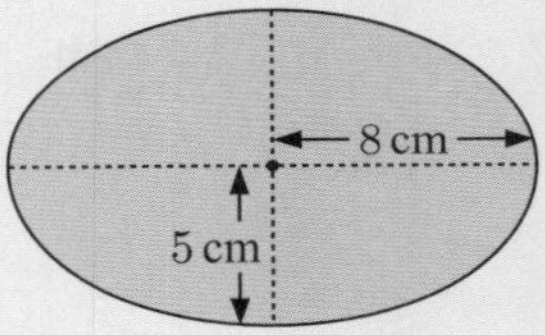

c

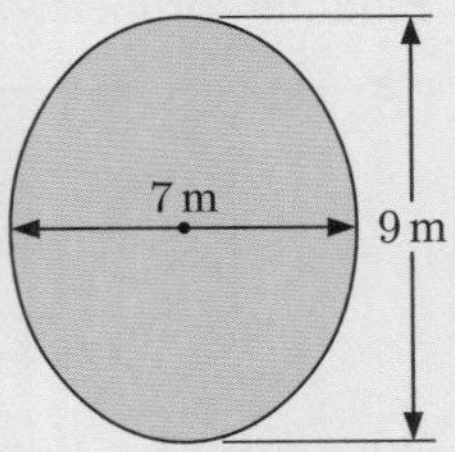

10 This circular pond has diameter 1.6 m.

a Find the area of plastic needed to line the bottom of the pond.

b A 10 cm wide strip filled with pebbles will surround the edge of the pond. What area will the pebbles cover?

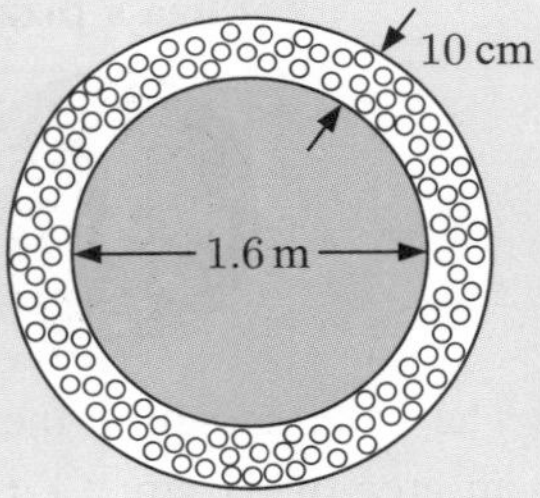

REVIEW SET 11B

1 Convert:

a 7260 m to km

b 38.7 cm to mm

c 340 cm^2 to mm^2

d 3270 m^2 to ha

2 Hayden bought a packet containing 60 m of dental floss. He uses 40 cm of floss each day. How long will he take to use the whole packet?

3 Find the area of the top of this piece of shortbread:

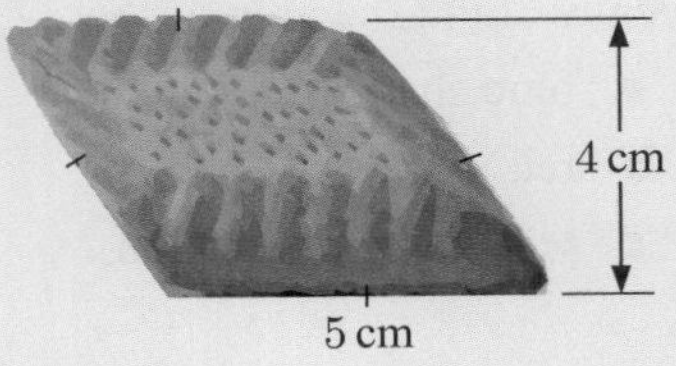

4 **a** Find the perimeter P of the figure alongside, giving your answer in simplest form.

b If the perimeter of the figure is 30 cm:

i find x

ii find the length of the longest side.

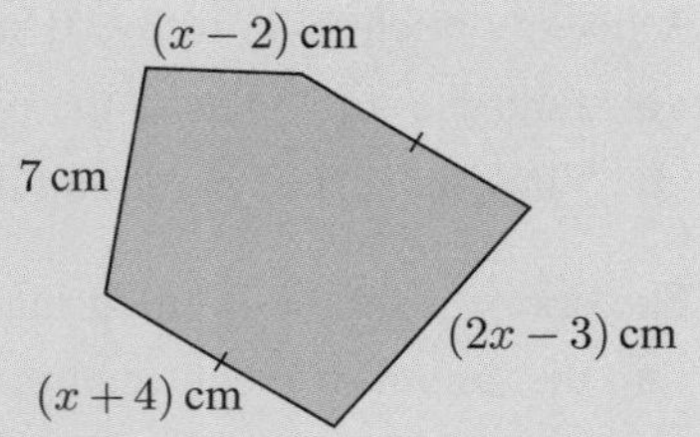

5 Find the area of:

a

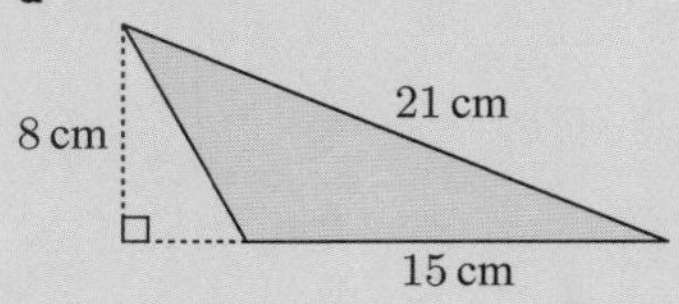

b

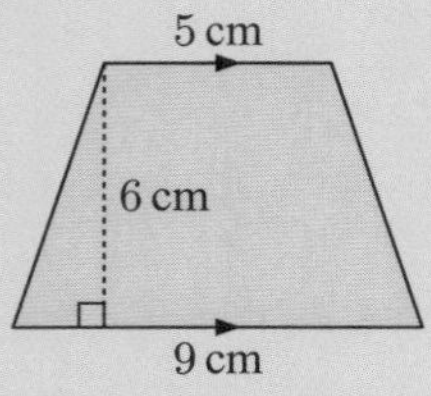

c

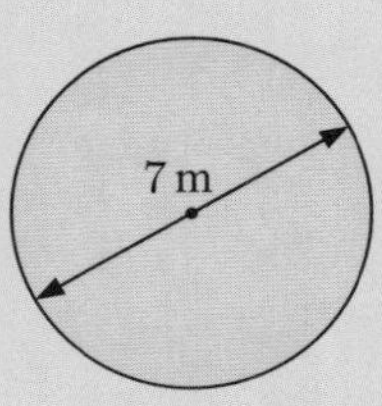

6 Find the perimeter P and area A of the following figures. Give your answers in simplest form.

a

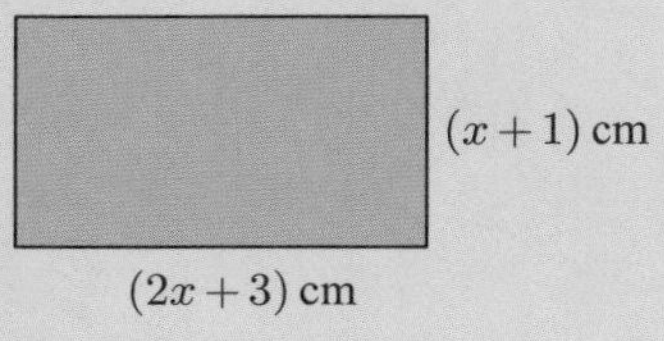

b

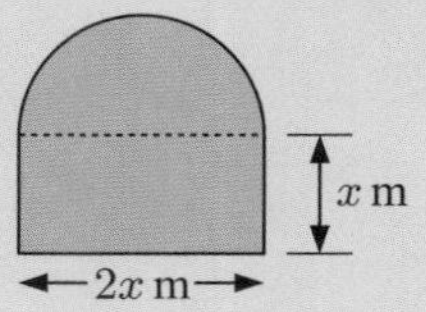

7 Whose pizza is larger?

Eliza's pizza

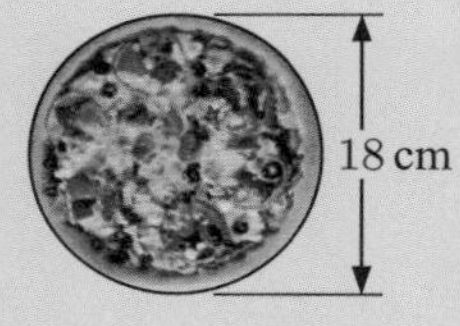

Claire's pizza

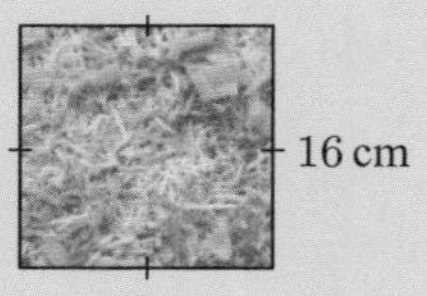

8 The outer square in the shape below has an area of 64 cm^2. Find the area of the yellow shaded region.

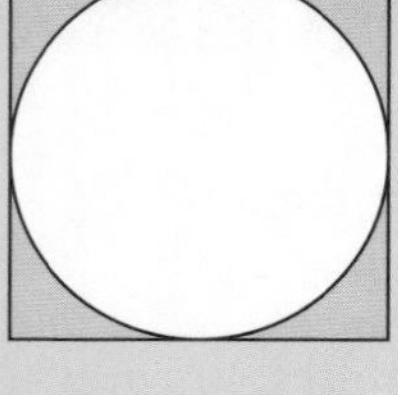

9 The flag of Nepal is shown below. Find its area.

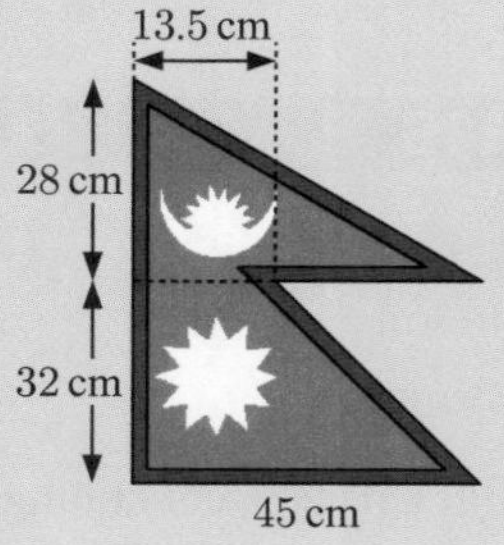

10 The circles and ellipse in this figure all have the same centre. Find the area of the:

a blue shaded region

b red shaded region

c yellow shaded region.

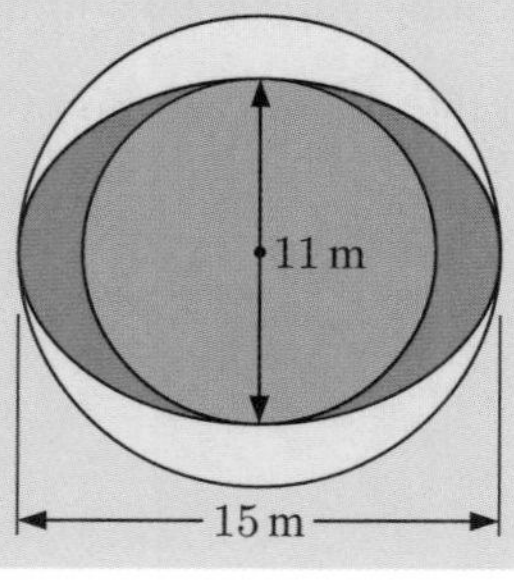

Chapter 12

Algebra: Patterns and formulae

Contents:

OPENING PROBLEM

Leonard builds ladders which are made from pieces of metal. The vertical and horizontal metal pieces are all the same length. The more pieces Leonard uses, the bigger the ladder he makes.

1 rung 5 pieces   2 rungs 8 pieces   3 rungs 11 pieces

Things to think about:

a How many metal pieces does Leonard require to make a:

i 4 rung ladder   **ii** 5 rung ladder   **iii** 12 rung ladder?

b Is there a formula which gives the number of metal pieces required to make a ladder with a given number of rungs?

In the **Opening Problem**, the *number of metal pieces* required is related to the *number of rungs* in the ladder. In this chapter we will learn how to find a **formula** which describes the relationship between these variables.

A **formula** is a rule which connects two or more variables.

The plural of formula is **formulae**.

We can use the formula to find the number of pieces required for longer ladders, without having to draw the diagram and count the pieces.

A GEOMETRIC PATTERNS

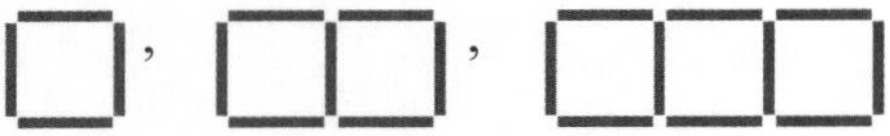 , ... and 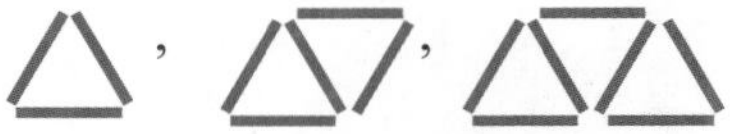 , ...

are examples of **geometric patterns** which continue indefinitely.

We often refer to them as **matchstick patterns** because we can construct them from matchsticks.

For the pattern  , ...

we may wish to know how many matchsticks are necessary to create the 10th figure.

Rather than draw the diagram, we can establish a **formula** which will tell us how many matchsticks there are in any figure further along the pattern.

Suppose the *figure number* is n and the *number of matches* is M.

From the first four figures in the pattern, we can create a **summary table**:

Figure number (n)	1	2	3	4
Number of matches (M)	4	7	10	13

$+3$ $+3$ $+3$

Each time the *figure number* n is increased by 1, the *number of matches* M increases by 3. This suggests we compare $n \times 3$ with M.

$n \times 3$	3	6	9	12
M	4	7	10	13

We can see that M is always one more than $n \times 3$, so the rule connecting the variables is $M = n \times 3 + 1$ or "the *number of matches* is the *figure number* times three, plus one".

This formula can be written more simply as $M = 3n + 1$.

To help understand how the formula relates to the pattern, we can construct a more detailed table:

Figure number	*Figure*	*Matches*	*Pattern*	*Explanation*
1		4	$1 \times 3 + 1$	
2	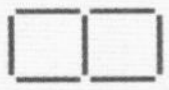	7	$2 \times 3 + 1$	
3		10	$3 \times 3 + 1$	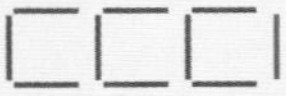
4		13	$4 \times 3 + 1$	

We can use the pattern to predict that the 10th figure has $10 \times 3 + 1 = 31$ matches,
and the 100th figure has $100 \times 3 + 1 = 301$ matches.

Example 1 **Self Tutor**

a Complete a table to describe the first four figures in the pattern: 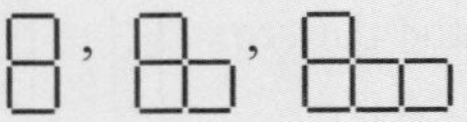 , ...

b Find how many matches are required to make the:
  i 10th figure **ii** 50th figure.

c Write a description of the pattern in words.

d Write a general rule for finding the number of matches M in the nth figure.

a

Figure number	*Figure*	*Matches*	*Pattern*	*Explanation*
1		7	$1 \times 3 + 4$	
2	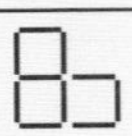	10	$2 \times 3 + 4$	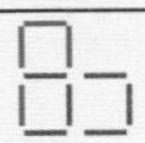
3		13	$3 \times 3 + 4$	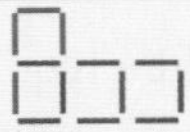
4		16	$4 \times 3 + 4$	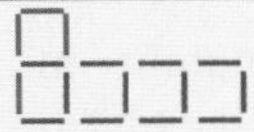

The number of matches increases by 3 each time, so we look for a pattern involving "the figure number times three".

b **i** The 10th figure requires $10 \times 3 + 4 = 34$ matches.
ii The 50th figure requires $50 \times 3 + 4 = 154$ matches.

c The number of matches is the figure number times three, plus four.

d For the nth figure the rule is $M = n \times 3 + 4$ or $M = 3n + 4$.

EXERCISE 12A

1 **a** Consider the pattern: _| , _|_| , _|_|_| , ...

Draw the next two figures and hence complete:

Figure number	*Figure*	*Matches*	*Pattern*	*Explanation*
1	_|	2	1×2	_|
2	_|_|	4	2×2	_| _|
3	_|_|_|			
4				_| _| _| _|
5			5×2	

b Find how many matches would be required to make the:
i 6th figure **ii** 30th figure.

c Copy and complete: "The number of matches is the figure number ......".

d Write a general rule for determining the number of matches M in the nth figure.

2 **a** Consider the pattern: 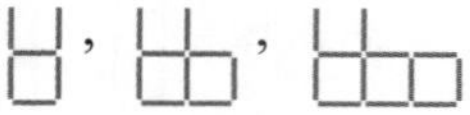 , ...

Draw the next two figures and hence complete:

Figure number	*Figure*	*Matches*	*Pattern*	*Explanation*
1		6	$1 \times 3 + 3$	
2		9	$2 \times 3 + 3$	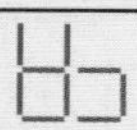
3	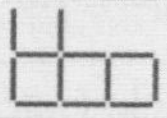			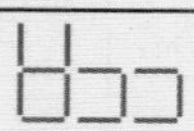
4			$4 \times 3 + 3$	
5				

b Find how many matches would be required to make the:
i 6th figure **ii** 20th figure.

c Copy and complete: "The number of matches is the figure number ......, plus ...... "

d Write a general rule for determining the number of matches M in the nth figure.

3 **a** Consider the pattern:  , ...

Draw the next two figures and hence complete:

Figure number	*Figure*	*Matches*	*Pattern*	*Explanation*
1		5		
2		9		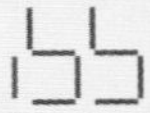
3				
4				
5				

b Find how many matches would be required to make the:

i 6th figure **ii** 15th figure.

c Write a description of the pattern in words.

d Write a general rule for determining the number of matches M in the nth figure.

B NUMBER CRUNCHING MACHINES

Rules or **formulae** which give the total number of matchsticks in patterns can be likened to *number crunching machines.*

For any **input number** fed into the machine, for example, 1, 2, 3, 4, 5, ..., the machine calculates an **output number** according to a rule.

input number

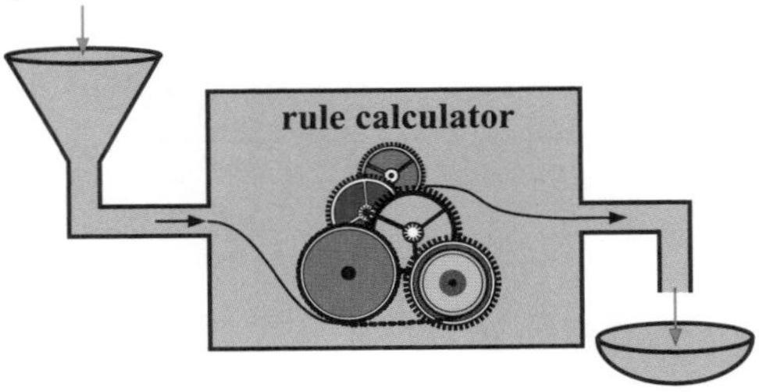

output number

For example, suppose the output number M is *'two times the input number n, plus seven'*, or $M = 2 \times n + 7$.

We can generate a table of values:

Input number (n)	*Calculation*	*Output number* (M)
1	$2 \times 1 + 7$	9
2	$2 \times 2 + 7$	11
3	$2 \times 3 + 7$	13
⋮	⋮	⋮

Example 2 **Self Tutor**

Consider the rule: *four times the input number, less one.* Calculate the output numbers when the input numbers are 1, 2, 3, and 10.

Let n represent the input number and M represent the output number.

In symbols, the rule is: $M = 4 \times n - 1$ or $M = 4n - 1$.

Input number (n)	*Output number* (M)
1	$4 \times 1 - 1 = 3$
2	$4 \times 2 - 1 = 7$
3	$4 \times 3 - 1 = 11$
10	$4 \times 10 - 1 = 39$

So, $1 \to \mathbf{3}$, $2 \to \mathbf{7}$, $3 \to \mathbf{11}$, $10 \to \mathbf{39}$.

EXERCISE 12B.1

1 For each of the following rules, calculate output numbers for the given input numbers:

a *The input number plus six*

Input number	*Output number*
1	
2	
3	
4	

b *Three times the input number*

Input number	*Output number*
2	
3	
6	
9	

c *Multiply by* 4 *then subtract* 3

Input number	*Output number*
1	
4	
9	
12	

d *Add* 5 *then double*

Input number	*Output number*
0	
3	
7	
10	

e *Multiply the input number by itself*

Input number	*Output number*
2	
5	
8	
10	

f *Halve the input number*

Input number	*Output number*
4	
8	
12	
20	

g *Subtract* 4 *then multiply by* 10

Input number	*Output number*
5	
7	
9	
11	

h *Add* 8 *then divide by* 3

Input number	*Output number*
7	
16	
22	
28	

FINDING THE 'NUMBER CRUNCHING RULE'

If we are given a table of input and output numbers, we can work out the 'number crunching rule' that was used.

Consider the following rules with input and output numbers:

Rule: *Two times the input number.*

Input number	*Output number*
1	2
2	4
3	6
4	8

(+2, +2, +2)

When the input number is increased by 1, the output number increases by 2.

Rule: *Three times the input number, plus one.*

Input number	*Output number*
1	4
2	7
3	10
4	13

(+3, +3, +3)

When the input number is increased by 1, the output number increases by 3.

Rule: *Five times the input number, minus two.*

Input number	*Output number*
1	3
2	8
3	13
4	18

(+5, +5, +5)

When the input number is increased by 1, the output number increases by 5.

In general, when we consider a table of input and output numbers:

> If the output number increases by k each time the input number increases by 1, the rule contains 'k times the input number'.

Example 3 — Self Tutor

Find the rule which connects these input numbers and their corresponding output numbers:

Input (n)	*Output* (M)
1	6
2	10
3	14
4	18

When the input number is increased by 1, the output number increases by 4.

$\therefore$ the rule contains 'four times the input number', and so we compare $4n$ with M.

$4n$	4	8	12	16
M	6	10	14	18

M is always 2 more than $4n$, so the rule is *four times the input number, plus two.*

$\therefore \quad M = 4n + 2.$

EXERCISE 12B.2

1 Find the rule which connects each set of input and output numbers.

a

Input (n)	*Output* (M)
1	4
2	5
3	6
4	7

b

Input (n)	*Output* (M)
1	5
2	10
3	15
4	20

c

Input (n)	*Output* (M)
1	5
2	7
3	9
4	11

d

Input (n)	*Output* (M)
1	6
2	10
3	14
4	18

e

Input (n)	*Output* (M)
1	2
2	5
3	8
4	11

f

Input (n)	*Output* (M)
1	5
2	11
3	17
4	23

2 For each of the following tables, write a formula connecting the variables. Check your formula for all of the number pairs given.

a

n	1	2	3	4	5	6
M	6	8	10	12	14	16

b

x	1	2	3	4	5	6
y	11	22	33	44	55	66

c

a	1	2	3	4	5	6
P	3	10	17	24	31	38

d

d	1	2	3	4	5	6
C	1	4	7	10	13	16

e

h	1	2	3	4	5	6
L	8	17	26	35	44	53

f

s	1	2	3	4	5	6
t	11	21	31	41	51	61

C SUBSTITUTING INTO FORMULAE

Having established a rule or formula connecting two variables, we can **substitute** the value of one variable to find the corresponding value of the other variable.

For example, suppose the cost C of hiring a volleyball court for h hours is given by the formula $C = 8h + 3$ euros.

To hire the court for 1 hour, we substitute $h = 1$ into the formula.
The cost is $C = 8 \times 1 + 3 = €11$.

To hire the court for $2\frac{1}{2}$ hours, we substitute $h = 2\frac{1}{2}$ into the formula.
The cost is $C = 8 \times 2\frac{1}{2} + 3 = €23$.

Example 4 **Self Tutor**

Consider the formula $D = 3x - 11$. Find the value of D when:

a $x = 10$ **b** $x = 2$.

a When $x = 10$,
$D = 3 \times 10 - 11$
$\therefore D = 30 - 11$
$\therefore D = 19$

b When $x = 2$,
$D = 3 \times 2 - 11$
$\therefore D = 6 - 11$
$\therefore D = -5$

EXERCISE 12C

1 Consider the formula $P = 2t + 7$. Find the value of P when:

a $t = 6$ **b** $t = -3$.

2 Consider the formula $C = 18 - 5d$. Find the value of C when:

a $d = 2$ **b** $d = 6$ **c** $d = -4$.

3 Consider the formula $K = 11 - 4n$.
Copy and complete the table of values:

n	-5	-2	0	2	9
K					

4 The cost C of hiring a bus for p people is given by $C = 12p + 80$ dollars.
Find the cost of hiring the bus for:

a 12 people **b** 20 people **c** 45 people.

5 The number of bread rolls in a bakery h hours after the bakery has opened, is given by $B = 400 - 50h$.

a Find B when $h = 0$. What does this mean?

b Find the number of bread rolls in the bakery after:

i 2 hours **ii** 5 hours **iii** 30 minutes.

6 The cost C of a mobile phone call overseas for t minutes is given by $C = 60t + 120$ cents.
Find the cost in *dollars* for a conversation that lasts:

a 5 minutes **b** 20 minutes **c** $1\frac{1}{2}$ hours.

7 If n overlapping circles are drawn on a sheet of paper, the maximum number of regions which can be formed is given by $R = n^2 - n + 2$.
For example, 2 circles can create a maximum of $R = (2)^2 - (2) + 2 = 4$ regions. Notice that outside of the circles is considered a region.

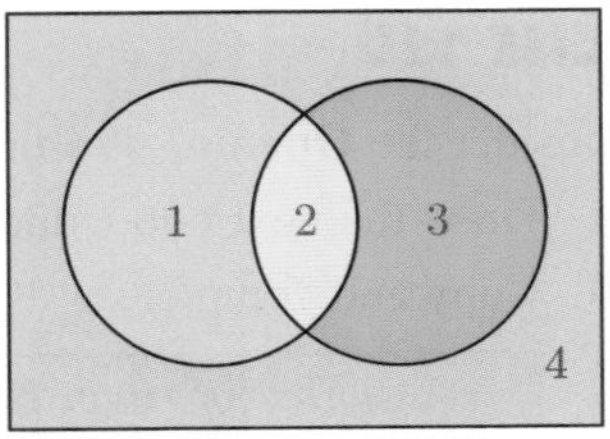

a Find the maximum number of regions which can be formed using:

i 1 circle **ii** 3 circles **iii** 4 circles.

Illustrate each of these cases.

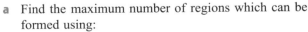

b Find the maximum number of regions which can be formed using 10 circles.

D USING PATTERNS

Many problems can be solved by observing patterns. We begin by looking at simple examples, and use them to find a **formula** connecting the variables. We then use the formula to find the solution to the problem.

Example 5 Self Tutor

Sam builds steel fences in sections.

 is called a 1-section and is made from 4 lengths of steel.

 is called a 2-section and is made from 7 lengths of steel.

How many lengths of steel does Sam need to make a 63-section fence?

First we sketch the next 2 or 3 cases to help establish a pattern.

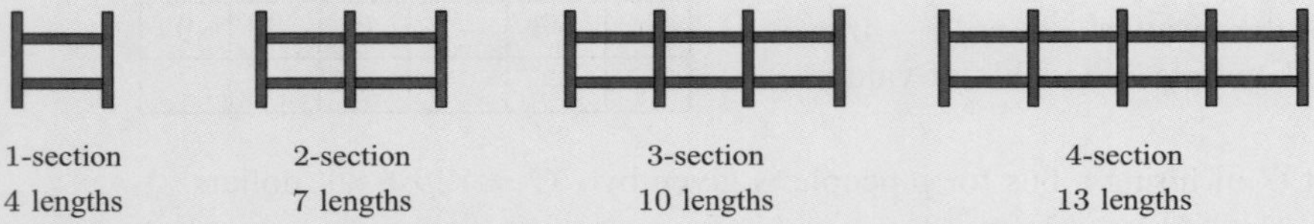

Let the number of sections be n and the number of steel lengths be S.

Number of sections (n)	1	2	3	4
Number of steel lengths (S)	4	7	10	13

+3 +3 +3

When n is increased by 1, S increases by 3. We therefore compare $3n$ with S.

$3n$	3	6	9	12
S	4	7	10	13

The S values are always 1 more than the $3n$ values, so $S = 3n + 1$.

When $n = 63$, $S = 3 \times 63 + 1 = 190$.

$\therefore$ 190 lengths of steel are needed.

EXERCISE 12D

1 Consider the **Opening Problem** on page **238**.

a Draw the next two ladder sizes.

b Copy and complete:

Number of rungs (n)	1	2	3	4	5
Number of metal pieces (M)	5	8			

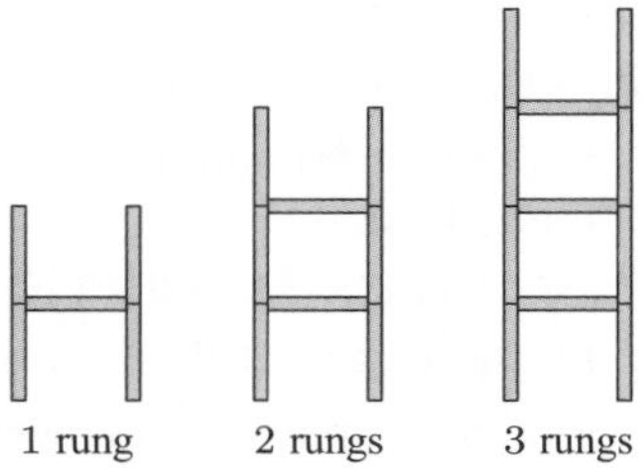

c Find the formula which connects M and n.

d How many metal pieces are required to build a ladder with 12 rungs?

2 Richard is experimenting with toothpicks to investigate housing designs:

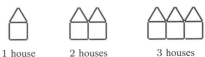

a Draw toothpick diagrams for 4 houses and 5 houses.

b Copy and complete:

Number of houses (h)	1	2	3	4	5
Number of toothpicks (T)					

c Find the formula which connects T and h.

d If Richard wanted to build 32 houses in a row, how many toothpicks would he need?

3 Mrs Moyle uses small pieces of cardboard to make pigeonholes for each student in her class.

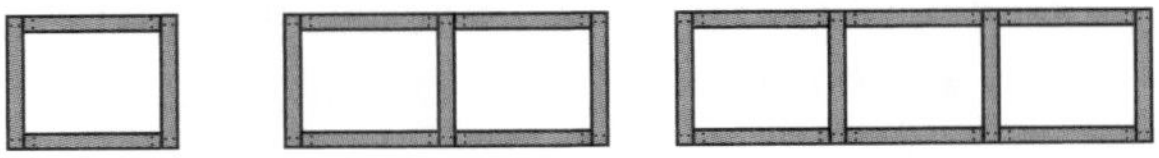

a Copy and complete the table:

b Find the formula that connects C and p.

c How many pieces of cardboard will Mrs Moyle need to construct 27 pigeonholes?

Pigeonholes (p)	1	2	3	4	5
Cardboard (C)					

4 Consider the pattern:

a Copy and complete the table:

Figure number (n)	1	2	3	4	5
Number of matchsticks (M)	5				

b Write a rule linking n and M.

c Find the number of matchsticks required for the 17th figure.

5 Consider the pattern:

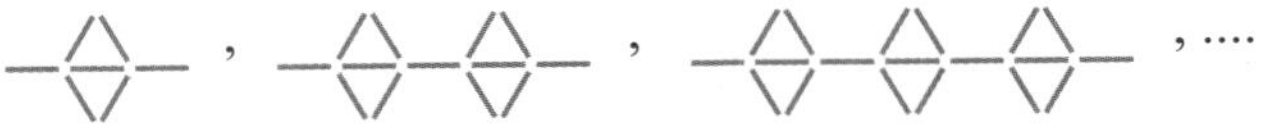

a Copy and complete the table:

Figure number (n)	1	2	3	4	5
Number of matchsticks (M)	7				

b Write a rule linking n and M.

c Find the number of matchsticks required for the:

i 14th figure **ii** 25th figure.

INVESTIGATION 1 THE CUBES PATTERN

What to do:

1 Use some cubes to form this pattern: 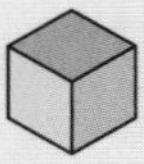 ,  , 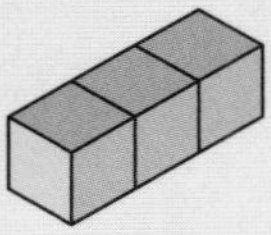 , ...

2 For each member of the pattern, count the number of cube faces that are exposed.

3 Copy and complete:

Number of cubes	1	2	3	4	5	6
Number of exposed cube faces	6	10				

4 Predict the number of exposed cube faces for the next three members of this pattern.

5 Check your prediction by arranging cubes and counting.

6 Write a formula for the number of exposed cube faces when there are n cubes.

7 Predict the number of exposed cube faces when there are:

a 10 cubes **b** 20 cubes **c** 100 cubes **d** 100 000 cubes.

INVESTIGATION 2 MAKING TRIANGLES

Consider the following triangles made out of dots.

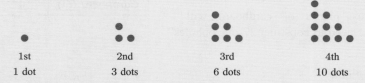

1st
1 dot
2nd
3 dots
3rd
6 dots
4th
10 dots

What to do:

1 Construct the next three triangles. Record the number of dots in a table:

Triangle (n)	1st	2nd	3rd	4th	5th	6th	7th
Number of dots (D)							

2 Predict the number of dots in the 8th, 9th, and 10th triangles.

3 Copy and complete: $\frac{1 \times 2}{2} = ...,$ $\frac{2 \times 3}{2} = ...,$ $\frac{3 \times 4}{2} = ...,$ $\frac{4 \times 5}{2} = ...$

Hence state a formula connecting D and n for the tabled values in **1**.

4 When Alan, Brenton, Claude, and Daniel shake hands in all possible ways, 6 handshakes take place. We can represent these as AB, AC, AD, BC, BD, and CD, where AB represents the Alan - Brenton handshake.

a Copy and complete:

Number of people (p)	2	3	4	5	6
Number of handshakes (H)					

b How is the number of handshakes related to the dot triangles above?

c State a formula connecting H and p.

d How many handshakes can take place within a group of 20 people?

E PRACTICAL PROBLEMS

The methods we have used for geometric patterns can also be used to solve more practical problems.

Consider the following example:

Milan is stacking boxes onto a wooden pallet. They contain the latest release crime novel to be sold in a bookshop.

The pallet weighs 20 kg, and each box of novels weighs 12 kg.

We can construct a table to show the total weight of the pallet and books as each carton of books is placed on the pallet.

Number of cartons	*Total weight*	
0	20 kg	
		$+12$
1	32 kg	
		$+12$
2	44 kg	
		$+12$
3	56 kg	
⋮	⋮	

The weight of c cartons of novels is $12c$ kg.

We then need to add the weight of the pallet, which is 20 kg.

So, the total weight W for a pallet with c cartons of novels, is $W = 12c + 20$ kg.

If Milan stacks 11 cartons of novels on the pallet, the total weight will be $(12 \times 11 + 20)$ kg $= 152$ kg.

Example 6 **Self Tutor**

Peter is a plumber. He charges a \$50 call-out fee plus \$40 for each hour spent working.

a What will t hours of labour cost?

b Find the total charge C dollars for a job taking t hours.

c Hence find the total charge for a job taking:

  i 5 hours **ii** $3\frac{1}{2}$ hours.

a 1 hour of labour will cost \$40.
2 hours of labour will cost $2 \times \$40 = \$80$.
$\therefore$ t hours of labour will cost $t \times \$40 = \$40t$.

b Total charge = cost of labour + call-out fee
$\therefore$ $C = 40t + 50$ dollars

c **i** When $t = 5$,
$C = 40 \times 5 + 50$
$= 250$
$\therefore$ the total charge is \$250.

ii When $t = 3.5$,
$C = 40 \times 3.5 + 50$
$= 190$
$\therefore$ the total charge is \$190.

EXERCISE 12E

1 For his birthday party, Desmond orders pizza from Domenica's Pizza House. Domenica charges €15 per pizza with a €5 surcharge for delivery.

 a What will p pizzas cost?
 b Find the total cost C euros of having p pizzas delivered to Desmond.
 c How much will Desmond have to pay for having:
  i 3 pizzas delivered ii 8 pizzas delivered?

2 Danielle inherits her great grandmother's shell collection containing 200 shells. Each month she adds another 7 shells to her collection.

 a Explain why the number of shells Danielle has in her collection after n months, is given by $S = 7n + 200$ shells.
 b How many shells will Danielle have in her collection after:
  i 3 months ii 1 year iii $2\frac{1}{4}$ years?

3 Mary has £5000 in her bank account. She withdraws £75 each week to pay her rent.

 a How much money will Mary have withdrawn for rent after n weeks?
 b Write a formula for the amount M pounds that Mary will have left in her bank account after n weeks, if she only uses the account to pay rent.
 c How much money will be in Mary's account after:
  i 8 weeks ii 1 year?

4 300 people went to the cinema to see a new film. However, they were so bored by the film that 5 people left the cinema every 10 minutes.

 a How many people had left the cinema after t lots of 10 minutes?
 b Find the total number of people P who were still in the cinema after t lots of 10 minutes.
 c Find the number of people still at the film after:
  i 40 minutes ii $1\frac{1}{2}$ hours.

5 A new manufacturer plans to make 12 000 greeting cards in the first year of production, and 8000 greeting cards each year after that.

 a In total, how many cards will have been manufactured after:
  i 2 years ii 3 years iii 4 years?
 b Write a formula for the total number of greeting cards C manufactured after n years.
 c Find the total number of greeting cards manufactured after 10 years.

F NUMBER SEQUENCES

In this Section we consider sequences of numbers which follow a pattern or rule. These rules often describe a member of the sequence in terms of the previous member.

For example, consider the number sequence 3, 7, 11, 15, 19, ...

We notice that
$$3+4=7$$
$$7+4=11$$
$$11+4=15$$
$$15+4=19$$

A rule connecting the members of the sequence is therefore:

"the next member is equal to the previous one plus 4".

However, not all number sequences increase by a fixed amount from one member to the next. You will need to practise your skills of observation to find the rules for each sequence.

Example 7 — Self Tutor

For each of these number sequences, write down the rule used to find the next member, and state the next three members:

a 1, 7, 13, 19, 25, ... **b** 50, 47, 44, 41, 38, ... **c** 2, 10, 50, 250, ...

a 1 $\xrightarrow{+6}$ 7 $\xrightarrow{+6}$ 13 $\xrightarrow{+6}$ 19 $\xrightarrow{+6}$ 25

Rule: "The next member is equal to the previous one plus 6."

∴ the next three members are: 31, 37, 43.

b 50 $\xrightarrow{-3}$ 47 $\xrightarrow{-3}$ 44 $\xrightarrow{-3}$ 41 $\xrightarrow{-3}$ 38

Rule: "The next member is equal to the previous one minus 3."

∴ the next three members are: 35, 32, 29.

c 2 $\xrightarrow{\times 5}$ 10 $\xrightarrow{\times 5}$ 50 $\xrightarrow{\times 5}$ 250

Rule: "The next member is equal to the previous one multiplied by 5."

∴ the next three members are: 1250, 6250, 31 250.

EXERCISE 12F

1 For each of these number sequences, write down the rule used to find the next member, and state the next three members:

a 1, 4, 7, 10, 13, ... **b** 11, 15, 19, 23, 27, ... **c** 2, 9, 16, 23, 30, ...

d 6, 12, 18, 24, ... **e** 13, 22, 31, 40, ... **f** 7, 20, 33, 46, ...

g 2, 1, 0, −1, ... **h** 8, 5, 2, ... **i** −11, −7, −3, ...

2 For each of these number sequences, write down the rule used to find the next member, and state the next three members:

- **a** 38, 36, 34, 32, 30, ...
- **b** 29, 26, 23, 20, ...
- **c** 57, 51, 45, 39, ...
- **d** 100, 97, 94, 91, ...
- **e** 250, 242, 234, 226, ...
- **f** 65, 61, 57, 53, 49, ...
- **g** 1, 2, 4, 8, 16, ...
- **h** 2, 6, 18, 54, ...
- **i** 2, 8, 32, 128, ...
- **j** 64, 32, 16, 8, 4, ...
- **k** 80, 40, 20, 10, ...
- **l** 243, 81, 27, 9, ...

3 Write down the missing number from each sequence:

- **a** 3, 9, □, 21, 27
- **b** 12, □, 36, 48, 60
- **c** 75, 60, □, 30, 15
- **d** 3, 6, □, 24, 48
- **e** 3, 9, 27, □, 243
- **f** 10, □, 32, 43
- **g** 100, 50, □, $12\frac{1}{2}$
- **h** 96, □, 6, $1\frac{1}{2}$
- **i** 2, 3, 5, □, 11, 13

4 State the next three members of these sequences.

- **a** 2, 3, 5, 8, 12, 17, ...
- **b** 2, 6, 24, 120, 720, ...
- **c** 2, 5, 11, 23, 47, ...
- **d** 1, 1, 2, 3, 5, 8, 13, ...

REVIEW SET 12A

1 Consider the pattern:

- **a** Copy and complete:

Figure number (n)	1	2	3	4	5
Number of matchsticks (M)					

- **b** Use the table of values to find the rule linking n and M.
- **c** Find the number of matchsticks required for the:
  - **i** 15th figure
  - **ii** 42nd figure.

2 Consider the rule:
four times the input number, minus five.
Calculate the output numbers for the input numbers given.

Input	Output
2	
5	
8	

3 Write a formula connecting the variables in each table:

a

n	1	2	3	4
M	5	9	13	17

b

x	1	2	3	4
y	5	12	19	26

4 Consider the formula $W = 6n - 13$. Find W when: **a** $n = 4$ **b** $n = -5$.

5 The following patterns are made with matchsticks:

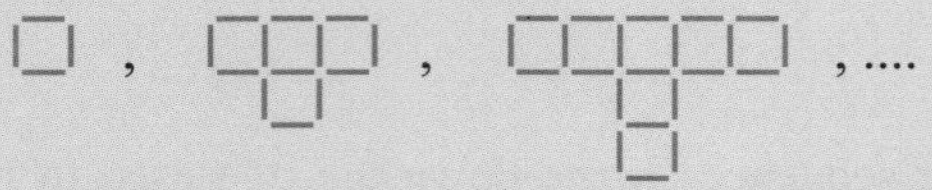

- **a** Copy and complete:

Figure number (n)	1	2	3	4	5
Number of matchsticks (M)					

b Use the table of values to find the rule linking the number of matchsticks M with the figure number n.

c Use the rule to find the number of matchsticks needed for the 30th figure.

6 The distance of a train from its destination after t hours of travel is given by the formula $D = 600 - 80t$ kilometres.

a Find D when $t = 0$. Interpret your answer.

b How far is the train from its destination after:

i 2 hours **ii** 5 hours?

7 Josie has \$450 in her savings account. Using the surplus from her pay, she is able to deposit \$25 per week into it. She does not withdraw any money.

a Find the amount of money that Josie will have deposited from her pay after w weeks.

b Find the *total* amount A dollars in the account after w weeks.

c How much money will Josie have in her account after:

i 4 weeks **ii** 6 months?

8 For each of these number sequences, write down the rule used to find the next member, and state the next three members:

a 3, 7, 11, 15, 19, ... **b** 38, 31, 24, 17, 10, ...

9 Carl is buying concert tickets online. Each ticket costs £19, and there is a fixed credit card fee of £3.

a Explain why the total cost of buying n tickets is $C = 19n + 3$ pounds.

b Find the total cost of buying: **i** 2 tickets **ii** 5 tickets.

10 Write down the missing number from each sequence:

a 1, 3, 9, □, 81, 243 **b** 120, 60, □, 15, $7\frac{1}{2}$

REVIEW SET 12B

1 Consider the rule:

treble the input number then add seven.

Calculate the output numbers for the input numbers given.

Input	*Output*
2	
9	
11	

2 Write a formula connecting the variables in each table:

a

p	1	2	3	4
Q	4	10	16	22

b

t	1	2	3	4
D	5	8	11	14

3 The cost of hiring a tennis court for t hours is given by $C = 15h + 8$ euros.
Find the cost of hiring the tennis court for:

a 12 hours **b** $4\frac{1}{2}$ hours.

4 For each of these number sequences, write down the rule used to find the next member, and state the next three members:

a -2, 6, 14, 22, 30, ... **b** 320, 160, 80, 40, ...

5 Consider the pattern:

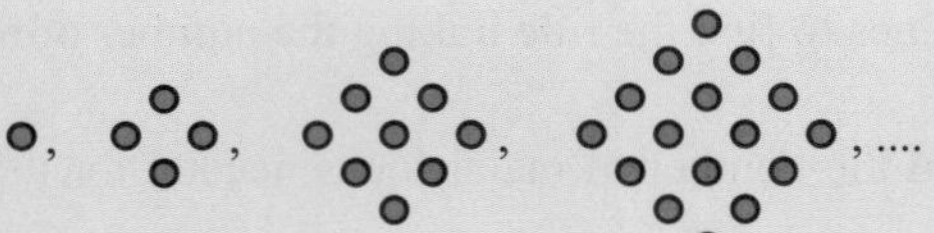

a Record the number of dots in each figure:

Figure (n)	1	2	3	4
Number of dots (D)				

b Predict the number of dots in the nth figure.

6 The mass of a basket containing n plums is $45n + 95$ grams.
Find the mass of a basket containing a dozen plums.

7 A school fundraising committee decides to hold a sausage sizzle.
They start with $60 in their money box, and they receive $1.50 for every sausage they sell.

a Find the amount of money raised by selling s sausages.

b Find the total amount A dollars in the money box after selling s sausages.

c How much money will be in the money box if they sell a total of:

i 20 sausages **ii** 50 sausages **iii** 150 sausages?

8 The following patterns are made with matchsticks:

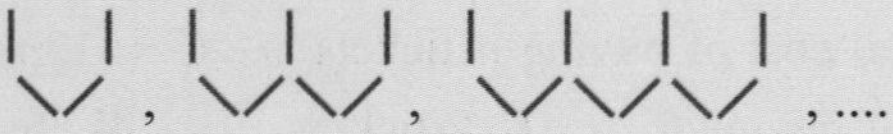

a Copy and complete:

Figure number (n)	1	2	3	4	5
Number of matchsticks (M)					

b Write the rule linking n and M.

c How many matchsticks would be required for the 25th figure?

9 Write down the missing number from each sequence:

a 12, 7, 2, □, −8 **b** 4, 20, □, 500

10 When a circle is divided by n distinct lines, the maximum number of regions which can be formed is given by the formula $R = \frac{1}{2}n^2 + \frac{1}{2}n + 1$.
For example, when a circle is divided by 2 lines, a maximum of 4 regions can be formed, as shown.

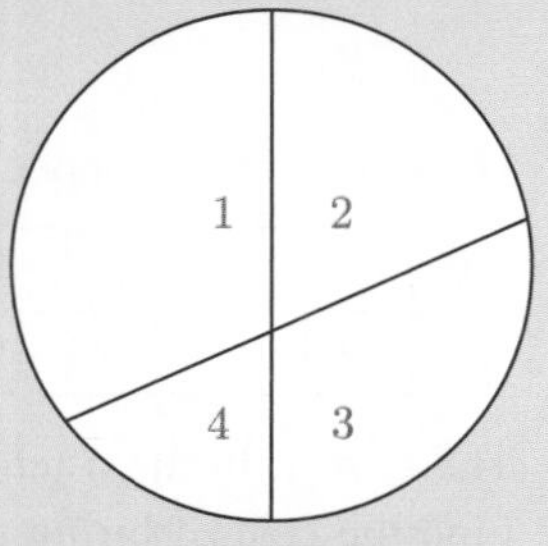

a Find the maximum number of regions formed when a circle is divided by:

i 3 lines **ii** 4 lines.

b Check your answers to **a** by illustrating each case.

c Find the maximum number of regions formed when a circle is divided by 12 lines.

d Find a formula for the *minimum* number of regions formed when a circle is divided by n distinct lines.

Chapter 13

Further measurement

Contents:

OPENING PROBLEM

Stuart has a 330 mL bottle of orange juice. He thinks he can pour it all into his glass, which is a cylinder with diameter 7 cm and height 8 cm. Stuart's friend Patrick thinks the glass will overflow.

Things to think about:

a If the glass was full, what *volume* of fluid would it contain?

b What is the relationship between *volume* and *capacity*?

c Will Stuart's glass overflow?

In this chapter we will extend our study of measurement to consider 3-dimensional objects.

A SURFACE AREA

The **surface area** of a solid is the sum of the areas of its surfaces.

To find the surface area of a solid, it is often helpful to draw the **net** of the solid.

Example 1 — Self Tutor

Find the total surface area of the rectangular box:

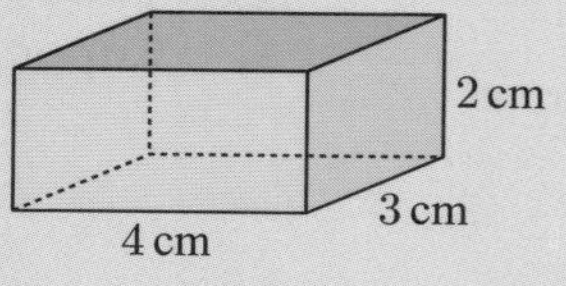

We first draw a net of the box:

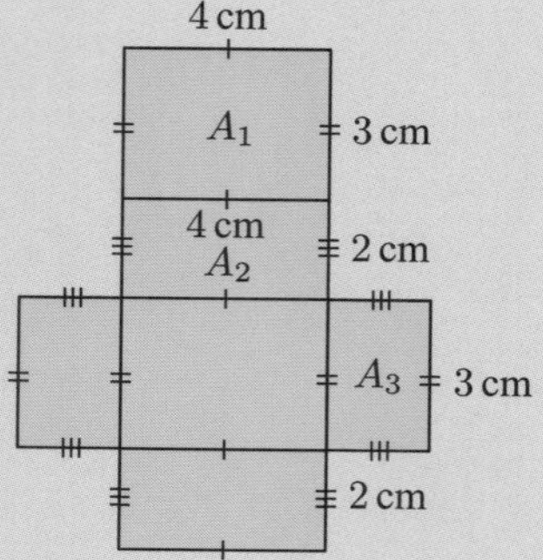

$A_1 = 4 \times 3 = 12$ cm^2 {bottom and top}

$A_2 = 4 \times 2 = 8$ cm^2 {front and back}

$A_3 = 2 \times 3 = 6$ cm^2 {sides}

$\therefore$ total surface area

$= 2 \times A_1 + 2 \times A_2 + 2 \times A_3$

$= (2 \times 12 + 2 \times 8 + 2 \times 6)$ cm^2

$= 52$ cm^2

So, the total surface area of the box is 52 cm^2.

EXERCISE 13A.1

1 Find the surface area of a cube with sides of length:

a 3 cm **b** 2 mm **c** 1.5 m

2 Find the surface area of the rectangular prism:

a

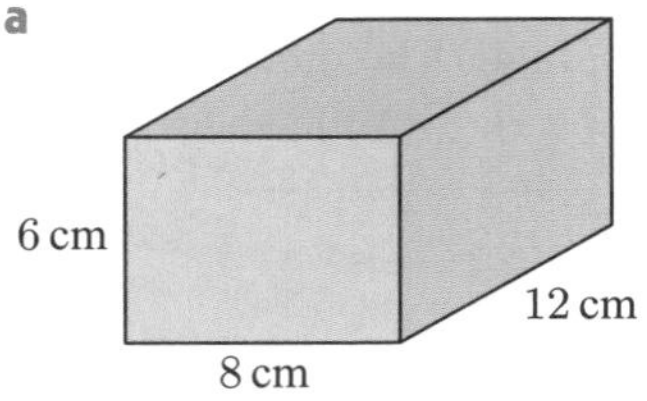

b

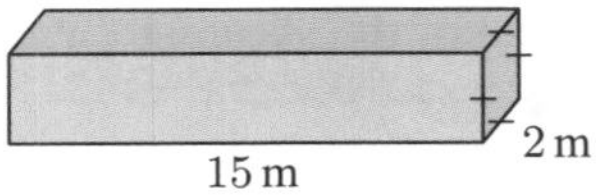

c

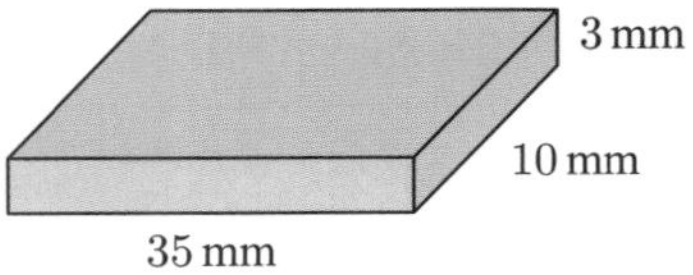

Example 2 **Self Tutor**

Find the total surface area of this wedge:

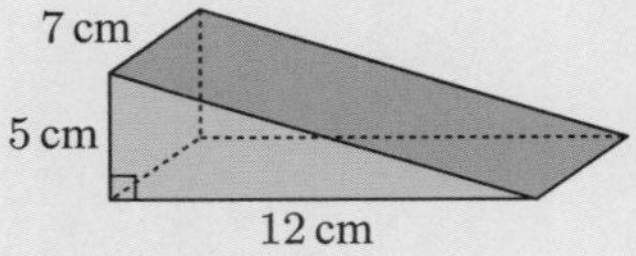

Let the length of the slanted edge be x cm.

We can now draw a net of the solid.

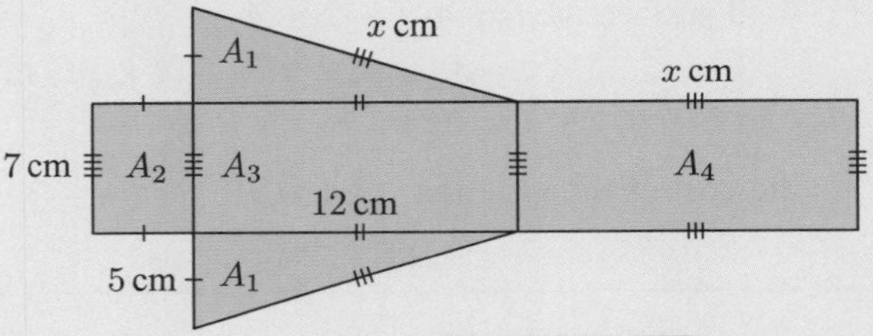

We find x using Pythagoras:

$$x^2 = 12^2 + 5^2$$
$$\therefore\ x^2 = 169$$
$$\therefore\ x = \sqrt{169} = 13 \quad \{\text{as } x > 0\}$$

$A_1 = \frac{1}{2}bh$
$= \frac{1}{2} \times 12 \times 5$
$= 30\ \text{cm}^2$

$A_2 = 7 \times 5$
$= 35\ \text{cm}^2$

$A_3 = 12 \times 7$
$= 84\ \text{cm}^2$

$A_4 = 13 \times 7$
$= 91\ \text{cm}^2$

Sometimes we need Pythagoras' theorem to find a missing length.

$\therefore$ total surface area $= 2 \times A_1 + A_2 + A_3 + A_4$
$= (2 \times 30 + 35 + 84 + 91)\ \text{cm}^2$
$= 270\ \text{cm}^2$

3 Find the surface area of the triangular prism:

a

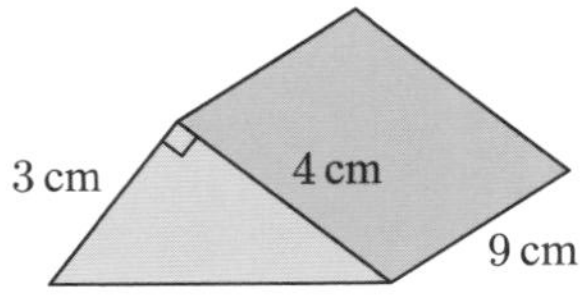

b

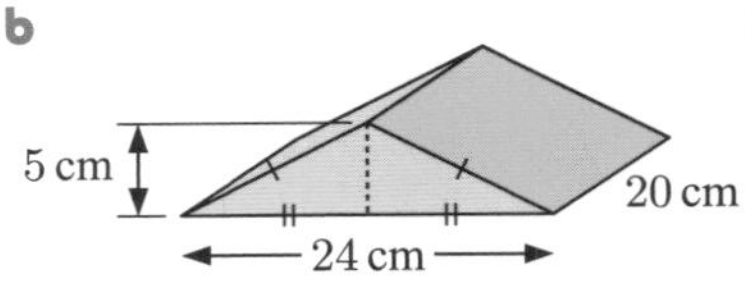

c

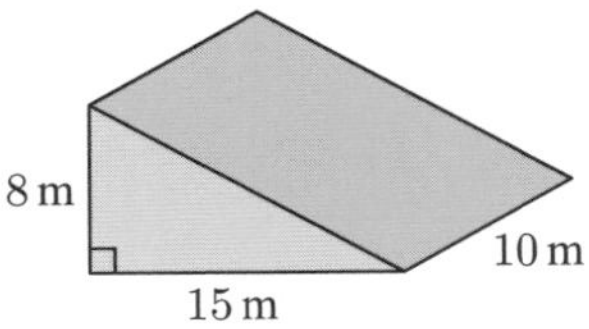

4 Find the surface area of the prism:

a

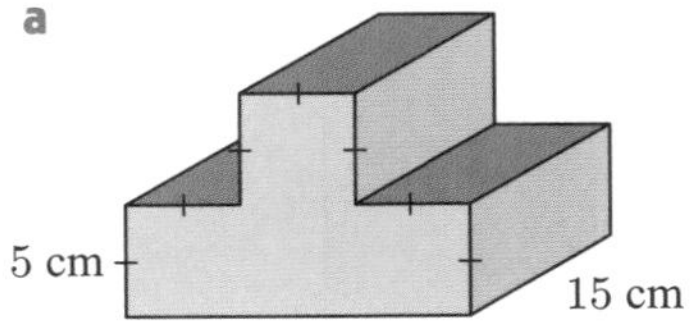

b

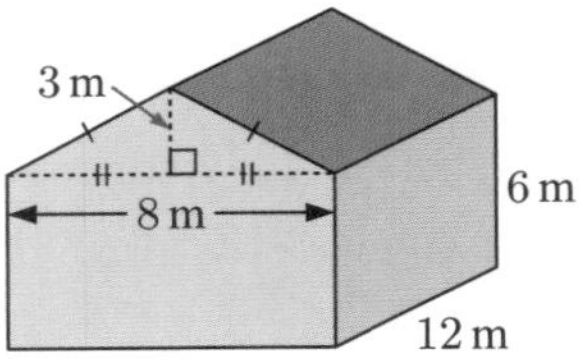

c

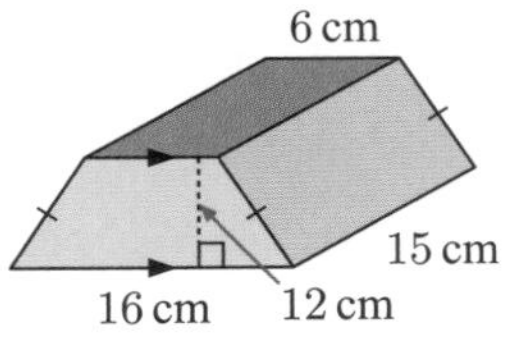

Example 3 ◀)) **Self Tutor**

Victor is erecting a 6 m by 4 m rectangular garden shed that is 2 m high. The metal sheeting costs
$15 per square metre. Find the cost of the sheeting for the sides and roof of the shed.

The shed: Net:

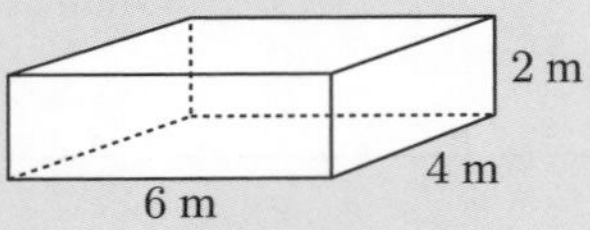

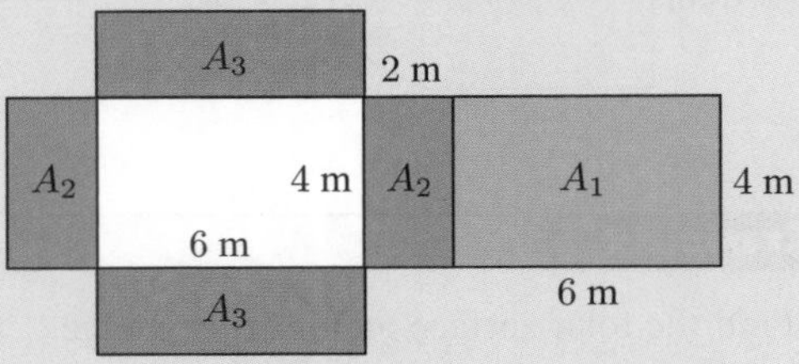

$$A_1 = 6 \times 4 \qquad\qquad A_2 = 4 \times 2 \qquad\qquad A_3 = 6 \times 2$$
$$ = 24 \text{ m}^2 \qquad\qquad = 8 \text{ m}^2 \qquad\qquad = 12 \text{ m}^2$$

∴ total surface area $= A_1 + 2 \times A_2 + 2 \times A_3$

$$= (24 + 2 \times 8 + 2 \times 12) \text{ m}^2$$
$$= 64 \text{ m}^2$$

We do not include
the area of the floor.

∴ the cost of the sheeting $= 64 \times \$15$
$$= \$960$$

5 A cellar has dimensions 4 m by 3 m by 2.4 m high. Find the cost of painting the walls and ceiling
of the cellar if 1 litre of paint costs €24.90, and each litre covers 15 square metres.

6

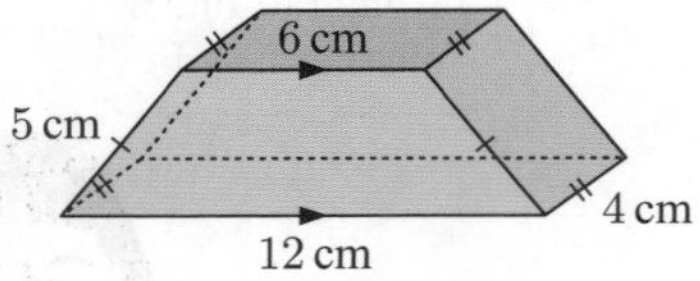

A box for a printer cartridge has the dimensions shown.
Find the area of cardboard needed to make the box.

7 The greenhouse shown is made from plastic
sheeting which costs $4.50 per m². The greenhouse
has no floor.
Find the total cost of the plastic sheeting.

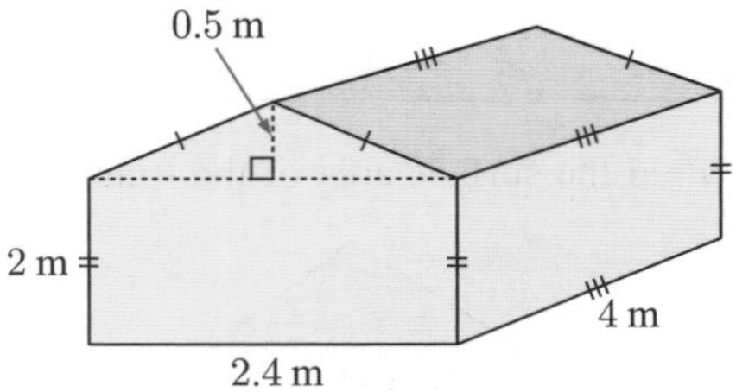

CYLINDERS

The cylinder shown has no top or bottom. If the cylinder is
cut, opened out, and flattened, it takes the shape of a rectangle.

You can verify this by peeling the label off a cylindrical can.

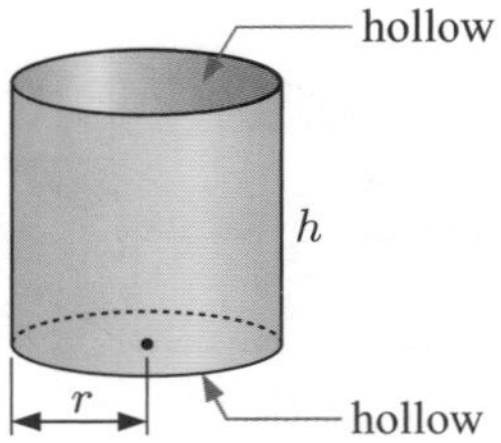

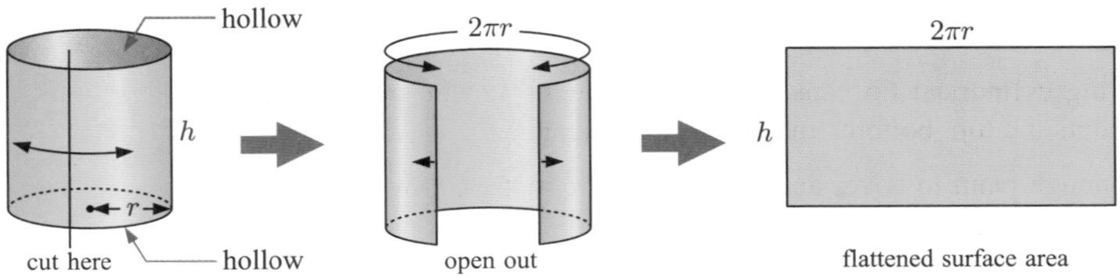

The length of the rectangle is the circumference of the cylinder.

$\therefore$ for a hollow cylinder, the outer surface area A = area of rectangle

$$\begin{aligned} A &= \text{area of rectangle} \\ &= \text{length} \times \text{width} \\ &= 2\pi r \times h \\ &= 2\pi r h \end{aligned}$$

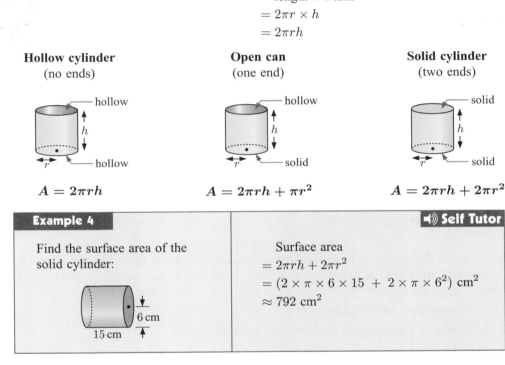

Hollow cylinder
(no ends)

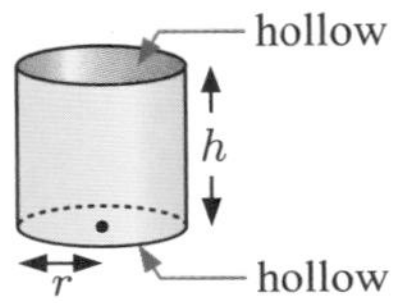

$\boldsymbol{A = 2\pi r h}$

Open can
(one end)

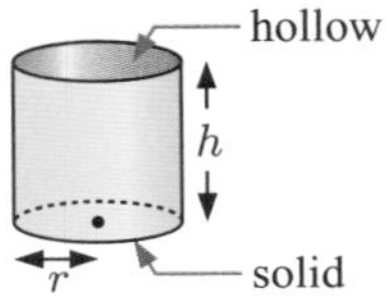

$\boldsymbol{A = 2\pi r h + \pi r^2}$

Solid cylinder
(two ends)

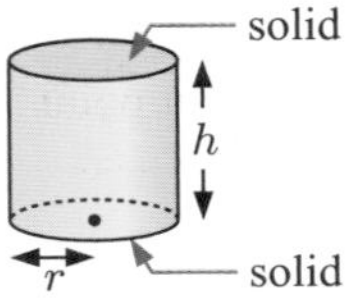

$\boldsymbol{A = 2\pi r h + 2\pi r^2}$

Example 4 — Self Tutor

Find the surface area of the solid cylinder:

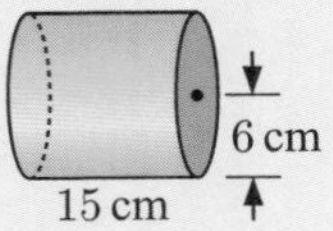

Surface area

$= 2\pi r h + 2\pi r^2$

$= (2 \times \pi \times 6 \times 15 + 2 \times \pi \times 6^2)\ \text{cm}^2$

$\approx 792\ \text{cm}^2$

EXERCISE 13A.2

1 Find, rounded to 3 significant figures, the outer surface area of the following cylinders:

a hollow throughout

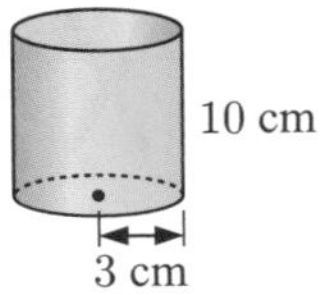

b solid

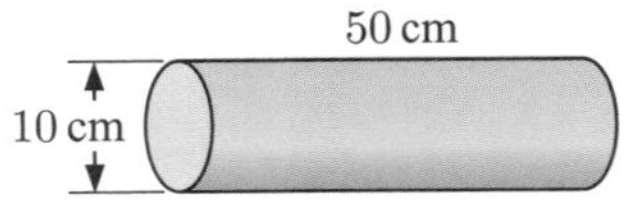

c can (no top)

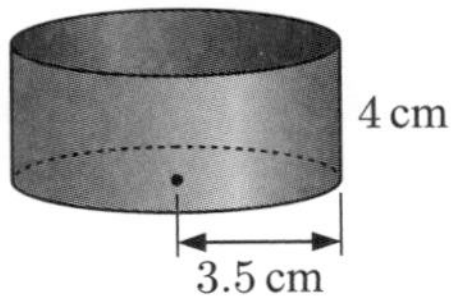

d solid

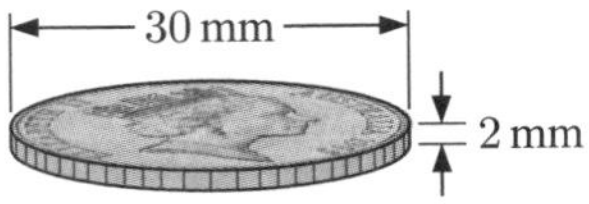

e tank (no top)

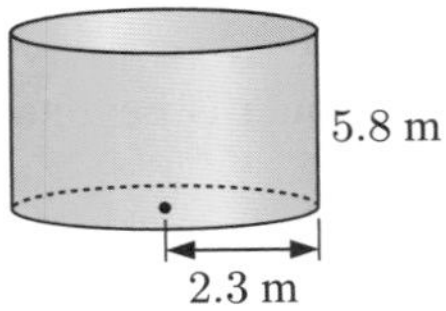

f hollow throughout

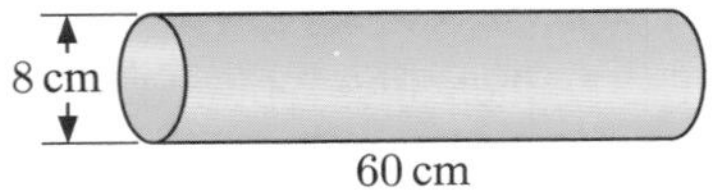

Example 5 **Self Tutor**

Jane is painting cylindrical tin cans which have height 12 cm and diameter 8 cm. She paints the top, bottom, and sides of each can.

If Jane has enough paint to cover an area of 5 square metres, how many cans is she able to paint?

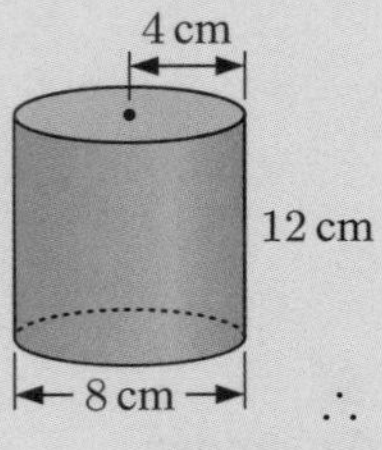

$$\begin{aligned}\text{Surface area} &= 2\pi rh + 2\pi r^2 \\ &= (2\times\pi\times 4\times 12 \;+\; 2\times\pi\times 4^2)\ \text{cm}^2 \\ &= (96\pi + 32\pi)\ \text{cm}^2 \\ &= 128\pi\ \text{cm}^2 \\ &\approx 402.12\ \text{cm}^2\end{aligned}$$

$$\begin{aligned}\therefore\ \text{the number of cans} &= 5\ \text{m}^2 \div 402.12\ \text{cm}^2 \\ &= (5\times 10\,000)\ \text{cm}^2 \div 402.12\ \text{cm}^2 \\ &= 50\,000\ \text{cm}^2 \div 402.12\ \text{cm}^2 \\ &\approx 124.34\end{aligned}$$

$\therefore$ Jane can paint 124 cans.

2 What area of sheet metal is needed to make the saucepan shown, excluding the handle? Round your answer to the nearest square centimetre.

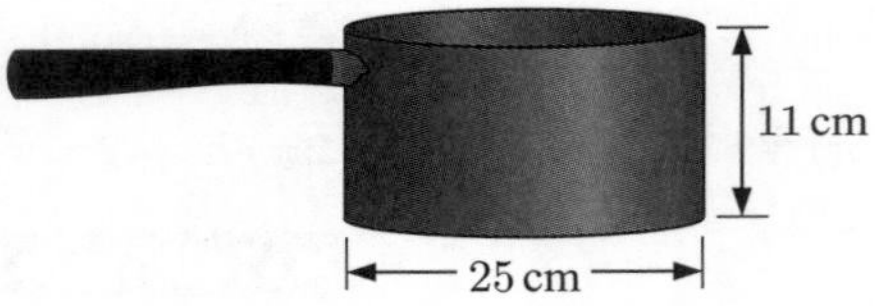

3 Fernandez has a collection of cylindrical jars with external radius 3 cm and height 10 cm. He needs to cover the curved side of each jar with a label. He has 2 square metres of sticky paper for the labels.

   a How many jars can Fernandez cover?

   b What assumption have you made in your calculation in **a**?

4 Determine how much paint is required to paint the outside of this tank, if each litre of paint covers 15 square metres.

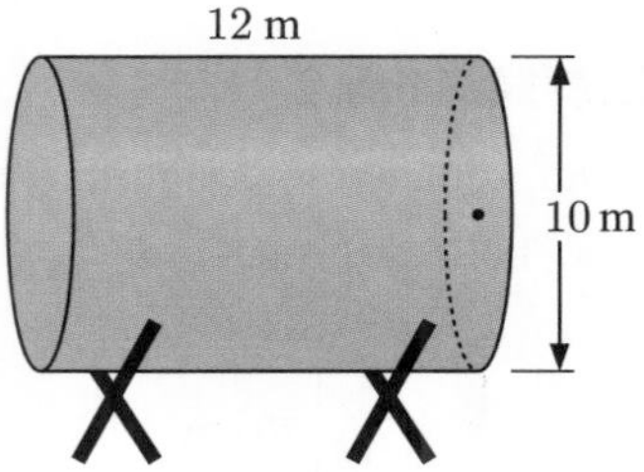

SPHERES

Surface area of a sphere $= 4\pi r^2$

The mathematics required to prove this formula is beyond the scope of this course.

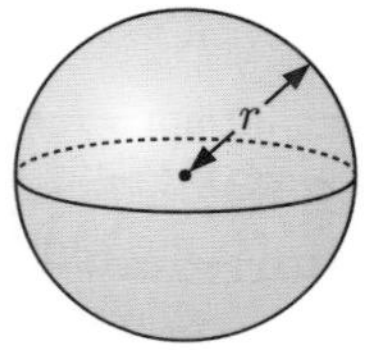

Example 6 — Self Tutor

Calculate the surface area of the sphere:

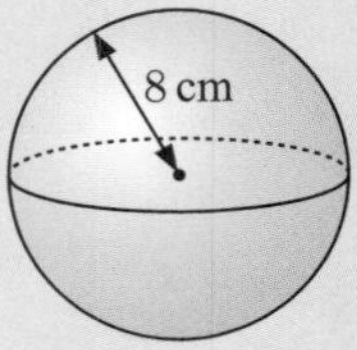

Surface area
$= 4\pi r^2$
$= 4 \times \pi \times 8^2\ \text{cm}^2$
$\approx 804\ \text{cm}^2$

EXERCISE 13A.3

1 Find the surface area of the following solids:

a

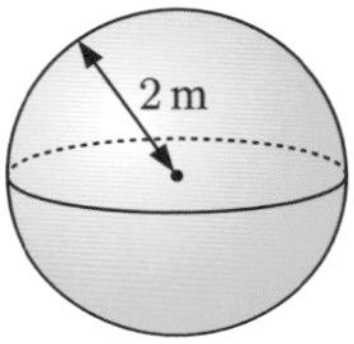

b

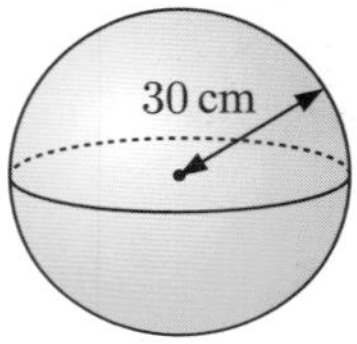

c

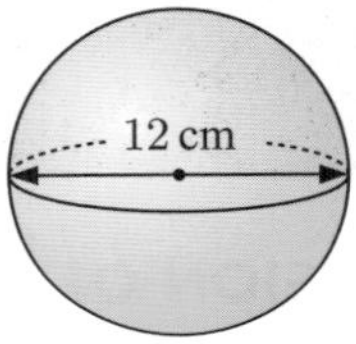

d

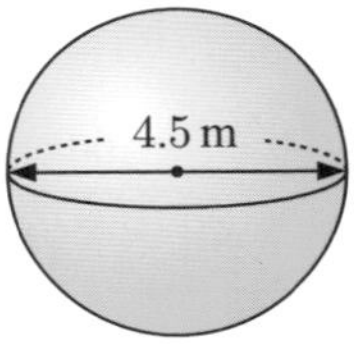

e

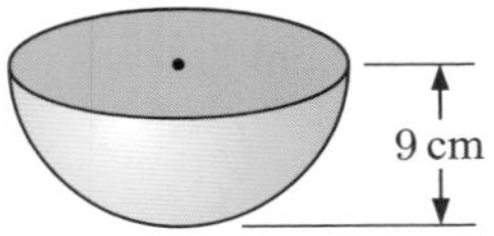

f

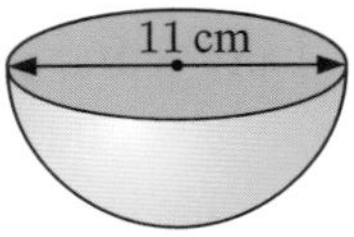

2 Find the surface area of a tennis ball with diameter 7 cm.

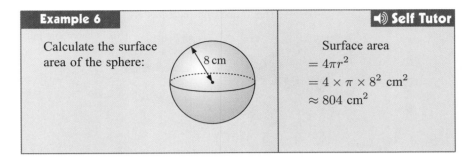

3 We use a sphere to model Earth, even though our planet is not a *perfect* sphere. Earth has a radius of approximately 6400 km. Estimate the surface area of Earth.

4 How many spherical balls of diameter 15 cm can be covered by 40 square metres of material?

5 A sphere has surface area 100 cm^2. Find the radius of the sphere.

B VOLUME

The **volume** of a solid is the amount of space it occupies.

We can measure volume in **cubic millimetres** (mm^3), **cubic centimetres** (cm^3), or **cubic metres** (m^3).

1 **cubic millimetre** is the volume of a cube with sides of length 1 mm.

1 **cubic centimetre** is the volume of a cube with sides of length 1 cm.

1 **cubic metre** is the volume of a cube with sides of length 1 m.

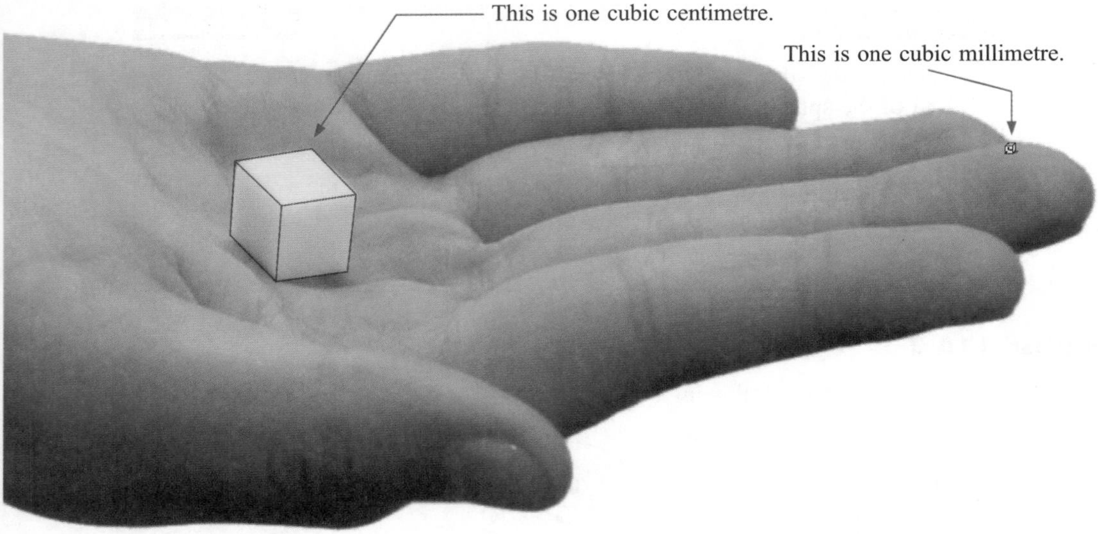

This is one cubic centimetre.
This is one cubic millimetre.

CONVERSION OF VOLUME UNITS

Since $1 \text{ cm} = 10 \text{ mm}$, we can see that

$$1 \text{ cm}^3 = 10 \text{ mm} \times 10 \text{ mm} \times 10 \text{ mm} = 1000 \text{ mm}^3$$

Likewise, $$1 \text{ m}^3 = 100 \text{ cm} \times 100 \text{ cm} \times 100 \text{ cm} = 1\,000\,000 \text{ cm}^3$$

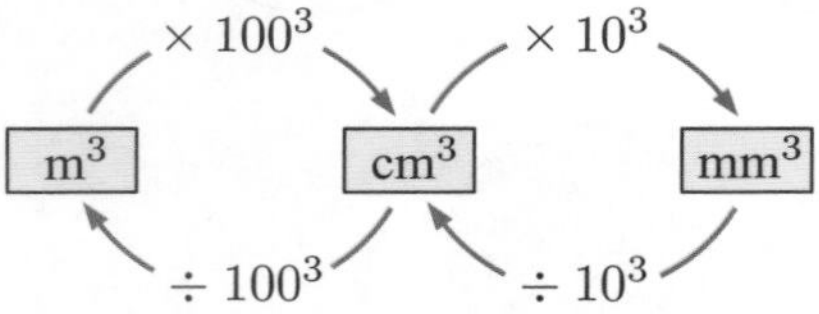

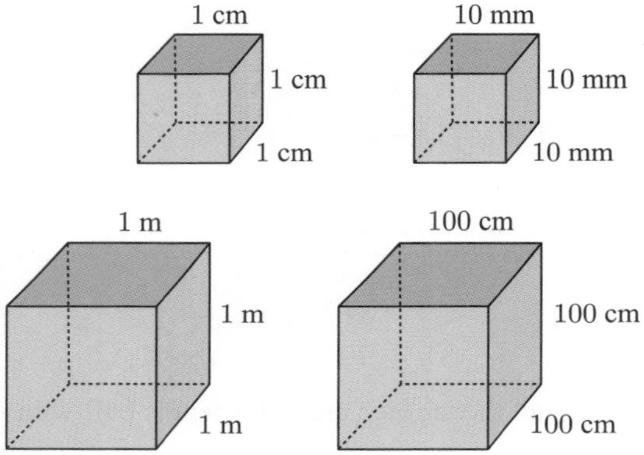

Example 7 **Self Tutor**

Convert:

a 23 cm^3 to mm^3 **b** $24\,000 \text{ cm}^3$ to m^3

a 23 cm^3
$= (23 \times 10^3) \text{ mm}^3$
$= 23\,000 \text{ mm}^3$

b $24\,000 \text{ cm}^3$
$= (24\,000 \div 100^3) \text{ m}^3$
$= (24\,000 \div 1\,000\,000) \text{ m}^3$
$= 0.024 \text{ m}^3$

To convert cm to mm we multiply by 10.

EXERCISE 13B.1

1 State which units of volume would be most suitable to measure the space occupied by:

a a can of dog food **b** a house **c** a stapler
d a small bead **e** a swimming pool **f** an eraser
g a mountain **h** a book **i** a grain of sand

2 Convert:

a $34\,000$ mm^3 to cm^3 **b** 7.9 m^3 to cm^3 **c** 6.1 mm^3 to cm^3

d $2\,820\,000$ cm^3 to mm^3 **e** 496 cm^3 to mm^3 **f** 8×10^{10} cm^3 to m^3

g $57\,700$ mm^3 to cm^3 **h** 1700 cm^3 to mm^3 **i** 0.074 m^3 to mm^3

3 There are 900 cm^3 of rice in a bag. If the average volume of each grain of rice is approximately 10 mm^3, estimate the number of rice grains in the bag.

VOLUME FORMULAE

RECTANGULAR PRISM

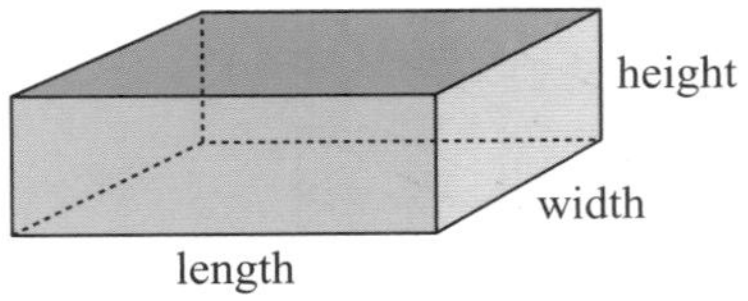

Volume = length × width × height

SOLIDS OF UNIFORM CROSS-SECTION

In the triangular prism alongside, any vertical slice parallel to the front triangular face will be the same size and shape as that face. Solids like this are called *solids of uniform cross-section.* The cross-section in this case is a triangle.

Solid **Cross-section**

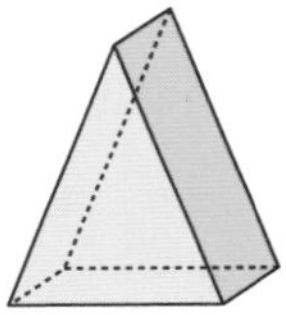

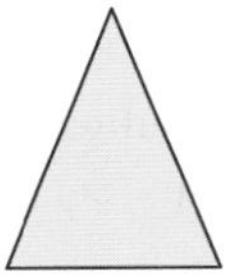

Another example is this hexagonal prism:

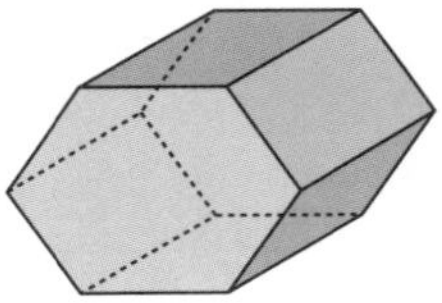

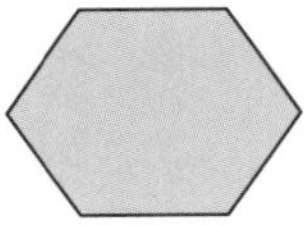

For any solid of uniform cross-section:

Volume = area of cross-section × length

Example 8 **Self Tutor**

Find the volume of each solid:

a

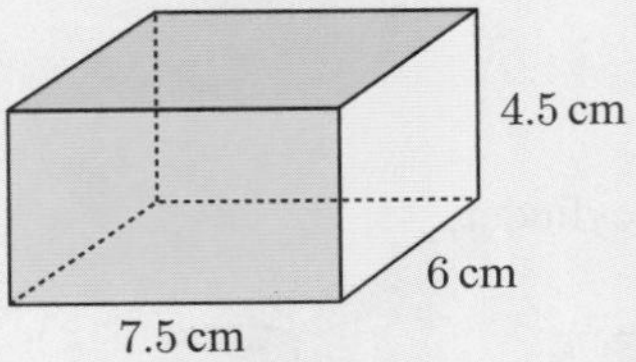

b

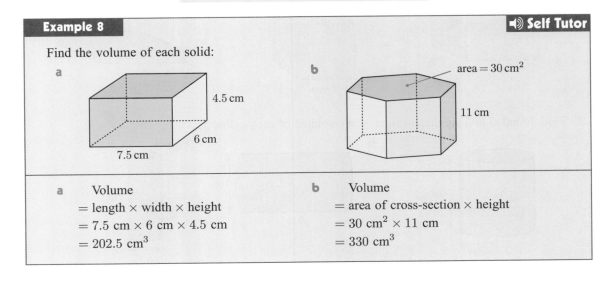

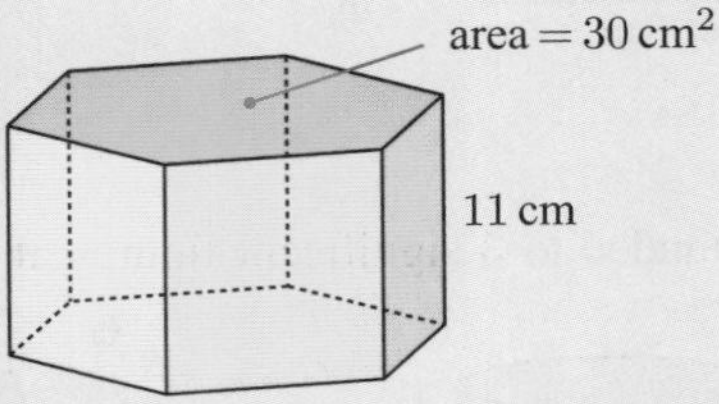

a Volume
= length × width × height
= 7.5 cm × 6 cm × 4.5 cm
= 202.5 cm^3

b Volume
= area of cross-section × height
= 30 cm^2 × 11 cm
= 330 cm^3

For a **cylinder**, the cross-section is a circle.

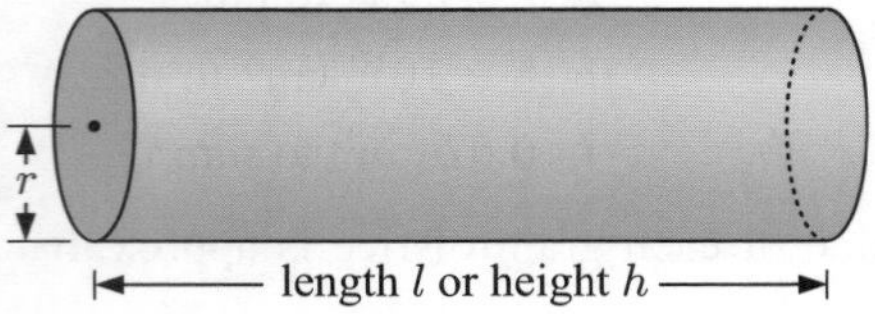

Volume = area of circle × length
$= \pi r^2 \times l$

$$V = \pi r^2 l \quad \text{or} \quad V = \pi r^2 h$$

Example 9 — Self Tutor

Find, rounded to 3 significant figures, the volume of each solid:

a

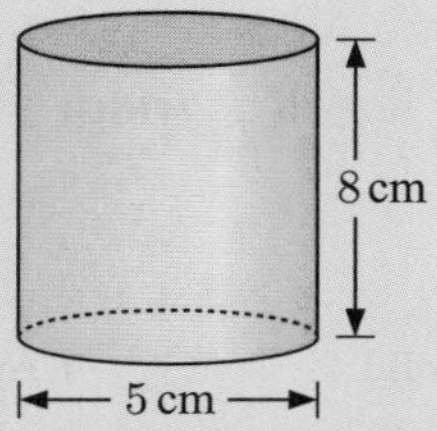

b

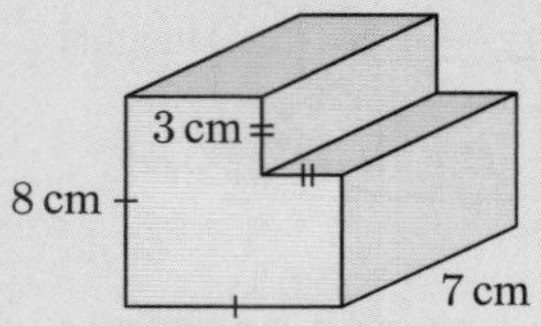

a The base has diameter 5 cm, so the radius is 2.5 cm.

$V = \pi r^2 h$
$= \pi \times 2.5^2 \times 8 \text{ cm}^3$
$\approx 157 \text{ cm}^3$

b area of cross-section
$= (8 \times 8 - 3 \times 3) \text{ cm}^2$
$= 55 \text{ cm}^2$

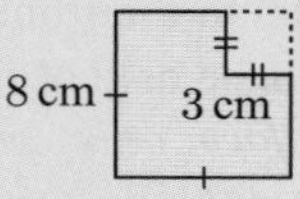

$\therefore$ volume
= area of cross-section × length
$= 55 \text{ cm}^2 \times 7 \text{ cm}$
$= 385 \text{ cm}^3$

EXERCISE 13B.2

1 Find the volume of each rectangular prism:

a

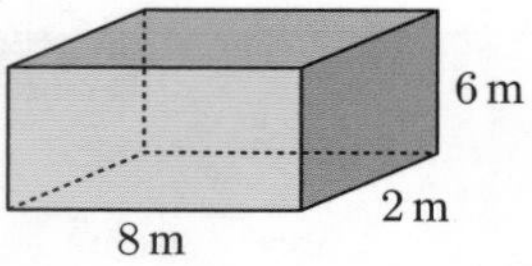

b

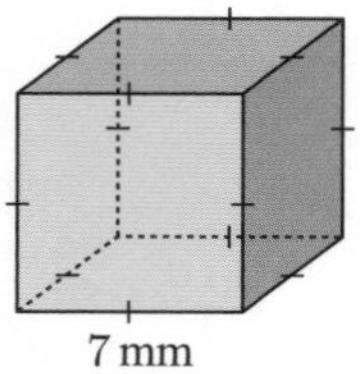

c

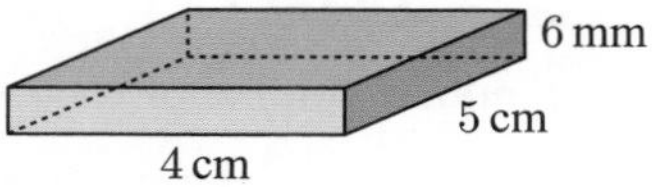

2 Find, rounded to 3 significant figures, the volume of each cylinder:

a

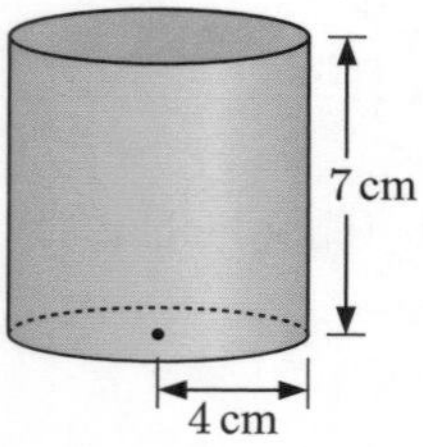

b

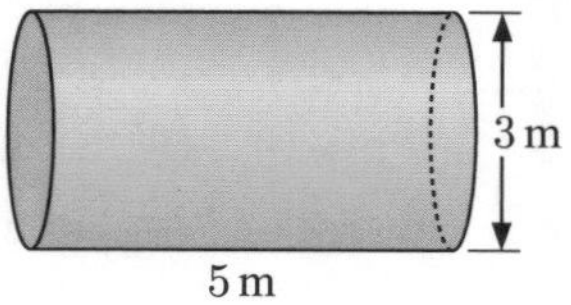

c

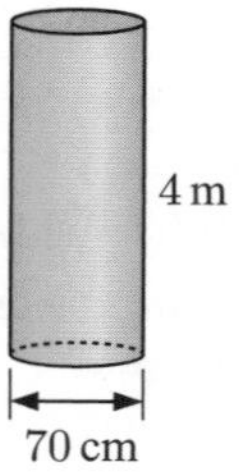

3 Find, rounded to 3 significant figures where necessary, the volume of each solid:

a

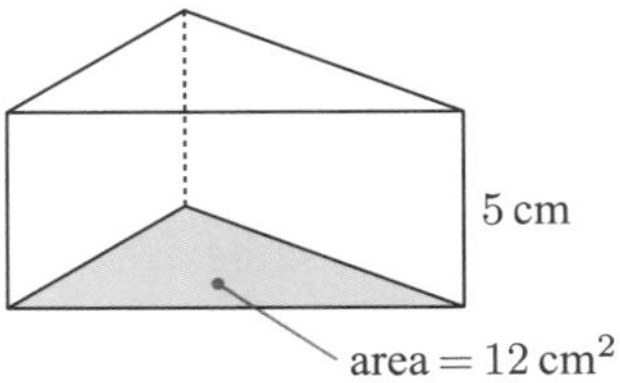

b

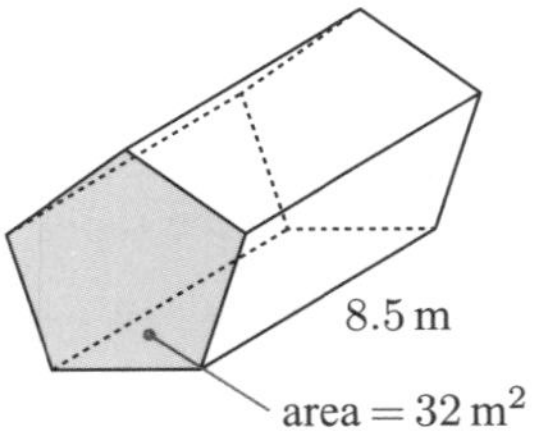

c

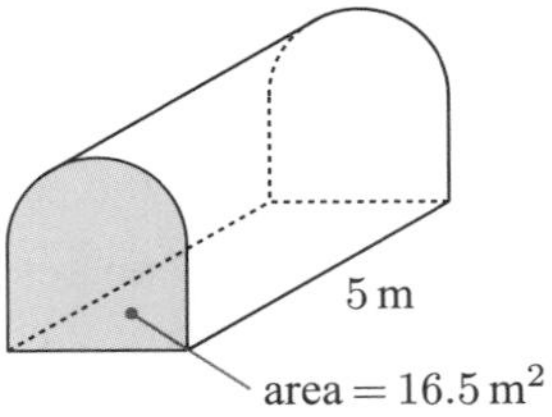

d

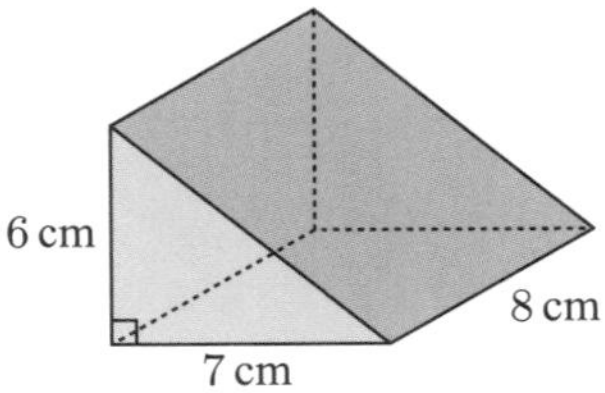

e

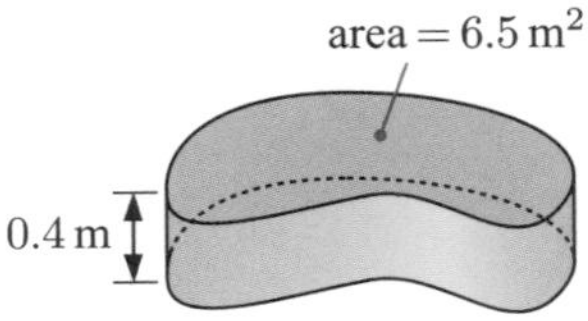

f

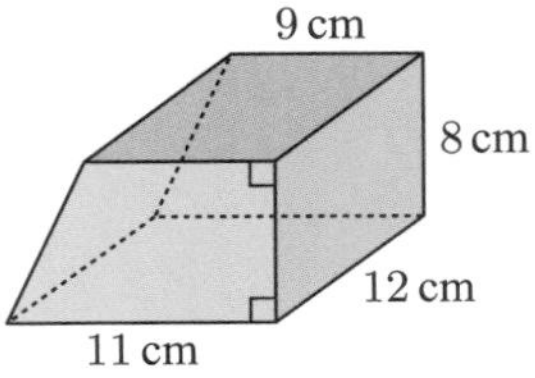

g

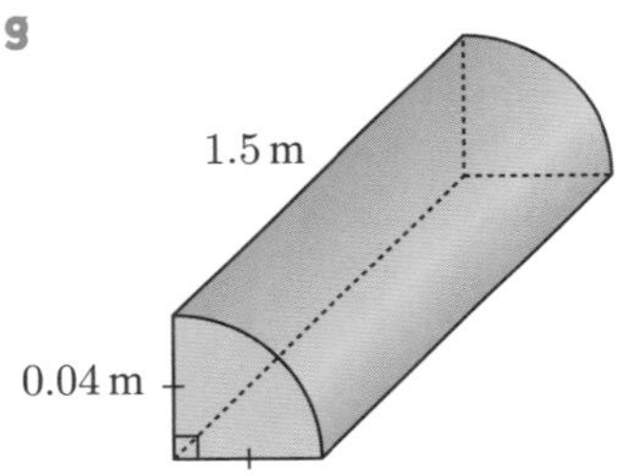

h

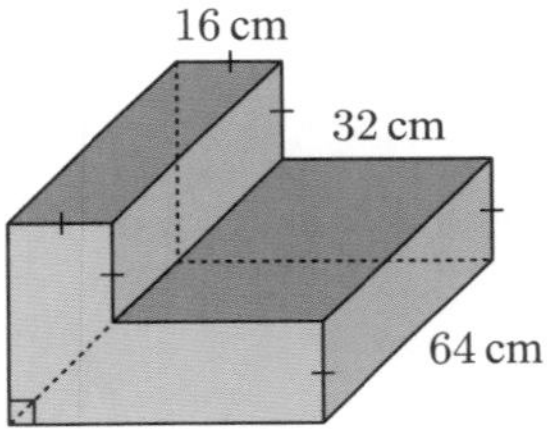

i

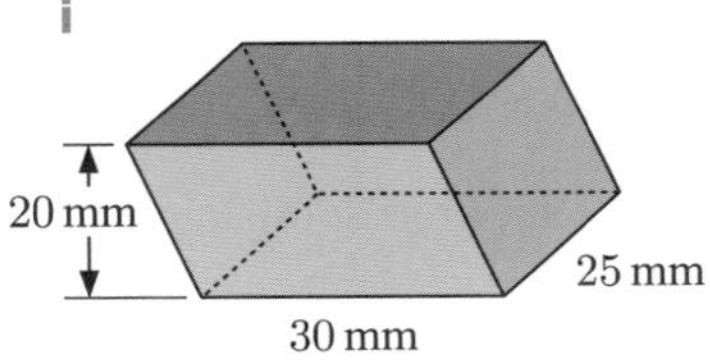

4 Find the volume of soil that can fit into this cylindrical pot.

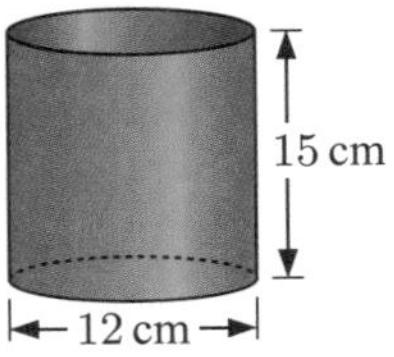

5 Find the volume of concrete required to make this ramp.

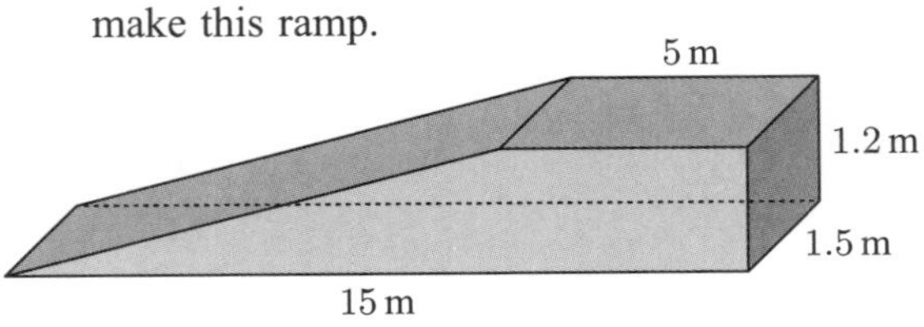

6 **a** Find the volume of air inside this letter box.

b Three rectangular envelopes with dimensions 23 cm by 12 cm by 5 mm are placed inside the letter box. What volume of air remains inside the letter box?

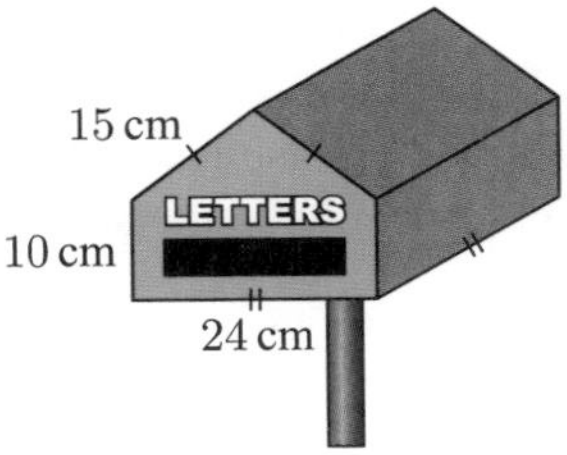

7 Find the volume of metal in this magnet.

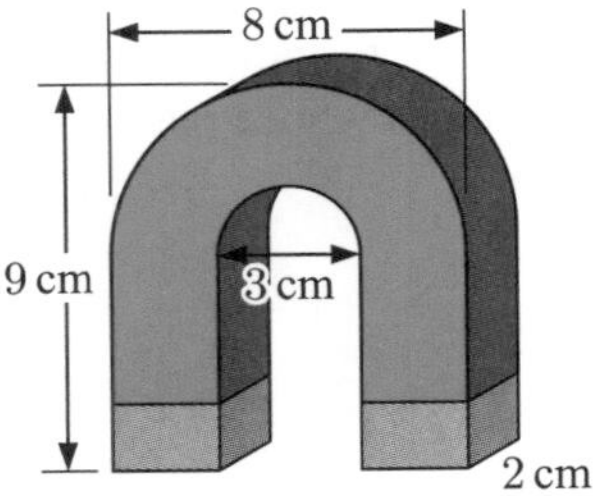

8 A section of concrete pipe has the dimensions shown.

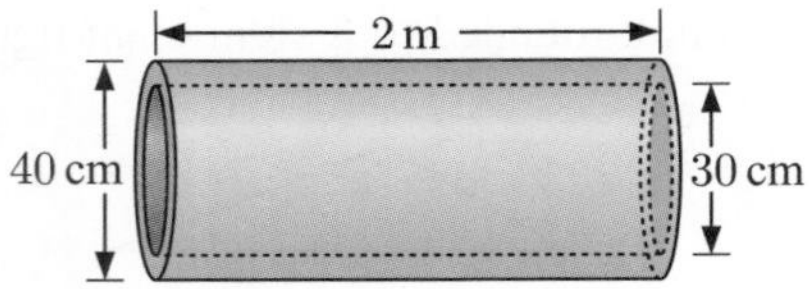

- **a** Find the area of one end of the pipe.
- **b** Hence, find the volume of the pipe.
- **c** If the concrete costs \$135 per cubic metre, find the cost of the concrete needed to make the pipe.
- **d** If the concrete weighs 2.43 grams per cm^3, find the weight of the pipe in kilograms.

9 Three faces of a rectangular prism have areas 6 cm^2, 10 cm^2, and 15 cm^2. Find the volume of the prism.

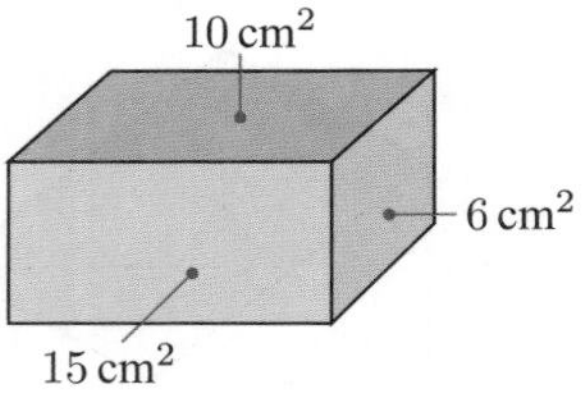

PYRAMIDS AND CONES

These **tapered solids** have a flat base and come to a point called the **apex**.

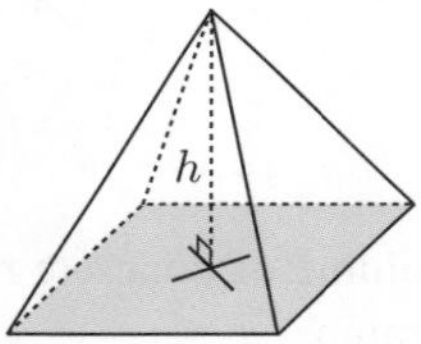

square-based pyramid

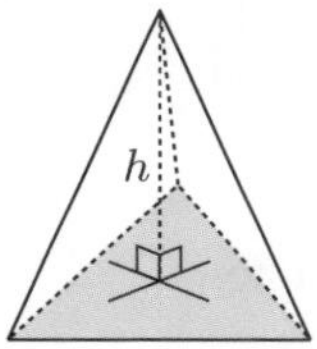

triangular-based pyramid

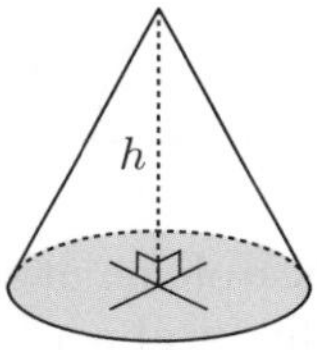

cone

They are *not* solids of uniform cross-section. The cross-sections always have the same shape, but not the same size.

The volume of a tapered solid is given by $\textbf{Volume} = \frac{1}{3} \times \textbf{area of base} \times \textbf{height}$

A formal proof of this formula is beyond the scope of this course. However, you can demonstrate that the formula is true by using water displacement. You should compare tapered solids with solids of uniform cross-section that have the same base and the same height.

For example, compare:

- a cone and a cylinder
- a square-based pyramid and a square-based prism.

You can also click on the icon to view a demonstration of the formula for the special case of a square-based pyramid whose base length is double its height.

DEMO

Example 10 — Self Tutor

Find the volume of each solid:

a

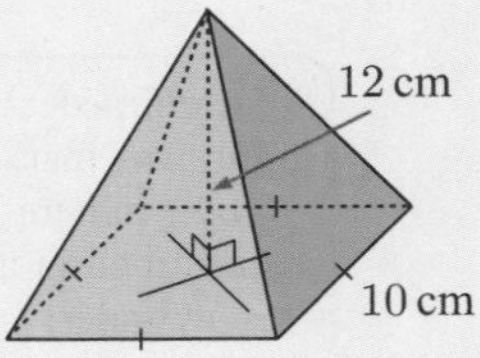

b

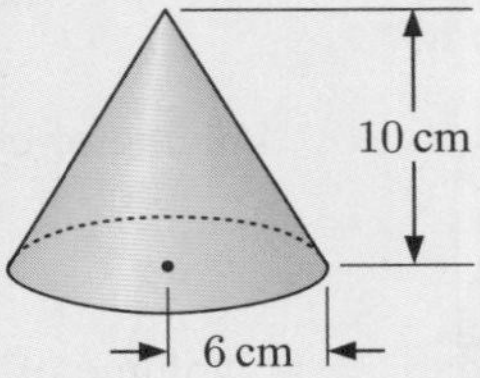

a Volume
$= \frac{1}{3} \times$ area of base $\times$ height
$= \frac{1}{3} \times 10 \times 10 \times 12 \text{ cm}^3$
$= 400 \text{ cm}^3$

b Volume
$= \frac{1}{3} \times$ area of base $\times$ height
$= \frac{1}{3} \times \pi \times 6^2 \times 10 \text{ cm}^3$
$\approx 377 \text{ cm}^3$

EXERCISE 13B.3

1 Find the volume of each tapered solid, rounded to 3 significant figures if necessary:

a

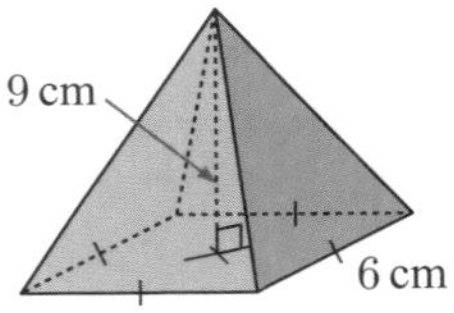

b

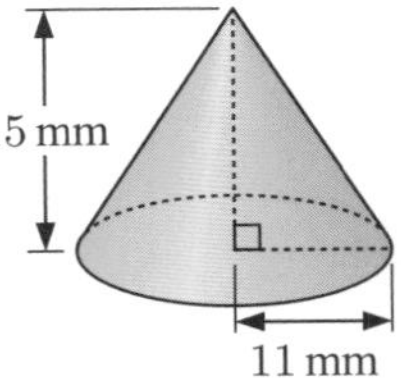

c

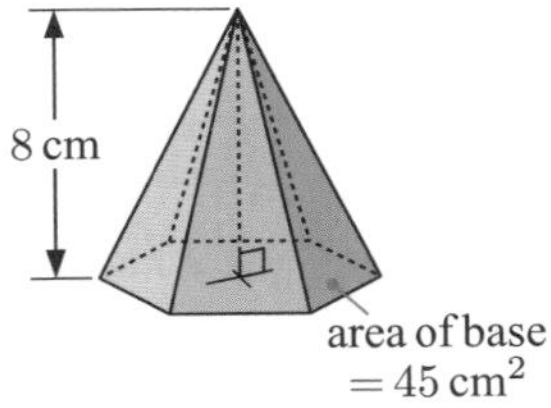

d

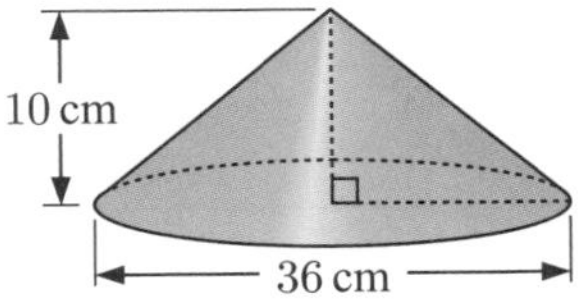

e

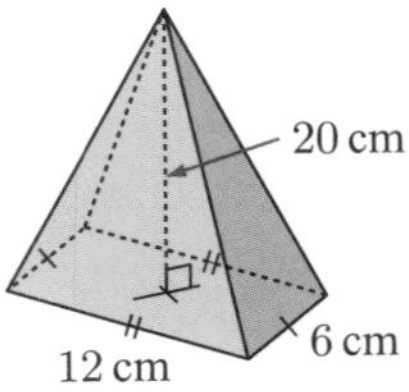

f

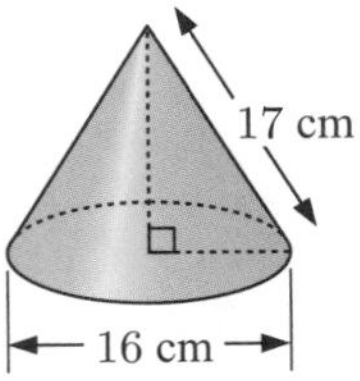

2 Find the volume of the triangular-based pyramid shown:

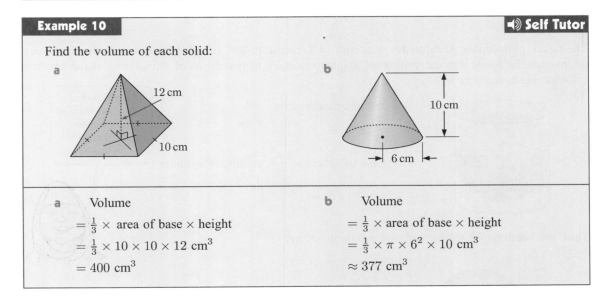

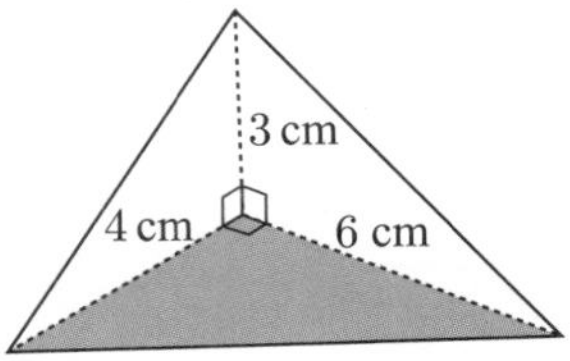

3 Sugar runs out from a hole in the bottom of a shipping container and forms a conical heap on the floor. The heap is 2.6 m in diameter and 0.83 m high. Find:

a the volume of the heap of sugar

b the total mass of sugar, given that 1 m^3 weighs 961 kg

c the total value of the sugar, given that 1 kg is worth €0.48 .

SPHERES

The Greek philosopher **Archimedes** was born in Syracuse in 287 BC. Amongst many other important discoveries, he found that the volume of a sphere is equal to two thirds of the volume of the smallest cylinder which encloses it.

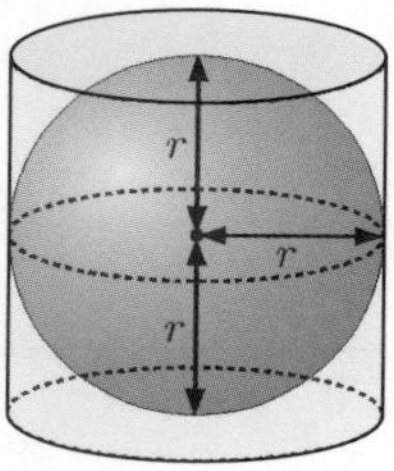

$$\begin{aligned}\text{Volume of cylinder} &= \pi r^2 \times h \\ &= \pi r^2 \times 2r \\ &= 2\pi r^3 \\ \therefore\ \text{volume of sphere} &= \tfrac{2}{3} \times \text{volume of cylinder} \\ &= \tfrac{2}{3} \times 2\pi r^3 \\ &= \tfrac{4}{3}\pi r^3\end{aligned}$$

Archimedes' tomb was marked by a sphere inscribed in a cylinder!

Thus, the volume of a sphere with radius r is given by:

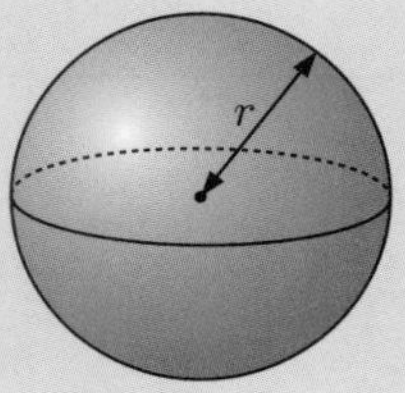

Sphere

$$V = \frac{4}{3}\pi r^3$$

Example 11 — Self Tutor

Find the volume of this sphere:

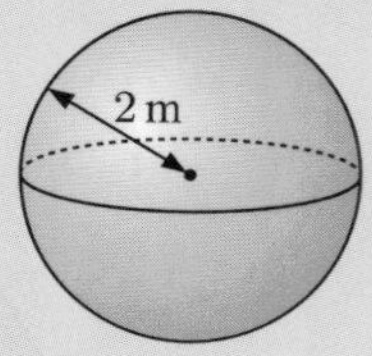

$$\begin{aligned}\text{Volume} &= \tfrac{4}{3}\pi r^3 \\ &= \tfrac{4}{3} \times \pi \times 2^3\ \text{m}^3 \\ &\approx 33.5\ \text{m}^3\end{aligned}$$

EXERCISE 13B.4

1 Find the volume of each solid:

a

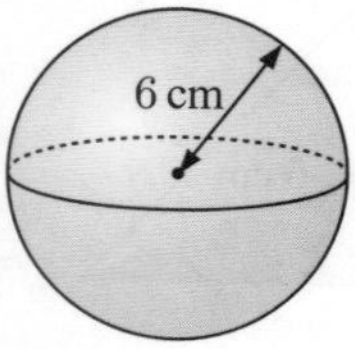

b

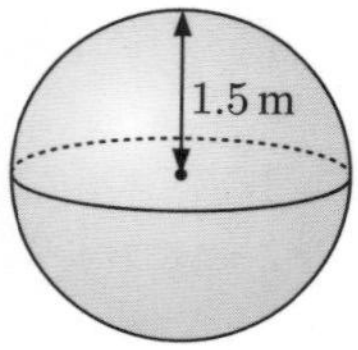

c

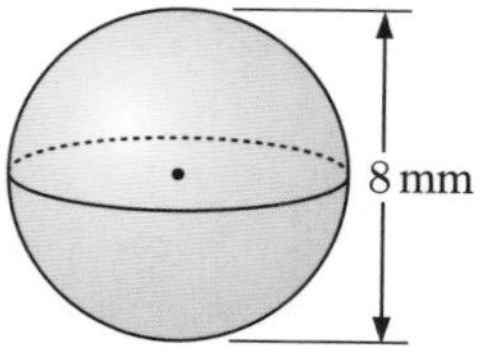

d

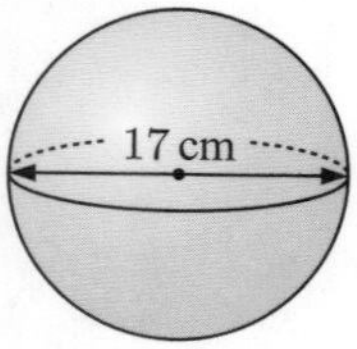

e

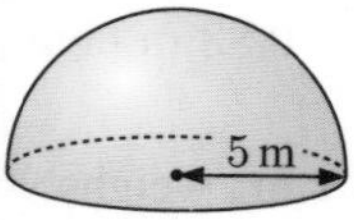

f

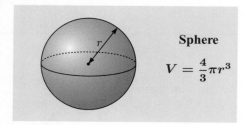

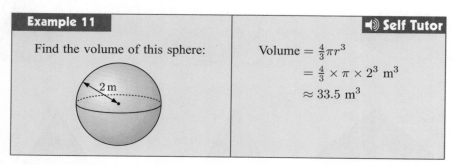

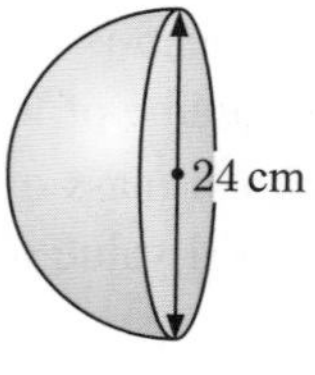

2 A spherical balloon has a radius of 13 cm. Find the volume of air inside the balloon.

3 Lucy's necklace contains 15 spherical glass beads of radius 8 mm, and 12 spherical glass beads of radius 5 mm. Find the total volume of glass in Lucy's necklace, giving your answer in:

a mm^3 **b** cm^3.

4 Jack shapes some clay into a sphere with diameter 9 cm.

a How much clay did Jack use?

b If instead Jack decided to shape this clay into a cube, what would the side length of the cube be?

C CAPACITY

The **capacity** of a container is the amount of material (solid or fluid) that it can contain.

The units for capacity are:

- millilitres (mL)
- litres (L)
- kilolitres (kL)
- megalitres (ML).

We measure the capacity of:

- a drinking glass in millilitres

400 mL

- a watering can in litres

12 L

- a petrol tanker in kilolitres

40 kL

- a lake in megalitres.

80 ML

CONVERSION OF CAPACITY UNITS

We can convert from one unit of capacity to another:

$1 \text{ L} = 1000 \text{ mL}$
$1 \text{ kL} = 1000 \text{ L}$
$1 \text{ ML} = 1000 \text{ kL}$

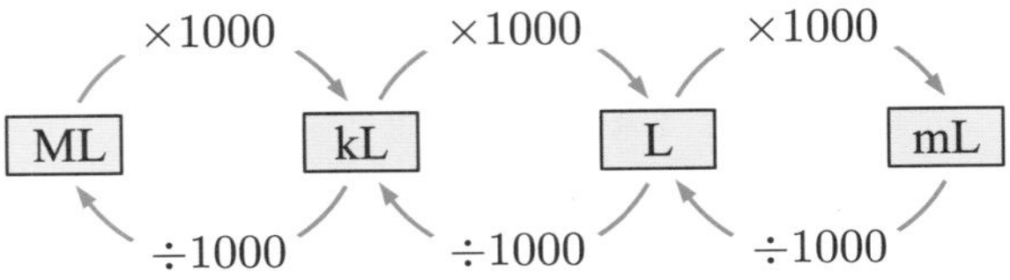

Example 12 **Self Tutor**

Convert:

a 8750 mL to L b 6.4 kL to L

a 8750 mL
$= (8750 \div 1000)$ L
$= 8.75$ L

b 6.4 kL
$= (6.4 \times 1000)$ L
$= 6400$ L

EXERCISE 13C.1

1 Which units would be most suitable for measuring the capacity of a:

a laundry sink
b test tube
c rainwater tank
d small water bottle
e reservoir
f swimming pool
g bucket
h shipping container?

2 Convert:

a 2960 mL to L
b 3.01 ML to kL
c 99.1 L to kL
d 1800 kL to ML
e 6.6 kL to L
f 18.7 L to mL
g 303 mL to L
h 56 L to kL
i 225 000 kL to ML
j 42 000 mL to L
k 0.35 kL to L
l 0.001 kL to mL

3 When a vending machine is fully stocked, it holds 144 cans of drink each with capacity 375 mL, and 96 bottles each with capacity 600 mL. Find, in litres, the total capacity of drink in the machine.

4 Water flows from Shelley's garden hose at 20 litres per minute. How long will it take for her to fill her outdoor spa with 1.5 kL of water?

VOLUME AND CAPACITY

There is a close relationship between the units of **capacity** and **volume**.

1 mL of fluid will fill a cube 1 cm × 1 cm × 1 cm.

1 mL is equivalent to 1 cm^3.
1 mL ≡ 1 cm^3

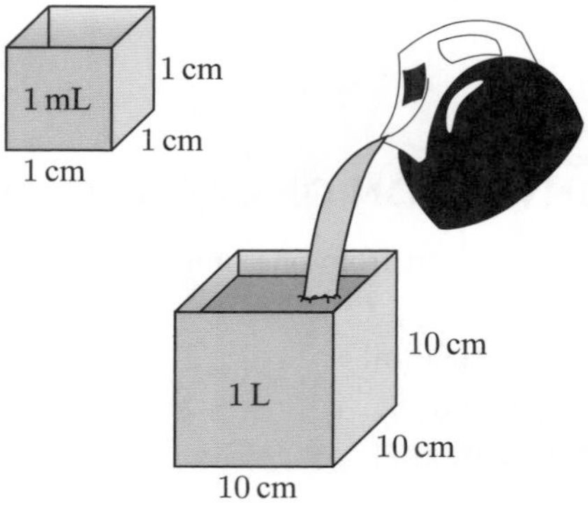

1 L of fluid will fill a cube 10 cm × 10 cm × 10 cm.

1 L is equivalent to 1000 cm^3.
1 L ≡ 1000 cm^3

1 kL of fluid will fill a cube $1 \text{ m} \times 1 \text{ m} \times 1 \text{ m}$.

1 kL is equivalent to 1 m^3.
$$1 \text{ kL} \equiv 1 \text{ m}^3.$$

You could pour 1000 L into this cube!

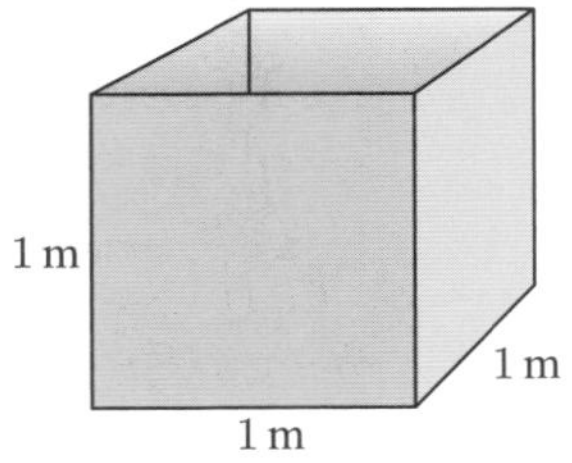

Example 13 🔊 **Self Tutor**

Find the capacity of this box:

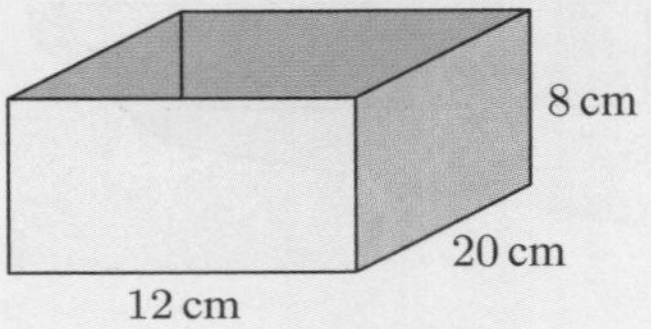

Volume $= 12 \times 20 \times 8 \text{ cm}^3$
$\qquad\; = 1920 \text{ cm}^3$

\therefore capacity $= 1920 \text{ mL} \quad$ {as $1 \text{ mL} \equiv 1 \text{ cm}^3$}
$\qquad\qquad\; = (1920 \div 1000) \text{ L}$
$\qquad\qquad\; = 1.92 \text{ L}$

EXERCISE 13C.2

1 Find the capacity of each container:

a 3 cm, 5 cm, 6 cm

b 10 cm, 25 cm, 30 cm

c 15 cm, 20 cm, 1.1 m

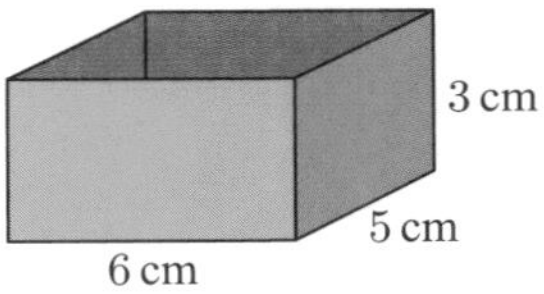

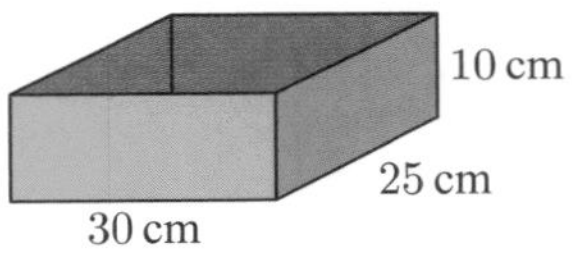

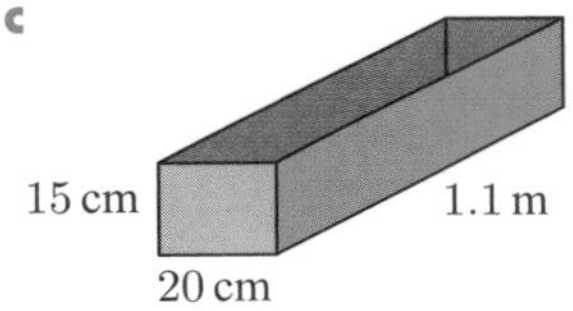

2 A fridge is 60 cm long, 50 cm wide, and 1.2 m high. Find the capacity of the fridge, in litres.

Example 14 🔊 **Self Tutor**

Find the capacity of a cylindrical rainwater tank with height 3 m and diameter 4 m. Give your answer in kilolitres.

The volume of the tank
$\qquad = \text{area of base} \times \text{height}$
$\qquad = \pi \times 2^2 \times 3 \text{ m}^3$
$\qquad = 12\pi \text{ m}^3$

\therefore capacity $= 12\pi \text{ kL} \quad$ {as $1 \text{ kL} \equiv 1 \text{ m}^3$}
$\qquad\qquad\; \approx 37.7 \text{ kL}$

3 m

4 m

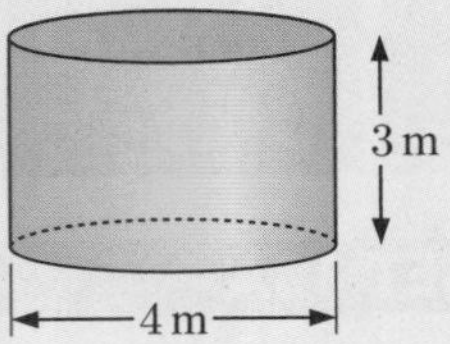

3 How many litres of oil can be stored in this drum?

57 cm

85 cm

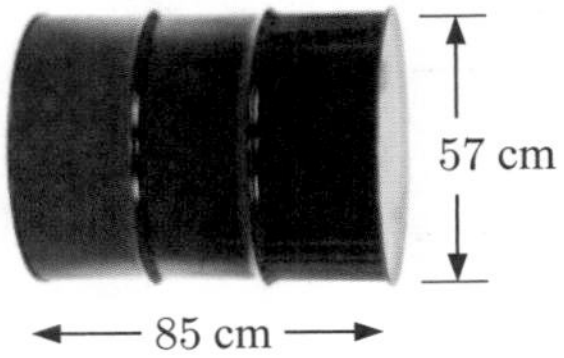

4 A cylindrical water tank with diameter 2 m contains water to a depth of 1.8 m. How many 10 L watering cans could be filled with water from the tank?

5 A children's lawn bowls set contains 8 spherical bowls of radius 6.1 cm, each of which is filled with water. Find the total amount of water in the bowls.

6 Answer the **Opening Problem** on page **256**.

7 Mrs Foster has made $3\frac{1}{2}$ L of marmalade. She ladles it into cylindrical jars which are 12 cm high, with 7 cm internal diameter. How many jars can she completely fill?

8 A conical tank has diameter 4 m and height 5 m. How many kilolitres of water could it contain?

9 Find the number of kilolitres of water required to fill this swimming pool:

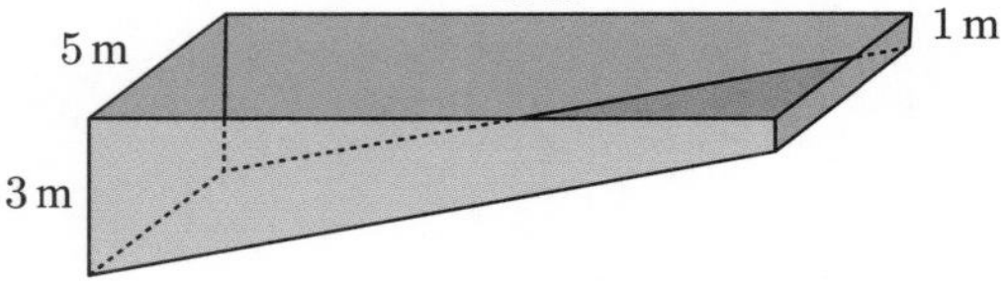

10

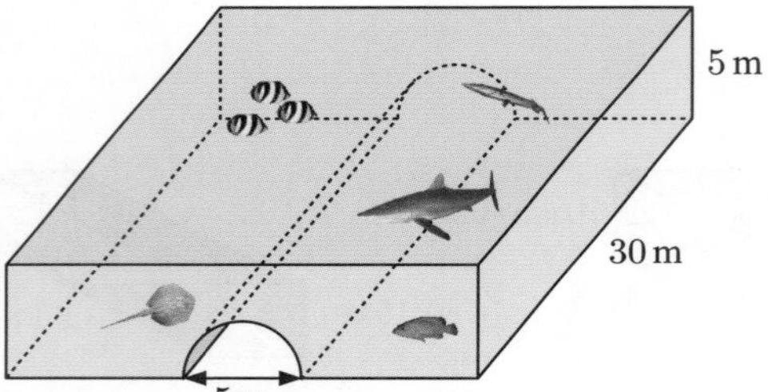

Find the amount of water in this aquarium, giving your answer in:

a kilolitres **b** megalitres.

Global context

Icebergs

Statement of inquiry:	Taking measurements allows us to be more aware of changes to our natural resources.
Global context:	Globalisation and sustainability
Key concept:	Form
Related concepts:	Measurement, Space
Objective:	Applying mathematics in real-life contexts
Approaches to learning:	Thinking, Communication

REVIEW SET 13A

1 Find the surface area of:

a

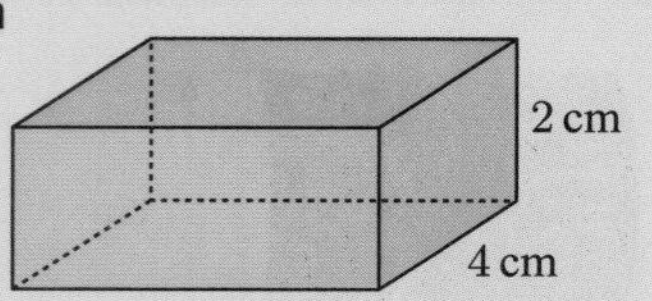

b

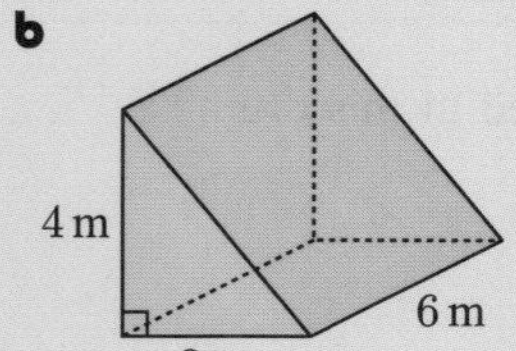

c open at the top

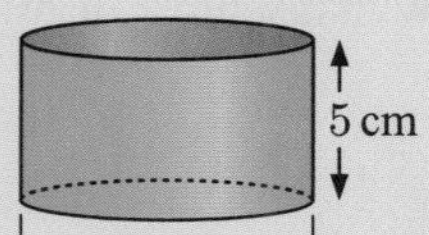

2 A sphere has diameter 7 cm. Find its:

a surface area **b** volume.

3 Convert:

a 2.8 m^3 to cm^3 **b** 4200 cm^3 to L **c** 1.1 cm^3 to mm^3

4 Which units would be most suitable to measure the space occupied by:

a a gluestick **b** a caravan?

5 Find the volume of:

a

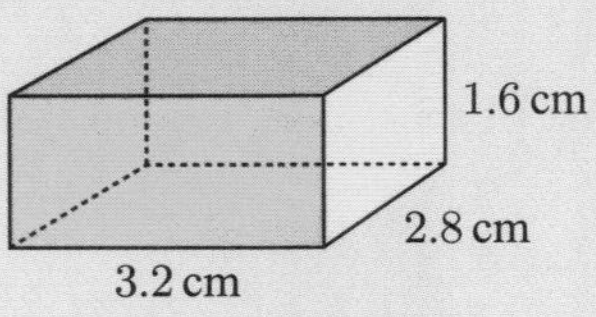

b

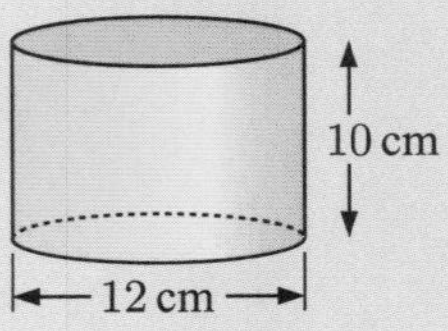

c

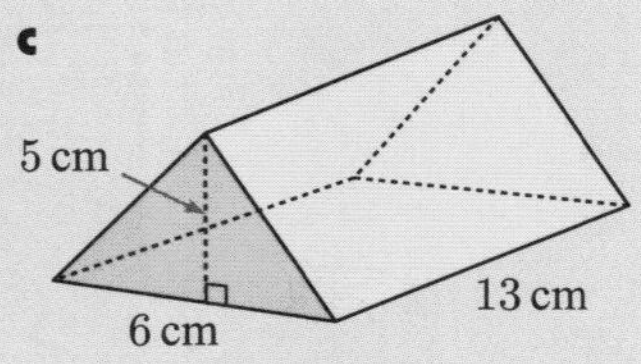

6 A semi-circular tunnel with the dimensions shown is made of concrete.

a Find the cross-sectional area of the tunnel.

b The tunnel is 200 m long, and concrete costs €120 per cubic metre. Find the cost of the concrete for the tunnel.

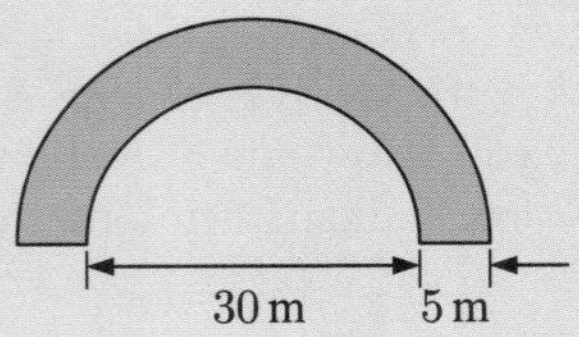

7 Ten glass bottles of lime cordial are lined up on a supermarket shelf. Marina accidentally knocks one off the shelf and it breaks. There is now a total of 6.75 L of lime cordial on the shelf. What is the capacity of each bottle?

8 Find the capacity of this can, to the nearest mL.

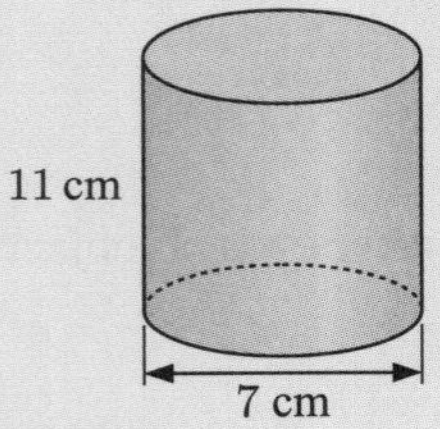

9 A petrol tank is a rectangular prism 80 cm by 120 cm by 50 cm. Find the capacity of the tank, in litres.

10 Tyson's Trophy Company makes wooden trophy bases with the dimensions shown.

a What volume of wood is required for the base?

b Find the surface area of the trophy base.

c Tyson paints his bases with black paint. He knows that one tin of paint covers 3 square metres. How many *complete* trophy bases can Tyson paint with one tin?

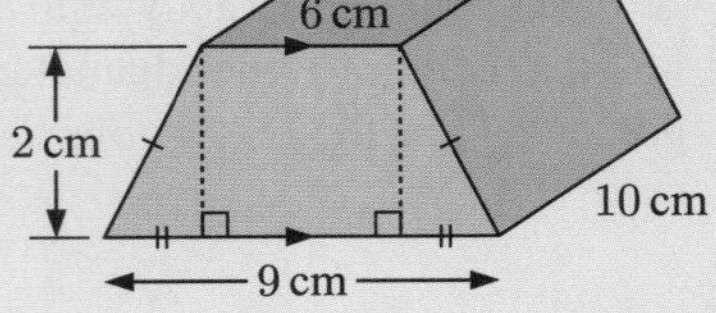

REVIEW SET 13B

1 Convert:

a 820 mL to L **b** 3.07 mL to kL **c** 1.2 m^3 to mm^3

2 How many cubic metres of molten metal would be required to fill 8000 moulds with 150 cm^3 of metal each?

3 Find the surface area of each solid:

a

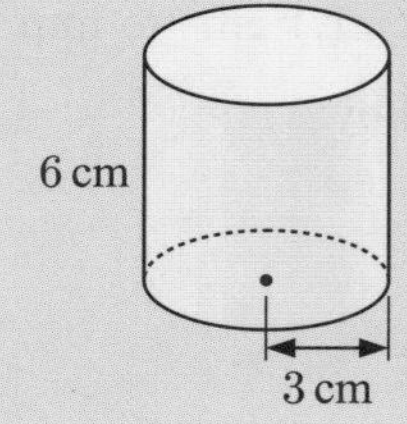

b

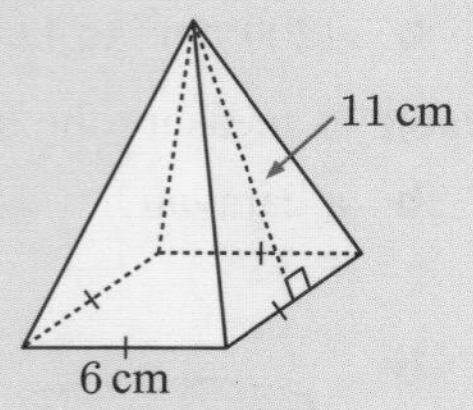

c

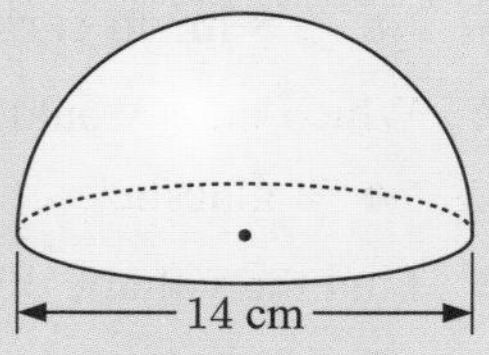

4

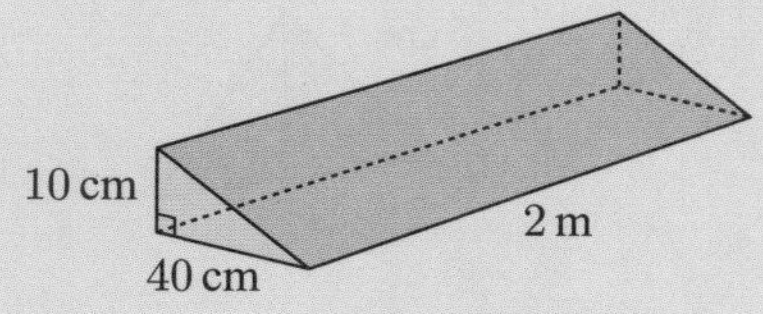

Find the volume of the wooden ramp illustrated.

5 A truck driver charges $16.20 per cubic metre for delivering soil. How much should the driver charge to fill a rectangular excavation 14 m long by 4 m wide by 2.5 m deep?

6

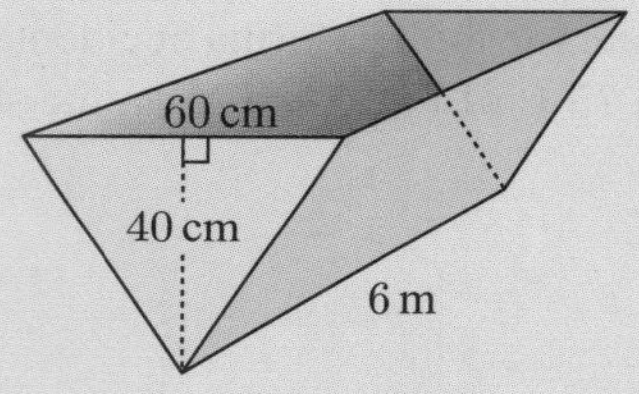

A water trough 6 m long has the triangular cross-section shown. Find the capacity of the trough in kilolitres.

7 Find the capacity of each object:

a

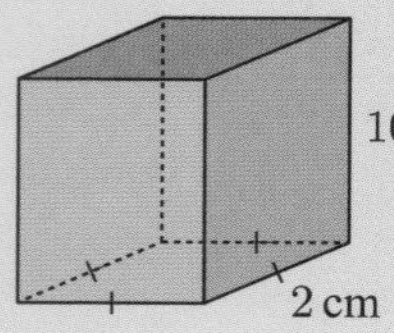

b

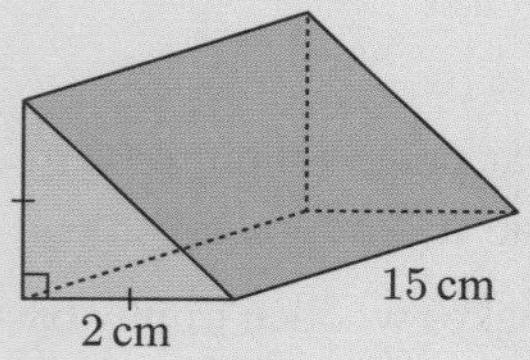

c

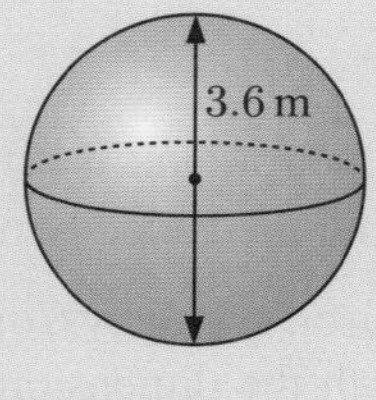

8 A basketball fits exactly into a cubic box which has side lengths equal to the diameter of the basketball. What percentage of the box's volume does the basketball occupy?

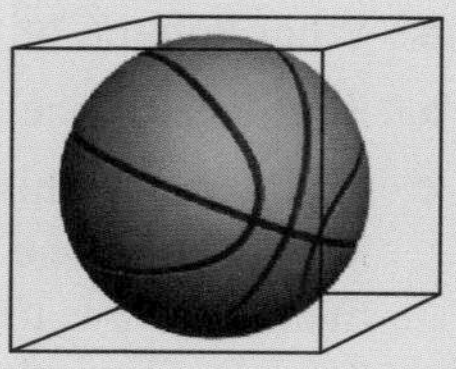

9 A garden shed is 3 m by 2.5 m by 2.2 m high. Find the cost of painting the outside walls and ceiling of the shed if 1 litre of paint costs £16 and covers 10 m^2.

10 A rectangular garden plot 8 m by 3 m is surrounded by a concrete path 1.2 m wide and 8 cm deep. The concrete costs $195 per cubic metre. Find the:

a area of the path **b** volume of concrete needed **c** cost of the path.

Chapter 14

Coordinate geometry

Contents:

OPENING PROBLEM

When Tiffany makes a mobile phone call, the *cost* of the call depends on the *time* that she spends on the call. The relationship between the cost and the time of the call is shown on the graph alongside.

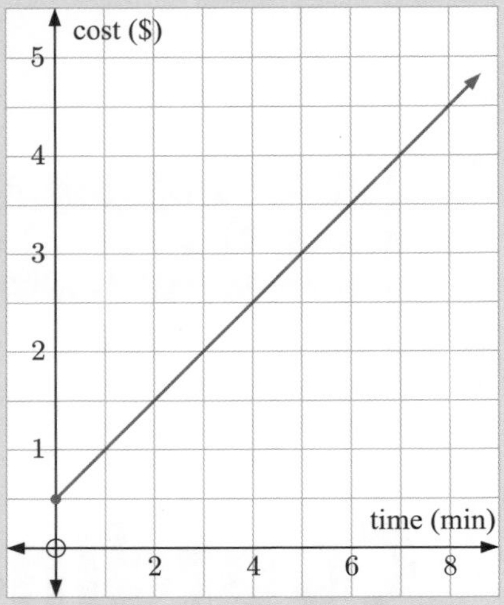

Things to think about:

a Is the relationship between *cost* and *time* linear?

b What is the *connection fee* or fixed cost charged for a very short phone call?

c By how much does the cost of the call increase for each minute spent on the call?

d Can you use this graph to determine:

  i the cost of a 3 minute call

  ii the length of a call which costs $4?

The graph in the **Opening Problem** is a straight line. We say there is a **linear relationship** between the variables.

HISTORICAL NOTE

Sir Isaac Newton is recognised as one of the great mathematicians of all time. His achievements are remarkable considering mathematics, physics, and astronomy were enjoyable pastimes after his main interests of chemistry, theology, and alchemy.

Despite his obvious abilities, there is a story from Newton's childhood which indicates that even the greatest thinkers can find silly solutions for simple problems. He was asked to go out and cut a hole in the bottom of the barn door for the cats to go in and out. He decided to cut two holes: one for the cat and a smaller one for the kittens.

After completing school, Newton was initially made to work on a farm, but when his uncle discovered his enthusiasm for mathematics it was decided that he should attend Cambridge University.

Newton's contribution to coordinate geometry included the introduction of negative values for coordinates. In his *Method of Fluxions*, Newton suggested eight new types of coordinate systems, one of which we know today as **polar coordinates**.

A THE CARTESIAN PLANE

The number grid alongside is a **Cartesian plane**, named after **René Descartes**. The numbers or **coordinates** on it allow us to locate the exact position of any point on the plane.

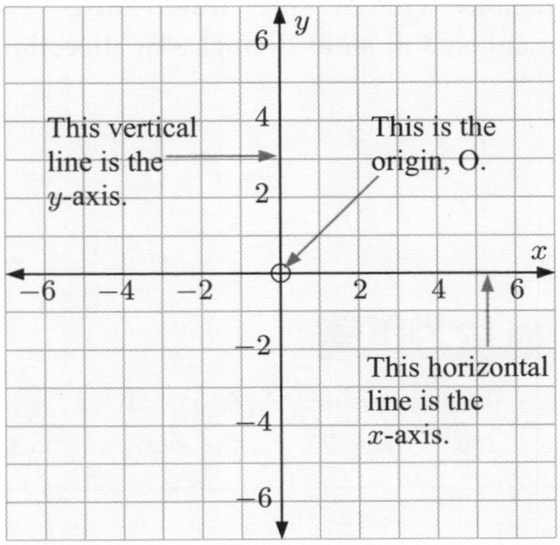

We start with a point of reference O called the **origin**. Through it we draw two fixed lines which are perpendicular to each other. They are a horizontal line called the ***x*-axis**, and a vertical line called the ***y*-axis**.

The ***x*-axis** is an ordinary number line with positive numbers to the right of O and negative numbers to the left of O. The ***y*-axis** has positive numbers above O and negative numbers below O.

PLOTTING POINTS ON THE CARTESIAN PLANE

To specify the position of a point on the number plane, we use an **ordered pair** of numbers in the form (x, y).

For example, on the grid alongside we see the point described by the ordered pair (3, 2). We say that the point has **coordinates** (3, 2).

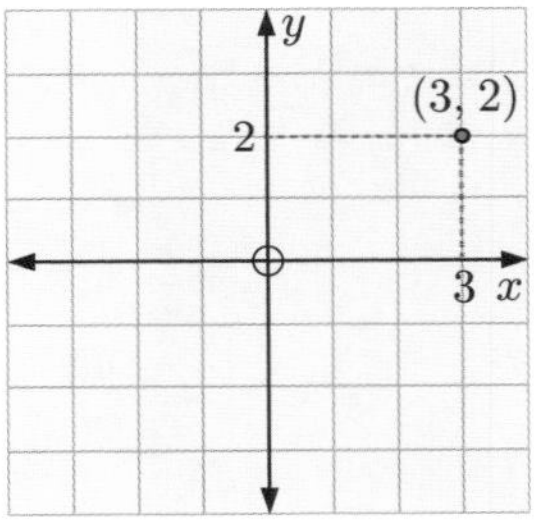

To help us identify particular points, we often refer to them using a capital letter. For example, consider the points A(1, 3), B(4, −3), and C(−4, −2).

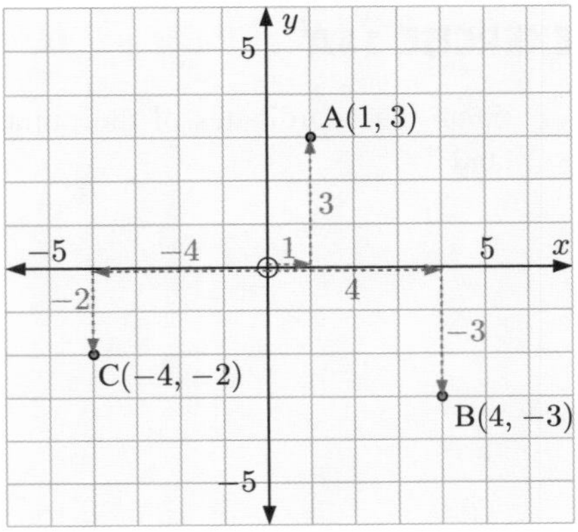

To plot the point A(1, 3):

- start at the origin O
- move right along the x-axis 1 unit
- then move upwards 3 units.

We say that 1 is the ***x*-coordinate** of A
and 3 is the ***y*-coordinate** of A.

To plot the point B(4, −3):

- start at the origin O
- move right along the x-axis 4 units
- then move downwards 3 units.

To plot the point C(−4, −2):

- start at the origin O
- move left along the x-axis 4 units
- then move downwards 2 units.

DEMO

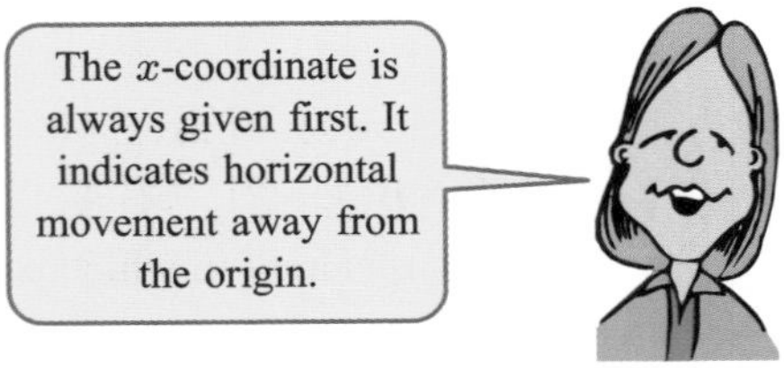

The x-coordinate is always given first. It indicates horizontal movement away from the origin.

QUADRANTS

The x and y-axes divide the Cartesian plane into four regions referred to as **quadrants**. These quadrants are numbered in an **anti-clockwise direction** as shown:

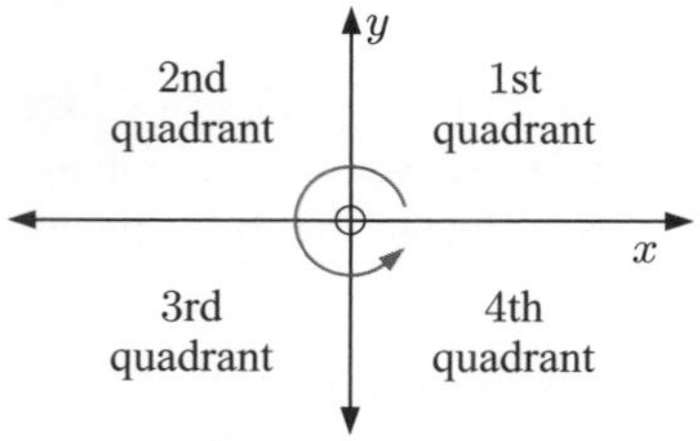

Example 1 — Self Tutor

Plot the points A(3, 5), B(−1, 4), C(0, −3), D(−3, −2), and E(4, −2) on the same set of axes.

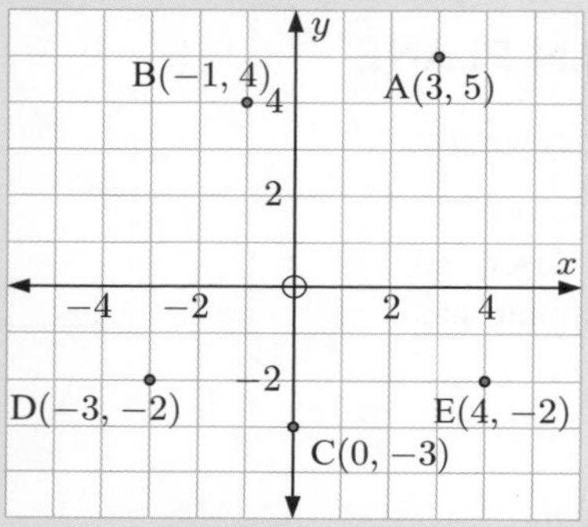

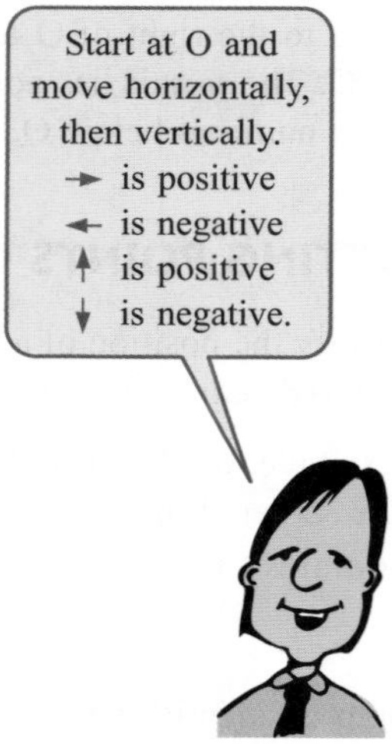

Start at O and move horizontally, then vertically.
→ is positive
← is negative
↑ is positive
↓ is negative.

EXERCISE 14A

1 State the coordinates of the points P, Q, R, S, and T:

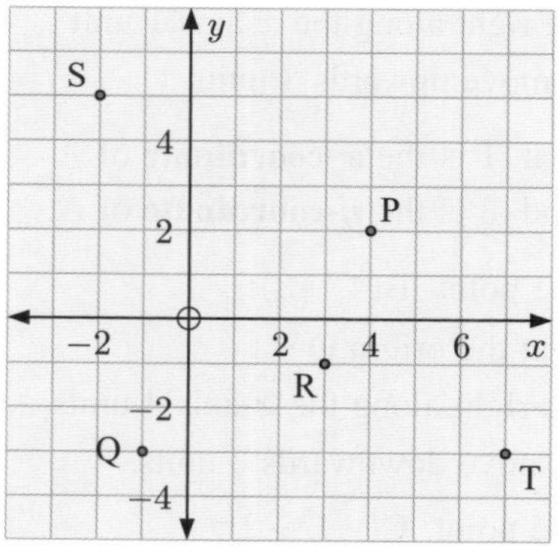

2 **a** On the same set of axes, plot the points:
A(2, 5), B(4, −2), C(−5, 0), D(−1, −4), E(−2, 3), F(0, 3), G(5, 1), and H(−5, −1).

b State the quadrant in which each point in **a** lies.

Example 2 — Self Tutor

On a Cartesian plane, show all the points with positive x-coordinate and negative y-coordinate.

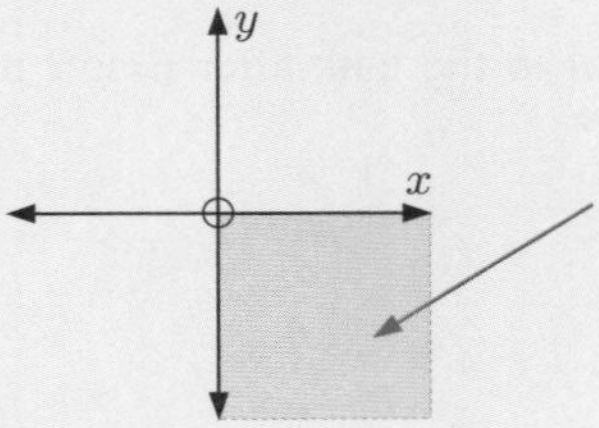

This shaded region contains all points where x is positive and y is negative.
The points on the axes are not included.

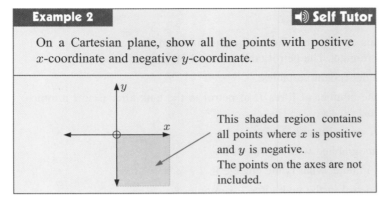

3 On different sets of axes, show all the points with:

- **a** x-coordinate equal to -1
- **b** y-coordinate equal to 3
- **c** x-coordinate equal to 0
- **d** y-coordinate equal to 0
- **e** negative x-coordinate
- **f** positive y-coordinate
- **g** negative x and y-coordinates
- **h** negative x-coordinate and positive y-coordinate.

4 State the quadrants in which I would find points whose coordinates have:

- **a** the same sign
- **b** different signs.

B LINEAR RELATIONSHIPS

Consider the pattern:

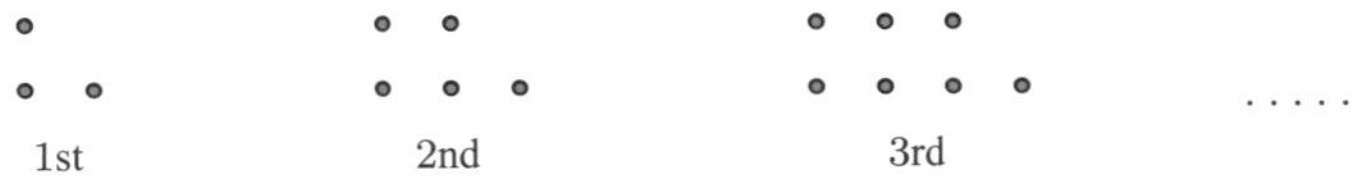

We can construct a **table of values** which connects the diagram number n to the number of dots D. To go from one diagram to the next we need to add *two more* dots.

n	1	2	3	4
D	3	5	7	9

+2 +2 +2

The **equation** which connects n and D in this case is $D = 2n + 1$.

The number of dots D *depends* on the diagram number n. We say that n is the **independent variable** and D is the **dependent variable**.

We can plot the relationship between D and n on a number plane. We place the independent variable n on the horizontal axis, and the dependent variable D on the vertical axis.

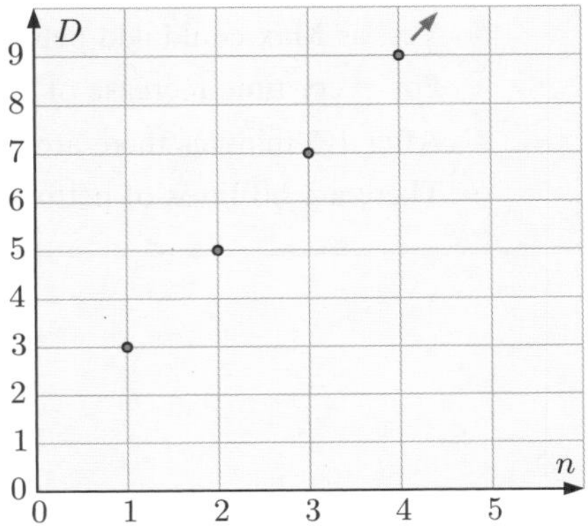

This is an example of a **linear relationship** because the points lie in a straight line.

In this case the values in between the points are meaningless. For example, we cannot have a $2\frac{1}{2}$th diagram. We therefore do not connect the points with a straight line.

However, there are many situations where it *is* sensible to connect the points with a straight line. In these cases, we can use the line to answer questions involving values between the given points.

Example 3 **Self Tutor**

Max has 10 litres of fuel left in his car's petrol tank. When he fills it at the petrol station, petrol runs into the tank at 15 litres per minute. The petrol tank can hold 70 litres.

a Identify the independent and dependent variables.

b Make a table of values for the number of litres L of petrol in the tank after time t minutes, and plot the graph of L against t.

c Is the relationship between L and t linear?

d Is it sensible to join the points graphed with a straight line?

e For every time increase of 1 minute, what is the change in L?

f Find the number of litres of petrol in the tank after 1.5 minutes.

g At what time will there be 50 litres of petrol in the tank?

---

a The *number of litres of petrol* in the tank depends on the *time* it has been filling.
$\therefore$ *time* is the independent variable and the *number of litres of petrol* is the dependent variable.

b Each minute the tank is filling adds another 15 litres of petrol.

t (min)	0	1	2	3	4
L (litres)	10	25	40	55	70

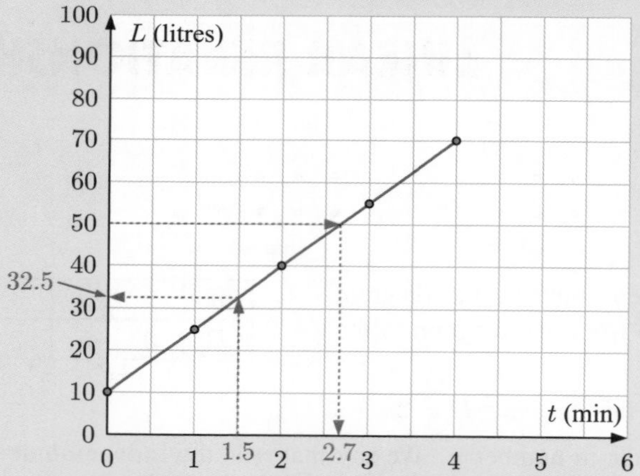

The independent variable is placed on the horizontal axis.

c The points lie in a straight line so the relationship is linear.

d Yes, as Max could add petrol for 2.5 minutes, say, or put 56 litres of petrol in the tank.

e For every time increase of 1 minute, L increases by 15 litres.

f After 1.5 minutes there are 32.5 litres of petrol in the tank.

g There are 50 litres of petrol in the tank after about 2.7 minutes.

EXERCISE 14B

1 Each week a department store employee receives a basic salary of \$300. In addition, she is paid a bonus of \$20 for each new member she signs up to the store's rewards club. Let I be the employee's income and m be the number of members she signs up to the rewards club.

- **a** What are the independent and dependent variables?
- **b** Construct a table of values for I, for $m = 0, 1, 2, 3, ..., 10$.
- **c** Hence draw a graph of I against m.
- **d** Is the relationship linear?
- **e** Is it sensible to join the points with a straight line? Explain your answer.
- **f** For each new member signed, what is the employee's increase in income?

2 Mangoes can be bought for €3.50 each.

- **a** Copy and complete the table:

Number of mangoes, n	0	1	2	3	4	5	6	7	8
Cost, €C									

- **b** Plot the graph of C against n.
- **c** Identify the independent and dependent variables.
- **d** Is the relationship between C and n linear?
- **e** Is it sensible to join the points with a straight line? Explain your answer.
- **f** For each extra mango bought, what is the change in C?
- **g** Find the cost of 5 mangoes.
- **h** How many mangoes could be bought for €24.50?

3 Simon is filling a large container with sports drink for his football team. It already contains 3 litres when he starts to fill it up using 2 L bottles.

- **a** Make a table of values for the volume of sports drink S in the container after Simon has emptied n bottles of sports drink into it. Consider $n = 0, 1, 2, ..., 8$.
- **b** What are the independent and dependent variables?
- **c** Plot the graph of S against n.
- **d** Is the relationship between S and n linear?
- **e** Is it sensible to join the points graphed with a straight line? Explain your answer.
- **f** For each full bottle of sports drink added, what is the change in S?
- **g** What volume of sports drink is in the container after Simon has emptied $2\frac{1}{2}$ bottles into it?
- **h** How many full bottles must be emptied into the container so it contains 15 L in total?

4 Adrian's cookbook gives the cooking temperatures in degrees Fahrenheit (°F). However, Adrian is only familiar with degrees Celsius (°C).

a Draw a set of axes as shown.

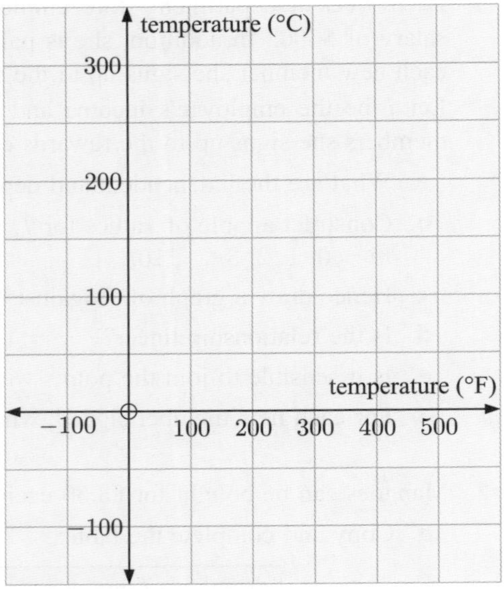

b Identify the independent and dependent variables.

c There is a linear relationship between °F and °C. The boiling point of water is 212 °F or 100 °C. The freezing point of water is 32 °F or 0 °C. Mark these points on your graph and join them with a straight line.

d Find the point where the number of degrees Celsius equals the same number of degrees Fahrenheit. What is the temperature?

e Help Adrian convert these temperatures into °C:

i a cake must be cooked at 350 °F

ii a roast must reach an internal temperature of 145 °F.

f Use your graph to complete the following table:

Temperature in °F	0	180		
Temperature in °C			150	200

PRINTABLE GRID

C GRADIENT

DISCUSSION — WHICH LINE IS STEEPER?

Look at the two lines alongside.

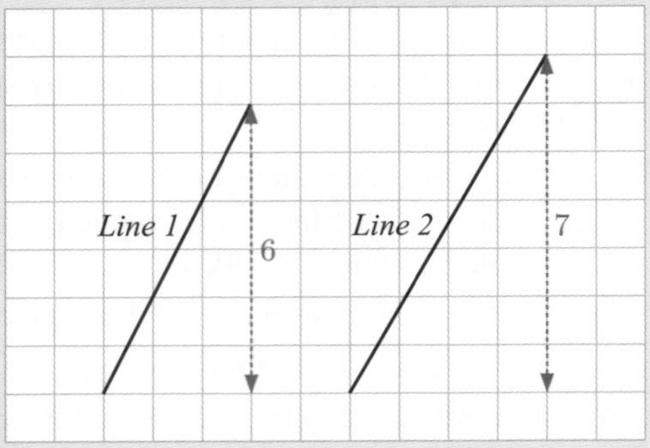

Justin thinks that *line 2* is steeper, because *line 2* rises 7 units vertically, whereas *line 1* only rises 6 units.

- Is Justin correct? Which line do you think is steepest?
- What does it mean to say that one line is *steeper* than another?
- How can we *measure* the steepness of a line?

The **gradient** of a line is a measure of its steepness.

In the **Discussion** above, *line 2* rises higher than *line 1*, but *line 1* is *steeper* because it rises at a greater *rate* than *line 2*.

We can calculate the rate at which a line rises or falls by choosing two points on the line, then dividing the vertical step between them by the horizontal step between them.

$$\text{gradient} = \frac{\text{vertical step}}{\text{horizontal step}}$$

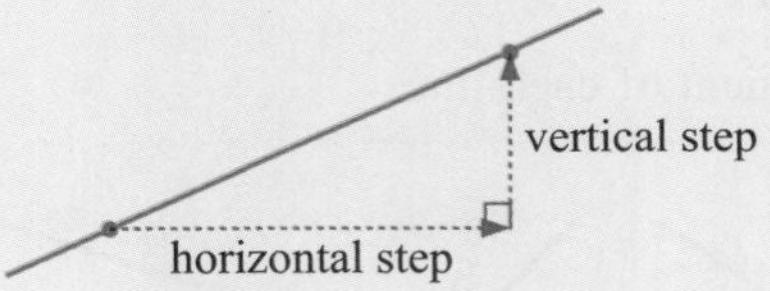

The gradient of *line 1* is $\frac{6}{3} = 2$. This means that for every 1 unit moved horizontally, the line moves 2 units upwards.

The gradient of *line 2* is $\frac{7}{4} = 1.75$. *Line 1* has a higher gradient than *line 2*, which means that *line 1* is steeper than *line 2*.

For an upwards sloping line, if the horizontal step is positive then the vertical step is positive.

Upward sloping lines have a **positive gradient**.

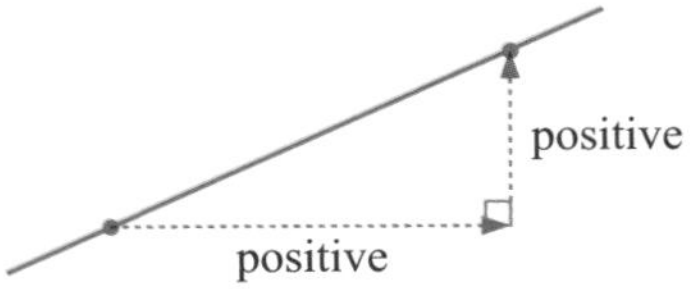

For a downward sloping line, if the horizontal step is positive then the vertical step is negative.

Downward sloping lines have a **negative gradient**.

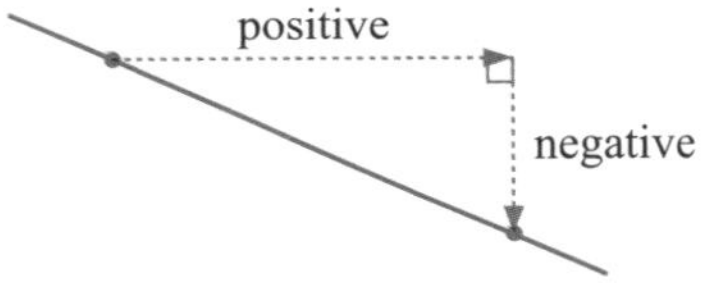

For a **horizontal line**, the vertical step is 0, so the **gradient of a horizontal line is 0**.
For a **vertical line**, the horizontal step is 0, so the **gradient of a vertical line is undefined**.

Example 4 Self Tutor

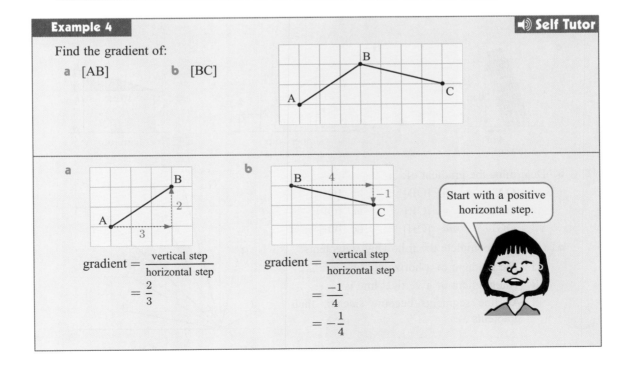

Find the gradient of:

a [AB] **b** [BC]

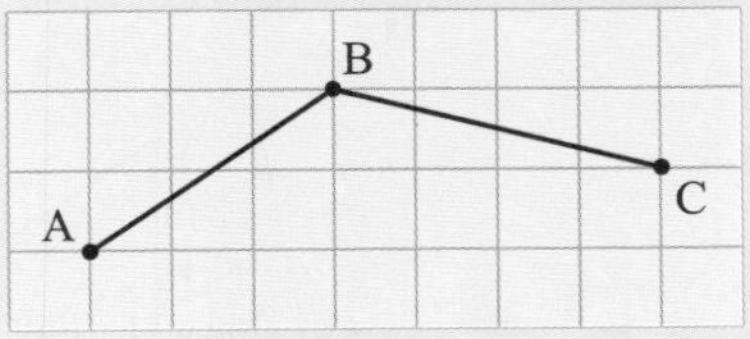

a

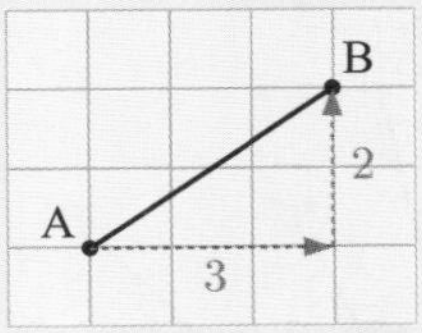

$$\text{gradient} = \frac{\text{vertical step}}{\text{horizontal step}} = \frac{2}{3}$$

b

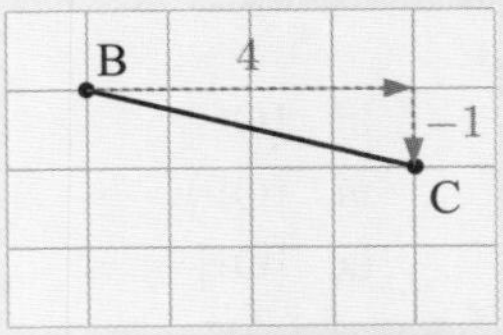

$$\text{gradient} = \frac{\text{vertical step}}{\text{horizontal step}} = \frac{-1}{4} = -\frac{1}{4}$$

EXERCISE 14C.1

1 State the gradient of each line:

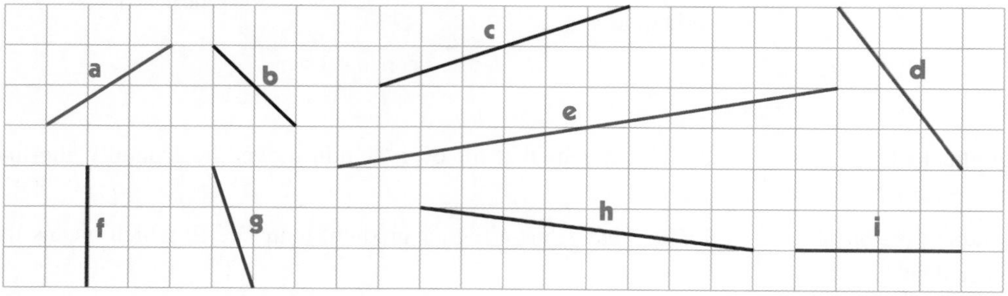

2 On grid paper, draw a line segment with gradient:

a $\frac{1}{2}$	**b** $\frac{2}{3}$	**c** $-\frac{1}{4}$	**d** $2 = \frac{2}{1}$	**e** 1	**f** -3
g $\frac{4}{3}$	**h** $-\frac{5}{2}$	**i** 0	**j** $1\frac{1}{5}$	**k** 5	**l** undefined

3 On grid paper, draw a triangle which has:

a all three sides with positive gradients
b two sides with positive gradients and one side with negative gradient
c two sides with negative gradients and one side with positive gradient
d all three sides with negative gradients.

4 Find the gradient of the following:

a

road uphill

b

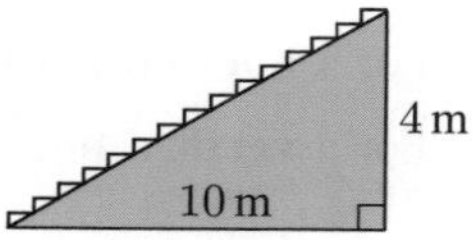

stairs

c

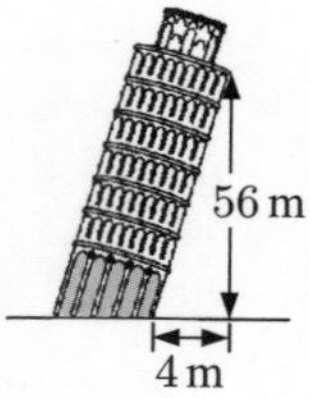

tower

d

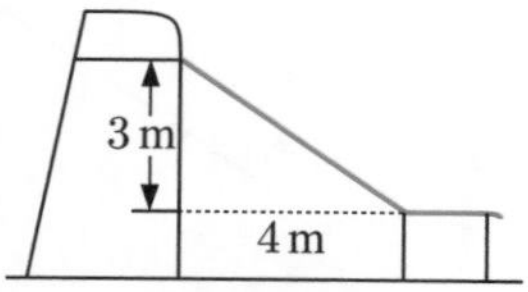

slippery-dip

e

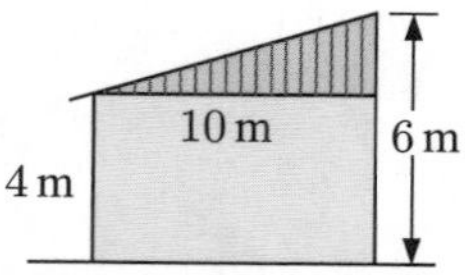

barn roof

5 **a** Determine the gradient of:

i [OA]	**ii** [OB]	**iii** [OC]
iv [OD]	**v** [OE]	**vi** [OF]
vii [OG]	**viii** [OH]	**ix** [OI]

b Copy and complete the following statements:

i The gradient of a horizontal line is ......
ii The gradient of a vertical line is ......
iii As line segments become steeper, their gradients ......

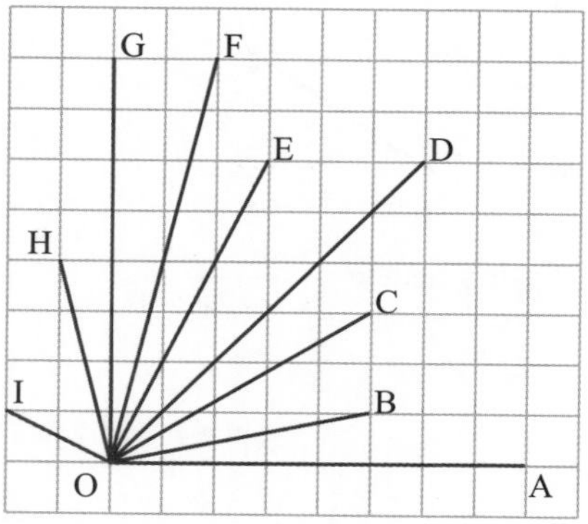

6

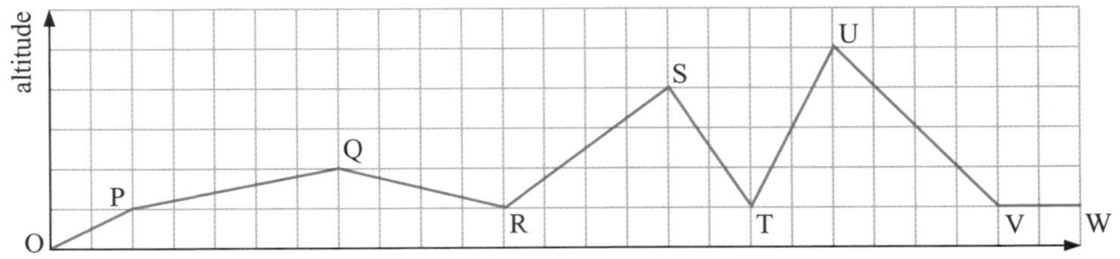

Imagine that you are walking across the countryside from O to W, from left to right. The vertical axis of the grid shows your altitude, or height above your starting point.

- **a** When are you going uphill?
- **b** When are you going downhill?
- **c** Where is the steepest positive gradient?
- **d** Where is the steepest negative gradient?
- **e** Where is the gradient 0?
- **f** Where is the least steep positive gradient?

Example 5 — Self Tutor

Draw a line through the point $(1, 1)$, with gradient $\frac{2}{3}$.

gradient $= \frac{2}{3}$ ← vertical step / ← horizontal step

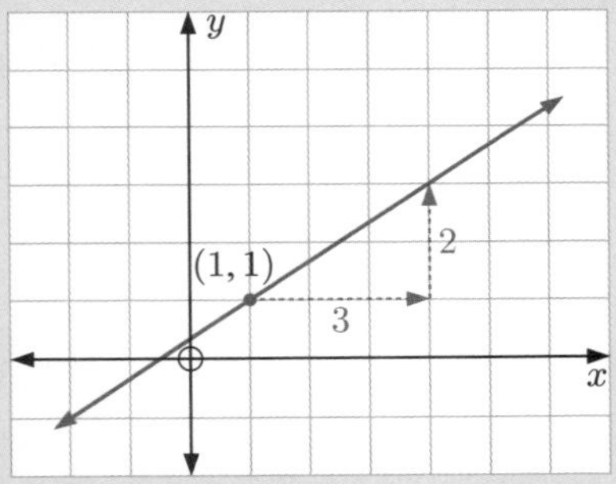

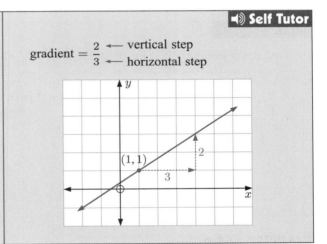

7 Draw a line through the point:

- **a** $(4, 1)$ with gradient $\frac{3}{2}$
- **b** $(3, -1)$ with gradient $\frac{1}{4}$
- **c** $(-2, 3)$ with gradient $-\frac{1}{5}$
- **d** $(0, 4)$ with gradient $-\frac{2}{3}$
- **e** $(0, -2)$ with gradient 3
- **f** $(-2, -1)$ with gradient -2
- **g** $(0, 6)$ with gradient $-\frac{5}{2}$
- **h** $(0, -3)$ with gradient $-\frac{3}{4}$.

8 By plotting the points on graph paper, find the gradient of the line segment joining:

- **a** O(0, 0) and A(2, 6)
- **b** O(0, 0) and B(−4, 2)
- **c** G(0, −1) and H(2, 5)
- **d** K(1, 1) and L(−2, −2)
- **e** M(3, 1) and N(−1, 3)
- **f** P(−2, 4) and Q(2, 0).

THE GRADIENT FORMULA

Although we can find gradients using steps on a diagram, it is often quicker to use a formula.

For points $A(x_1,\ y_1)$ and $B(x_2,\ y_2)$, the vertical step is $y_2 - y_1$, and the horizontal step is $x_2 - x_1$.

$\therefore$ the gradient is $\dfrac{y_2 - y_1}{x_2 - x_1}$.

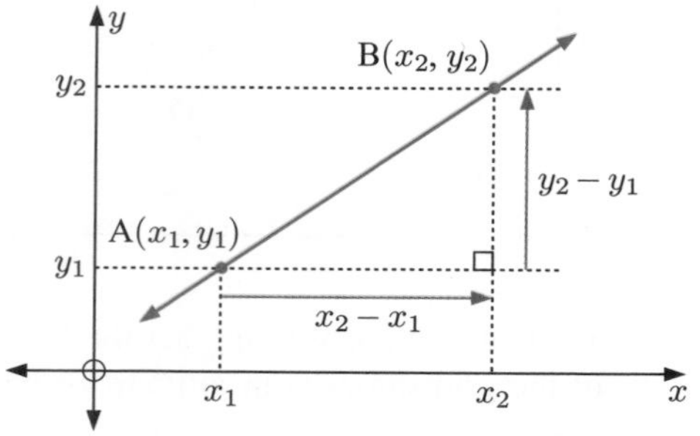

The **gradient** of the line through $(x_1,\ y_1)$ and $(x_2,\ y_2)$ is $\dfrac{y_2 - y_1}{x_2 - x_1}$.

Example 6 — Self Tutor

Find the gradient of [PQ] for $P(1,\ 3)$ and $Q(4,\ -2)$.

$P(1\ ,\ 3)$ with $x_1 = 1$, $y_1 = 3$; $Q(4\ ,\ -2)$ with $x_2 = 4$, $y_2 = -2$

$$\text{gradient of [PQ]} = \frac{y_2 - y_1}{x_2 - x_1} = \frac{-2-3}{4-1} = \frac{-5}{3} = -\frac{5}{3}$$

By using a formula, we do not have to plot the points on a graph.

EXERCISE 14C.2

1 For each graph, find the gradient of the line using:

  i horizontal and vertical steps **ii** the gradient formula.

a

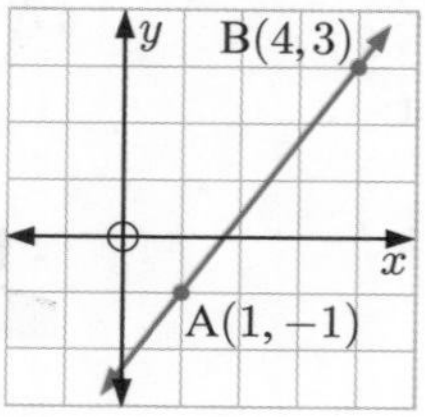

b

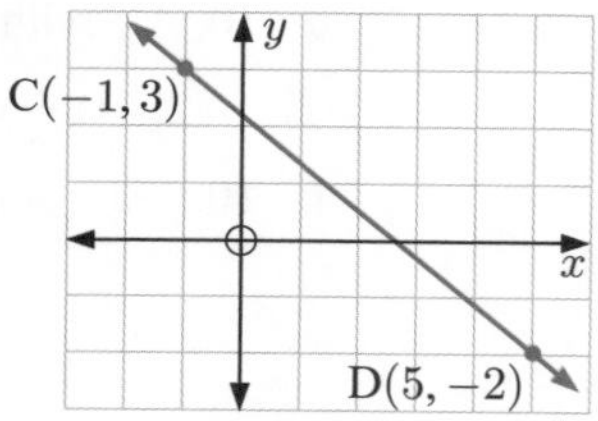

c

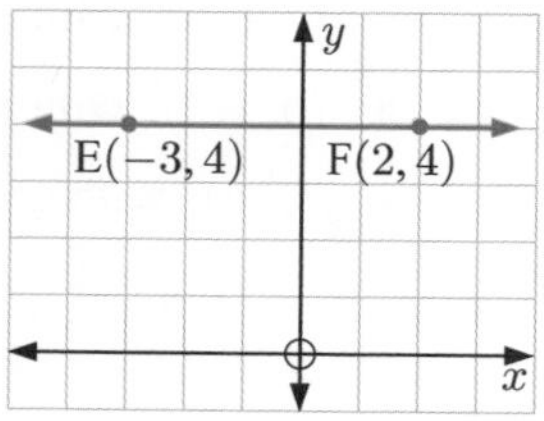

2 Use the gradient formula to find the gradient of the line segment joining:

a $O(0,\ 0)$ and $A(2,\ 6)$ **b** $O(0,\ 0)$ and $B(-4,\ 2)$ **c** $O(0,\ 0)$ and $C(2,\ -12)$

d $O(0,\ 0)$ and $D(1,\ -5)$ **e** $E(1,\ 0)$ and $F(1,\ 5)$ **f** $G(0,\ -1)$ and $H(2,\ -1)$

g $I(1,\ 1)$ and $J(3,\ 3)$ **h** $S(2,\ 3)$ and $T(-2,\ -7)$ **i** $J(4,\ 1)$ and $K(-2,\ 3)$

j $A(4,\ 6)$ and $B(-8,\ -3)$. **k** $P(1,\ -3)$ and $Q(-5,\ -7)$ **l** $M(6,\ 2)$ and $N(-2,\ -16)$.

3 Which method do you think is better to find the gradient of the line joining $R(-50,\ 460)$ and $S(115,\ 55)$? Explain your answer.

4 A(−2, 3), B(3, 6), C(6, 2), and D(−4, −4) are vertices of a quadrilateral. The sides [AB] and [CD] are parallel.

a Plot quadrilateral ABCD on a graph.

b What type of quadrilateral is ABCD?

c Find the gradient of:

i [AB] ii [BC] iii [CD] iv [DA]

d What do you suspect we can say about the gradients of parallel lines?

D AXES INTERCEPTS

When we are investigating lines on a number plane, it is useful to know where the line cuts the x and y-axes.

The **x-intercept** of a line is the x-coordinate of the point where the line cuts the x-axis.
The **y-intercept** of a line is the y-coordinate of the point where the line cuts the y-axis.

Example 7 Self Tutor

Find the x and y-intercepts of the line given:

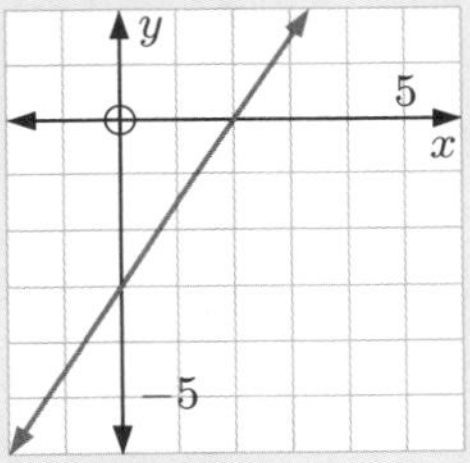

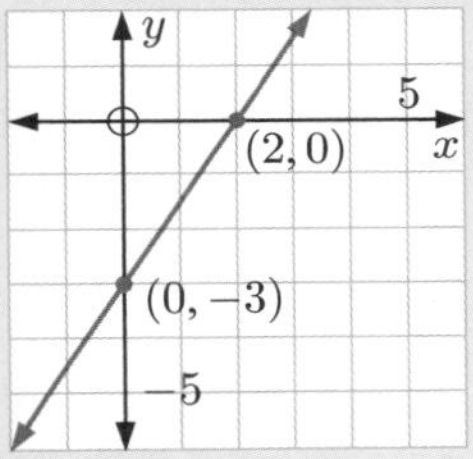

The line cuts the x-axis at (2, 0), so the x-intercept is 2.

The line cuts the y-axis at (0, −3), so the y-intercept is −3.

If the axes intercepts of a line are non-zero, we can quickly sketch the line and find its gradient.

Example 8 Self Tutor

Draw the graph of the line with x-intercept −2 and y-intercept −3.
Find the gradient of the line.

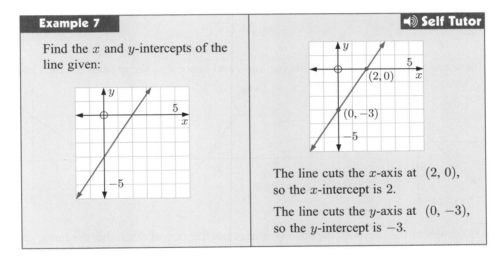

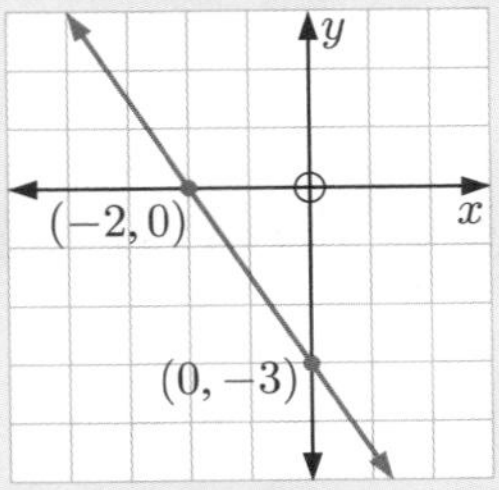

The line passes through (−2, 0) and (0, −3).

Its gradient is $\dfrac{-3-0}{0-(-2)} = \dfrac{-3}{2}$

$= -\dfrac{3}{2}$

EXERCISE 14D

1 Find the x and y-intercepts of the following lines:

a

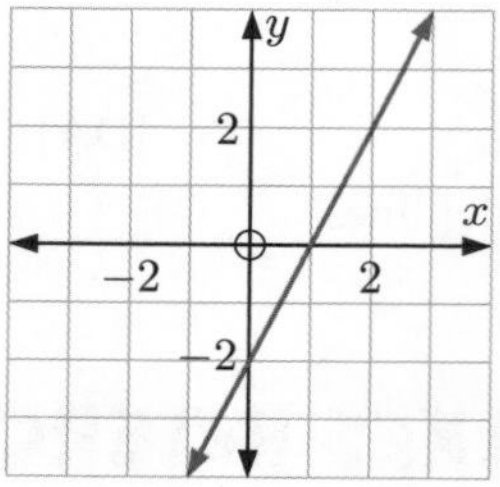

b

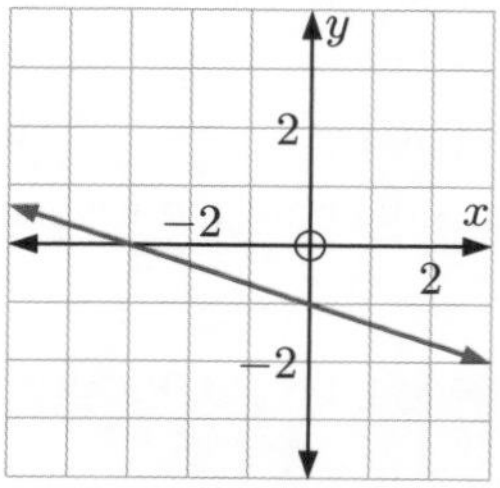

c

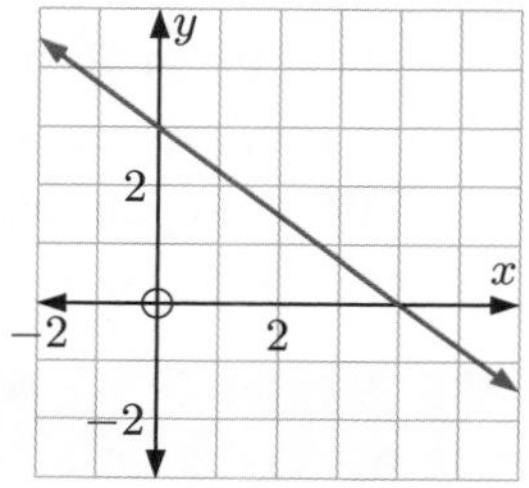

d

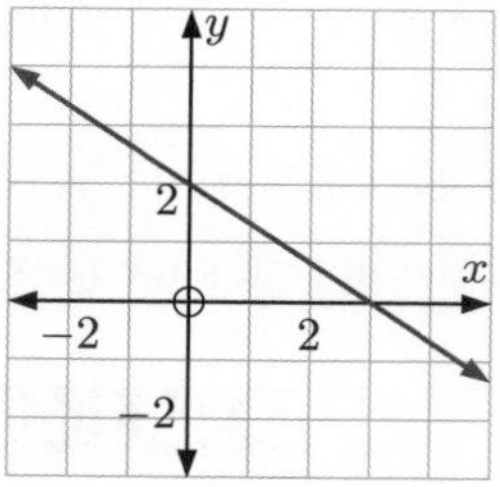

e

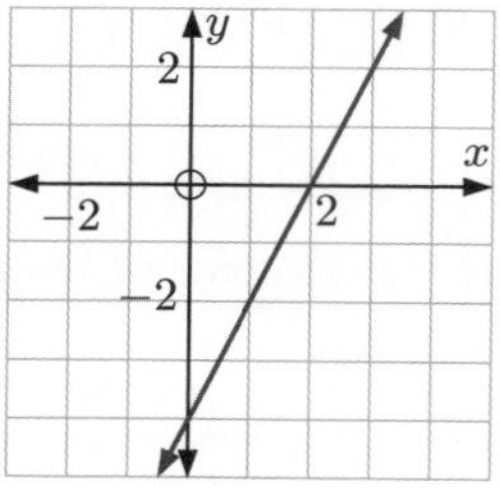

f

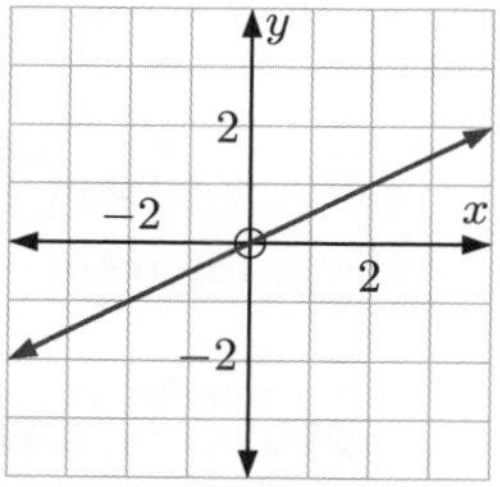

2 Find the x and y-intercepts of the following lines, and hence find the gradient of each line:

a

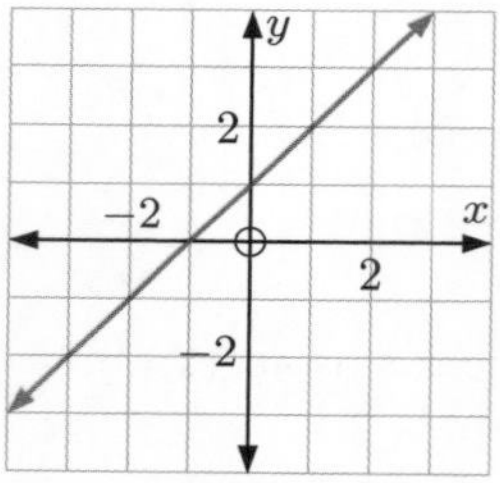

b

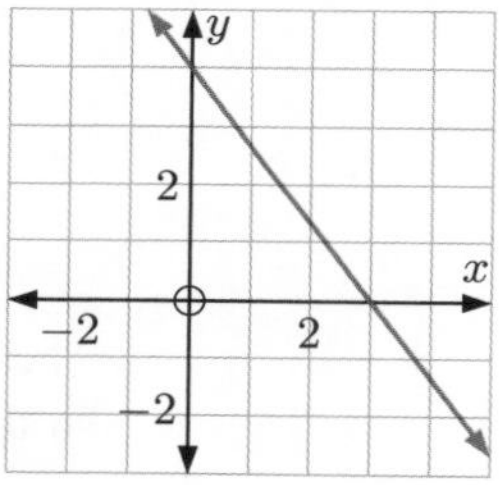

c

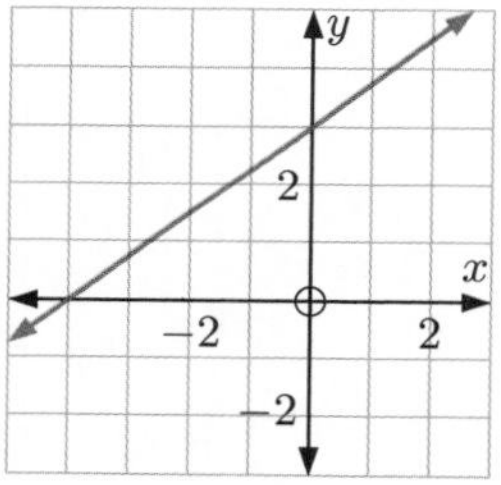

3 Draw the graph of the line with the following axes intercepts, and determine the line's gradient:

a x-intercept -1 and y-intercept 2

b x-intercept 2 and y-intercept 6

c x-intercept 3 and y-intercept -5

d x-intercept -4 and y-intercept -2.

DISCUSSION

Under what circumstances can we *not* determine the gradient of a line from the axes intercepts?

E THE EQUATION OF A LINE

The **equation of a line** is a rule which connects the x and y-coordinates of **all** points on the line.

For any line that is not horizontal or vertical, the rule can be written in the form $y = mx + c$ where m and c are constants.

Consider the line with equation $y = 2x$.

For all points on the line, the y-coordinate is double the x-coordinate.

Example 9 Self Tutor

State in words, the meaning of the equation $y = 3x + 7$.

$y = 3x + 7$ connects the x and y-coordinates of every point on a straight line.

For any point on the line, the y-coordinate is three times the x-coordinate, plus 7.

A **table of values** is often used to display the coordinates (x, y) for points on a line.

For example, this table of values corresponds to the line with equation $y = 2x$. It tells us that the points $(-2, -4)$, $(-1, -2)$, $(0, 0)$, $(1, 2)$, $(2, 4)$, and $(3, 6)$ all lie on the line.

x	-2	-1	0	1	2	3
y	-4	-2	0	2	4	6

Example 10 Self Tutor

By inspection only, find the equation of the straight line passing through the following points:

a

x	1	2	3	4	5
y	-3	-6	-9	-12	-15

b

x	1	2	3	4	5
y	5	4	3	2	1

The line in **b** could be written as $y = -x + 6$.

a Each y-value is -3 times its corresponding x-value, so $y = -3x$.

b The sum of each x and y-value is always 6, so $x + y = 6$.

A point lies on a line if, and only if, its coordinates satisfy the equation of the line.

Example 11 Self Tutor

Determine whether $(2, 5)$ and $(-1, -5)$ lie on the line with equation $y = 4x - 3$.

The point on the line with x-coordinate 2, has y-coordinate $= 4 \times 2 - 3$
$= 8 - 3$
$= 5$ ✓

So, $(2, 5)$ does lie on the line.

The point on the line with x-coordinate -1, has y-coordinate $= 4 \times (-1) - 3$
$= -4 - 3$
$= -7$

Since the y-coordinate $\neq -5$,
$(-1, -5)$ does not lie on the line.

EXERCISE 14E

1 State in words, the meaning of the equation:

a $y = x + 3$ **b** $y = 5x$ **c** $y = 2x - 6$ **d** $x + y = 5$

2 By inspection only, find the equation of the straight line passing through the following points:

a

x	1	2	3	4	5
y	4	8	12	16	20

b

x	2	3	4	5	6
y	4	5	6	7	8

c

x	0	1	2	3
y	0	-2	-4	-6

d

x	0	1	2	3
y	3	2	1	0

e

x	1	2	3	4	5
y	3	5	7	9	11

f

x	1	2	3	4	5
y	1	3	5	7	9

3 Determine whether the point:

a (3, 4) lies on the line $y = 2x - 2$

b $(-1, 4)$ lies on the line $y = x + 6$

c $(-2, 10)$ lies on the line $y = -3x + 4$

d $(\frac{1}{2}, -6)$ lies on the line $y = 2x - 8$.

4 Consider the line $y = 2x - 3$.

a Find the y-coordinate of the point on the line with x-coordinate 4.

b Find the x-coordinate of the point on the line with y-coordinate -4.

5 Consider the line $y = 5 - 2x$.

a Find the y-coordinate of the point on the line with x-coordinate -2.

b Find the x-coordinate of the point on the line with y-coordinate -3.

6 Consider the line $y = 4 + x$.

a Find the y-coordinate of the point on the line with x-coordinate 0.

b Find the x-coordinate of the point on the line with y-coordinate 0.

c Hence state the axes intercepts of the line.

F GRAPHING LINES FROM EQUATIONS

If we are given the equation of a line, we can draw its graph:

- by constructing a **table of values**
- using its **gradient** and **y-intercept**.

GRAPHING LINES BY CONSTRUCTING A TABLE OF VALUES

For any given value of x, we can use the equation of the line to find the corresponding value of y.

Consider the equation $y = \frac{1}{2}x - 1$.

When $x = -2$, $y = \frac{1}{2}(-2) - 1$
$= -1 - 1$
$= -2$

When $x = 2$, $y = \frac{1}{2}(2) - 1$
$= 1 - 1$
$= 0$

By continuing this process, we construct the **table of values**:

x	-3	-2	-1	0	1	2	3
y	$-2\frac{1}{2}$	-2	$-1\frac{1}{2}$	-1	$-\frac{1}{2}$	0	$\frac{1}{2}$

The points $(-3, -2\frac{1}{2})$, $(-2, -2)$, $(-1, -1\frac{1}{2})$, $(0, -1)$, $(1, -\frac{1}{2})$, $(2, 0)$, and $(3, \frac{1}{2})$ all satisfy $y = \frac{1}{2}x - 1$ and lie on its graph.

The graph of $y = \frac{1}{2}x - 1$ is the line which passes through these points.

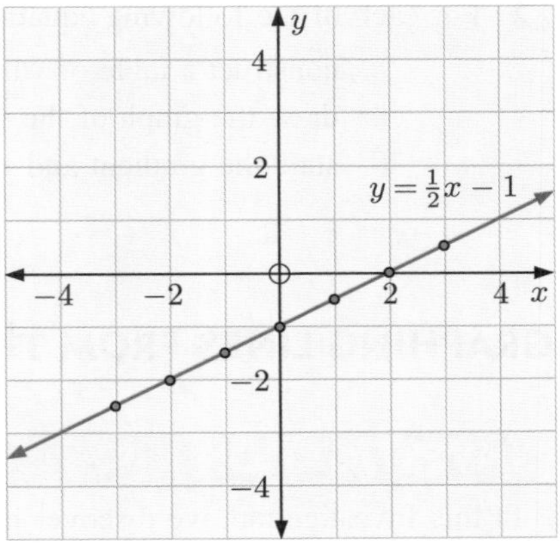

Example 12 **Self Tutor**

Consider the equation $y = x - 2$.

a Construct a table of values using $x = -3, -2, -1, 0, 1, 2$, and 3.

b Hence draw the graph of $y = x - 2$.

a

x	-3	-2	-1	0	1	2	3
y	-5	-4	-3	-2	-1	0	1

b

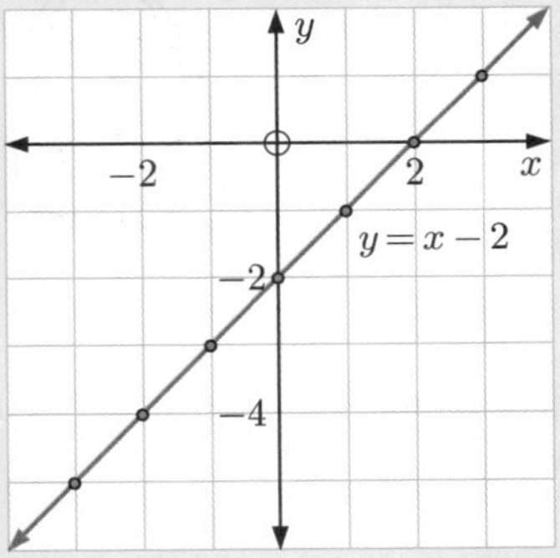

EXERCISE 14F.1

1 For each of the following equations:

- **i** construct a table of values using $x = -3, -2, -1, 0, 1, 2, 3$
- **ii** draw the graph of the straight line.

a $y = x$ **b** $y = -x$ **c** $y = 2x$

d $y = -2x$ **e** $y = 2x - 1$ **f** $y = -2x - 1$

g $y = \frac{1}{4}x + 2$ **h** $y = -\frac{1}{4}x + 2$ **i** $y = 2 - x$

j $y = 3x - 2$ **k** $y = 1 - 2x$ **l** $y = -1.5x - 1$

Use your **graphics calculator** or the **graphing package** to check your answers.

GRAPHICS CALCULATOR INSTRUCTIONS

GRAPHING PACKAGE

2 For each of the following equations:

- **i** construct a table of values using $x = -3, -2, -1, 0, 1, 2, 3$
- **ii** draw the graph of the straight line
- **iii** state the gradient and y-intercept of the line.

a $y = x + 3$ **b** $y = -2x + 1$ **c** $y = \frac{1}{3}x - 1$

GRAPHING LINES FROM THE GRADIENT AND y-INTERCEPT

INVESTIGATION — GRAPHING LINES

In this Investigation, we discover how the equation of a line relates to the *gradient* and *y-intercept* of the line.

What to do:

GRAPHING PACKAGE

1 Draw the graph of each line given. You can do this using a **table of values**, your **graphics calculator**, or the **graphing package**. Hence write down the gradient and y-intercept of each line.

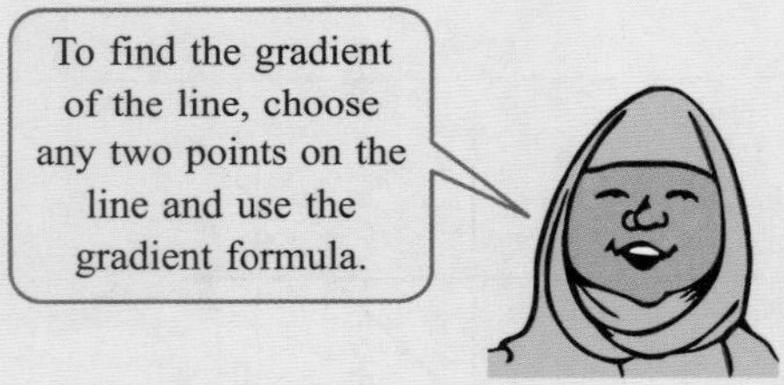
To find the gradient of the line, choose any two points on the line and use the gradient formula.

	Equation of line	*Gradient*	*y-intercept*
a	$y = 2x + 1$	2	1
b	$y = 3x - 2$		
c	$y = -x + 3$		
d	$y = 4x$		
e	$y = -2x + 2$		
f	$y = \frac{1}{2}x - 1$		
g	$y = -\frac{1}{3}x + 1$		

2 Copy and complete: "For a line with equation $y = mx + c$, the gradient is ...... and the y-intercept is ...."

You should have discovered that:

> $y = mx + c$ is the equation of a straight line with gradient m and y-intercept c.

Example 13 — Self Tutor

State the gradient and y-intercept of the line with equation:

a $y = 3x - 2$ **b** $y = 7 - 2x$ **c** $y = 0$

a $y = 3x - 2$ has $m = 3$ and $c = -2$
$\therefore$ the gradient is 3 and the y-intercept is -2.

b $y = 7 - 2x$ can be written as $y = -2x + 7$, with $m = -2$ and $c = 7$
$\therefore$ the gradient is -2 and the y-intercept is 7.

c $y = 0$ can be written as $y = 0x + 0$, with $m = 0$ and $c = 0$
$\therefore$ the gradient is 0 and the y-intercept is 0.

To draw the graph of $y = mx + c$:

- Use the y-intercept c to plot the point $(0, c)$.
- Starting from $(0, c)$, use horizontal and vertical steps from the gradient m to locate another point on the line.
- Join the two points and extend the line in either direction.

Example 14 — Self Tutor

Draw the graph of: **a** $y = \frac{2}{3}x + 1$ **b** $y = -2x - 3$.

a For $y = \frac{2}{3}x + 1$:
- the y-intercept is $c = 1$
- the gradient is

$m = \frac{2}{3}$ ← vertical step / ← horizontal step

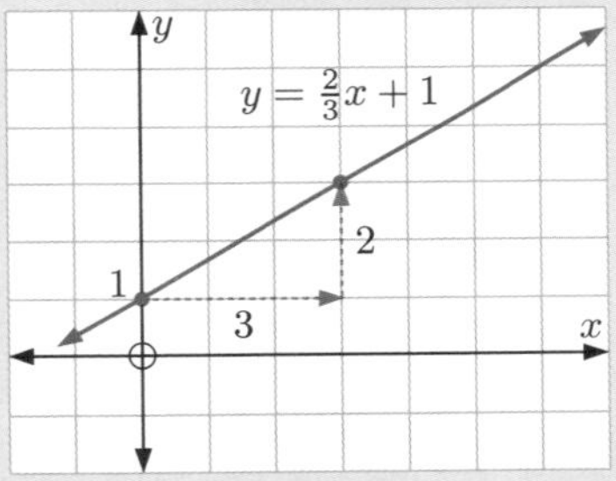

b For $y = -2x - 3$:
- the y-intercept is $c = -3$
- the gradient is

$m = \frac{-2}{1}$ ← vertical step / ← horizontal step

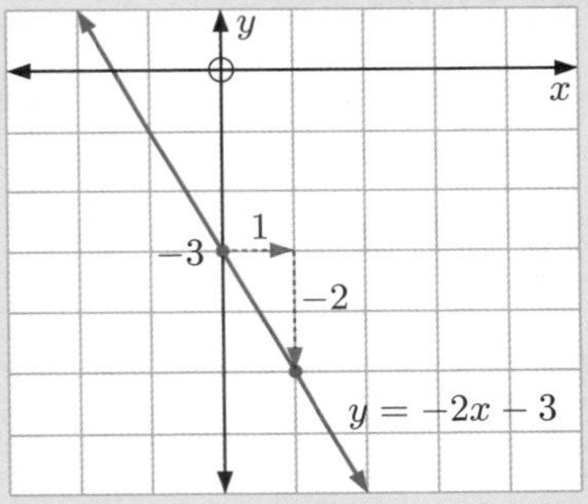

EXERCISE 14F.2

1 State the gradient and y-intercept of the line with equation:

a $y = 4x + 8$ **b** $y = -3x + 2$ **c** $y = 6 - x$
d $y = -2x + 3$ **e** $y = -2$ **f** $y = 11 - 3x$
g $y = \frac{1}{2}x - 5$ **h** $y = 3 - \frac{3}{2}x$ **i** $y = \frac{2}{5}x + \frac{4}{5}$
j $y = \frac{x+1}{2}$ **k** $y = \frac{2x-10}{5}$ **l** $y = \frac{11-3x}{2}$

2 Draw the graph of:

a $y = x + 3$ **b** $y = -x + 4$ **c** $y = 2x + 2$
d $y = -3x - 2$ **e** $y = \frac{1}{2}x - 1$ **f** $y = \frac{2}{3}x + 4$
g $y = 3x$ **h** $y = -\frac{1}{2}x$ **i** $y = -2x + 1$
j $y = 3 - \frac{1}{3}x$ **k** $y = \frac{3}{4}x - 2$ **l** $y = -\frac{1}{4}x - 3$

3 Consider the line with equation $y = -\frac{2}{3}x + 2$.

a Find the: **i** gradient **ii** y-intercept **iii** x-intercept.

b Draw the graph of the line. **c** Does the point $(4, -\frac{2}{3})$ lie on the line?

G VERTICAL AND HORIZONTAL LINES

Vertical and horizontal lines are special cases which we need to treat with care.

VERTICAL LINES

For all points on a vertical line, the x-coordinate is constant regardless of the value of the y-coordinate.

The graph alongside shows the vertical lines $x = -1$ and $x = 3$.

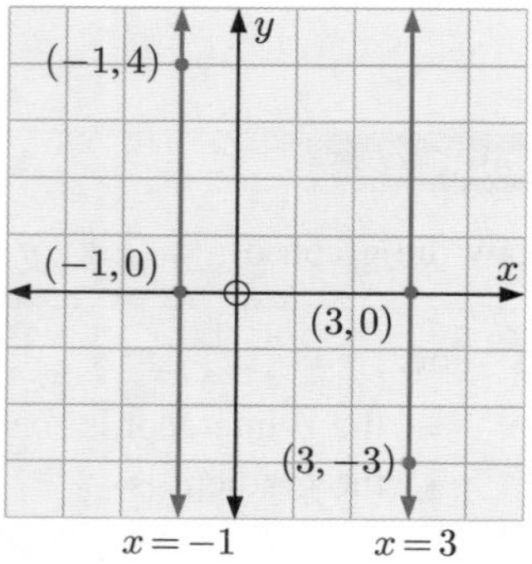

All **vertical** lines have equations of the form $x = a$.

The gradient of a vertical line is **undefined**.

HORIZONTAL LINES

For all points on a horizontal line, the y-coordinate is constant regardless of the value of the x-coordinate.

The graph alongside shows the horizontal lines $y = -2$ and $y = 1$.

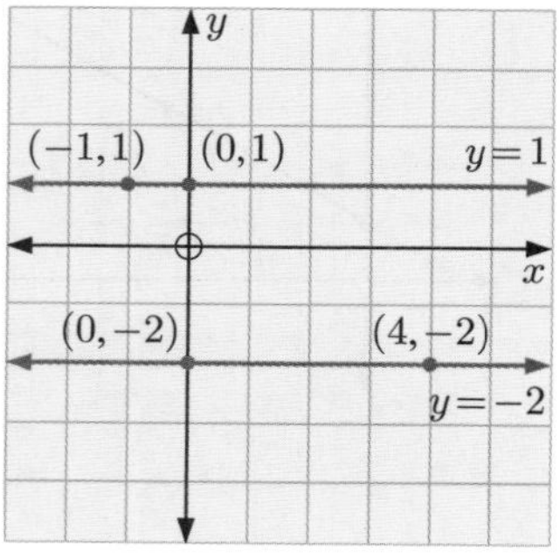

All **horizontal** lines have equations of the form $y = c$.

The gradient of a horizontal line is **zero**.

EXERCISE 14G

1 Draw the graph of the line with equation:

a $x = 2$ **b** $y = 3$ **c** $y = -4$ **d** $x = -3$

e $y = 1.5$ **f** $x = -\frac{5}{2}$ **g** $y = 0$ **h** $y = -\frac{1}{4}$

2 Find the gradient of each line in **1**.

3 Suppose l_1 is the line with equation $x = 5$, and l_2 is the line with equation $y = -3$.

a Graph l_1 and l_2 on the same set of axes.

b Suppose l_1 cuts the x-axis at A, and l_2 cuts the y-axis at B. Find:

i the coordinates of A and B **ii** the gradient of [AB].

4 **a** On the same set of axes, graph the lines $x = -2$, $x = 6$, $y = 5$, and $y = -6$.

b Consider the quadrilateral formed by the intersection points of these lines.

i What type of quadrilateral is it?

ii Find the area of the quadrilateral.

iii Find the gradient of the diagonals of the quadriateral.

H FINDING EQUATIONS FROM GRAPHS

If we know the y-intercept c and one other point on a graph, then we can find the gradient m using the gradient formula.

We can then write down the equation of the line as $y = mx + c$.

Example 15 — Self Tutor

For the graph alongside, determine:

a the gradient of the line

b the y-intercept

c the equation of the line.

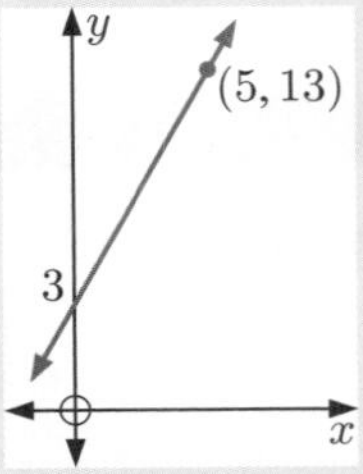

a (0, 3) and (5, 13) lie on the line

$\therefore$ the gradient $m = \dfrac{13-3}{5-0}$

$= \frac{10}{5}$

$= 2$

b The y-intercept is 3.

c The equation of the line is $y = 2x + 3$.

EXERCISE 14H

1 For each of the following lines, find:

i the gradient **ii** the y-intercept **iii** the equation of the line.

a

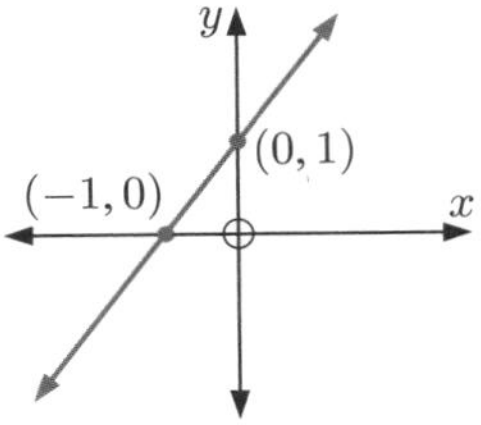

b

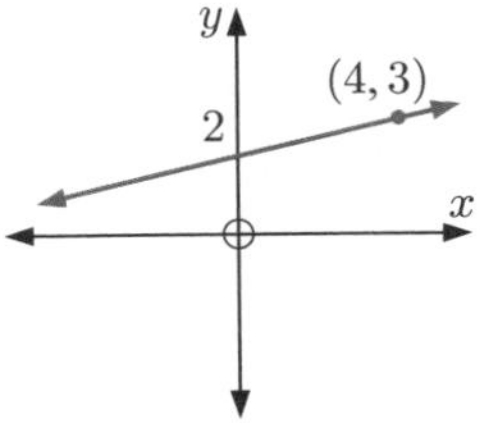

c

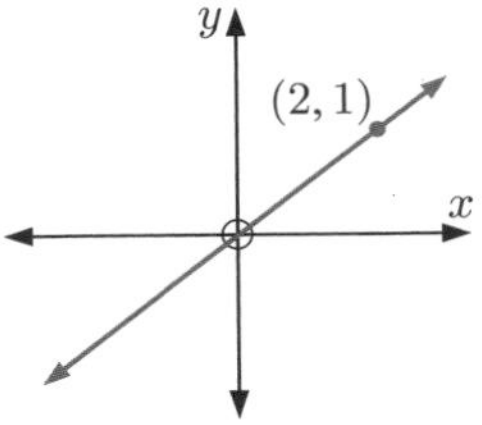

d

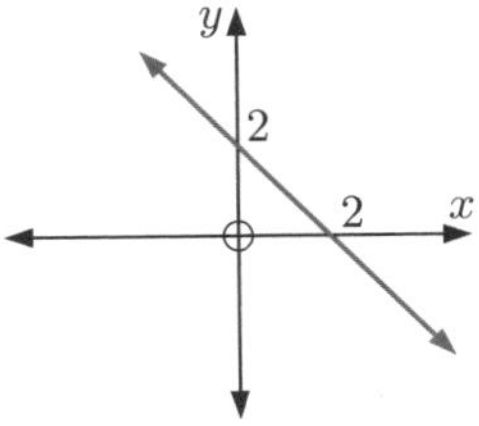

e

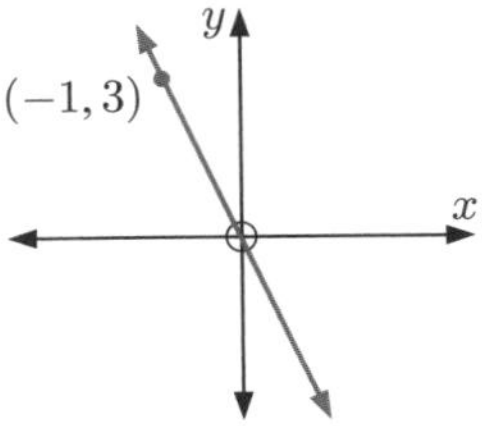

f

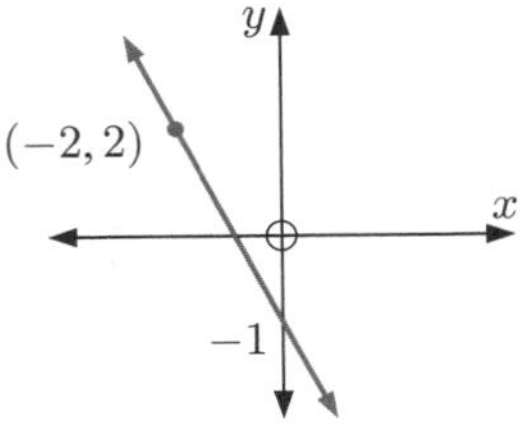

g

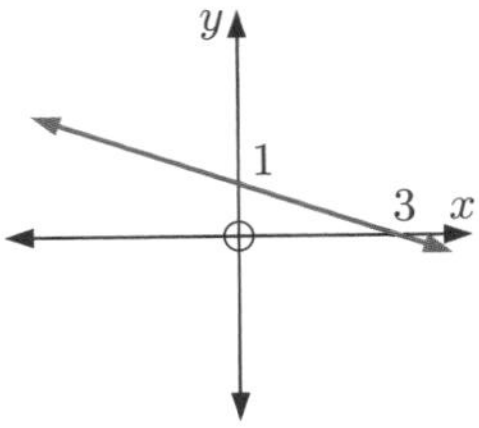

h

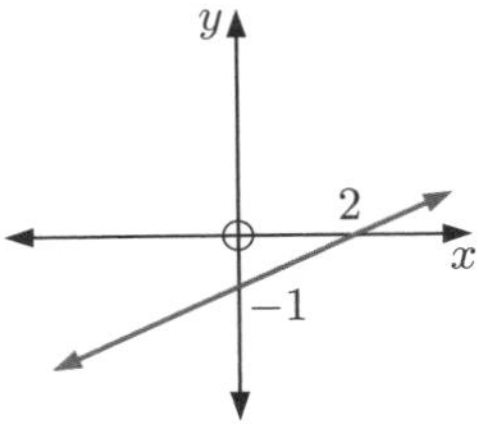

i

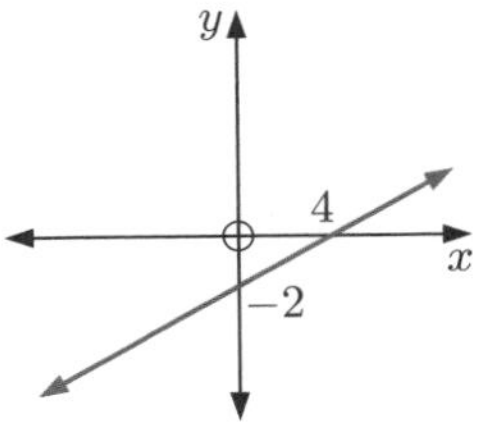

2 Find the rule connecting the variables in:

a 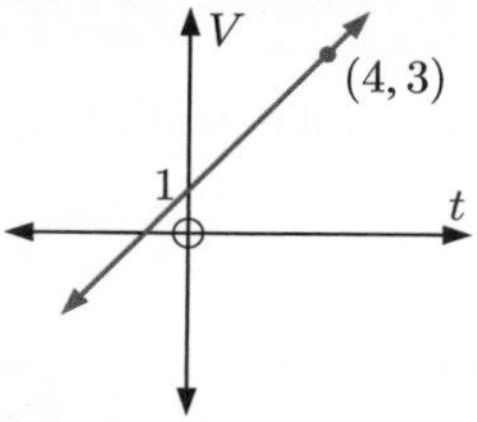

b 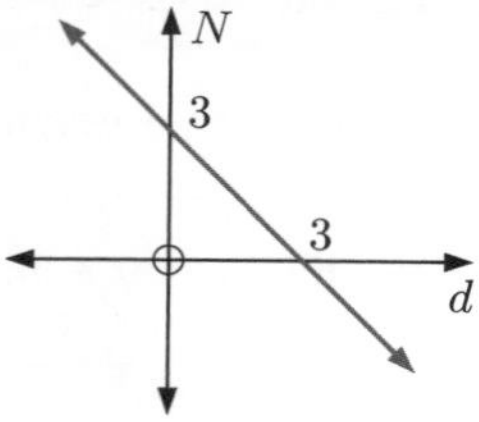

c 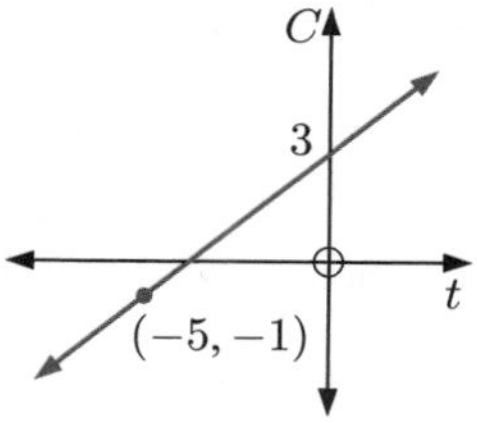

REVIEW SET 14A

1 State the coordinates of the points A, B, C, D, and E.

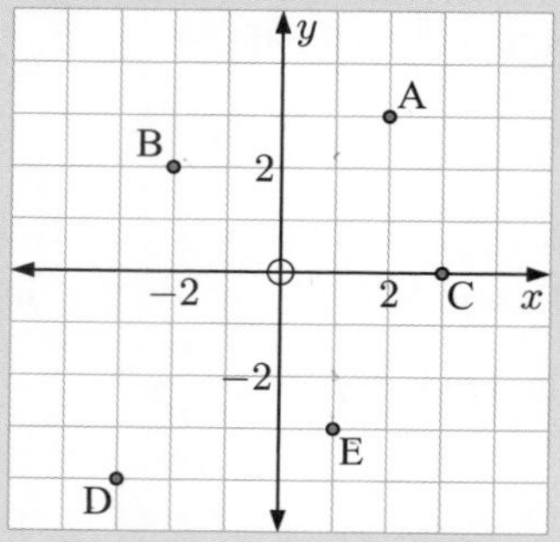

2 On a set of axes, illustrate all the points which have equal x and y-coordinates.

3 For the equation $y = 4 - 3x$:

a construct a table of values with $x = -3, -2, -1, 0, 1, 2, 3$

b draw the graph of the straight line

c state the gradient and y-intercept of the line.

4 An accountant charges a £70 consultation fee and then £120 per hour thereafter.

a Identify the independent and dependent variables.

b Make a table of values for the cost £C of an appointment with the accountant for t hours where $t = 0, 1, 2, 3, 4$.

c Draw a graph of C against t.

d Is the relationship between C and t linear?

e Is it sensible to join the points graphed with a straight line? Explain your answer.

f For every increase in t of 1 hour, what is the change in C?

5 State the gradient of each line:

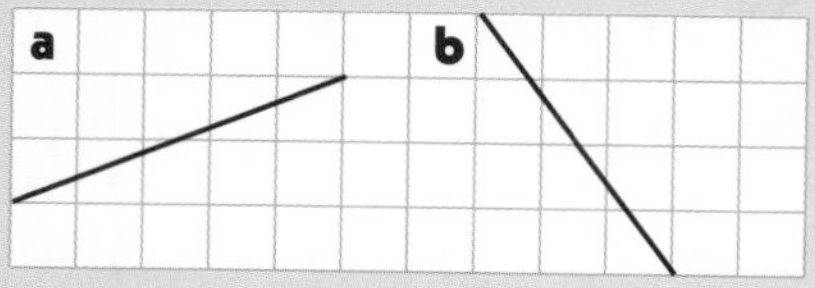

6 On the same set of axes, draw graphs of the lines with equations $x = -2\frac{1}{2}$ and $y = -4$.

7 State the gradient and y-intercept of the line with equation:

a $y = 4x - 3$ **b** $y = 2 - x$ **c** $y = \dfrac{3x - 1}{2}$

8 Find the x and y-intercepts of each of the following lines, and hence find the gradient of the line:

a

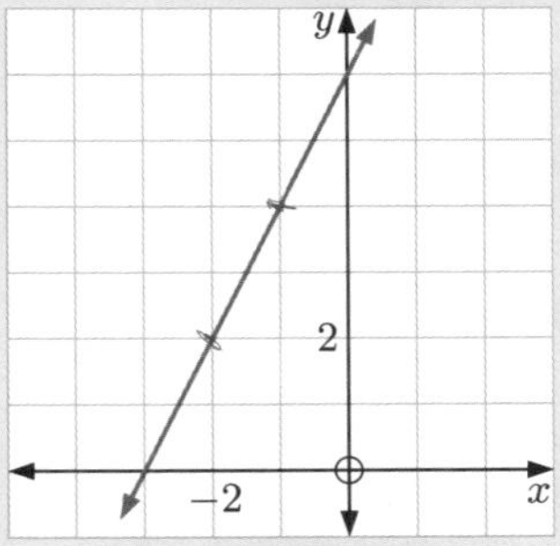

b

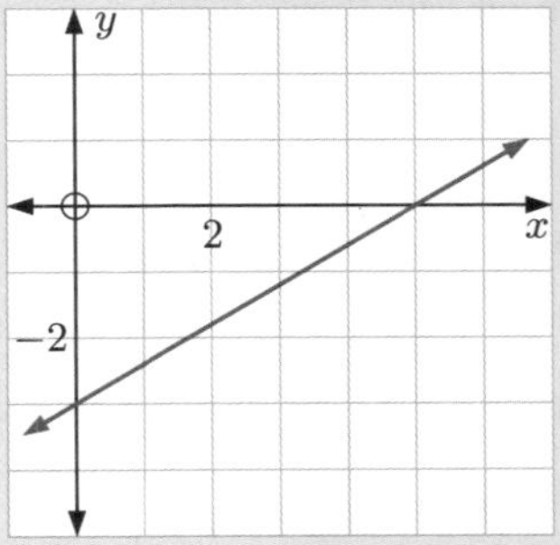

c

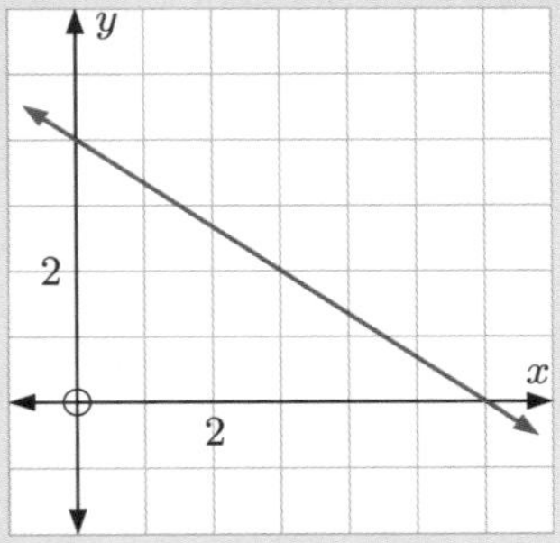

9 For each of the following lines:

i state the gradient and y-intercept **ii** draw the graph of the line.

a $y = 2x - 3$ **b** $y = \frac{1}{3}x + 1$ **c** $y = 8 - 3x$

10 Find the equation of each line:

a

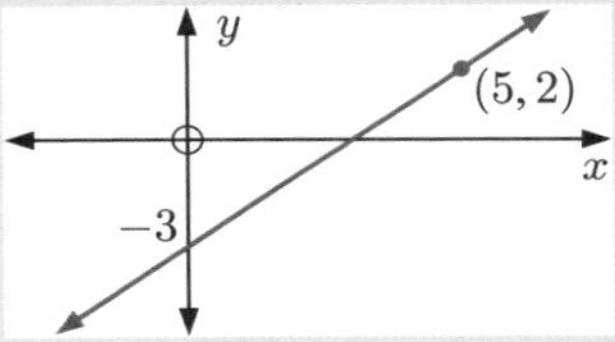

b

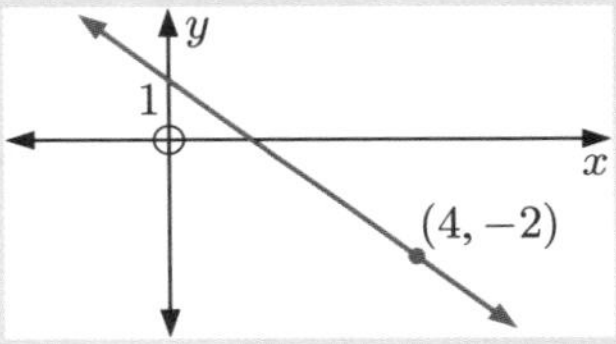

REVIEW SET 14B

1 Plot the points P(2, 5), Q(3, −3), R(−4, 0), and S(−2, −4) on a set of axes.

2 Find, by inspection, the equation of the straight line passing through these points:

x	0	1	2	3	4	5
y	3	2	1	0	−1	−2

3 A tank contains 400 litres of water. The tap is left on and 20 litres of water escape per minute. Suppose V is the volume of water remaining in the tank t minutes after the tap is turned on.

a What are the independent and dependent variables?

b Make a table of values for V and t, for $t = 0$, 2, 4, 6, 8, 10 minutes.

c Draw the graph of V against t.

d Is the relationship between V and t linear?

e Is it sensible to join the points graphed with a straight line? Explain your answer.

f For every increase of 1 minute for t, what is the change in V?

g How much water is left in the tank after $2\frac{1}{2}$ minutes?

h How long will it take for the volume of water in the tank to fall to 310 litres?

4 On grid paper, draw a line with a gradient of:

a $\frac{2}{5}$ **b** $-\frac{4}{3}$ **c** 0

5 Find the gradient of the straight line through the points:

a $(2, 1)$ and $(8, 13)$ **b** $(-2, 3)$ and $(1, -4)$

c $(-1, -5)$ and $(9, 3)$ **d** $(2, -3)$ and $(-7, 12)$.

6 Draw a line through the point:

a $(3, 5)$ with gradient $\frac{1}{4}$ **b** $(-2, 3)$ with gradient -2.

7 Determine whether the point $(-2, 5)$ lies on the line with equation $y = -2x + 1$.

8 For each of the following lines:

i state the gradient and y-intercept **ii** draw the graph of the line.

a $y = -\frac{1}{3}x + 2$ **b** $y = \frac{3}{4}x - 3$

9 Find the equation of each line:

a

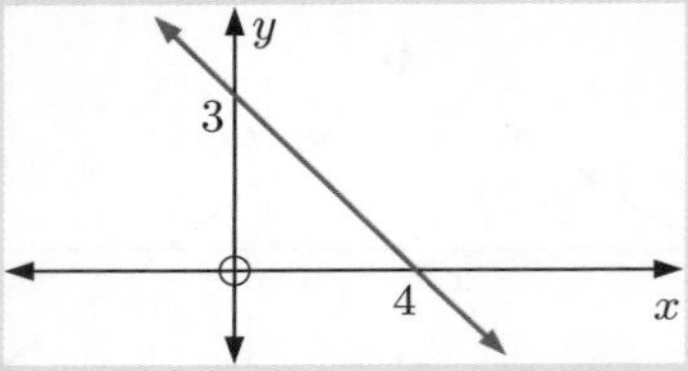

b

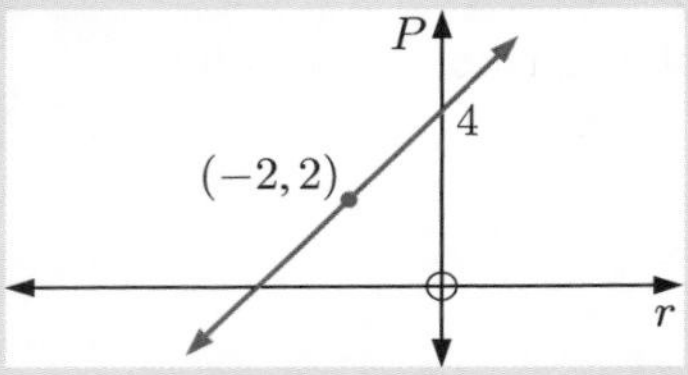

10

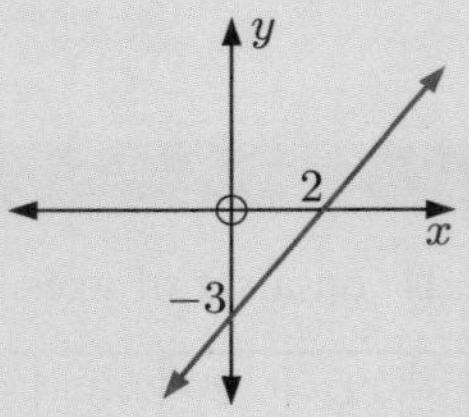

For the line given, find the:

a x-intercept

b y-intercept

c equation of the line.

Chapter 15

Simultaneous equations

Contents:

OPENING PROBLEM

At the summer sales, Cassandra buys a dress and a skirt. Together they cost \$30. The dress cost \$8 more than the skirt.

Suppose the dress cost $\$x$, and the skirt cost $\$y$.

Things to think about:

a Can you explain why:
  i $x + y = 30$ **ii** $x - y = 8$?

b How many solutions are there to the equation:
  i $x + y = 30$ **ii** $x - y = 8$?

c Which solution satisfies *both* equations at the same time?

We have previously studied equations involving one variable.

For example, the linear equation $3x + 5 = 14$ has exactly one solution, $x = 3$.

Some equations have more than one variable, and more than one solution.

Consider the equations in the **Opening Problem**:

- $x + y = 30$ has infinitely many solutions. They lie in a straight line on the Cartesian plane. $x = 1$, $y = 29$ is one solution, and $x = 2$, $y = 28$ is another.
- $x - y = 8$ also has infinitely many solutions which lie in a straight line. They include $x = 9$, $y = 1$, and $x = 10$, $y = 2$.

To find a solution which satisfies *both* equations at the same time, we need to solve the equations *simultaneously*. We say they are **simultaneous equations**.

There is in fact only *one* solution to the simultaneous equations
$$\begin{cases} x + y = 30 \\ x - y = 8 \,. \end{cases}$$

The solution occurs at the point where the two lines intersect.

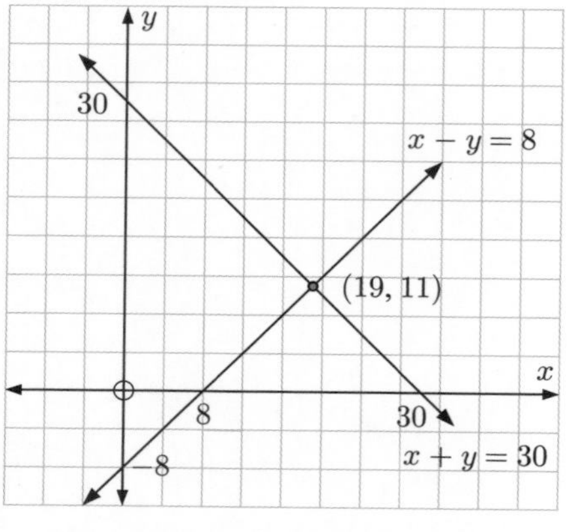

The solution $x = 19$, $y = 11$ satisfies both equations at the same time, since $19 + 11 = 30$ and $19 - 11 = 8$.

So, Cassandra paid \$19 for the dress and \$11 for the skirt.

A TRIAL AND ERROR SOLUTION

One way to solve simultaneous equations is by **trial and error**. We list possible solutions to *one* of the equations, and look for the solution which also satisfies the *other* equation.

Example 1 — Self Tutor

Solve $\begin{cases} x + y = 8 \\ 2x - y = 7 \end{cases}$ simultaneously by trial and error.

We consider solutions to $x + y = 8$, and find the solution which also satisfies $2x - y = 7$.

The solution is $x = 5$, $y = 3$.

x	y	$x+y$	$2x-y$	
0	8	8	−8	
1	7	8	−5	
2	6	8	−2	
3	5	8	1	
4	4	8	4	
5	3	8	7	✓

EXERCISE 15A

1 Determine whether the given values satisfy the pair of simultaneous equations:

a $\begin{cases} x - y = 3 \\ 2x + y = 11 \end{cases}$ $(x = 5,\ y = 2)$

b $\begin{cases} x + y = 9 \\ 2x - y = 6 \end{cases}$ $(x = 5,\ y = 4)$

c $\begin{cases} a + b = 2 \\ a - b = 8 \end{cases}$ $(a = 5,\ b = -3)$

d $\begin{cases} 2p + q = 7 \\ 3p + 2q = 10 \end{cases}$ $(p = 4,\ q = -1)$

2 Given that the solutions are integers, solve the following by trial and error:

a $\begin{cases} x + y = 4 \\ 3x + 5y = 14 \end{cases}$

b $\begin{cases} x + y = 11 \\ 4x + 3y = 40 \end{cases}$

c $\begin{cases} y = x + 2 \\ 9x - 4y = 7 \end{cases}$

d $\begin{cases} y = 6 + x \\ 8x - 3y = -3 \end{cases}$

e $\begin{cases} x + y = 4 \\ 2x - y = 5 \end{cases}$

f $\begin{cases} x + y = 6 \\ 2x + y = 10 \end{cases}$

g $\begin{cases} a - b = 1 \\ 2a + 3b = 2 \end{cases}$

h $\begin{cases} p - q = 3 \\ 5p + 2q = 29 \end{cases}$

i $\begin{cases} 3x + 2y = 17 \\ -y + x = -21 \end{cases}$

DISCUSSION

1 Attempt to solve the following simultaneous equations by trial and error:

a $\begin{cases} 3x + 7y = 1 \\ 6x - 14y = -4 \end{cases}$

b $\begin{cases} 2x - y = 8 \\ -4x + 2y = 9 \end{cases}$

c $\begin{cases} x - y = 2 \\ 2y - 2x = -4 \end{cases}$

2 Discuss your answers to **1** with your class. In particular:

- For **a** and **b**, did anyone find a solution? *Is* there a solution?
- For **c**, did you all find the same solution? Are all of the solutions you found valid?
- Discuss the problems with using trial and error to solve simultaneous equations.

B GRAPHICAL SOLUTION

Suppose we are given two linear equations involving x and y. The solutions to each equation will form a straight line. If we graph the two equations on the same set of axes, any **point of intersection** corresponds to a **simultaneous solution** of the equations.

- If the lines are not parallel, the lines will meet in exactly one point. The simultaneous equations have *exactly one solution.*

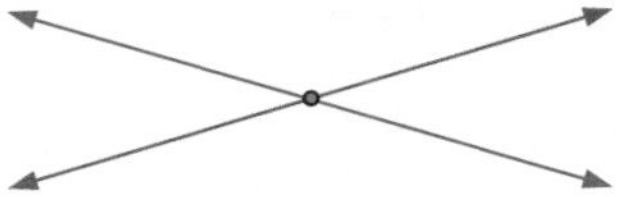

- If the lines are parallel but not identical, the lines will never meet. The simultaneous equations have *no solutions.*

- If the lines are identical, there will be infinitely many points of intersection. The simultaneous equations have *infinitely many solutions.*

Example 2 **Self Tutor**

Solve the simultaneous equations graphically: $\begin{cases} y = 2x + 5 \\ y = -x - 1 \end{cases}$

For $y = 2x + 5$:
when $x = 0$, $y = 5$ and when $y = 0$, $x = -\frac{5}{2}$.

For $y = -x - 1$:
when $x = 0$, $y = -1$ and when $y = 0$, $x = -1$.

We draw the graphs of $y = 2x + 5$ and $y = -x - 1$ on the same set of axes.

The graphs meet at the point $(-2, 1)$.

$\therefore$ the solution is $x = -2$, $y = 1$.

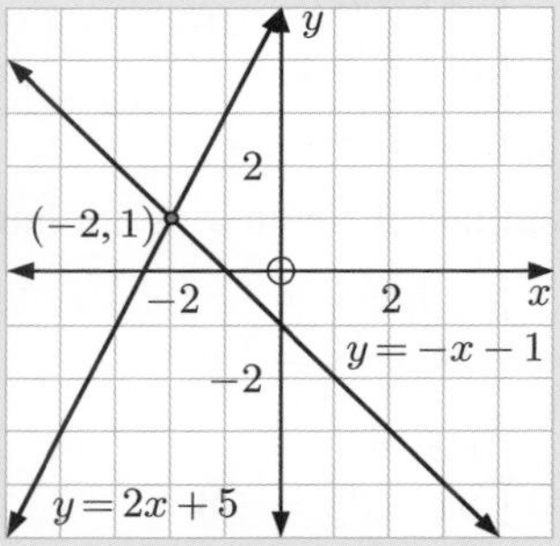

EXERCISE 15B

1 Solve the simultaneous equations graphically:

a $\begin{cases} y = x \\ y = 2 - x \end{cases}$ b $\begin{cases} y = x + 3 \\ y = -2x \end{cases}$ c $\begin{cases} y = 3x + 2 \\ y = x - 4 \end{cases}$

d $\begin{cases} y = -2x + 3 \\ y = 5 - x \end{cases}$ e $\begin{cases} y = 2 - 3x \\ y = x - 2 \end{cases}$ f $\begin{cases} y = 3x + 4 \\ y = 2x + 1 \end{cases}$

You can check your answer by substituting into the original equations.

2 Solve the simultaneous equations graphically:

a $\begin{cases} y = x + 1 \\ y = 2x - 3 \end{cases}$ b $\begin{cases} y = x + 4 \\ y = -x + 2 \end{cases}$ c $\begin{cases} y = x + 2 \\ y = -2x + 5 \end{cases}$

d $\begin{cases} y = 2x - 2 \\ y = 1 - x \end{cases}$ e $\begin{cases} y = 3x - 1 \\ y = 2x - 2 \end{cases}$ f $\begin{cases} y = -2x + 3 \\ y = x + 6 \end{cases}$

y=-x+1

3 Graph the following pairs of lines to find how many solutions these simultaneous equations have. In each case explain your answer.

a $\begin{cases} y = 2x + 3 \\ y = 2x - 2 \end{cases}$ **b** $\begin{cases} x + y = 2 \\ y = 2 - x \end{cases}$ **c** $\begin{cases} y = 2.3x - 3.6 \\ y = -1.2x + 5.7 \end{cases}$

DISCUSSION

Discuss the advantages and disadvantages of solving simultaneous equations by graphical methods.

C SOLUTION BY EQUATING VALUES OF y

We will now consider some **algebraic** methods for solving linear simultaneous equations. Algebraic methods are often quicker than trial and error or graphing. They are also more accurate if the solutions are not integers.

If y is the subject of *both* equations, we equate the y values and solve for x.

For example, consider the simultaneous equations $\begin{cases} y = 2x - 1 \\ y = x + 3\,. \end{cases}$

We equate the RHS of each equation to give $2x - 1 = x + 3$. We solve the resulting equation to find x, then substitute this value of x into one of the original equations to find y.

Example 3 **Self Tutor**

Solve the simultaneous equations: $\begin{cases} y = 2x - 1 \\ y = x + 3 \end{cases}$

If $y = 2x - 1$ and $y = x + 3$, then

$2x - 1 = x + 3$ {equating ys}

$\therefore\ 2x - 1 - x = x + 3 - x$ {subtracting x from both sides}

$\therefore\ x - 1 = 3$

$\therefore\ x = 4$ {adding 1 to both sides}

Now $y = x + 3$

$\therefore\ y = 4 + 3$

$\therefore\ y = 7$

The solution is $x = 4$, $y = 7$.

Check: In $y = 2x - 1$, $y = 2 \times 4 - 1 = 8 - 1 = 7$ ✓

Always check your solution in *both* equations.

EXERCISE 15C

1 Solve these simultaneous equations by equating values of y:

a $\begin{cases} y = x + 1 \\ y = 2x - 3 \end{cases}$ **b** $\begin{cases} y = x + 4 \\ y = -x + 2 \end{cases}$ **c** $\begin{cases} y = x + 2 \\ y = -2x + 5 \end{cases}$

2 Solve by equating values of y:

a $\begin{cases} y = -2x - 4 \\ y = x - 4 \end{cases}$ b $\begin{cases} y = -x + 4 \\ y = 2x - 8 \end{cases}$ c $\begin{cases} y = -2 - x \\ y = 2x + 13 \end{cases}$

d $\begin{cases} y = 3x + 7 \\ y = -x - 6 \end{cases}$ e $\begin{cases} y = 2x - 10 \\ y = 3x - 18 \end{cases}$ f $\begin{cases} y = 5 - 3x \\ y = 10 - 6x \end{cases}$

3 Try to solve by equating values of y:

a $\begin{cases} y = 2x + 3 \\ y = 2x - 2 \end{cases}$ b $\begin{cases} y = 2.3x - 3.6 \\ y = -1.2x + 5.7 \end{cases}$

Comment on your results.

D SOLUTION BY SUBSTITUTION

The method of **substitution** is used when a variable is given as the subject of *one* of the equations.

For example, in the equations $\begin{cases} y = 2x + 3 \\ 3x - 4y = 8 \end{cases}$ we see that y is the subject of the first equation.

We substitute the expression for y on the RHS into the second equation.

Example 4 **Self Tutor**

Solve simultaneously by substitution: $\begin{cases} y = 2x + 3 \\ 3x - 4y = 8 \end{cases}$

$y = 2x + 3$ .... (1)
$3x - 4y = 8$ .... (2)

Substituting (1) into (2) gives $3x - 4(2x + 3) = 8$

$\therefore\ 3x - 8x - 12 = 8$

$\therefore\ -5x - 12 = 8$

$\therefore\ -5x = 20$

$\therefore\ x = -4$

Substituting $x = -4$ into (1) gives $y = 2(-4) + 3$

$\therefore\ y = -8 + 3$

$\therefore\ y = -5$

The solution is $x = -4$, $y = -5$.

Check: $3x - 4y = 3(-4) - 4(-5) = -12 + 20 = 8$ ✓

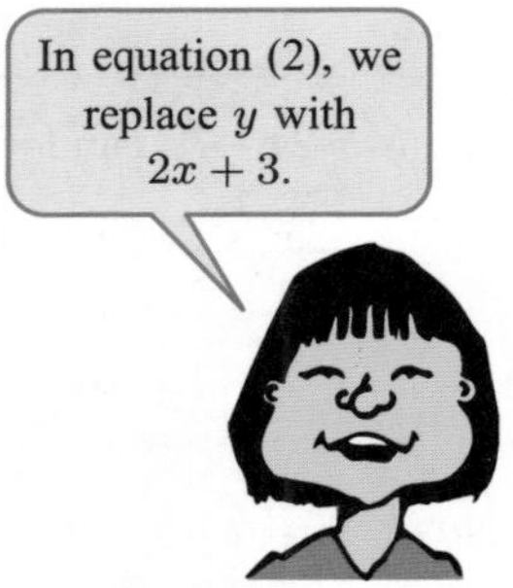
In equation (2), we replace y with $2x + 3$.

EXERCISE 15D

1 Use the method of substitution to solve:

a $\begin{cases} y = x + 2 \\ 3x + 2y = 19 \end{cases}$ b $\begin{cases} y = 2x + 1 \\ 5x - 4y = 2 \end{cases}$ c $\begin{cases} 4x + 3y = -14 \\ y = -3x - 3 \end{cases}$

d $\begin{cases} x = 3y + 2 \\ 2x - 5y = 1 \end{cases}$ e $\begin{cases} 7x - 2y = -6 \\ x = y - 3 \end{cases}$ f $\begin{cases} y = 3x + 2 \\ 4x + 2y = -1 \end{cases}$

2 Use the method of substitution to solve:

a $\begin{cases} 3x - 7y = 11 \\ x = 4y + 6 \end{cases}$ **b** $\begin{cases} y = 8 - 4x \\ 12x - y = 12 \end{cases}$ **c** $\begin{cases} 2x - 5y = 0 \\ y = 5 - 3x \end{cases}$

3 Try to solve using substitution:

a $\begin{cases} y = 3x - 5 \\ 12x - 4y = 7 \end{cases}$ **b** $\begin{cases} 6x + 3y = 15 \\ y = 5 - 2x \end{cases}$

Comment on your results.

E SOLUTION BY ELIMINATION

Solution by **elimination** is used to solve simultaneous equations such as $\begin{cases} 3x + 4y = 10 \\ 5x - 4y = 6 \end{cases}$ where neither variable is given as the subject of an equation.

In this method, we make the coefficients of x (or y) the **same size** but **opposite in sign**.

We then **add** the equations, which has the effect of **eliminating** one of the variables.

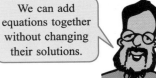

We can add equations together without changing their solutions.

The method of elimination uses the fact that:

If $a = b$ and $c = d$ then $a + c = b + d$.

This allows us to add the equations together without changing their solutions.

Example 5 **Self Tutor**

Solve simultaneously, by elimination: $\begin{cases} 3x + 2y = 5 \\ x - 2y = 3 \end{cases}$

The coefficients of y are the same size but opposite in sign.

We **add** the LHSs and the RHSs to get an equation which contains x only.

$$\begin{aligned} 3x + 2y &= 5 \quad .... (1) \\ x - 2y &= 3 \quad .... (2) \\ \hline \text{Adding,} \quad 4x \qquad &= 8 \\ \therefore \quad x &= 2 \end{aligned}$$

Substituting $x = 2$ into (1) gives

$$\begin{aligned} 3(2) + 2y &= 5 \\ \therefore \quad 6 + 2y &= 5 \\ \therefore \quad 2y &= -1 \\ \therefore \quad y &= -\tfrac{1}{2} \end{aligned}$$

The solution is $x = 2, \quad y = -\frac{1}{2}$.

Check: In (2), $(2) - 2(-\frac{1}{2}) = 2 + 1 = 3$ ✓

In problems where the coefficients of x (or y) are *not* the same size and opposite in sign, we first need to **multiply** an equation by a constant.

Example 6 — Self Tutor

Solve $\begin{cases} 3x + 2y = -2 \\ 5x - y = 27 \end{cases}$ using the method of elimination.

$3x + 2y = -2$ .... (1)
$5x - y = 27$ .... (2)

We have $+2y$ in (1), so we obtain $-2y$ from (2) by multiplying both sides of (2) by 2.

$$\begin{aligned} 3x + 2y &= -2 \quad &\{(1)\} \\ 10x - 2y &= 54 \quad &\{(2) \times 2\} \\ \hline \text{Adding, } 13x \quad &= 52 \\ \therefore x &= 4 \end{aligned}$$

It is easier to eliminate y in this case.

Substituting $x = 4$ into (1), $3(4) + 2y = -2$
$\therefore 12 + 2y = -2$
$\therefore 2y = -14$
$\therefore y = -7$

The solution is $x = 4$, $y = -7$.

Check: In (2), $5(4) - (-7) = 20 + 7 = 27$ ✓

Sometimes it is easier to eliminate a variable if we multiply *both* equations by constants.

Example 7 — Self Tutor

Solve simultaneously, by elimination: $\begin{cases} 5x + 3y = 12 \\ 7x + 2y = 19 \end{cases}$

$5x + 3y = 12$ .... (1)
$7x + 2y = 19$ .... (2)

We can multiply (1) by 2 and (2) by -3:

$$\begin{aligned} 10x + 6y &= 24 \quad &\{(1) \times 2\} \\ -21x - 6y &= -57 \quad &\{(2) \times -3\} \\ \hline \text{Adding, } -11x \quad &= -33 \\ \therefore x &= 3 \end{aligned}$$

Substituting $x = 3$ into (1), $5(3) + 3y = 12$
$\therefore 15 + 3y = 12$
$\therefore 3y = -3$
$\therefore y = -1$

The solution is $x = 3$, $y = -1$.

Check: In (2), $7(3) + 2(-1) = 21 - 2 = 19$ ✓

EXERCISE 15E

1 What equation results when the following are added vertically?

a $\begin{cases} 5x + 3y = 12 \\ x - 3y = -6 \end{cases}$ **b** $\begin{cases} 2x + 5y = -4 \\ -2x - 6y = 12 \end{cases}$ **c** $\begin{cases} 4x - 6y = 9 \\ x + 6y = -2 \end{cases}$

d $\begin{cases} 12x + 15y = 33 \\ -18x - 15y = -63 \end{cases}$ **e** $\begin{cases} 5x + 6y = 12 \\ -5x + 2y = -8 \end{cases}$ **f** $\begin{cases} -7x + y = -5 \\ 7x - 3y = -11 \end{cases}$

2 Solve using the method of elimination:

a $\begin{cases} 2x + y = 3 \\ 3x - y = 7 \end{cases}$ **b** $\begin{cases} 4x + 3y = 7 \\ 6x - 3y = -27 \end{cases}$

c $\begin{cases} 2x + 5y = 16 \\ -2x - 7y = -20 \end{cases}$ **d** $\begin{cases} 3x + 5y = -11 \\ -3x - 2y = 8 \end{cases}$

e $\begin{cases} 4x - 7y = 41 \\ 3x + 7y = -6 \end{cases}$ **f** $\begin{cases} -4x + 3y = -25 \\ 4x - 5y = 31 \end{cases}$

You can choose to eliminate either x or y, depending on which is easier.

3 Give the equation that results when both sides of the equation:

a $3x + 4y = 2$ are multiplied by 3

b $x - 4y = 7$ are multiplied by -2

c $5x - y = -3$ are multiplied by 5

d $7x + 3y = -4$ are multiplied by -3

e $-2x - 5y = 1$ are multiplied by -4

f $3x - y = -1$ are multiplied by -1.

4 Solve using the method of elimination:

a $\begin{cases} 4x - 3y = 6 \\ -2x + 5y = 4 \end{cases}$ **b** $\begin{cases} 2x - y = 9 \\ x + 4y = 36 \end{cases}$ **c** $\begin{cases} 3x + 4y = 6 \\ x - 3y = -11 \end{cases}$

d $\begin{cases} 4x + 3y = 17 \\ 5x - 9y = 34 \end{cases}$ **e** $\begin{cases} 2x - 7y = -5 \\ 6x + 5y = -15 \end{cases}$ **f** $\begin{cases} 5x + 8y = 8 \\ 9x + 2y = 33 \end{cases}$

5 Solve using the method of elimination:

a $\begin{cases} 2x + 3y = 7 \\ 3x - 2y = 4 \end{cases}$ **b** $\begin{cases} 4x - 3y = 6 \\ 6x + 7y = 32 \end{cases}$ **c** $\begin{cases} 7x - 3y = 29 \\ 3x + 4y + 14 = 0 \end{cases}$

d $\begin{cases} 2x + 5y = 20 \\ 3x + 2y = 19 \end{cases}$ **e** $\begin{cases} 3x - 2y = 10 \\ 4x + 3y = 19 \end{cases}$ **f** $\begin{cases} 3x + 4y + 11 = 0 \\ 5x + 6y + 7 = 0 \end{cases}$

6 Use the method of elimination to attempt to solve:

a $\begin{cases} 3x + y = 8 \\ 6x + 2y = 16 \end{cases}$ **b** $\begin{cases} 2x + 5y = 8 \\ 4x + 10y = -1 \end{cases}$

Comment on your results.

F PROBLEM SOLVING WITH SIMULTANEOUS EQUATIONS

In this Section we deal with problems given in sentences. We need to interpret the information and use it to write two equations in two unknowns. We use the techniques we have learnt during the chapter to solve the equations simultaneously, and hence answer the original problem.

Example 8 Self Tutor

Two numbers have a difference of 7 and an average of 4. Find the numbers.

Let x and y be the unknown numbers, where $x > y$.

The difference between x and y is $x - y = 7$ .... (1)

The average of x and y is $\dfrac{x+y}{2} = 4$ .... (2)

$$\begin{aligned} x - y &= 7 \quad &\{(1)\} \\ x + y &= 8 \quad &\{(2) \times 2\} \\ \hline \text{Adding,}\quad 2x &= 15 \\ \therefore\ x &= \tfrac{15}{2} \end{aligned}$$

Substituting $x = \frac{15}{2}$ into (1) gives $\frac{15}{2} - y = 7$

$\therefore\ y = \frac{15}{2} - 7$

$\therefore\ y = \frac{1}{2}$

When solving problems with simultaneous equations we must find two equations containing two unknowns.

The numbers are $\frac{1}{2}$ and $\frac{15}{2}$.

Check: (1) $\frac{15}{2} - \frac{1}{2} = 7$ ✓ (2) $\dfrac{\frac{15}{2} + \frac{1}{2}}{2} = 4$ ✓

Example 9 Self Tutor

At a clearance sale, all CDs are sold for one price and all DVDs are sold for another price. Marisa bought 3 CDs and 2 DVDs for a total of $34.50. Nico bought 2 CDs and 5 DVDs for a total of $56. Find the cost of each item.

Let x cents be the cost of one CD, and y cents be the cost of one DVD.

3 CDs and 2 DVDs cost $34.50, so $3x + 2y = 3450$ .... (1)

2 CDs and 5 DVDs cost $56, so $2x + 5y = 5600$ .... (2)

We will eliminate x by multiplying equation (1) by 2 and equation (2) by -3.

$$\begin{aligned} \therefore\ 6x + 4y &= 6900 \quad &\{(1) \times 2\} \\ -6x - 15y &= -16\,800 \quad &\{(2) \times -3\} \\ \hline \text{Adding,}\quad -11y &= -9900 \\ \therefore\ y &= 900 \end{aligned}$$

Substituting $y = 900$ into (1) gives $3x + 2(900) = 3450$

$\therefore 3x + 1800 = 3450$

$\therefore 3x = 1650$

$\therefore x = 550$

The cost of one CD is \$5.50, and the cost of one DVD is \$9.

EXERCISE 15F

1. Two numbers have a sum of 200 and a difference of 37. Find the numbers.
2. The difference between two numbers is 84, and their sum is 278. What are the numbers?
3. Find two numbers whose difference is 8 and whose average is 13.
4. The larger of two numbers is four times the smaller. The sum of the numbers is 85. Find the two numbers.
5. Two hammers and a screwdriver cost a total of €34. A hammer and 3 screwdrivers cost a total of €32. Find the price of each type of tool.
6. Four adults and three children go to a theatre for £148. Two adults and five children are charged £116 for the same performance. Find the price of an adult's ticket and a child's ticket.
7. Three blankets and a sheet cost me \$90. Two sheets and a blanket cost a total of \$55. Find the cost of one blanket and one sheet.

Example 10 **Self Tutor**

A carpenter makes cabinets and desks. These items use the same types of doors and drawers. Each cabinet has 2 doors and 3 drawers, and each desk has 1 door and 5 drawers. The carpenter has 41 doors and 100 drawers available. How many of each item should he make to use his entire supply of doors and drawers?

Suppose the carpenter makes x cabinets and y desks.

$\therefore 2x + y = 41$ .... (1) {total number of doors}

$3x + 5y = 100$ .... (2) {total number of drawers}

Item	*Number*	*Doors*	*Drawers*
Cabinet	x	$2x$	$3x$
Desk	y	y	$5y$
	Total	41	100

We will eliminate y by multiplying equation (1) by -5.

$-10x - 5y = -205$ {(1) × −5}

$3x + 5y = 100$ {(2)}

Adding, $-7x = -105$

$\therefore x = 15$

Substituting $x = 15$ into (1) gives $2(15) + y = 41$

$\therefore 30 + y = 41$

$\therefore y = 11$

The carpenter should make 15 cabinets and 11 desks.

8 A purse contains \$3.75 in 5 cent and 20 cent coins. There are 33 coins altogether. How many of each type of coin are in the purse?

9 A yard contains rabbits and pheasants only. There are 35 heads and 98 feet in the yard. How many rabbits and pheasants does the yard contain?

10 Milk is sold in one litre and two litre cartons. A delicatessen owner orders 120 litres of milk, and receives 97 cartons. How many of each type did she receive?

Example 11 **Self Tutor**

An equilateral triangle has sides of length $(3x-y)$ cm, $(x+5)$ cm, and $(y+3)$ cm. Find the length of each side.

The sides of an equilateral triangle are equal.

$\therefore\ y+3=x+5$ .... (1) and

$3x-y=x+5$ .... (2)

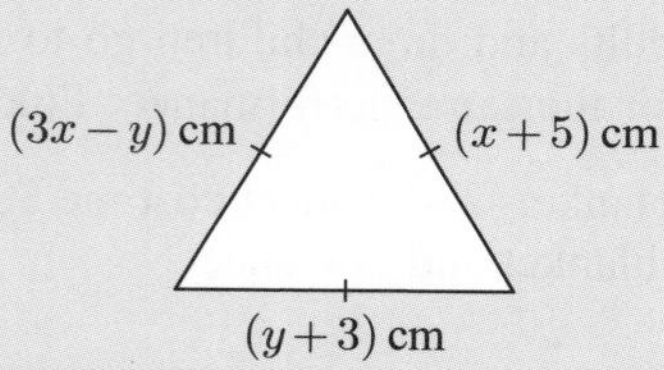

Using (1), $y=x+2$

Substituting into (2), $3x-(x+2)=x+5$

$\therefore\ 2x-2=x+5$

$\therefore\ x=7$

Substituting $x=7$ into (1), $y+3=7+5$

$\therefore\ y=9$

Substituting $x=7$ and $y=9$ into the side lengths:

$3x-y=21-9$ $=12$ $\qquad x+5=7+5$ $=12$ $\qquad y+3=9+3$ $=12$

The sides of the triangle are 12 cm long.

11 The figure below is a rectangle.

a Find x and y.

b Hence, find the area of the rectangle.

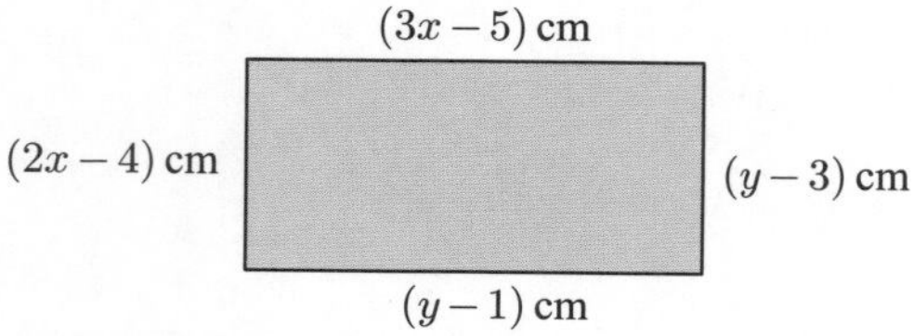

12 KLM is an isosceles triangle.

a Find x and y.

b Hence, find the measure of $L\widehat{K}M$.

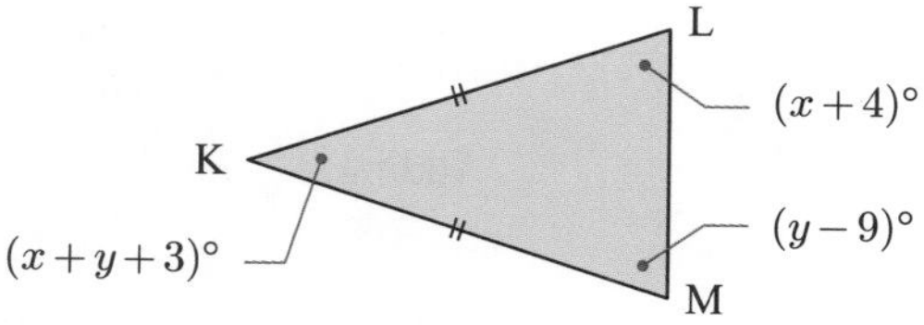

13 Twelve years ago, Jane was five times as old as Anne. In three years' time, Anne will be half Jane's age. How old is each woman at the moment?

14 Nine years ago, a woman was three times as old as her son. In eight years from now, the sum of their ages will be 78. How old are they today?

15 In this figure, [AM] has length $\sqrt{3}$ cm and [CN] has length $\sqrt{7}$ cm. Find the length of [AC].

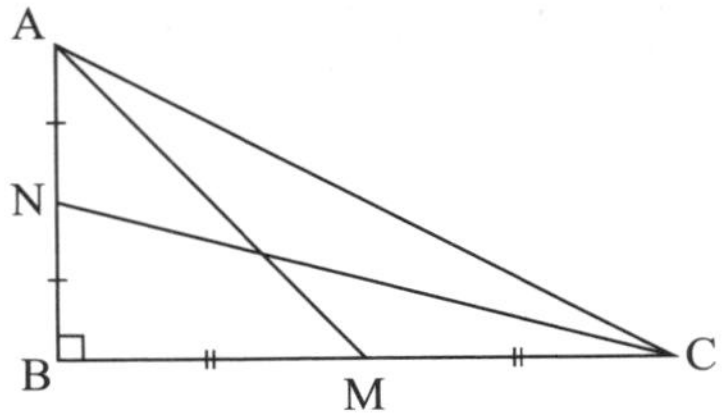

REVIEW SET 15A

1 By trial and error, find integers x and y which satisfy both $y = 2x + 1$ and $x + y = 7$.

2 Solve graphically: $\begin{cases} y = 2x - 1 \\ y = x - 2 \end{cases}$

3 Solve by substitution: $\begin{cases} y = 11 - 3x \\ 4x + 3y = -7 \end{cases}$

4 Solve by equating values of y:

a $\begin{cases} y = 2x + 3 \\ y = x - 2 \end{cases}$ **b** $\begin{cases} y = -5x + 1 \\ y = -5x - 1 \end{cases}$

5 Solve simultaneously:

a $\begin{cases} 3x - 2y = 16 \\ y = 2x - 10 \end{cases}$ **b** $\begin{cases} 3x - 5y = 11 \\ 4x + 3y = 5 \end{cases}$

6 Two pencils and a ruler cost 98 cents in total. One pencil and two rulers cost $1.24 in total. Find the cost of each item.

7 Flour is sold in 5 kg and 2 kg packets. The 5 kg packets cost $2.75 each, and the 2 kg packets cost $1.25 each. If I bought 67 kg of flour and the total cost was $38.50, how many of each size of packet did I buy?

8 **a** Rearrange $4x + y = 29$ to make y the subject of the formula.

b Hence, use the method of substitution to solve simultaneously: $\begin{cases} 4x + y = 29 \\ 2x - 3y = 25 \end{cases}$

9 Solve by elimination: $\begin{cases} 2x - 3y = 18 \\ 4x + 5y = -8 \end{cases}$

10 The figure alongside is a rectangle.

a Find x and y.

b Hence, find the area of the rectangle.

$(2x+3y+5)$ cm

$(x+y+3)$ cm

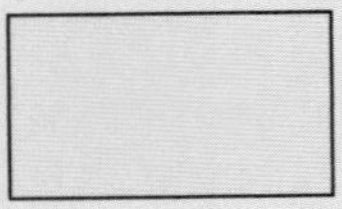

$(2x-y+6)$ cm

$(3x-y+16)$ cm

REVIEW SET 15B

1 **a** By drawing their graphs on the same set of axes, find the point of intersection of $y = 3x - 2$ and $y = 2x + 1$.

b Hence, solve the simultaneous equations: $\begin{cases} y = 3x - 2 \\ y = 2x + 1 \end{cases}$

2 Solve by equating values of y: $\begin{cases} y = 16 - 3x \\ y = 2x - 4 \end{cases}$

3 Solve by substitution: $\begin{cases} y = 2x - 3 \\ 3x - 2y = 4 \end{cases}$

4 Given that the solutions are integers, solve by trial and error: $\begin{cases} 5x + y = 4 \\ y = 3x - 12 \end{cases}$

5 Solve simultaneously:

a $\begin{cases} y = 2x - 5 \\ 3x - 2y = 11 \end{cases}$ **b** $\begin{cases} 3x + 5y = 1 \\ 4x - 3y = 11 \end{cases}$

6 The difference between two numbers is 11, and their sum is 85. Find the numbers.

7 A bus company uses two different sized buses. One day it used 7 small buses and 5 large buses to transport 331 students to a swimming carnival. The next day it used 4 small buses and 9 large buses to take 398 people to a concert. In both of these situations, all of the buses were full. Determine the number of people each bus can carry.

8 Sally has only 10 cent and 50 cent coins in her purse. She has 21 coins altogether with a total value of \$5.30. How many of each coin type does she have?

9 Solve simultaneously:

a $\begin{cases} 3x + y = -4 \\ y = -2x + 5 \end{cases}$ **b** $\begin{cases} y = 3x + 2 \\ y = 3x - 5 \end{cases}$

10

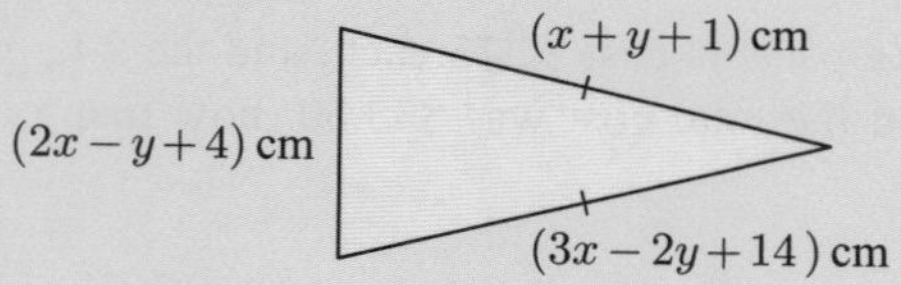

The perimeter of this triangle is 29 cm.

a Find x and y.

b Hence, find the length of the equal sides of the triangle.

Chapter 16

Probability

Contents:

OPENING PROBLEM

Maude wants to know the probability that a person who enters her store will buy something. One morning she counts 25 people entering her store. 9 of the people buy something.

Things to think about:

a Can you use this information to estimate the probability that a person entering Maude's store will buy something?

b How accurate do you think the estimate is?

c How can the accuracy of the estimate be improved?

Probability deals with the **chance** or likelihood of an event occurring.

We can determine probabilities based on:

- what we theoretically expect to happen (theoretical probability)
- observing the results of an experiment (experimental probability).

In this chapter we consider both theoretical and experimental probabilities.

A PROBABILITY

The **probability** of an event is a measure of the chance or likelihood of it occurring.

Probabilities can be given as percentages from 0% to 100%, or as proper fractions or decimal numbers between 0 and 1.

An **impossible** event has 0% chance of happening, and is assigned the probability 0.

A **certain** event has 100% chance of happening, and is assigned the probability 1.

All other events are assigned a probability between 0 and 1.

The number line below shows how we could interpret different probabilities:

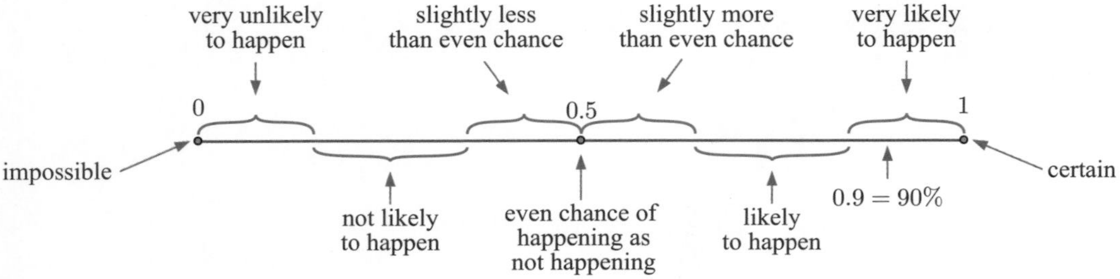

For example, suppose that the weather forecast says there is a 90% chance of rain tomorrow. We would say it is *very likely* that it will rain tomorrow.

Example 1 **Self Tutor**

Use the number line on the previous page to describe the probability of these events:

a There is a 75% chance that Ted will be on time for school tomorrow.

b There is a 40% chance that Claire will burn her toast.

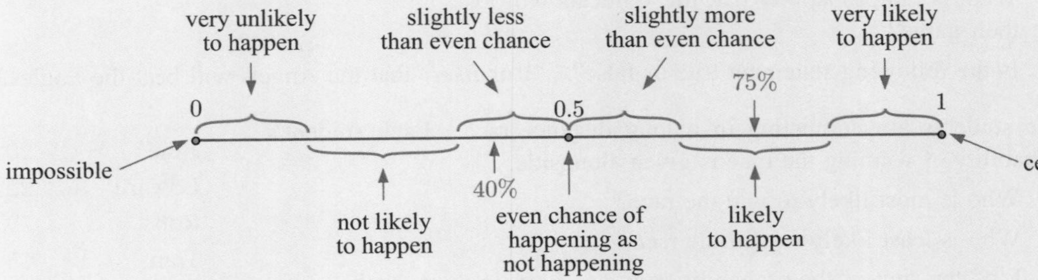

a It is *likely* that Ted will be on time for school tomorrow.

b There is a *slightly less than even chance* that Claire will burn her toast.

In probability, we can use capital letters to represent events.

In **Example 1**, we could let E be the event that Ted will be on time for school tomorrow. The probability that event E occurs is written $\text{P}(E)$, so we write $\text{P}(E) = 75\%$ or $\text{P}(E) = 0.75$.

COMPLEMENTARY EVENTS

Two events are **complementary** if exactly one of them *must* occur.

The probabilities of complementary events sum to 1.

The **complement** of event E is denoted E'. It is the event that E *does not* occur.

> For any event E with **complementary** event E',
> $\text{P}(E) + \text{P}(E') = 1$ or $\text{P}(E') = 1 - \text{P}(E)$.

If E is the event that Ted will be on time for school tomorrow, then E' is the event that Ted will *not* be on time for school tomorrow, and $\text{P}(E') = 1 - 0.75 = 0.25$.

EXERCISE 16A

1 Use the terms on the number line on the previous page to describe the probability of these events:

a There is a 25% chance that Ella will score a goal in her next football match.

b There is a 60% chance that the restaurant will be booked out on Saturday night.

c There is a 5% chance that William will forget to take his lunch to school tomorrow.

2 The next four games in a baseball season are listed alongside, including the probability of each team winning.

32%	Cubs vs Lions	68%
59%	Wildcats vs Flames	41%
73%	Eagles vs Angels	27%
20%	Pumas vs Strikers	80%

- **a** Which team is most likely to win the game between the Cubs and the Lions?
- **b** Which team is most likely to win their game?
- **c** What is the probability that the Wildcats will lose their game?
- **d** Is the following statement true or false? "It is *likely* that the Angels will beat the Eagles."

3 Five students are competing in a long distance race. Each student's probability of winning the race is given alongside.

Julie	20%
Edward	22%
Rob	7%
Tran	15%
Patricia	36%

- **a** Who is most likely to win the race?
- **b** Who is least likely to win the race?
- **c** Find the sum of the probabilities given. Explain your result.
- **d** Find the probability that either Julie or Tran will win the race.
- **e** Describe in words, the probability that Rob will win the race.
- **f** Let E be the event that Edward will win the race.
  - **i** Find $P(E)$.
  - **ii** State the complementary event E'.
  - **iii** Find $P(E')$.

4 Suppose a bag is filled with balls, and one ball is chosen at random. Use a term on the number line to describe the probability of choosing a *red* ball, if the bag contains:

- **a** 1 red ball and 1 blue ball
- **b** 5 red balls
- **c** 2 blue balls and 3 green balls
- **d** 1 red ball and 10 blue balls.

5 Suppose S is the event that it will snow tomorrow, and $P(S) = 0.03$.

- **a** State the complementary event S'.
- **b** Find $P(S')$.
- **c** Use a term on the number line to describe the probability of:
  - **i** S occurring
  - **ii** S' occurring.

B SAMPLE SPACE

The **outcome** of an experiment is the result we obtain in one trial of the experiment.

Before we can calculate the probabilities of obtaining certain results in an experiment, we must first understand what outcomes can occur.

The **sample space** of an experiment is the set of its possible outcomes.

For example, consider the following experiment:

We have 5 cards numbered 1 to 5. The cards are placed in a hat, and one card is drawn out at random.

If we draw out the card numbered 4, the outcome of the experiment is 4.

There are 5 possible outcomes for this experiment. These outcomes are the numbers from 1 to 5.

We say the *sample space* of the experiment is $\{1, 2, 3, 4, 5\}$.

EXERCISE 16B.1

1 List the sample space for:

- **a** tossing a coin
- **b** picking a counter at random from a bag that contains a pink counter, a green counter, and a blue counter
- **c** rolling an ordinary 6-sided die
- **d** twirling a spinner with 3 segments marked A, B, and C
- **e** choosing a random month of the year
- **f** taking a card from a pack of playing cards and looking at its suit
- **g** choosing a two digit number which is less than 20
- **h** choosing a multiple of 5 which is less than 50.

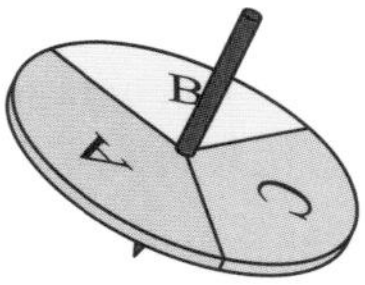

2 State the number of possible outcomes for each of the experiments in **1**.

2-DIMENSIONAL GRIDS

If an experiment involves two operations, we can use a **2-dimensional grid** to display the set of possible outcomes.

For example, the grid alongside displays the sample space for spinning these spinners:

Spinner 1

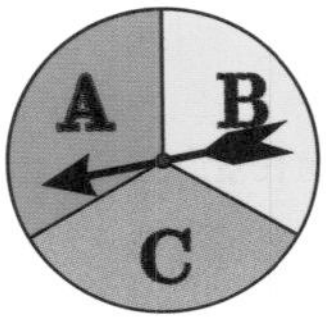

Spinner 2

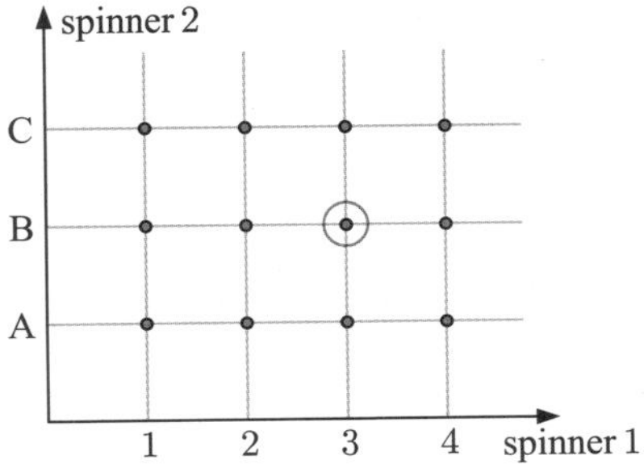

The four possibilities for spinner 1 are listed on the horizontal axis, and the three possibilities for spinner 2 are listed on the vertical axis.

Each point on the grid represents one of the 12 possible outcomes. For example, the red circled point represents spinning a 3 with spinner 1 and a B with spinner 2.

EXERCISE 16B.2

1 Draw a 2-dimensional grid to display the sample space for:

- **a** tossing two coins
- **b** rolling a die and spinning a spinner marked 1, 2, and 3
- **c** selecting a ticket from each of the boxes alongside
- **d** selecting one consonant and one vowel from the letters in the name SINGAPORE.

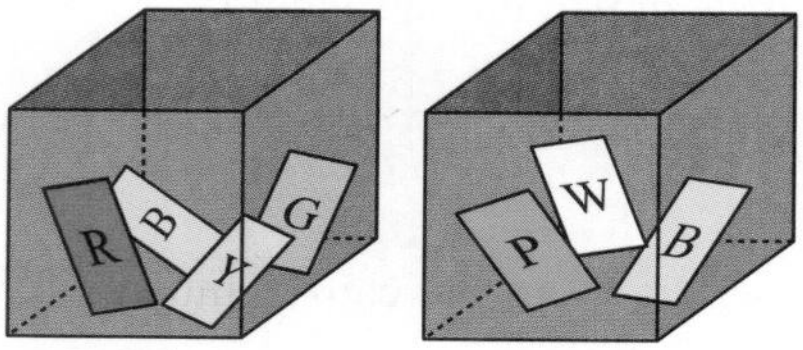

Box 1 **Box 2**

2 State the number of possible outcomes for each of the experiments in **1**.

3
- **a** Draw a 2-dimensional grid to display the sample space for rolling a die and spinning a spinner marked A, B, C, and D.
- **b** How many possible outcomes are there?
- **c** Draw a red circle around the outcome of rolling a 5 and spinning a C.
- **d** Draw green circles around the outcomes of rolling an even number and spinning an A.

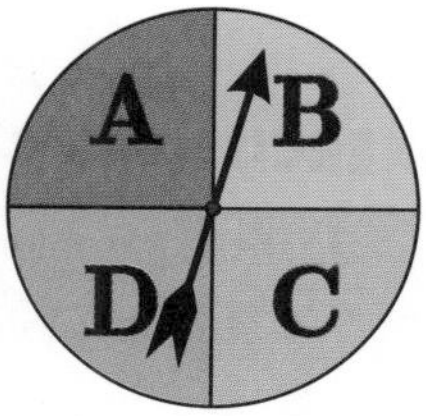

C THEORETICAL PROBABILITY

Consider the **octagonal spinner** shown. The sample space for spinning it is $\{1, 2, 3, 4, 5, 6, 7, 8\}$, and there are 8 possible outcomes.

Since the spinner is symmetrical, the arrowed marker could finish with **equal likelihood** on each of the numbers.

We can use this symmetry to calculate the probability of a particular event occurring.

For example, consider the event *spinning a* 5. Only one outcome of the eight possible outcomes corresponds to this event. The *likelihood* of spinning a 5 is therefore

$$1 \text{ chance in } 8, \quad \frac{1}{8}, \quad 12\frac{1}{2}\%, \quad \text{or} \quad 0.125.$$

This is a **mathematical** or **theoretical** probability, and is based on what we theoretically expect to occur.

We write $P(5) = \frac{1}{8}$.

Now consider the event of *spinning a* 6 *or more*. Out of the eight possible outcomes, there are three outcomes (6, 7, or 8) that correspond to this event. Each of the outcomes is equally likely to occur.

So, the probability of spinning 6 or more is $\frac{3}{8}$. We write $P(6 \text{ or more}) = \frac{3}{8}$.

In general, for an event E containing **equally likely** possible outcomes:

$$P(E) = \frac{\textbf{the number of outcomes corresponding to } E}{\textbf{the total number of possible outcomes}}.$$

Example 2 Self Tutor

A spinner with equal sectors labelled A, B, C, D, and E is spun. Determine the probability of spinning:

a D **b** a vowel.

The sample space is {A, B, C, D, E}, so there are 5 possible outcomes.

a Only one of the five possible outcomes is a D.

$\therefore \quad P(D) = \frac{1}{5}$

b Two of the outcomes (A and E) correspond to *spinning a vowel.*

$\therefore \quad P(\text{a vowel}) = \frac{2}{5}$

Example 3 Self Tutor

A ticket is *randomly selected* from a basket containing 3 green, 4 yellow, and 5 blue tickets. Determine the probability of getting:

a a green ticket
b a green or yellow ticket
c an orange ticket
d a green, yellow, or blue ticket.

There are $3 + 4 + 5 = 12$ tickets which could be selected with equal chance.

a $P(\text{green}) = \frac{3}{12}$
$= \frac{1}{4}$

b $P(\text{a green or a yellow}) = \frac{3+4}{12}$
$= \frac{7}{12}$

c $P(\text{orange}) = \frac{0}{12}$
$= 0$

d $P(\text{green, yellow, or blue}) = \frac{3+4+5}{12}$
$= \frac{12}{12}$
$= 1$

There is *no chance* of selecting an orange ticket.

We are *certain* to choose a green, yellow, or blue ticket.

EXERCISE 16C

1 An ordinary die is rolled once. Determine the probability of rolling:

a a 4
b an odd number
c a number greater than 1
d a multiple of 3.

2 Ten cards with the numbers 1 to 10 written on them are placed in a bag. A card is chosen from the bag at random. Determine the probability of choosing:

a 7 **b** 9 or 10 **c** a multiple of 3
d a number greater than 4 **e** a prime number.

3 A standard set of balls for a pool table is shown alongside.
If a ball is chosen at random, determine the probability of choosing:

a the white ball **b** a green ball
c a number less than 8.

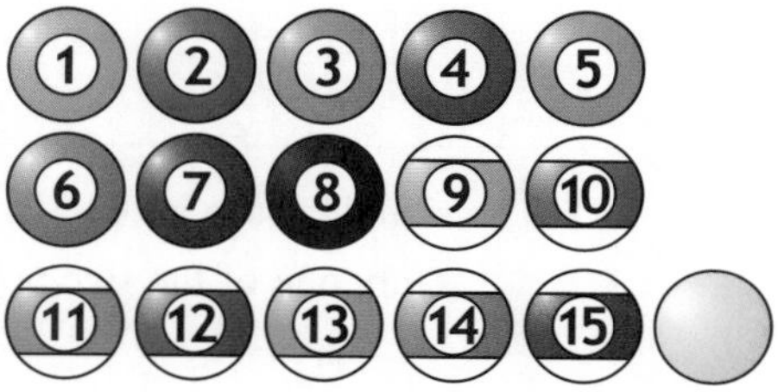

4 A carton contains eight brown and four white eggs. Find the probability that an egg selected at random is:

a brown **b** white.

5 A ticket is randomly selected from a box containing 3 yellow, 4 green, and 8 blue tickets. Determine the probability that the ticket is:

a yellow **b** green **c** blue
d red **e** not yellow **f** yellow or blue.

6 For each of the following spinners:

i find the probability of spinning *red*
ii determine whether it is more likely that red will be spun, or that blue will be spun.

a

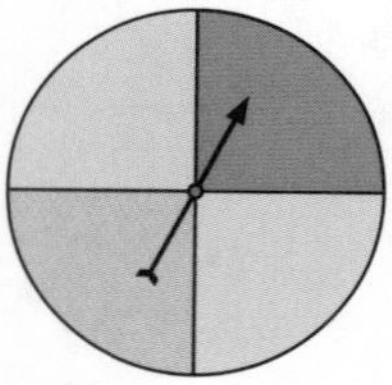

b

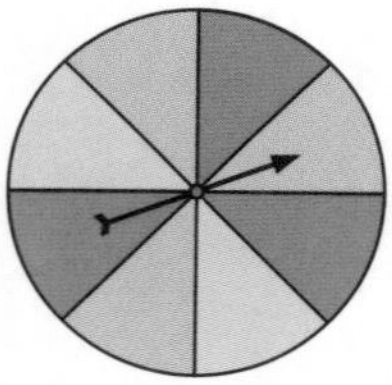

c

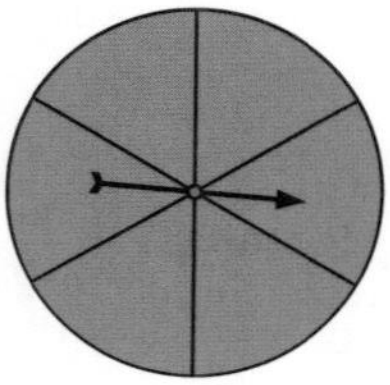

7 At the local cinema, one movie session sells 20 adult tickets, 16 concession tickets, and 9 child tickets. One person from the audience is selected at random. Find the probability that this person has:

a a concession ticket **b** an adult ticket
c a child or a concession ticket.

8 A jigsaw puzzle for a small child is shown alongside.
If a piece of the puzzle is chosen at random, determine the probability of choosing:

a a corner piece
b an edge piece
c a corner or an edge piece
d a piece which is neither a corner nor an edge.

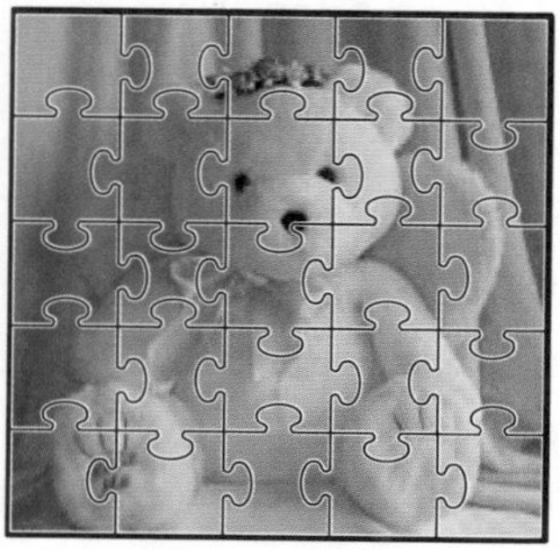

9 The layout of seats on an aeroplane is given alongside. The seats that are already occupied are shaded in red.
If you are allocated an unoccupied seat at random, determine the probability of getting:

a a front row seat
b a seat in the emergency row
c a window seat
d an aisle seat.

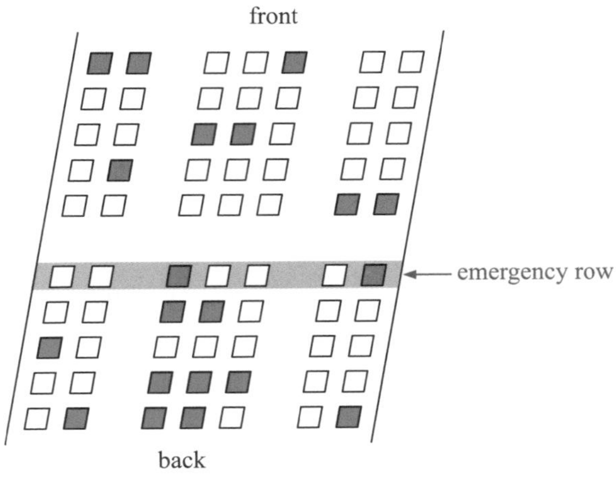

D USING 2-DIMENSIONAL GRIDS

We have seen that for an experiment involving two operations, the sample space of possible outcomes can be shown on a 2-dimensional grid.

If the outcomes of the experiment are equally likely, we can use the grid to find the probability of an event occurring. We count the number of outcomes corresponding to the event, and divide by the total number of possible outcomes.

Example 4 — Self Tutor

A coin is tossed and a die is rolled simultaneously.

a Use a grid to illustrate the sample space.
b Find the probability of getting:
i a tail and a 5 **ii** a head and a number less than 3 **iii** a tail or a 5.

a

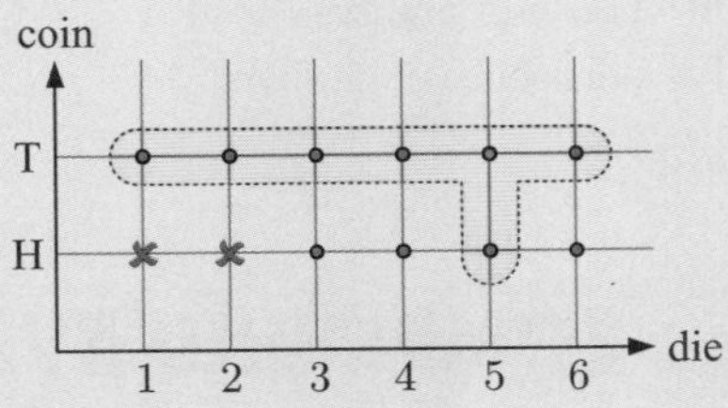

b The sample space has 12 members, each of which is equally likely to occur.

i P(tail and a 5) $= \frac{1}{12}$ {•}

ii P(head and a number less than 3)
$= \frac{2}{12} = \frac{1}{6}$ {crossed points}

iii P(tail or a 5) $= \frac{7}{12}$ {the enclosed points}

EXERCISE 16D

1 **a** A 5 cent and a 10 cent coin are tossed simultaneously. Draw the grid of the sample space.
b How many possible outcomes are there?
c Determine the probability of getting:
i two heads **ii** exactly one head **iii** at least one head.

2 **a** A coin is tossed, and a spinner with 3 equal sectors A, B, and C is twirled. Use a grid to illustrate the sample space.

b How many outcomes are possible?

c Use your grid to determine the chance of getting:

- **i** an A and a head
- **ii** a head but *not* an A
- **iii** an A
- **iv** an A or a B, and a tail
- **v** an A, or, a B and a tail.

3 Bag A contains one red disc and one blue disc. Bag B contains one red, one blue, and one white disc. One disc is taken at random from each bag.

a Draw a grid of the sample space.

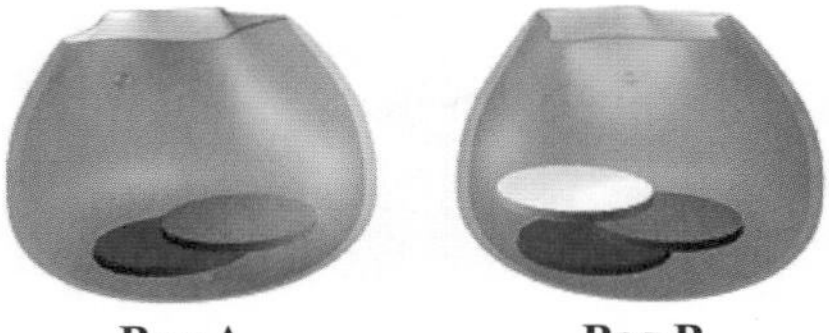

Bag A **Bag B**

b Hence determine the probability of getting:

- **i** two red discs
- **ii** two discs the same colour
- **iii** a white disc
- **iv** two discs which are different in colour.

4 Two spinners with equal sectors 1, 2, and 3 are twirled simultaneously.

a Draw a grid to display the sample space.

b Determine the probability of getting:

- **i** two 2s
- **ii** two odd numbers
- **iii** a 2 and a 3
- **iv** two numbers whose sum is 3
- **v** two numbers the same
- **vi** two numbers whose sum is 3 or 5.

5 Erika has separated the integers from 2 to 10 into primes and composites. She now selects one number from each group at random.

a Draw a grid of the sample space.

b Find the probability that Erika selects:

- **i** 3 and 8
- **ii** two odd numbers
- **iii** two numbers whose sum is 13
- **iv** consecutive numbers.

E COMPOUND EVENTS

When we calculate the probability of two or more events occurring, we are calculating the probability of **compound events** or **combined events**.

Suppose a ball is randomly selected from each of these boxes. What is the probability of selecting a red ball from box X *and* a blue ball from box Y?

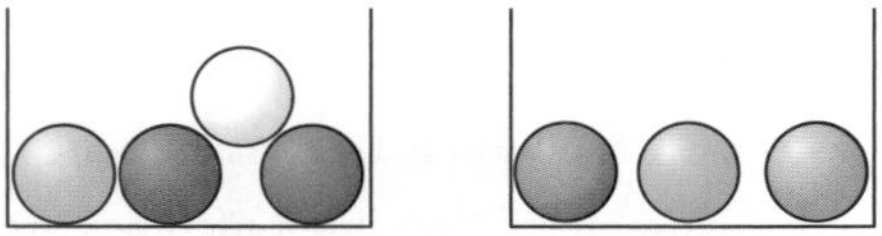

Box X **Box Y**

By illustrating the sample space on a 2-dimensional grid, we see that only 1 of the 12 outcomes is a red from X and a blue from Y.

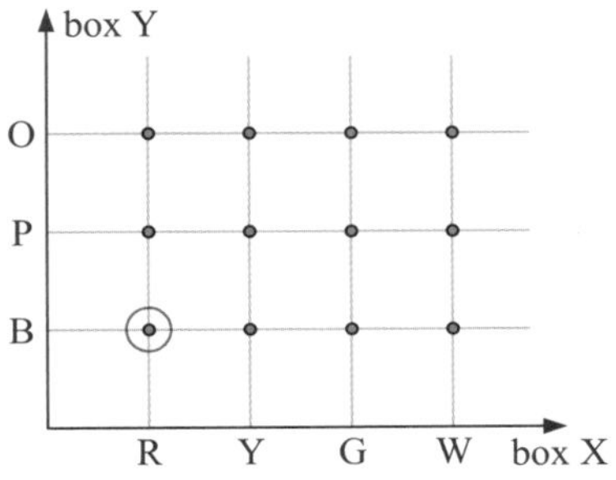

So, P(red from X *and* blue from Y) $= \frac{1}{12}$.

However, we can calculate this probability without having to draw a grid.

Notice that P(red from X) $= \frac{1}{4}$ and P(blue from Y) $= \frac{1}{3}$.

$\therefore$ P(red from X **and** blue from Y) = P(red from X) $\times$ P(blue from Y).

INDEPENDENT EVENTS

Two events are **independent** if the occurrence of each event does not affect the occurrence of the other.

The two events 'selecting a red from X' and 'selecting a blue from Y' are independent events, since the result of one selection has no effect on the result of the other.

If two events A and B are **independent** then P(A **and** B) = P(A) $\times$ P(B).

Example 5 — Self Tutor

The two spinners alongside are spun. Find the probability that a 'green' and a '3' result.

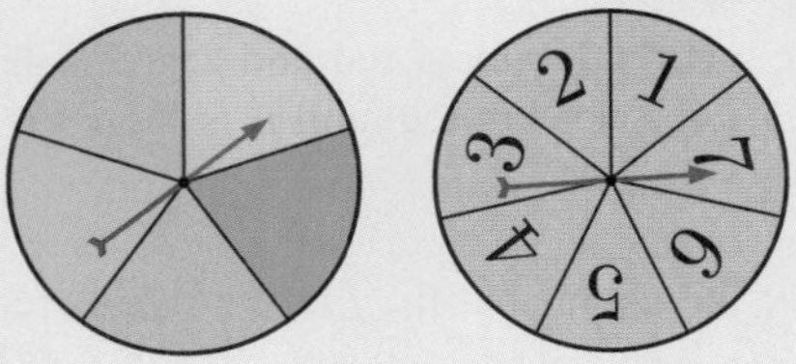

The events 'spinning a green' and 'spinning a 3' are independent events, since the outcome from one spinner does not affect the outcome from the other.

$\therefore$ P(a green and a 3) = P(a green) $\times$ P(a 3)

$$= \frac{2}{5} \times \frac{1}{7}$$

$$= \frac{2}{35}$$

EXERCISE 16E.1

1 A coin and a pentagonal spinner with edges marked A, B, C, D, and E are tossed and twirled simultaneously. Find the probability of getting:

a a head and a D
b a tail and either an A or a D.

2 A spinner with 6 equal sides has 3 red, 2 blue, and 1 yellow edge. A second spinner with 7 equal sides has 4 purple and 3 green edges. The spinners are twirled simultaneously. Find the probability of getting:

a a red and a green
b a blue and a purple
c a yellow and a green
d a red and a purple.

3 Janice and Lee take set shots at a netball goal from 3 m. From past experience, Janice throws a goal on average 2 times in every 3 shots, whereas Lee throws a goal 4 times in every 7 shots. If the two girls both shoot for goals, determine the probability that:

- **a** both score a goal
- **b** both miss
- **c** Janice scores a goal but Lee misses.

4 Tei has probability $\frac{1}{3}$ of hitting a target with an arrow, while See has probability $\frac{2}{5}$.

- **a** If they both fire at the target, determine the probability that:
  - **i** both hit the target
  - **ii** both miss the target
  - **iii** Tei hits the target and See misses
  - **iv** Tei misses the target and See hits.
- **b** Which of the outcomes in **a** is most likely?

5 Vicky and Paul are taking their driving test tomorrow. Vicky has 70% chance of passing the test, and Paul has 60% chance of passing the test. Find the probability that:

- **a** they both pass the test
- **b** at least one of them fails the test.

DEPENDENT EVENTS

Suppose a cup contains 4 red and 2 green marbles. One marble is randomly chosen, its colour is noted, and it is then put aside. A second marble is then randomly selected.

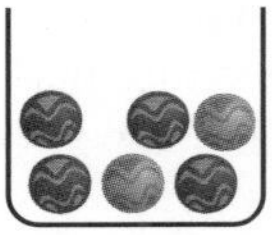

Let A be the event that the *first* marble is red, and B be the event that the *second* marble is red.

We take out the first marble.

Either: A occurs, so there are now 3 red and 2 green marbles in the cup. We take out the second marble.

$\therefore \quad P(B) = \frac{3}{5}$ ← 3 reds remaining, ← 5 to choose from

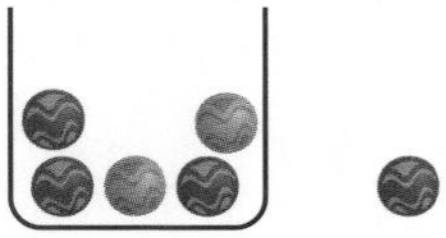

or: A does *not* occur, so there are now 4 red and 1 green marble in the cup. We take out the second marble.

$\therefore \quad P(B) = \frac{4}{5}$ ← 4 reds remaining, ← 5 to choose from

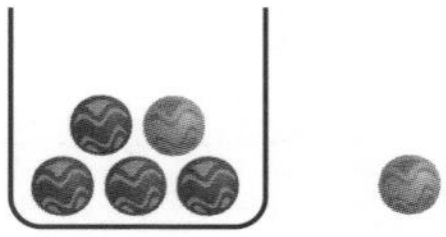

The probability of B occurring depends on whether A occurs, so we say that A and B are **dependent events**.

> Two or more events are **dependent** if they are **not independent**.
>
> **Dependent** events are events for which the occurrence of one event *does affect* the occurrence of the other event.

For compound events which are dependent, the following product rule applies:

> If A and B are dependent events then $P(A \textbf{ and } B) = P(A) \times P(B \text{ given that } A \text{ has occurred})$.

Example 6 **Self Tutor**

A box contains 4 blue and 3 yellow buttons of the same size. Two buttons are randomly selected from the box without replacement. Find the probability that:

a both are yellow **b** the first is yellow and the second is blue.

a P(both are yellow)

= P(first is yellow *and* second is yellow)

= P(first is yellow) × P(second is yellow given that the first is yellow)

$= \frac{3}{7} \times \frac{2}{6}$ ← 2 yellows remaining / ← 6 to choose from

$= \frac{1}{7}$

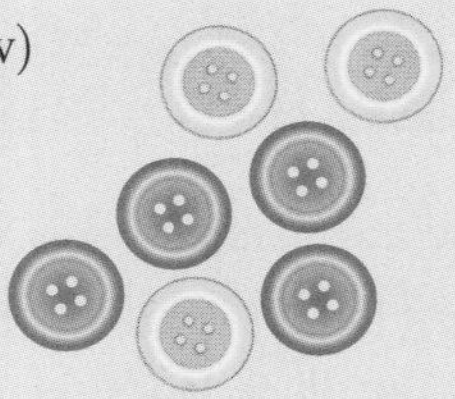

b P(first is yellow and second is blue)

= P(first is yellow) × P(second is blue given that the first is yellow)

$= \frac{3}{7} \times \frac{4}{6}$ ← 4 blues remaining / ← 6 to choose from

$= \frac{2}{7}$

EXERCISE 16E.2

1 A packet contains 8 identically shaped jelly beans. 5 are green and 3 are yellow. Two jelly beans are randomly selected without replacing the first before the second is drawn.

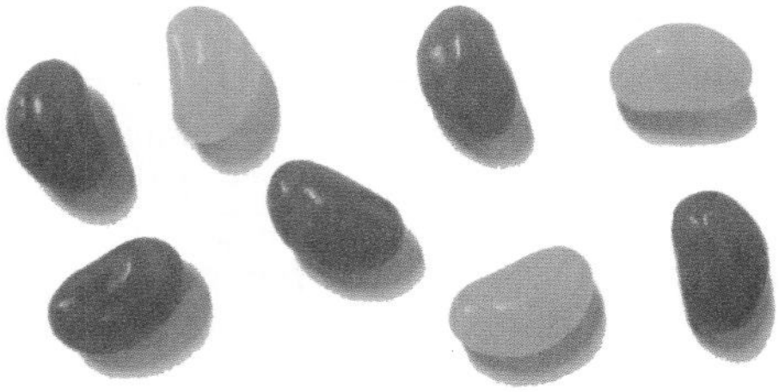

- **a** Determine the probability of getting:
  - **i** two green jelly beans
  - **ii** a green then a yellow jelly bean
  - **iii** a yellow then a green jelly bean
  - **iv** two yellow jelly beans.
- **b** Explain why your answers in **a** add up to 1.

2 From a squad of 3 male and 5 female badminton players, two players are randomly selected to play an exhibition match. Find the probability that both players are female.

3 Tickets numbered 1 to 20 are placed in a hat. Two tickets are drawn out at random, without replacement. Find the probability that:

- **a** the first number drawn is even and the second number is odd
- **b** both of the numbers are prime.

4 A jar contains 4 purple, 3 blue, and 1 gold ticket. Three tickets are selected without replacement. Find the probability that:

- **a** all of the tickets are purple
- **b** all of the tickets are blue
- **c** the first two are purple and the third is gold
- **d** none of the tickets is blue.

5 A ball is randomly selected from bag A, and is then placed in bag B. A ball is then randomly selected from bag B. Find the probability that the selected balls are both:

a red **b** blue.

F EXPERIMENTAL PROBABILITY

Isaac has made a paper plane. He throws it up into the air, and observes how it lands. He notices that there are two possible outcomes:

1 the plane lands the right way up **2** the plane lands upside down.

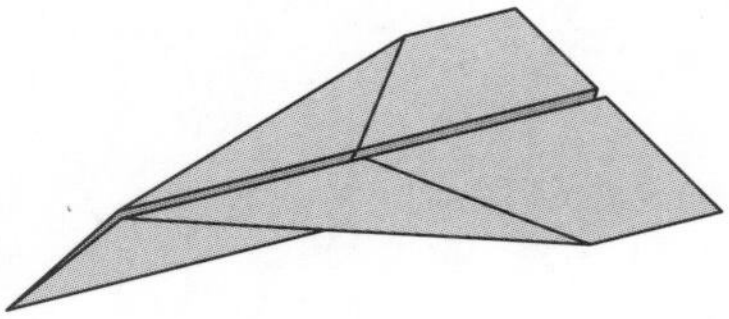

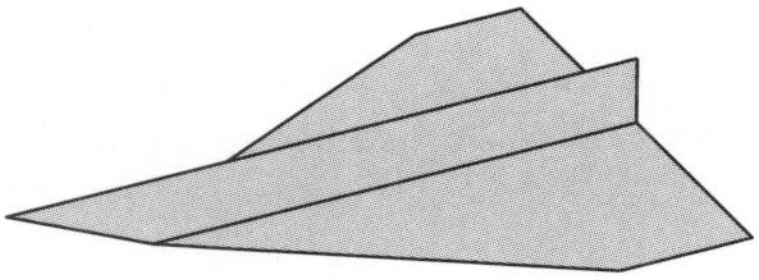

We cannot argue that the probability of each outcome occurring is $\frac{1}{2}$, because there is no reason to think that these outcomes are equally likely. Depending on the design of the plane, it may be more likely to land the right way up, or it may be more likely to land upside down.

In a situation like this, we can *estimate* the probability of each outcome occurring by **experimentation**.

Suppose Isaac throws his plane into the air 50 times. It lands the right way up 31 times, and it lands upside down 19 times. This suggests that the plane is more likely to land the right way up than upside down.

Since the plane has landed the right way up 31 times out of 50, we *estimate* that the probability of the plane landing the right way up is $\frac{31}{50} = 0.62$. This is called the **experimental probability**.

In a probability experiment:

- the **frequency** of a particular event is the number of times that this event is observed
- the **relative frequency** of an event is the frequency of that event divided by the total number of trials
- we use the relative frequency, usually written as a decimal, to estimate the probability of an event.

So, we would write P(right way up) $\approx \frac{31}{50} \approx 0.62$, and P(upside down) $\approx \frac{19}{50} \approx 0.38$.

These are not the *exact* probabilities for how the plane will land, but they are the best *estimates* we can make based on the information we have.

DISCUSSION

If Isaac threw his plane in the air another 50 times, would you expect it to again land the right way up exactly 31 times?

Example 7 Self Tutor

A ball is thrown to Joel 40 times. He catches the ball 29 times. Estimate the probability that Joel will:

a catch the next throw

b drop the next throw.

Joel caught the ball 29 times, and dropped it 11 times.

a P(catch)
$\approx$ relative frequency of a catch
$\approx \frac{29}{40}$
≈ 0.725

b P(drop)
$\approx$ relative frequency of a drop
$\approx \frac{11}{40}$
≈ 0.275

EXERCISE 16F.1

1 Adam is practising hitting baseballs in a cage. Out of 52 attempts, he hits the ball 38 times. Estimate the probability that Adam will hit the next baseball pitched at him.

2 When Aina is taking her washing off the line, she throws her pegs at the peg basket nearby. When she has nearly finished, she realises that she threw 34 pegs into the basket and 17 pegs missed.

a Estimate the probability that Aina will throw the next peg into the basket.

b Does this mean the events of hitting and missing the basket are equally likely? Explain your answer.

3 Read the **Opening Problem** on page **314**. Estimate the probability that a person who enters Maude's store will buy something.

4 Paula catches a bus to her daily yoga class. During a period of 66 days, she arrives at class on time on 47 occasions. Estimate the probability that tomorrow Paula will:

a arrive on time

b arrive late.

5 Jeffrey asked 80 people how many cousins they had. 6 people did not have any cousins, and 10 people only had one cousin. Estimate the probability that a randomly selected person has:

a one cousin

b more than one cousin.

6 When a nut was tossed 400 times, it finished on its edge 84 times and on its side for the rest.

a Find the experimental probability that when this nut is tossed, it will finish on its edge.

b Hence estimate the probability that when two identical nuts are tossed:

i they both fall on their edges

ii they both fall on their sides.

ACTIVITY — PAPER PLANES

PAPER PLANE INSTRUCTIONS

What to do:

1. Make a paper plane of your own. Predict how often it will land the right way up.
2. Throw your plane in the air 50 times, and record how many times it lands the right way up.
3. Use your results to estimate the probability that your plane will land the right way up.
4. Compare your estimate with those of your classmates.

THE ACCURACY OF EXPERIMENTAL PROBABILITIES

The more times an experiment is repeated, the more accurate the experimental probabilities will be.

We can demonstrate this by studying experimental probabilities for a situation for which we can also calculate theoretical probabilities.

INVESTIGATION 1 — TOSSING A COIN

SIMULATION

Click on the icon to run a simulation for tossing a coin.

For each toss, the probability that the coin lands on *heads* is $\frac{1}{2}$ or 0.5.

What to do:

1. Use the simulation to toss a coin 10 times.
2. Repeat this 9 more times, so in total you have tossed the coin 10 lots of 10 times. Record your results in a table like the one alongside.
3. Given that the probability of a head with any toss is 0.5, what percentage of heads do you *expect* to get with each trial?
4. What percentage of heads did you get for each group of 10 tosses? In general, how close is this to what you expected in **3**?

Trial	*Number of heads*	*Percentage of heads*
1		
2		
3		
4		
5		
6		
7		
8		
9		
10		

5. Run the simulation 10 times for 100 tosses.
   - **a** Construct a table like the one above to display your results.
   - **b** In general, are the percentages of heads closer to what you expected in **3**?
6. Repeat for 10 trials of 1000 tosses, and 10 trials of 10 000 tosses.

From the **Investigation** you should have seen that as the number of tosses increases, the experimental probability of obtaining a head gets closer to the theoretical probability of 0.5. This means that the accuracy of the estimate improves as the number of trials increases.

EXERCISE 16F.2

1 Don threw a tin can into the air 180 times. In these trials it landed on its side 137 times. Later that afternoon he threw the same tin can into the air 75 more times. It landed on its side 46 times.

- **a** Find the experimental probability of the can landing on its side for both sets of trials.
- **b** List possible reasons for the differences in the results.
- **c** Which probability is likely to be more accurate? Explain your answer.

2
- **a** In the first round of a competition, Sasha recorded 77 hits out of 80 shots at her target. Use this result to estimate her chances of hitting the target.
- **b** On the next day Sasha scored 185 hits out of 200 shots. Use the results of this round to estimate her chances of hitting the target.
- **c** Which of these estimates is more likely to reflect Sasha's actual probability of hitting the target?

3 Kelly rolled a die 200 times, and Lucy rolled a die 50 times. Their experimental probabilities for obtaining each number are given in the tables below. Suggest which set of results is Kelly's, and which is Lucy's. Explain your answer.

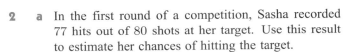

A

1	2	3	4	5	6
0.16	0.3	0.1	0.24	0.08	0.12

B

1	2	3	4	5	6
0.2	0.14	0.18	0.16	0.18	0.14

4 Keith and Megan want to find the probability that a randomly chosen person is vegetarian. Keith surveyed 150 people, and found that 18 of them were vegetarian. Megan surveyed 60 people, and found that 9 of them were vegetarian.

- **a** Estimate the probability that a randomly chosen person is vegetarian, using:
  - **i** Keith's results
  - **ii** Megan's results.
- **b** Which estimate is likely to be more accurate? Explain your answer.
- **c** Combine Keith's and Megan's results to obtain an even more accurate estimate.

INVESTIGATION 2 THE CEREAL BOX PROBLEM

There is a plastic toy animal inside each box of Weet-Plus cereal. There are six different animals to collect: an elephant, a bear, a buffalo, a lion, a tiger, and a giraffe. The animals are equally likely to occur in any given box.

Over a period of time, Gareth's mother buys 8 boxes of Weet-Plus cereal. What is the probability that Gareth will have a complete set of animals?

What to do:

Since the animals are equally likely to occur in any given box, the result from each cereal box can therefore be simulated using a roll of a die, with each number corresponding to a different animal:

1 = elephant 2 = bear 3 = buffalo 4 = lion 5 = tiger 6 = giraffe

1 Roll a die 8 times.

2 Determine whether each number has appeared at least once, indicating that Gareth has collected the complete set.

3 Repeat the experiment 50 times. Record your observations in a table like the one alongside:

Trial	*Rolls*	*Complete set?*
1	1, 4, 4, 6, 5, 3, 5, 1	No
2	2, 5, 1, 1, 3, 6, 6, 4	Yes
3	5, 2, 2, 6, 1, 5, 3, 2	No
⋮	⋮	⋮

4 Use your results to estimate the probability that Gareth will collect a complete set of animals from 8 cereal boxes.

5 Compare your results with those of your classmates.

6 A large number of trials is often required to obtain an accurate probability estimate. It is therefore sometimes helpful to use technology to simulate many trials of an experiment.

SPREADSHEET

Click on the icon to open the spreadsheet. This spreadsheet is set up to run 500 trials of the experiment.

	A	B	C	D	E	F	G	H	I	J	K	L	M	N
1	Trial		Box 1	Box 2	Box 3	Box 4	Box 5	Box 6	Box 7	Box 8		Complete Set?		Probability
2														
3	1		1	5	1	5	5	1	6	4		No		0.106
4	2		4	1	3	6	5	4	2	6		Yes		
5	3		4	6	2	3	5	6	5	5		No		

The results in column L indicate whether each trial generates a complete set of animals.
The value in cell N3 gives the experimental probability of obtaining the complete set based on these trials.
Pressing **F9** will generate a new set of random numbers, and a new experimental probability.

7 Compare these results with the ones from your own experiment. Which results do you expect to be more accurate?

G PROBABILITIES FROM TABLED DATA

When data is collected, it is often summarised and displayed in a frequency table. We can use such a table to help calculate probabilities.

Example 8 — Self Tutor

A marketing company surveys 50 randomly selected people to discover what brand of toothpaste they use. The results are given in the table.

Brand	*Frequency*	*Relative frequency*
Shine	10	
Starbright	14	
Brite	4	
Clean	12	
No Name	10	
Total	50	

a Copy and complete the table.

b Estimate the probability that a randomly selected community member uses:

i Starbright ii Clean.

a

Brand	*Frequency*	*Relative frequency*
Shine	10	$\frac{10}{50} = 0.2$
Starbright	14	$\frac{14}{50} = 0.28$
Brite	4	$\frac{4}{50} = 0.08$
Clean	12	$\frac{12}{50} = 0.24$
No Name	10	$\frac{10}{50} = 0.2$
Total	50	1.00

b i P(Starbright) ≈ 0.28

ii P(Clean) ≈ 0.24

EXERCISE 16G.1

1 A corner shop sells shortbread and chocolate chip biscuits. In one week 187 biscuits are sold.

a Copy and complete the table.

b Estimate the probability that the next customer will buy:

i a shortbread biscuit

ii a chocolate chip biscuit.

Type	*Frequency*	*Relative frequency*
Shortbread	62	
Chocolate chip		
Total	187	

2 A football club has three types of membership: platinum, gold, and silver.
A summary of the membership appears in the table.

Type	*Frequency*	*Relative frequency*
Platinum	419	
Gold	628	
Silver	921	
Total		

a Copy and complete the table.

b How many members of the football club are there?

c Estimate the probability that the next membership sold is:

i silver **ii** not platinum.

3 A café sells four types of hot drinks. Over a one week period, it sells the numbers shown in the table.

Type	*Frequency*	*Relative frequency*
Espresso	49	
Milk coffee	187	
Tea	150	
Hot chocolate	113	
Total		

a Copy and complete the table.

b Estimate the probability that the next customer will buy hot chocolate.

c Estimate the probability that the next customer will buy an espresso or a tea.

TWO-WAY TABLES

Sometimes data is categorised by not just one, but two variables. The data is represented in a **two-way table**. We can estimate probabilities from a two-way table just as we do from a regular frequency table.

Example 9 Self Tutor

60 students were randomly selected and asked whether they studied Physics and English.

a Copy and complete the table by finding the total of each row and column.

b What does the 13 in the table represent?

c Estimate the probability that a randomly selected student studies English but not Physics.

		Physics		
		Yes	No	*Total*
English	Yes	15	12	
	No	13	20	
	Total			

a

		Physics		
		Yes	No	*Total*
English	Yes	15	12	27
	No	13	20	33
	Total	28	32	60

b 13 of the selected students study Physics but do not study English.

c 12 out of the 60 students study English but not Physics.

$\therefore$ P(student studies English but not Physics) $\approx \frac{12}{60} \approx 0.2$

Since the data only represents a sample of the population, the results are only **estimates** of the true probabilities.

EXERCISE 16G.2

1 The Year 8 students at a school were asked whether they completed their homework for English and Mathematics.

a Copy and complete the table.

b How many students were surveyed?

c What does the 14 indicate?

d Estimate the probability that a randomly chosen student completed their Mathematics homework.

		Mathematics		
		Yes	No	*Total*
English	Yes	59	11	
	No	14	23	
	Total			

2 200 randomly chosen people were surveyed to determine whether they enjoyed a new television show. The results were categorised by age, and are shown in the table.

		Preference			
		Like	Dislike	Undecided	*Total*
Age	Under 40	29	49	26	
	Over 40	48	14	34	
	Total				

a Copy and complete the table.

b What does the 49 indicate?

c Estimate the probability that a randomly chosen person:

i will dislike the new television show

ii is over 40 and undecided.

3 A sample of teenagers was asked whether they had ever learnt to play a musical instrument. The results were further categorised by gender as shown.

a Copy and complete the table.

b Estimate the probability that a randomly chosen teenager has learnt to play an instrument.

c Estimate the probability that a randomly chosen teenager is male, and has never learnt to play an instrument.

		Gender		
		Male	Female	*Total*
Instrument	Yes	39	44	
	No	17	12	
	Total			

4 40 students were asked what grades they achieved for Mathematics and Science last term.

a Copy and complete the table.

b Estimate the probability that a randomly selected student:

i scored an A for Mathematics and a B for Science

ii scored an A for at least one of the subjects

iii scored the same grade for the two subjects.

		Mathematics			
		A	B	C	*Total*
Science	A	7	5	3	
	B	6	8	4	
	C	4	1	2	
	Total				

c If we know that a student scored an A for Mathematics, estimate the probability that the student scored a C for Science.

H EXPECTATION

Suppose a die is rolled 120 times. On how many occasions would you *expect* the result to be a '5'?

The possible outcomes when rolling a die are 1, 2, 3, 4, 5, and 6. Each of these outcomes is equally likely, so we would expect $\frac{1}{6}$ of them to be a '5'.

Since $\frac{1}{6}$ of 120 is 20, we expect 20 of the 120 rolls to be a '5'.

> If there are n trials of an experiment and the probability of an event occurring in each trial is p, then the **expectation** of the occurrence of that event is np.

Example 10 — Self Tutor

Every bottle of Cola-Pop comes with a 1 in 3 chance of winning a prize. In one month Stan buys 6 bottles of Cola-Pop. How many prizes would you expect him to win?

$p = \text{P(bottle wins a prize)} = \frac{1}{3}$

For $n = 6$ bottles, the expected number of prizes is $np = 6 \times \frac{1}{3}$
$= 2$

EXERCISE 16H

1 a What is the probability that when a coin is tossed, it will land heads up?
  b If the coin is tossed 500 times, how many times would you *expect* the coin to land heads up?

2 Each time Darren takes the train, he has probability $\frac{5}{8}$ of getting a seat. In 120 train trips, how many times can Darren expect to get a seat?

3 Turtle hatchlings only have probability 0.01 of surviving to adulthood. If 500 000 eggs hatch in one year, how many of the hatchlings are expected to survive to adulthood?

4 A library has found that the probability of a borrowed book being returned on time is 0.68. In one day the library lent 837 books. How many of those books can the library expect to be returned on time?

5 Suppose the spinner alongside is spun 200 times. How many times would you expect the result to be:
  a blue
  b red
  c yellow
  d green?

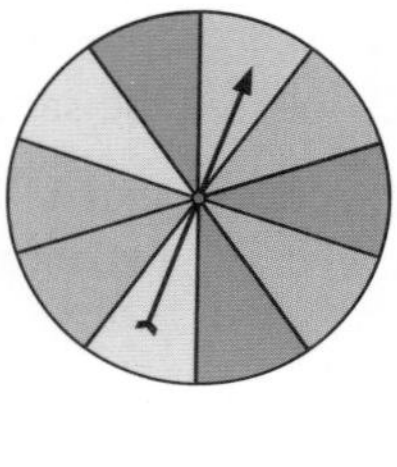

6 Suppose a pair of dice is rolled 900 times. How many times would you expect to get:

a a pair of 6s
b a 5 and a 2
c two odd numbers
d two prime numbers
e two numbers whose sum is 10
f two numbers whose product is 12?

REVIEW SET 16A

1 List the sample space for:

a selecting a letter of the alphabet
b spinning the spinner shown.

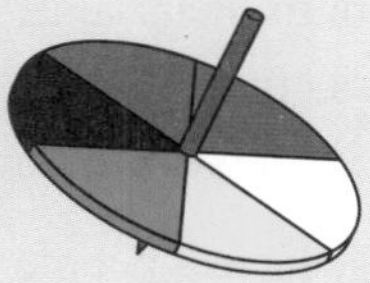

2 A survey of forty five 18 year olds was conducted. It was found that 19 enjoyed camping.

a Estimate the probability that a randomly selected 18 year old likes camping.
b How can the accuracy of this estimate be improved?

3 One lollipop is chosen at random from a tub of lollipops. Find the chance of picking an orange lollipop if the tub contains:

a 2 orange, 5 strawberry, and 1 lemon lollipop
b 3 apple and 7 blackberry lollipops
c 5 watermelon, 10 blackberry, 2 strawberry, and 3 orange lollipops.

4 A farmer fences his rectangular property into 9 rectangular paddocks as shown. A paddock is selected at random. Find the probability that it has:

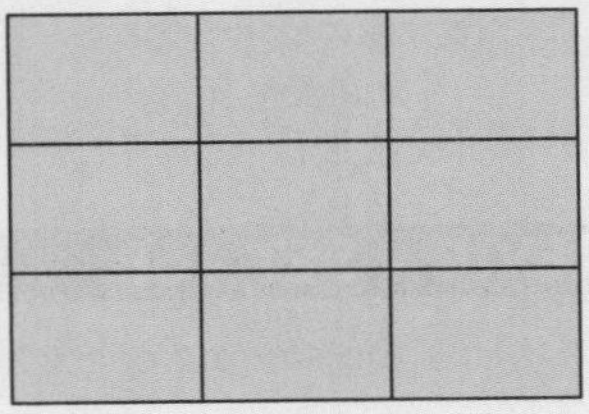

a no fences on the boundary of the property
b one fence on the boundary of the property
c two fences on the boundary of the property.

5 A coin is tossed, and a spinner with equal sectors numbered 1, 2, 3, 4, and 5 is spun.

a Use a 2-dimensional grid to show the sample space of possible outcomes.
b Find the chance of getting:
  i a head and a 5
  ii a head or a 5.

6 A marketing company was commissioned to investigate the main reason teenagers used their home computers. The results of the survey are shown alongside.

Reason	*Frequency*	*Relative frequency*
Homework	29	
Social networking	43	
Playing games	15	
Downloading music	69	
Total		

a How many teenagers were surveyed?
b Copy and complete the table.
c Estimate the probability that a randomly selected teenager mainly uses their computer for:
  i homework
  ii something other than downloading music.

7 A bag contains 4 green and 3 red marbles. Two marbles are randomly selected from the bag without replacement. Determine the probability that:

a both are green **b** both are red.

8 Jeff and Santi are baking a cake in a cooking class. Jeff has a 20% chance of burning his cake, and Santi has a 15% chance of burning his cake. Find the probability that:

a they both burn their cakes

b neither burns their cake

c Jeff burns his cake, but Santi does not.

9 300 randomly selected people were asked whether they attended a sporting event. The results are categorised by gender.

	Yes	*No*	*Total*
Male	71	77	
Female	87	65	
Total			

a Copy and complete the table.

b Estimate the probability that a randomly chosen person:

i attended the event **ii** is male and did not attend the event.

10 When a high jump bar is set at 1.90 metres, Steve has probability 0.26 of successfully completing the jump.

a Let E be the event that Steve successfully completes a jump.

i State the complementary event E'. **ii** Find $P(E')$.

b Steve performs 50 jumps at this height. How many of them would you expect to be successful?

REVIEW SET 16B

1 List the sample space for:

a randomly selecting a disc from a bag containing a red disc, a pink disc, a white disc, and a brown disc

b selecting a 2 digit multiple of 5.

2 Let L be the event that Lionel will pass his English exam, and that $P(L) = 0.57$.

a State the complementary event L'. **b** Find $P(L')$.

c Use a word or phrase to describe the probability of:

i L occurring **ii** L' occurring.

3 A variety box contains 6 packets of plain chips, 6 packets of salt and vinegar chips, 4 packets of chicken chips, and 4 packets of barbecue chips. If a packet is chosen at random from the box, determine the probability it contains:

a barbecue chips **b** chicken chips or plain chips.

4 In the previous week, Aaron received 12 emails from his friend Patrick, 2 from his mother, 4 from his father, and 11 spam emails. Estimate the probability that the next email Aaron receives will be from:

a Patrick **b** one of his parents.

5 When a metal nut was tossed 500 times, it finished on its edge 156 times, and on a flat side for the rest.

Result	*Frequency*	*Relative frequency*
Edge		
Flat		
Total	500	

a Copy and complete the table.

b Estimate the probability that a tossed nut will finish on a flat side.

6 Are you more likely to select a prime number by randomly choosing a whole number from 1 to 20, or by randomly choosing a whole number from 1 to 40?

7 A ball is removed from each of these boxes.

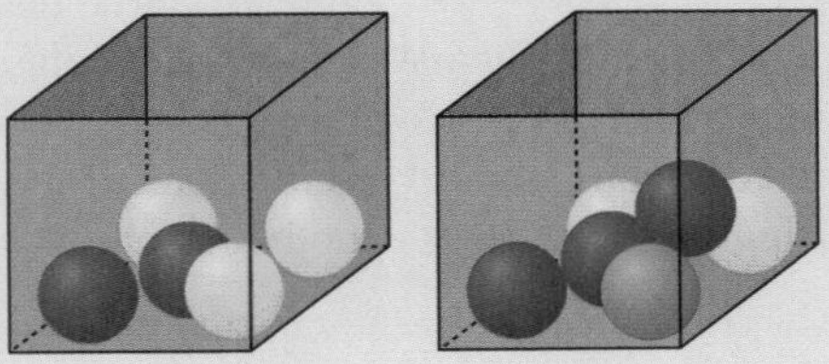

a Find the probability that both balls removed are yellow.

b Suppose this experiment is performed 60 times. How many times would you expect both balls removed to be yellow?

8 Tickets numbered 1 to 15 are placed in a hat. Two tickets are drawn out at random, without replacement. Find the probability that:

a both numbers are greater than 9

b the first number is prime, and the second number is composite.

9 150 people were randomly selected and asked what radio station they listen to. The results were categorised by age, and are shown in the table.

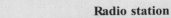

		Radio station			
		Mash	Planet	Gold	*Total*
Age	Under 30	43	14	24	
	Over 30	12	35	22	
	Total				

a Copy and complete the table.

b Estimate the probability that a randomly chosen person:

i is under 30 and listens to Gold

ii listens to Mash

iii does not listen to Planet.

10 The two spinners alongside are twirled simultaneously.

a Draw a 2-dimensional grid to illustrate the sample space.

b Find the probability of spinning:

i the same number with both spinners

ii two odd numbers

iii two numbers whose sum is 4.

HISTORICAL NOTE MARIA GAETANA AGNESI 1718 - 1799

Maria Gaetana Agnesi was born in 1718 in Italy. Her father, Pietro Agnesi, was a professor of mathematics at the University of Bologna. Maria was the eldest of 21 children, and her family was both wealthy and cultured.

While she was still very young, it was clear that Maria was talented at languages, in particular Latin. This was important as it was the language spoken by scholars all over Europe.

Encouraged by her parents, Maria engaged in discussions on abstract mathematical and philosophical topics with other intellectuals from all over Europe. However, being shy, she asked to be excused from these meetings at the age of 21, using the death of her mother as an excuse.

Maria then took over the management of the household, and also her own mathematical development. She became fascinated by the developent of calculus by Leibniz and Newton. Since these works appeared in a variety of languages and papers, she decided to produce a book of clarity to cover the topic.

The result of ten years work, her two volume *Analytical Institutions* brought fame not only to Maria, but to the cause of women by demonstrating that women could compete with men in abstract reasoning. She was highly honoured for this work and praised by the French Academy, but could not be admitted as a member because she was female.

Maria was offered the professorship at the University of Bologna in 1752 when her father died, but she declined and retired from academic pursuits. The last 40 years of her life were spent assisting the sick and the poor. There is some dispute as to whether Maria actually became a nun, but she certainly lived and worked the simple life of a nun and eventually became director of a hospital for the poor in Milan.

Chapter 17

Problem solving

Contents:

OPENING PROBLEM

Kevin, Mai, and Bruce had breakfast at an all-you-can-eat pancake parlour. Bruce ate twice as many pancakes as Kevin. Mai ate one more pancake than Kevin. Between them they ate 13 pancakes.

Things to think about:

a How can we represent this problem using the language of algebra?

b How many pancakes did Kevin eat?

Many problems we encounter are presented in sentence form, rather than using symbols. You need to be familiar with a variety of techniques for solving these problems.

In this chapter we will examine some problem solving techniques, including:

- writing the problem as an algebraic equation
- problem solving by search
- problem solving by working backwards.

A WRITING PROBLEMS AS EQUATIONS

One of the hardest things to do when solving problems is to write the information given as an equation using the language of algebra.

We write each step of the problem using symbols, taking care to use brackets when necessary.

Example 1 **Self Tutor**

Express the following problem algebraically:

"I start with a number, add 4, then multiply by 3. The result is 33."

Suppose the number we start with is n.

Start with a number	n
add 4	$n+4$
multiply by 3	$3(n+4)$
the result is 33	$3(n+4)=33$

So, the equation $3(n+4)=33$ represents the problem.

EXERCISE 17A

1 Starting with the number n, rewrite the following in algebraic form:

- **a** I think of a number and subtract 7 from it, getting an answer of 11.
- **b** I think of a number and divide it by 8, getting an answer of 5.
- **c** I think of a number, multiply it by 3, and then add 5. The result is 23.
- **d** I think of a number, add 1 to it, divide the result by 4, and get an answer of 10.
- **e** I think of a number, subtract 3, then multiply the result by 9. The result is 36.
- **f** I think of a number, divide it by 4, then add 11 to the result. The answer is 18.
- **g** I think of a number, multiply it by 5, then subtract 8. The result is 4 more than the original number.

Example 2 **Self Tutor**

Write the following information in an algebraic equation:

"Greg is x years old. Dylan is 3 years older than Greg. Their combined age is 31 years."

Greg is x years old, so Dylan is $(x+3)$ years old.

Their combined age is 31 years, so $x + (x+3) = 31$ is the equation which represents the information.

2 Write the following information in an algebraic equation:

- **a** Clint has x sons and 3 daughters. He has 5 children in total.
- **b** Beth took x minutes to walk to the shops, and the same amount of time to walk back. She spent 15 minutes at the shops, and the trip took 37 minutes in total.
- **c** Stan weighs x kg, and Ted is 6 kg heavier than Stan. Their combined weight is 100 kg.
- **d** Sylvia has $\$x$ in her bank account. If she deposits \$100 into her account, this would triple the amount of money there.

B PROBLEM SOLVING WITH ALGEBRA

In **Section A** we saw how worded problems can be written as algebraic equations. We can solve these equations using the techniques in **Chapter 8**, thus providing answers to the problems.

We use these steps:

Step 1: Examine the problem carefully.
Step 2: Select a letter or symbol to represent the unknown quantity to be found.
Step 3: Write an equation using the information in the question.
Step 4: Solve the equation.
Step 5: Write the answer to the question in a sentence.
Step 6: *Check* that your answer satisfies the given conditions.

Example 3 ◀)) **Self Tutor**

I think of a number, double it, then subtract 7. The result is 10. Find the number.

Let x be the number, so $2x$ is the number doubled.

$\therefore \quad 2x - 7$ is the number doubled minus 7.

$\therefore \quad 2x - 7 = 10$

$\qquad \therefore \quad 2x = 17 \qquad$ {adding 7 to both sides}

$\qquad \therefore \quad x = 8\frac{1}{2} \qquad$ {dividing both sides by 2}

Thus, the number is $8\frac{1}{2}$.

Check: LHS $= 2 \times 8\frac{1}{2} - 7 = 17 - 7 = 10 =$ RHS \checkmark

> Always check that your solution makes the original equation true **and** answers the original question.

Example 4 ◀)) **Self Tutor**

A set of cricket wickets consists of 3 stumps and 2 bails. Each bail weighs 100 g, and the total weight of the wickets is 1.7 kg.

Find the weight of each stump.

bail ⟶

stump ⟶

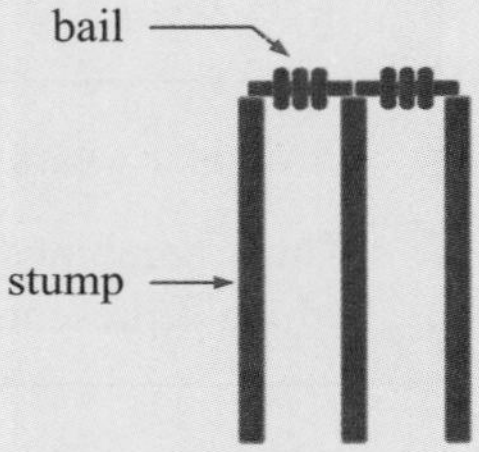

Let the weight of each stump be x g.

$\qquad \therefore \quad 3 \times x + 2 \times 100 = 1700 \qquad$ {total weight of the wickets $= 1700$ g}

$\qquad \therefore \quad 3x + 200 = 1700$

$\qquad\qquad \therefore \quad 3x = 1500 \qquad$ {subtracting 200 from both sides}

$\qquad\qquad \therefore \quad x = 500 \qquad$ {dividing both sides by 3}

Each stump weighs 500 g.

EXERCISE 17B

1 Find the unknown numbers using equations:

 a If a certain number is doubled, the result is -12. Find the number.

 b A third of a number is 15. Find the number.

 c 4 more than a number is -5. Find the number.

 d When a number is decreased by 14, the result is 22. Find the number.

2 Use equations to solve the following problems:

 a I think of a number, treble it, then subtract 8. The result is -5. Find the number.

 b When twice a certain number is increased by 7, the result is 31. Find the number.

 c When 3 is subtracted from a certain number and the result is divided by 4, the result is 10. What is the number?

d When 4 is added to a certain number and the result is doubled, the result is 6 more than the number. What is the number?

e When a certain number is added to 8, the result is the same as when the number is subtracted from 36. Find the number.

f The average of a certain number and 5 is one less than the number. What is the number?

g When a number is halved and 5 is added, the result is 8 more than the original number. Find the number.

3 I think of a number, double it, add 2, halve the result, then subtract 1.
Explain why the result is always the original number.

4 A market stall has 13 bags of apples, and 11 loose apples on display. In total there are 141 apples at the stall. How many apples are in each bag?

5 A packet of lollies is shared equally among 5 friends. Layla eats two of her lollies and has five left. How many lollies were in the packet?

6 Leanne cuts some roses in her front garden, and another 20 roses in her back garden. She uses one quarter of her roses to make a bouquet of a dozen flowers. How many roses did Leanne cut in her front garden?

Example 5 **Self Tutor**

I have one rake and two identical shovels for sale. Each shovel is worth \$7 more than the rake. If the total value of the items is \$59, find the value of the rake.

Let the rake cost $\$r$, so each shovel costs $\$(r+7)$.

$\therefore\ r + 2(r+7) = 59$ {the total value is \$59}

$\therefore\ r + 2r + 14 = 59$ {expanding}

$\therefore\ 3r + 14 = 59$ {simplifying}

$\therefore\ 3r = 45$ {subtracting 14 from both sides}

$\therefore\ r = 15$ {dividing both sides by 3}

$\therefore$ the rake is for sale at \$15.

Check: LHS $= 15 + 2(15+7) = 15 + 2(22) = 59 =$ RHS ✓

7 The Firebirds won last night's netball match, scoring 12 more goals than the Swifts. In total, 108 goals were scored in the match. How many goals did the Firebirds score?

8 Class A had 33 students and class B had 21 students. A number of students were moved from class A to class B so the classes now have the same number of students. How many students were moved?

9 In a group of 5 friends, the average height is 153 cm. Ken is 148 cm tall, Maria is 145 cm, and Marcus is 162 cm. The other two are the same height. How tall are they?

10 At a grocery store, Mandy bought some apples which weighed 100 g each, and some oranges which weighed 150 g each. She bought 10 pieces of fruit, with total weight 1.35 kg. How many apples did Mandy buy?

11 The Norton family went out for dinner, and paid for their meal with a €100 note. The change they received was one seventh of the cost of the meal. Find the cost of the meal.

Example 6 — Self Tutor

A rectangle has length 2 cm longer than its width. If the rectangle has perimeter 52 cm, find its width.

Let the width be x cm, so the length is $(x+2)$ cm.

$\therefore\ 2[x+(x+2)] = 52$ {the perimeter is 52 cm}

$\therefore\ x+(x+2) = 26$ {dividing both sides by 2}

$\therefore\ 2x+2 = 26$ {simplifying}

$\therefore\ 2x = 24$ {subtracting 2 from both sides}

$\therefore\ x = 12$ {dividing both sides by 2}

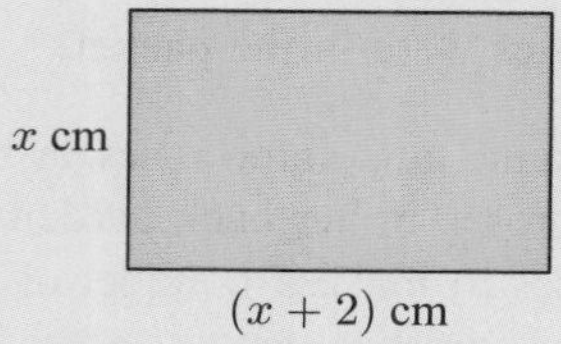

So, the width of the rectangle is 12 cm.

12 The length of a rectangle is double its width. The perimeter is 54 cm. Find the width of the rectangle.

13 The length of a rectangle is 7 cm longer than its width. The perimeter is 74 cm. Find the width of the rectangle.

14 The equal sides of an isosceles triangle are twice the length of the base. The perimeter of the triangle is 60 cm. Find the length of the base.

15 The parallelogram ABCD has perimeter 56 m.
[AD] is twice as long as the height, and [CD] is 1 m longer than the height.
Find the area of the parallelogram.

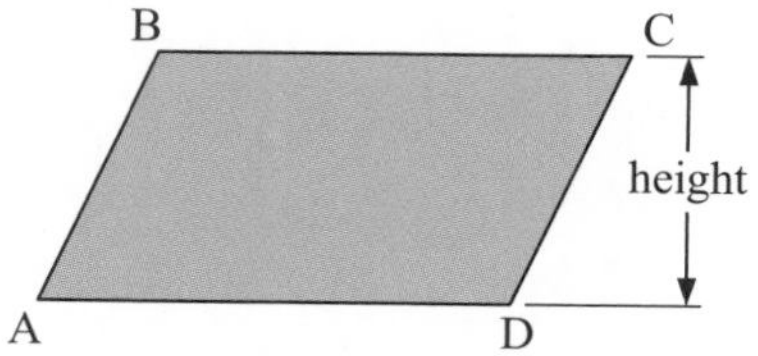

C PROBLEM SOLVING BY SEARCH

With some problems it is either difficult to write down an equation, or the equation may be difficult to solve. In some cases the equation may have more than one solution.

If the number of possibilities for the solution is small, it may be quickest to search through them all to find the solutions which work. In other cases a search through particular values may reveal what the correct solution must be.

Example 7 — Self Tutor

What rectangle with perimeter 24 cm has the greatest area?

The perimeter is 24 cm, so $2(\text{length} + \text{width}) = 24$ cm

$\therefore \text{length} + \text{width} = 12$ cm

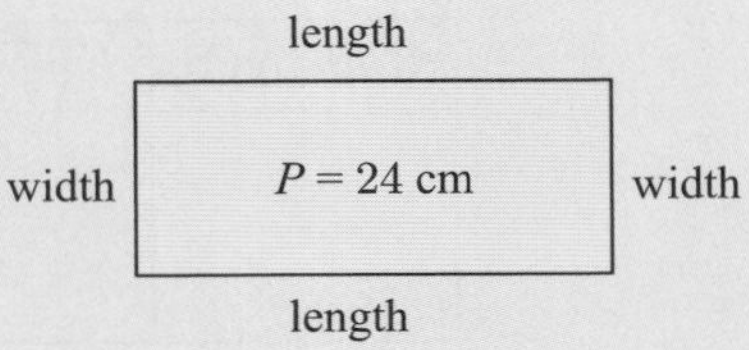

Trials:

Length (cm)	*Width* (cm)	*Area* (cm^2)
1	11	$1 \times 11 = 11$
2	10	$2 \times 10 = 20$
3	9	$3 \times 9 = 27$
4	8	$4 \times 8 = 32$
5	7	$5 \times 7 = 35$
6	6	$6 \times 6 = 36$
7	5	$7 \times 5 = 35$
8	4	$8 \times 4 = 32$

It appears that the area is largest when the rectangle is a 6 cm by 6 cm square.

EXERCISE 17C

1 Consider the equation $3x + 4y = 30$ where x is a positive integer and y is positive.

a Explain why x cannot be greater than 9.

b Copy and complete the following table for possible values of x and y.

x	1	2	3	4	5	6	7	8	9
y									

For example, when $x = 1$, $3(1) + 4y = 30$

$\therefore 4y = 27$

$\therefore y = \frac{27}{4} \quad (= 6\frac{3}{4})$

c Find the solutions to $3x + 4y = 30$ for which x and y are both positive integers.

2 Find positive integers x and y that satisfy the rule $9x + 6y = 90$.

3 **a** Find the smallest positive number greater than 3 which, when divided by 4 and 5, leaves a remainder of 3. Try 4, 5, 6, ...

b Is there a quicker way of finding this number? Explain how this may be done.

4 A rectangle has a perimeter of 32 cm and an area of 48 cm^2. Find the dimensions of the rectangle.

5 Find all positive integers less than 40 which *cannot* be written as a sum of a perfect square and a perfect cube.

Hint: Be systematic in your approach.

Calculate $0^2 + 1^3$ $\quad 1^2 + 0^3$ and so on.
$0^2 + 2^3$ $\quad 1^2 + 1^3$
$0^2 + 3^3$ $\quad 1^2 + 2^3$
$0^2 + 4^3$ $\quad 1^2 + 3^3$

A *perfect* square or cube is the square or cube of a whole number.

6 Find the smallest integer greater than 1 which is both a perfect square *and* a perfect cube.

7 Three sides of a rectangle have lengths which add to 32 cm. If the rectangle has the maximum area possible, what dimensions must it have?

Hint: Copy and complete:

Width (cm)	*Length* (cm)	*Area* (cm^2)
1	30	30
2	28	56
⋮	⋮	⋮

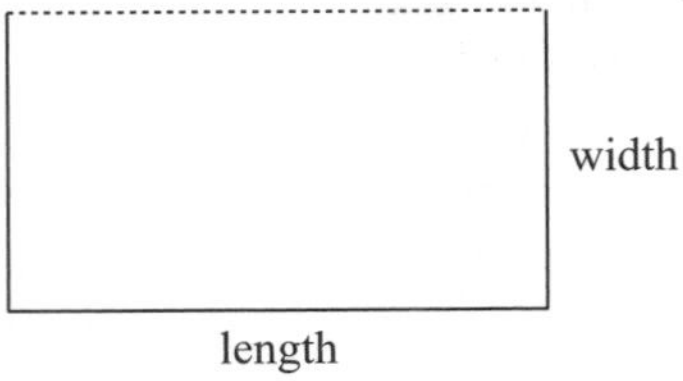

8 A number is called **perfect** if the sum of its factors, excluding itself, is equal to itself. For example, 6 is a perfect number because its factors are 1, 2, 3, and 6, and $1+2+3=6$.
There is one other perfect number less than 40. What is it?

9 Leslie has bought ten presents for her two sons. The price of each present is shown below:

\$20 \$18 \$10 \$24 \$5 \$1 \$8 \$35 \$15 \$2

Leslie wants to divide the presents into two groups of five presents. The total value of the presents in each group must be the same. How can Leslie do this?

10 If a and b are positive integers and $2a+b=40$, find the greatest possible value of ab^2.

D PROBLEM SOLVING BY WORKING BACKWARDS

In mathematics, we usually begin with an initial condition and work systematically towards an end point.

However, sometimes we are given details about the final situation, and need to determine what the situation was initially. In these cases we need to **work backwards**.

Example 8 Self Tutor

My friend lost \$5 from her wallet, but she then doubled what remained in her wallet by selling a book to me. She then had \$50 in her wallet. How much did she have in her wallet initially?

My friend doubled her money to reach \$50.

Double means multiply by 2, so to work backwards we need to divide by 2.

$\therefore$ she had $\$50 \div 2 = \$25$ in her wallet before selling the book to me.

Lose \$5 means subtract \$5, so to work backwards we need to add \$5.

Before losing the \$5, she must have had $\$25 + \$5 = \$30$.

My friend had \$30 in her wallet initially.

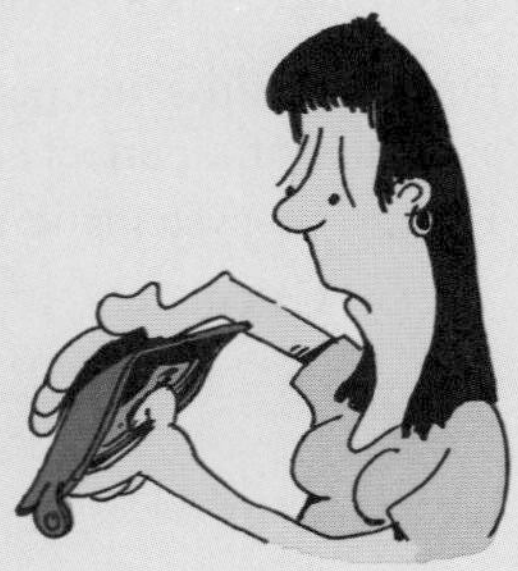

Example 9 **Self Tutor**

A teacher offers members of the class a peppermint for every problem they get right, but he takes back *two* for each incorrect answer. Barry stored up his peppermints over a week. On Thursday he got 8 questions right and 2 wrong. On Friday he got 9 right and 1 wrong. He finished the week with 16 peppermints.

How many did he have at the start of Thursday?

Friday: 9 right and 1 wrong is a gain of $9 - 2 = 7$ peppermints.

$\therefore$ he had $16 - 7 = 9$ peppermints at the start of Friday.

Thursday: 8 right and 2 wrong is a gain of $8 - 2 \times 2 = 4$ peppermints.

$\therefore$ he had $9 - 4 = 5$ peppermints at the start of Thursday.

Barry had 5 peppermints at the start of Thursday.

EXERCISE 17D

1 I think of a number. I multiply it by 7, add 1, divide by 8, subtract 2, then divide by 3. The result is 2. What was my number?

2 A breeder sold half of his horses, then another two. He then sold half of his remaining horses, then another two. He then only had his one favourite horse left. How many horses did he have initially?

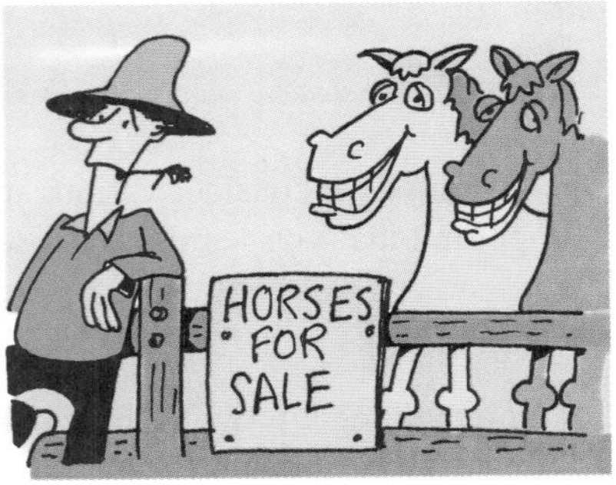

3 Xuen and Xia are sisters. Xia grew 4 cm in 2012 and Xuen grew 3 cm more than Xia in that year. In 2013 Xuen grew 3 cm and Xia grew 2 cm. When measured at the end of 2013, both girls were 140 cm tall. What was the height of each girl at the end of 2011?

4

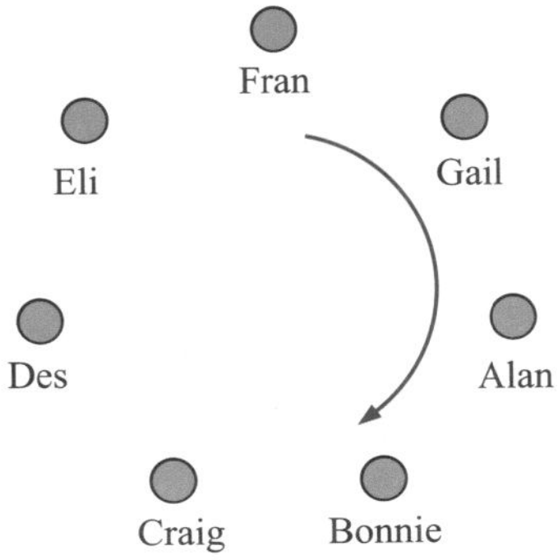

In the game '101', students sit in a circle. Going around in a clockwise direction, students call out the prime numbers in increasing order, starting with '2', '3', '5', and so on. The student who calls out '101' is the winner.

Fran will decide who should start the game. Which player should Fran choose so that Fran ends up winning?

Example 10 | Self Tutor

Sally rides $\frac{1}{3}$ of the way to school, and then is driven the remaining 6 km by a friend's family. How far does she live from her school?

She rides $\frac{1}{3}$ of the way, and so is driven $\frac{2}{3}$ of the way.

$\therefore$ 6 km is $\frac{2}{3}$ of the way.

$\therefore$ 3 km is $\frac{1}{3}$ of the way.

$\therefore$ Sally lives 6 km + 3 km = 9 km from her school.

5 Joe and Jerry went for a bike trek during the holidays. On the first day they rode $\frac{1}{3}$ of the total distance. On the second day they were tired and only rode $\frac{1}{4}$ of the remaining distance. On the third day they rode half of the distance left. The last day they rode the remaining 18 km. How far did they ride altogether?

6 Two bottles X and Y contain some water. From bottle X we pour into bottle Y twice as much water as bottle Y already contains. We then pour from bottle Y into bottle X as much water as bottle X now contains. Both bottles now contain 200 mL. How much water was in each bottle to start with?

E MISCELLANEOUS PROBLEMS

In this **Exercise** we consider various problems which can be solved using the techniques in this chapter. It is important that you learn to choose which is the most appropriate technique for each problem.

EXERCISE 17E

1 I am thinking of two numbers. One of them is 5 more than the other, and their sum is 53. What are the numbers?

2 One number is three times as large as another, and a third number is 13 less than the smaller one. If the sum of the three numbers is 42, find the largest number.

3 Tim bought 4 packets of nails from a hardware store. He used 10 nails to fix his gate, and put the remaining 50 nails in his toolbox. How many nails were there in each packet?

4 Colleen has three daughters. The sum of her daughters' ages is 13, and the product of their ages is 48. Find the ages of the daughters.

5 Ashley brought some biscuits for morning tea at work. Her colleagues ate $\frac{7}{9}$ of them, then her boss came by and ate two biscuits. When Ashley came to eat some, there were only four left. How many biscuits did she bring for morning tea?

6 The equal sides of an isosceles triangle are 6 cm longer than the third side. The perimeter of the triangle is 33.6 cm. Find the length of the third side.

7 A TV set costs £100 more than a DVD player. If the two of them cost a total of £654, find the cost of the TV set.

8 When Samuel was 7, Claire was 34. Claire's age is now double Samuel's age. How old will Samuel be in 10 years' time?

9 In a multiple choice test there are 20 questions. A correct answer to a question earns 2 marks, and an incorrect answer results in a deduction of 1 mark. Sarah achieved a mark of 19. How many questions did she get right?

10 If x can take any whole number value from 1 to 10, find the smallest possible value of $x^2 - 8x + 25$.

11 A Russian Blue kitten costs \$150 more than a Manx kitten. 9 Russian Blue kittens and 8 Manx kittens cost \$14 100 in total. Find the cost of:

a a Russian Blue kitten

b a Manx kitten.

12 Half an unknown number is the same as the number subtracted from forty eight. What is the number?

13 Each day, Sam the dog drinks half of the water remaining in his bowl. His owner then adds another 200 mL of water to the bowl.
There was 500 mL of water in the bowl at the end of Thursday. How much water was in the bowl at the start of Wednesday?

14 Nine more than a number is the same as a quarter of the number, subtracted from twenty four. What is the number?

15 John can walk at 5 km/h and run at 15 km/h. A and B are two bus stops on a road. Both are 2 km from John's home H. The bus takes 3 minutes to get from A to B.

a The bus leaves from A in 15 minutes. How far can John walk from home before he has to run to catch the bus at A?

b If John catches the bus at B, how much less running does he have to do?

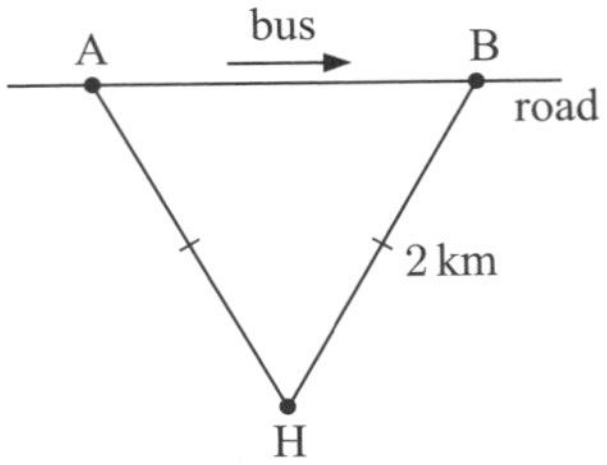

16 A pair of shoes costs €5 more than twice the cost of a tie. If Grant buys two pairs of shoes and three ties, the total cost is €255. Find the cost of:

a a tie **b** a pair of shoes.

17 Juan has two sets of metallic balls. Each red ball weighs twice as much as each green ball. He knows that two red balls plus a five gram weight balance three green balls plus an eight gram weight. Find the weight of each red ball.

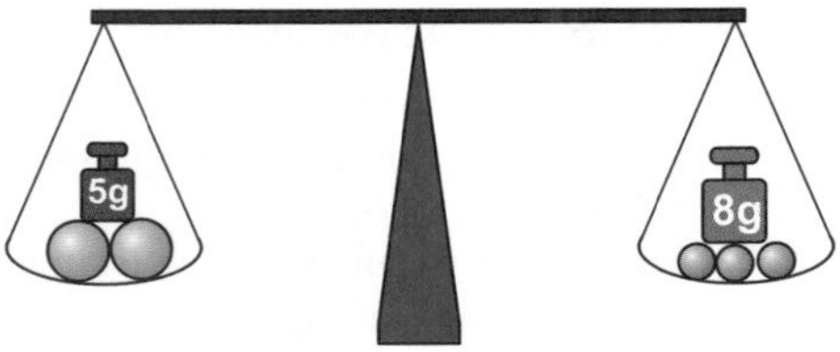

18 A 2-digit number is four times as large as the sum of its digits. Show that there are four possible numbers with this property.
Hint: The number with 'tens' digit x and 'units' digit y is $10x + y$.

19 A 6-digit number begins with a 1. However, if the 1 is put at the other end of the number instead of at the start, the resulting 6-digit number is 3 times the original number. Find the number.

20 A motorcyclist and a cyclist travel from A to B. They leave simultaneously from A at 12 noon. The motorcyclist arrives at B after $1\frac{1}{2}$ hours, and the cyclist arrives 30 minutes later. At what time was the cyclist twice as far from B as the motorcyclist was?

ACTIVITY 1 — LATERAL THINKING

For some problems in mathematics, we need to put aside standard techniques we have been taught, and instead allow ourselves to think differently.

The problems in this Activity will require you to carefully analyse the information given to you, and think logically about what you need to do.

What to do:

1

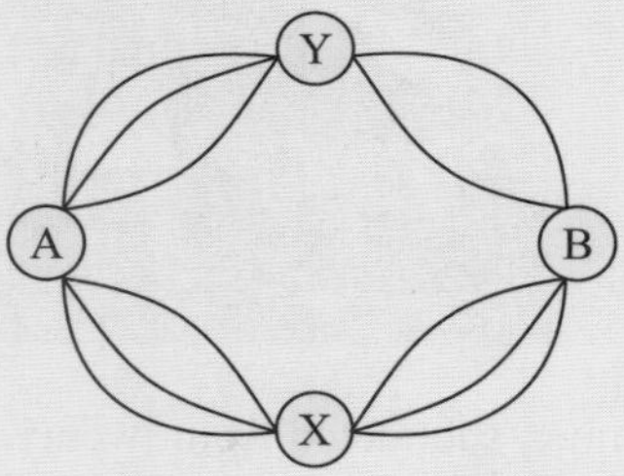

Two towns A and B are connected by the series of roadways going through two other towns X and Y.

a How many different paths exist going from A to B
  i through X
  ii through Y
  iii through X or Y?

b If X and Y were connected by a road, how many different paths would now go from A to B?

2 How many natural numbers between 0 and 100 (not including 0 and 100) have an odd number of factors?

3

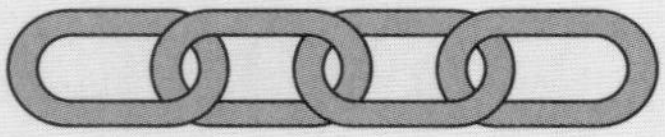

You have 6 chains, each of 4 links, as shown. You wish to make one chain of 24 links. If it costs \$2 to cut each link and \$5 to weld a link, explain how to do this in the most economical way.

4 Find the missing digits in the addition problem. The missing digits are not necessarily the same number.

$$\begin{array}{r} 3\ 8\ 7 \\ 6\ 4\ \square \\ +\ 2\ \square\ 3 \\ \hline \square\ \square\ 0\ 5 \end{array}$$

5 The diagram shows 5 squares built from 16 matches. By moving **2 matches only**, form 4 squares equal in area to one of the original squares. Each square must have a single match for each of its sides. You must use all of the matches.

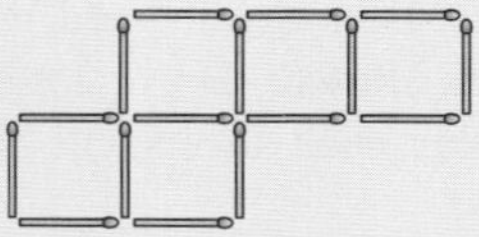

6 

Is it possible to draw 4 straight lines through all of the 9 points without taking your pen off the paper?

7 Some years ago, MENSA inserted the notice alongside in a newspaper. This is really a mathematical problem. Can you see what the problem is? What is the solution to the problem?

MENSA's contribution to Road Safety Week

```
  C R O S S
  R O A D S
-----------
D A N G E R
```

given that **CAR = 956**

8 

How many cubes are in the illustrated solid?

9 On a clear day, sound travels 335 m every second. Pam at A, shouts across the valley and notices that her echo returns in 6 seconds. How far is it across the valley?

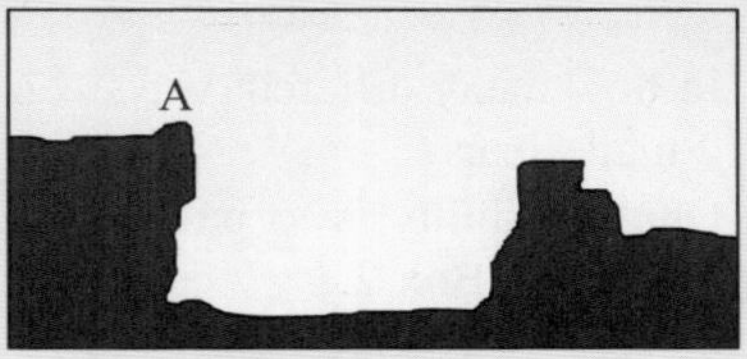

10 Two men dig a trench 30 m long in 3 days. How long would it take three men to dig a trench 15 m long working at the same rate?

11 How many triangles does this figure contain?

12 S, H, and E are different digits. What are they?

```
    H E
  × H E
  -----
  S H E
```

13 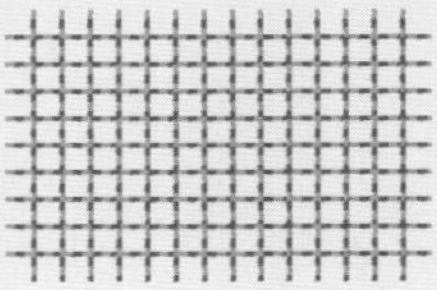

A cord fishing net is 100 m long and 4 m wide. The cord lengths are fixed 5 cm apart, so 5 cm by 5 cm holes are created. How many holes has the net?

14 9 sheep are located in a square paddock, as shown. Draw 2 squares of fencing so that each sheep will be in a pen by itself.

15 If you have a balance and single masses of 9 kg, 3 kg, and 1 kg, explain how you could measure the mass of any whole number from 1 kg to 13 kg.

16 King Arthur, Sir B, Sir C, and Sir D sit around a round table. Show that there are 6 different seating arrangements.

Hint: 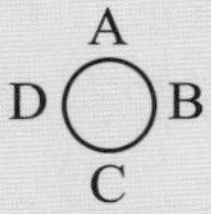

is the same as 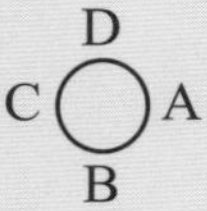

since each person has the same right-hand and left-hand neighbours.

17 In an enclosure at the zoo there are ostriches and giraffes. The total number of heads is 17, and the total number of legs is 50. How many of each animal are present?

18 In how many different ways can 3 letters be mailed into 2 mail boxes?
One possibility is to put letters A and B in Box 1 and letter C in Box 2.

19 Two wheels touch at their blue marks. The large wheel has diameter 20 cm and the smaller one 10 cm. The larger wheel moves clockwise, and no slipping between the wheels occurs.

- **a** In which direction does the smaller wheel move?
- **b** After how many revolutions of the smaller wheel will the wheels once again touch at their blue marks?

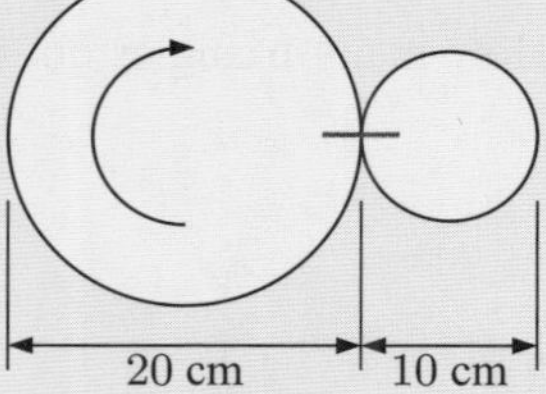

20 Using exactly four 4s and any of the operations $+$, $-$, $\times$, $\div$, find expressions for as many of the integers from 1 to 20 as you can.

$$\frac{4}{4} \div \frac{4}{4} = 1$$

$$\frac{4}{4} + \frac{4}{4} = 2$$

$$\frac{4+4+4}{4} = 3$$

21 Store A reduces its prices by 10%. One week later it increases its prices by $x\%$ so that its prices are back to what they were originally. Find x.

22 The diagram alongside shows piles of tennis balls.

- **a** How many balls are in pile 4?
- **b** How many balls are in pile 8?

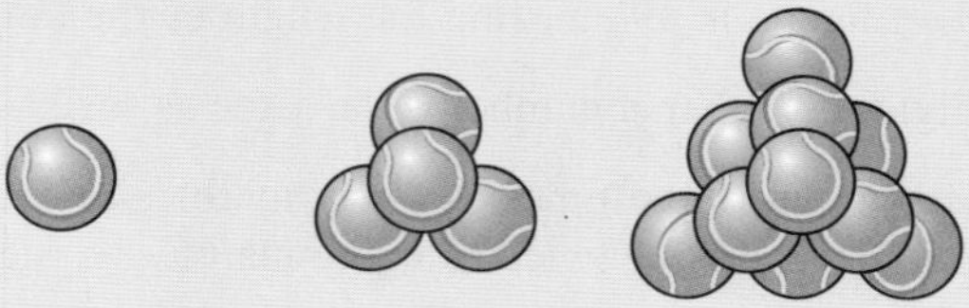

23 Cecil Pitt makes cylindrical tanks. The dimensions of his tanks are such that:

- the radius and height are a whole number of metres
- the surface area in m^2 and volume in m^3 have the same value.

Show that there are three sizes of tanks Cecil could produce at his factory.

24 Pete takes 3 days to dig a well working at a constant rate. Matt takes 5 days to dig the same sized well, in the same soil, also working at a constant rate.
If they work together to dig the well, each working at the same rate as before, how long will they take to dig the well?

25 The current flow in a river is 5 km/h. When a boat travels at maximum speed against the current, it reaches its destination in 2 hours. On the return trip it takes just $1\frac{1}{2}$ hours.

- **a** What is the boat's maximum speed?
- **b** How far does the boat travel against the current?

26

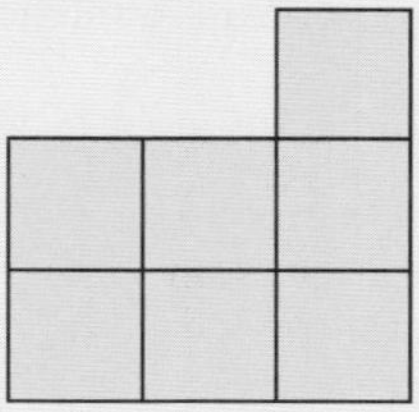

Where should point B be located along [PS] such that [AB] divides the figure into equal areas?

27 A log is sawn into 7 pieces in 7 minutes. How long would it have taken to saw the same log into 4 pieces?

28 Two real numbers differ by 3, and the sum of their squares is 8. Find the product of the numbers.

29 To pick all of the oranges in an orchard, it should take 14 people a total of 10 days. If 3 of the workers are sick and cannot work, and 2 others can only work at half the usual rate, how long will it take to pick all of the oranges?

30 Two consecutive squares differ by 71. Find the smaller of the two squares.

REVIEW SET 17A

1 Use equations to solve the following problems:

- **a** When a certain number is halved, the answer is 19. Find the number.
- **b** I think of a number, multiply it by 7, then subtract 2. The result is 26. What is the number?

2 A rectangle has length 5 cm longer than its width. If the perimeter of the rectangle is 50 cm, find its length.

3 The equal sides of an isosceles triangle are 6 cm shorter than the third side. If the perimeter of the triangle is 39 cm, find the length of the third side.

4 Eight more than a number is the same as seven added to twice the number. What is the number?

5 George has three times as many marbles as Steph. If George gives 5 of his marbles to Steph, George will have twice as many marbles as Steph. How many marbles does Steph have?

6 There is only one integer value of x such that $2x - 7$ and $14 - 3x$ are both positive. What is it?

7 There are 5 bowls of cupcakes on a table. Four children sit between the bowls as shown. Each child can reach cupcakes in the bowls either side of them. The diagram alongside indicates the number of cupcakes each child can reach. Given that there are 6 cupcakes in bowl 5, how many are there in bowl 1?

8 Consider the equation $3x + 4y = 40$ where x is a positive integer and y is positive.

a Explain why x cannot be greater than 13.

b Copy and complete:

x	1	2	3	4	5	6	7	8	9	10	11	12	13
y													

c Find the solutions to $3x + 4y = 40$ for which x and y are positive integers.

9 The base of an isosceles triangle is 10 cm longer than its height. Its area is 48 cm^2 and its perimeter is 36 cm.

a Find the height of the triangle, given that the length of its base is an integer.

b Find the lengths of the equal sides of the triangle.

10

When Leonard the lion goes to sleep at night, he sleeps the same number of hours before and after midnight. For example, if he goes to sleep at 9 pm, he wakes up at 3 am.

Leonard stays awake for 15 hours each day, then goes to sleep again.

If he wakes up at 5 am Friday morning, what time did he go to sleep Wednesday night?

REVIEW SET 17B

1 Use equations to solve the following problems:

a I think of a number, double it, then subtract 7. The result is 23. Find the number.

b When half of a number is subtracted from 20, the result is 14. Find the number.

2 At the supermarket a tin of hot chocolate costs \$1.20 more than a bag of marshmallows. If 4 tins of hot chocolate and 7 bags of marshmallows cost \$32.30, how much does a bag of marshmallows cost?

3 A necklace costs twice as much as a bracelet. I bought 4 necklaces and 3 bracelets for a total of €121. Find the cost of each item.

4 The sum of three consecutive numbers is 54. Find the middle number.

5 a and b are positive integers, and $3a + 4b = 22$. Find the greatest possible value of ab.

6 Jo spent half of the money in her wallet on a new cardigan. She then spent £4.50 on a cup of coffee. After drinking her coffee, she spent three quarters of the money remaining in her wallet on a book. If Jo is left with £8 in her wallet, how much did she have in her wallet initially?

7 Brothers Joe and Phil have a mother named Sue. A year ago, Sue was three times as old as Joe. Four years ago, Sue was four times as old as Phil. If Phil is 13 years old, how old is Joe?

8 Karen takes 4 minutes longer to make a pizza than she does to make a pasta dish. She can make 4 pasta dishes in the time it takes to make 3 pizzas. How long does Karen take to make a pasta dish?

9 Reiko and Josie are buying food for their party. They find that a doughnut costs 80 cents more than a lamington.
The girls buy 8 doughnuts and 12 lamingtons, spending a total of $25.40. Find the cost of each item.

10 Ange, Bill, Chad, Dean, and Eve are kicking a football amongst themselves.

Ange only kicks the ball to Dean.
Bill only kicks the ball to Eve.
Chad only kicks the ball to Ange.
Dean kicks the ball to either Bill or Eve.
Eve kicks the ball to either Ange or Chad.

a If Chad currently has the ball, who will have the ball in two kicks' time?

b If Bill currently has the ball, who had the ball two kicks ago?

c If Eve currently has the ball, name the people who could have had the ball three kicks ago.

ACTIVITY 2 VANISHING TRIANGLES

Draw an equilateral triangle and write a positive integer at each vertex. At the midpoint of each side, write down the positive difference between the integers at the ends of each side. Join these midpoints, and repeat the procedure on the newly formed triangle.

Continue this procedure until either the numbers created are identical in consecutive triangles, or a pattern emerges.

For example, if the numbers 6, 12, and 14 are chosen, after three steps the figure will be as shown alongside.

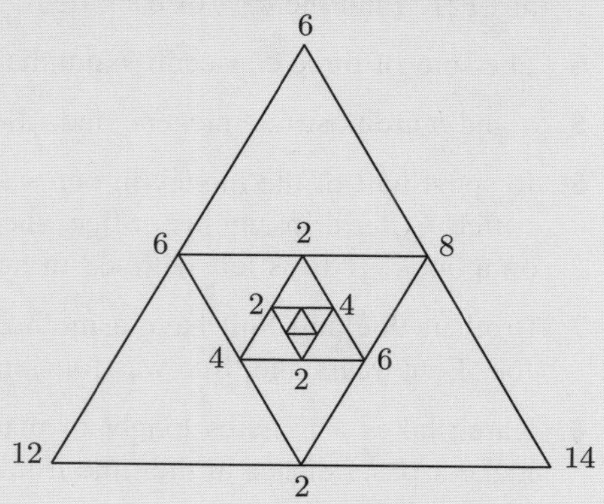

What to do:

1. Copy and complete the given example, making sure your original triangle is large enough.
2. Try triangles with the following combinations of integers:
   - **a** three even integers
   - **b** two even integers
   - **c** one even integer
   - **d** no even integers.

   Can you draw any general conclusions?

3. Now try the same procedure starting with a square instead of an equilateral triangle. For example, starting with 1, 17, 6, and 25, a square produces the figure alongside.
   Can you suggest a general result for the case of a square?

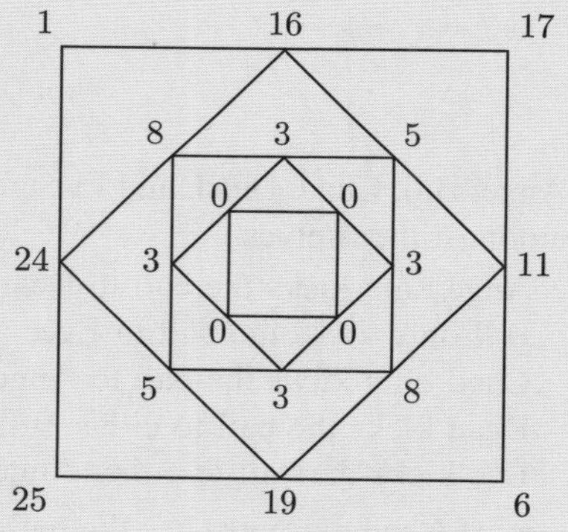

Chapter 18

Similarity and congruence

Contents:

OPENING PROBLEM

Jane cut two triangular slices of cheesecake, and gave one to her brother Nathan.

"That's not fair", Nathan said, "your slice is bigger than mine".

Jane used a ruler to measure the sides of each slice. "See, my slice has sides 5 cm, 6 cm, and 7 cm, and so does yours. That means the slices are the same size."

"Not necessarily", said Nathan, "the slices might have the same sides, but the angles might be different".

Things to think about:

a Who do you think is correct?

b What mathematical argument can you use to justify your answer?

In this chapter we will look at how the **enlargement** and **reduction** transformations are used to create **similar figures**, which are figures with the same shape but not necessarily the same size. We will also study **congruent figures**, which are identical in both shape and size.

A ENLARGEMENTS AND REDUCTIONS

The rectangles below are clearly not the same *size*, but they do have the same *shape*. Their side lengths are in the same proportions.

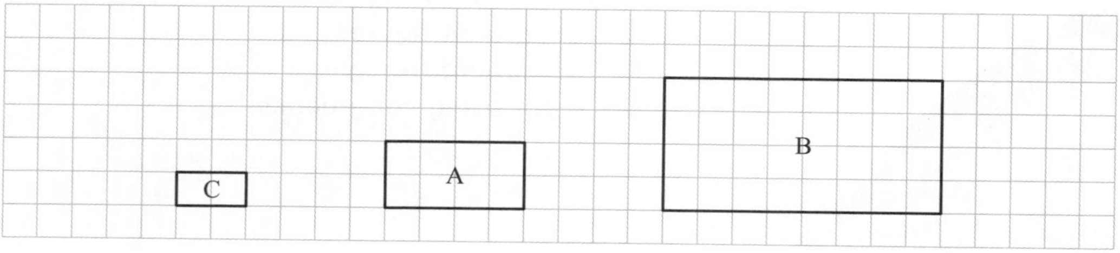

B is an **enlargement** of A, and C is a **reduction** of A.

When A is enlarged to B, the lengths are *doubled*.
We say that the scale factor $k = 2$.

When A is reduced to C, the lengths are *halved*.

We say that the scale factor $k = \frac{1}{2}$.

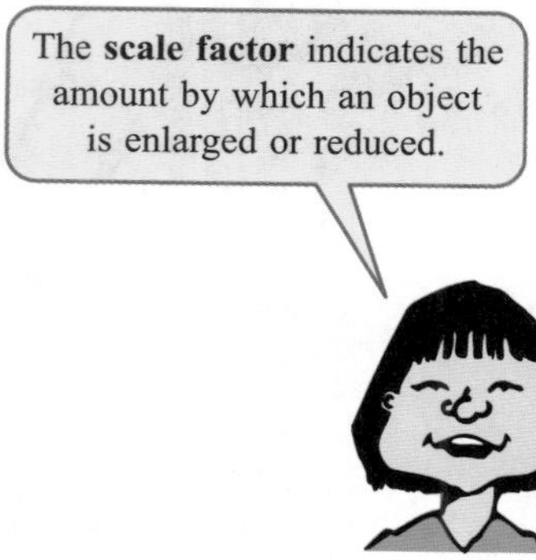

The **scale factor** indicates the amount by which an object is enlarged or reduced.

If the scale factor is greater than 1, an **enlargement** occurs.

If the scale factor is less than 1, a **reduction** occurs.

Example 1 Self Tutor

Enlarge or reduce the given figure using a scale factor of:

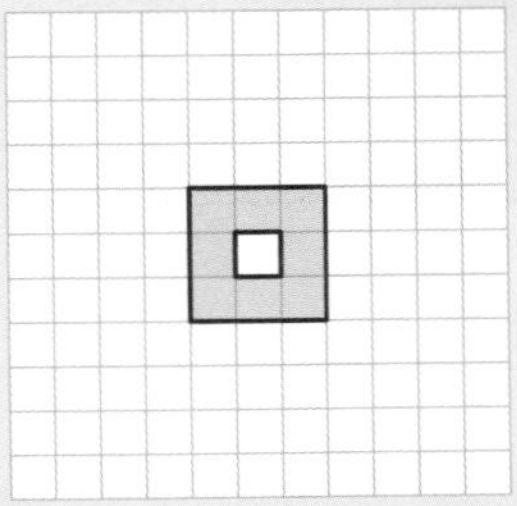

a 3 **b** $\frac{1}{2}$.

a For a scale factor of 3, the side lengths are *tripled*.

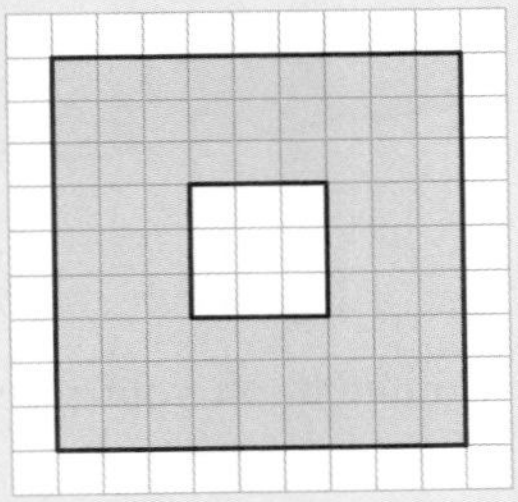

b For a scale factor of $\frac{1}{2}$, the side lengths are *halved*.

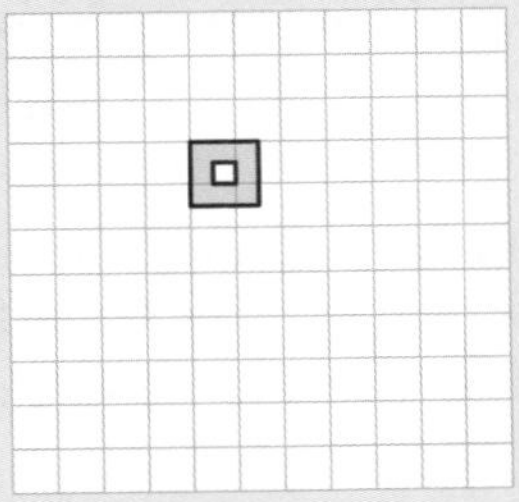

If A is enlarged or reduced to A′, we say that A is the **object** and A′ is the **image**. The figures do not need to have the same orientation.

EXERCISE 18A

1 For each of the following:

i state whether the transformation from A to B is an enlargement or a reduction

ii find the scale factor for the enlargement or reduction.

a

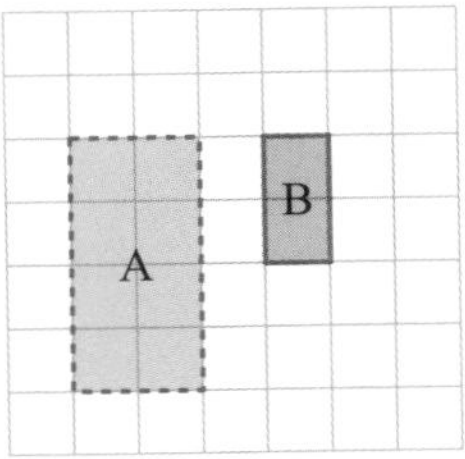

b

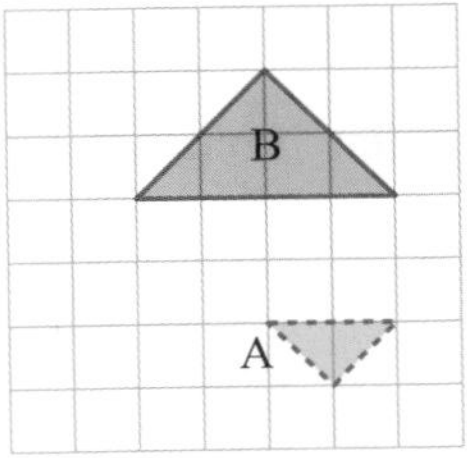

c

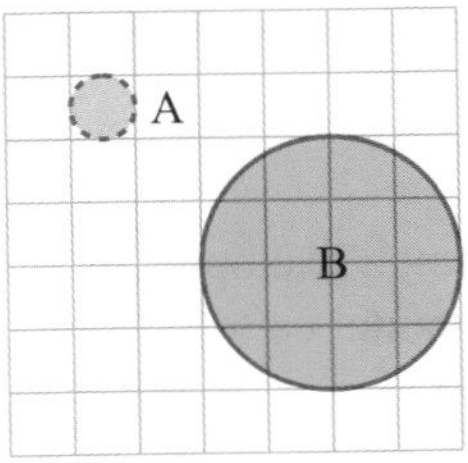

d

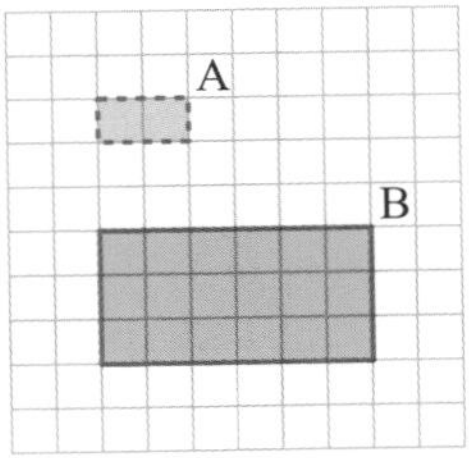

e

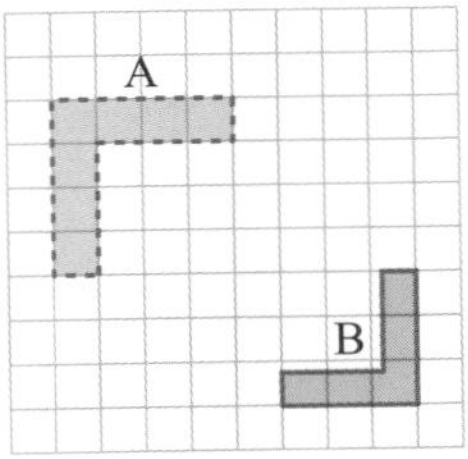

f

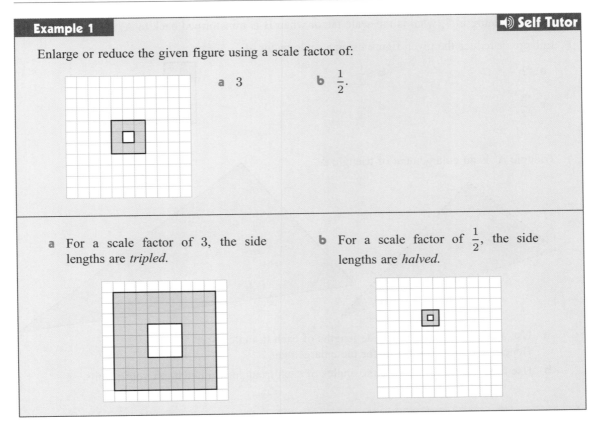

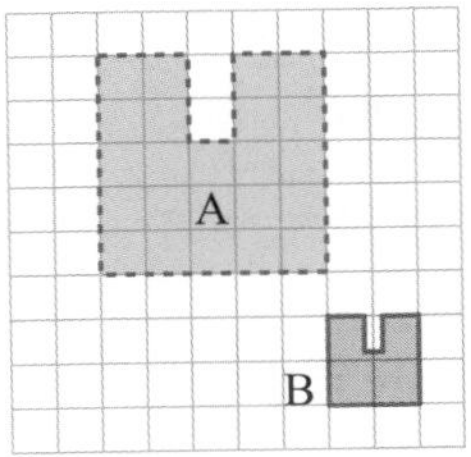

2 For each figure in **1**, what is the scale factor when B is transformed back to A?

3 Enlarge or reduce the given figure using a scale factor of:

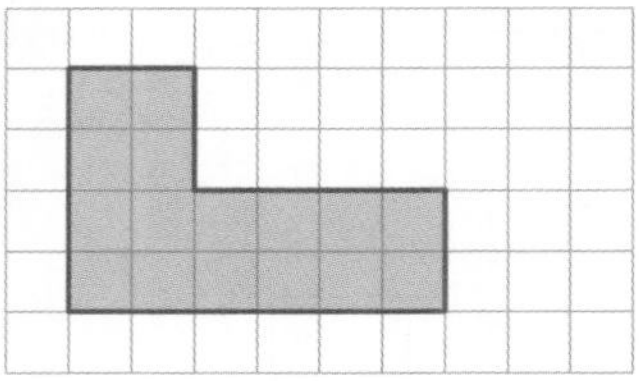

a 2

b $\frac{1}{2}$

c $\frac{3}{2}$

d $\frac{1}{4}$

4 Triangle A′ is an enlargement of triangle A.

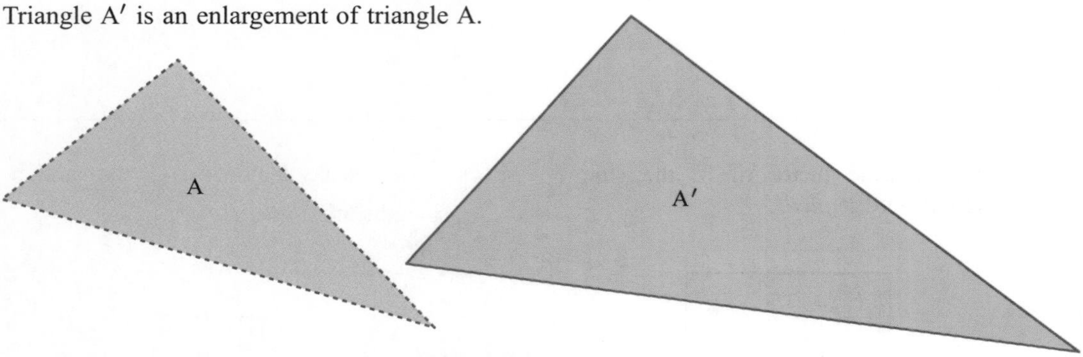

a Use a ruler to measure the side lengths of each triangle. Hence, find the scale factor for the enlargement.

b Use a protractor to measure the angles of each triangle. Comment on your results.

DISCUSSION

When a figure is enlarged or reduced, do the sizes of the angles within the figure change?

B SIMILAR FIGURES

The word *similar* suggests a comparison between objects which have some, but not all, properties in common. In mathematics, similar figures have the same **shape**, but not necessarily the same **size**.

Two figures are **similar** if one is an enlargement of the other.

Common examples of similar figures include television images, photo enlargements, house plans, maps, and model cars.

A′B′C′D′ is an enlargement of ABCD with scale factor 3. The two figures are therefore similar.

Notice that

$$\frac{A'B'}{AB} = \frac{B'C'}{BC} = \frac{C'D'}{CD} = \frac{D'A'}{DA} = 3,$$

so the corresponding side lengths are in the **same ratio**.

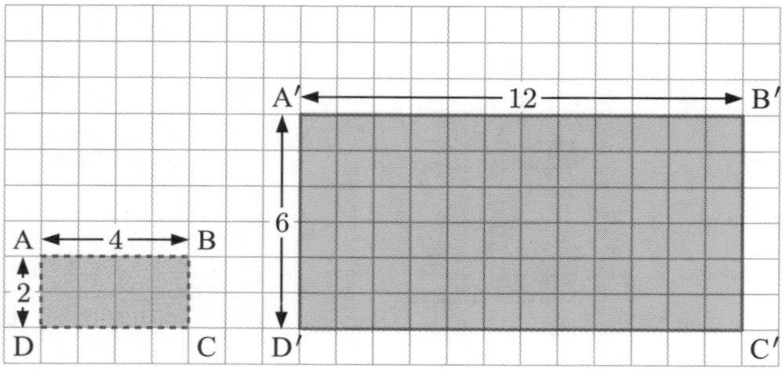

When a figure is enlarged or reduced, the sizes of its angles do not change. The figures are therefore **equiangular**.

> Two figures are **similar** if:
> - the figures are **equiangular** *and*
> - the corresponding side lengths are in the **same ratio**.

Example 2 — Self Tutor

Determine whether the following pairs of figures are similar:

a

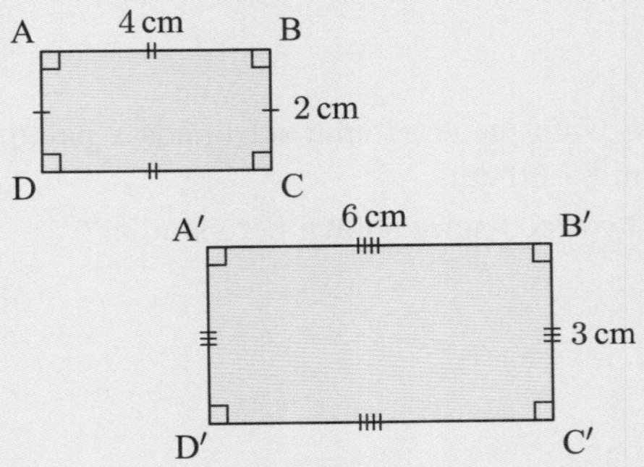

b

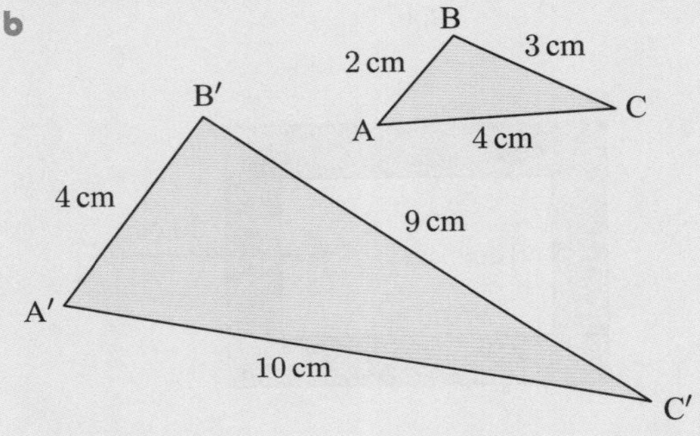

a $\frac{A'B'}{AB} = \frac{6}{4} = \frac{3}{2}$ and $\frac{B'C'}{BC} = \frac{3}{2}$

$\therefore$ the corresponding side lengths are in the same ratio.

The figures are also equiangular, so the figures are similar.

b $\frac{A'B'}{AB} = \frac{4}{2} = 2$ and $\frac{B'C'}{BC} = \frac{9}{3} = 3$

$\therefore$ the corresponding side lengths are *not* in the same ratio.

$\therefore$ the figures are not similar.

DISCUSSION

Are these figures similar?

Justify your answer using the definition of similar figures.

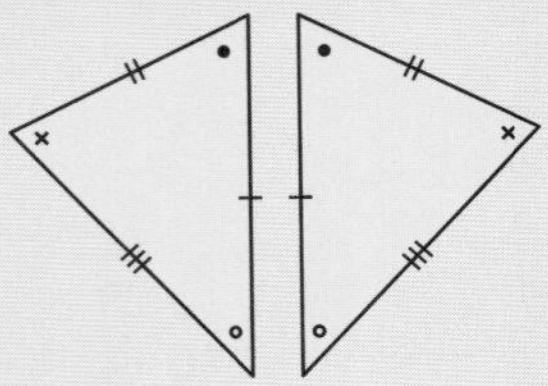

EXERCISE 18B

1 Determine whether the following pairs of figures are similar:

a

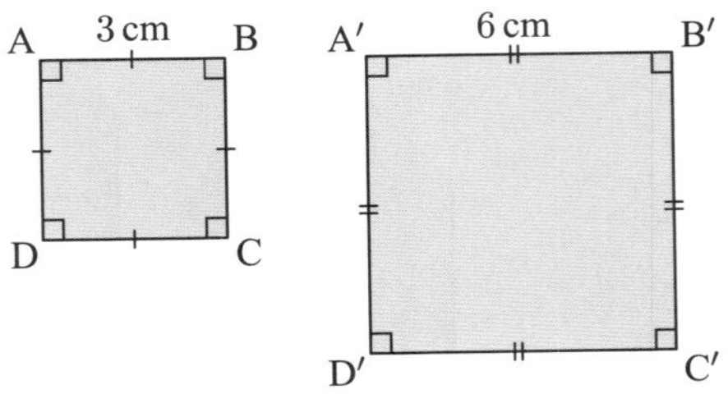

b

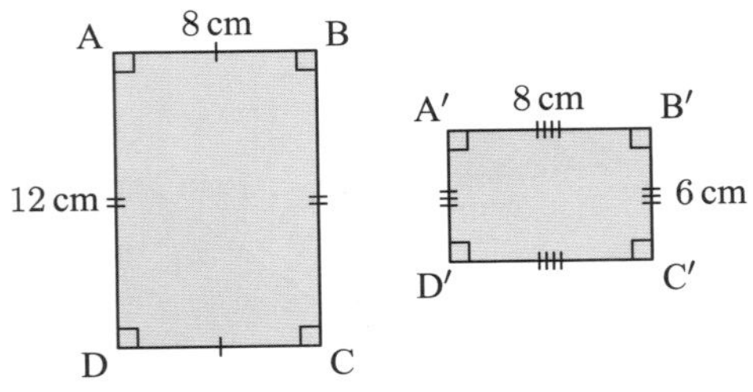

c

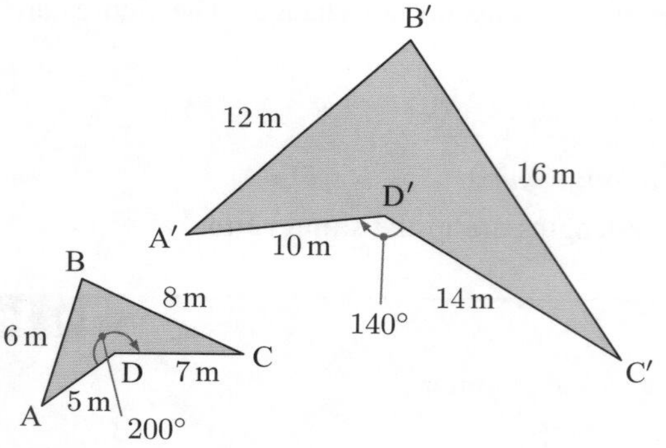

d

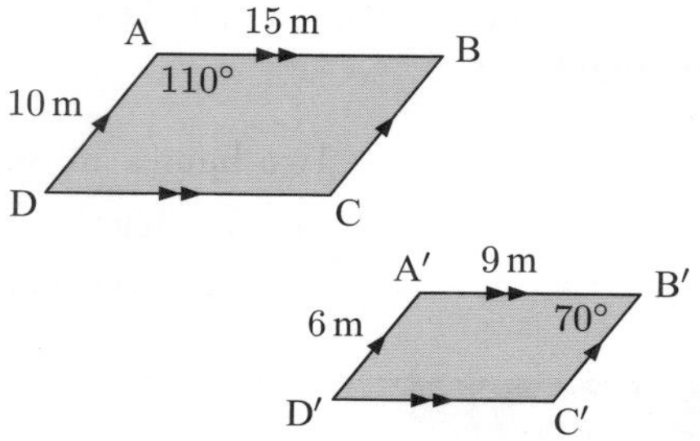

2

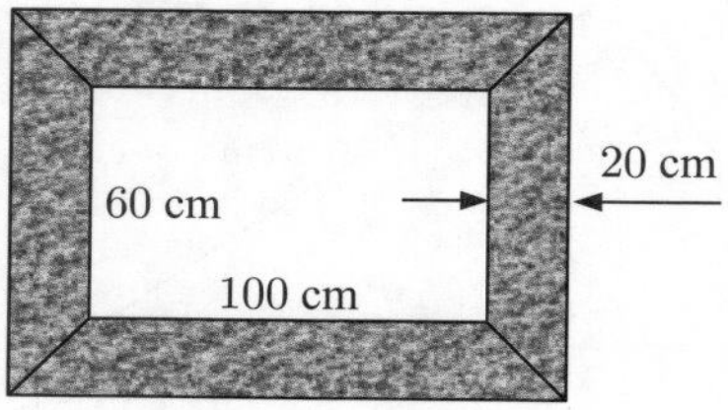

A 20 cm wide picture frame surrounds a painting which is 100 cm by 60 cm.
Are the two rectangles shown here similar?

3 Comment on the truth of the following statements. For any statement which is false, you should justify your answer with an illustration.

a All circles are similar.
b All parallelograms are similar.
c All squares are similar.
d All rectangles are similar.

Example 3 **Self Tutor**

These figures are similar.
Find x, rounded to 2 decimal places.

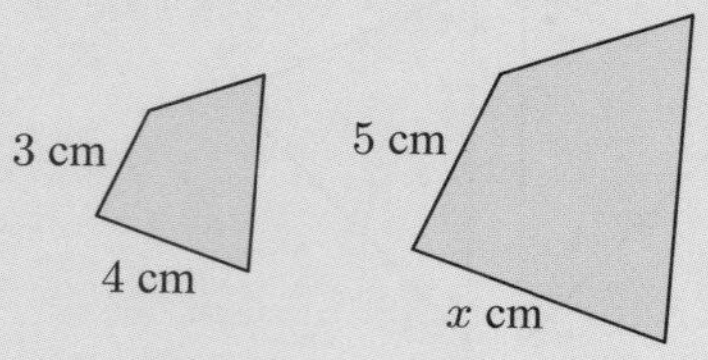

Since the figures are similar, their corresponding sides are in the same ratio.

$$\therefore \quad \frac{x}{4} = \frac{5}{3}$$

$$\therefore \quad x = \frac{5}{3} \times 4$$

$$\therefore \quad x = \frac{20}{3}$$

$$\therefore \quad x \approx 6.67$$

4 These figures are similar. Find x, rounded to 2 decimal places:

a

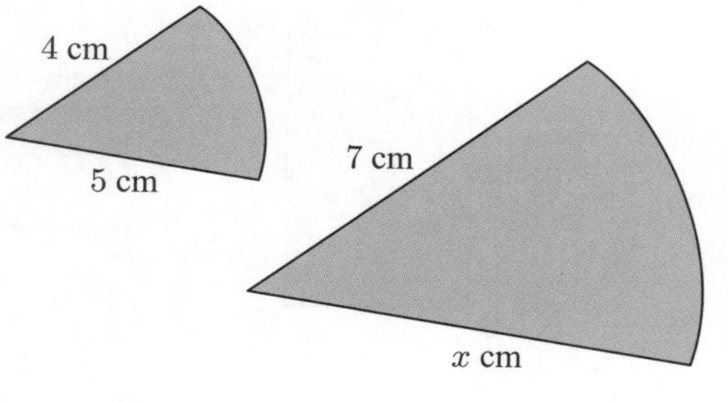

b

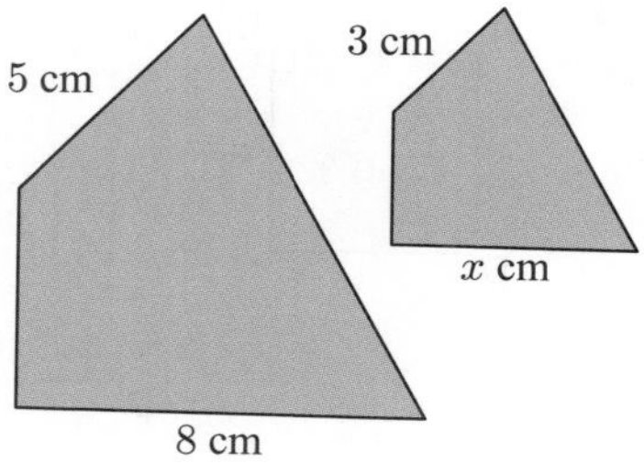

c

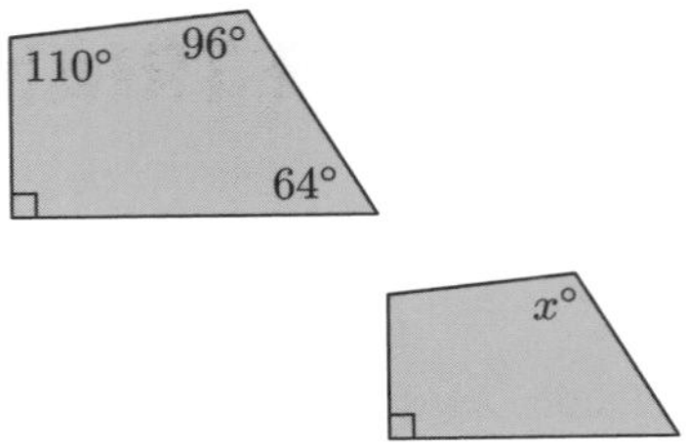

d

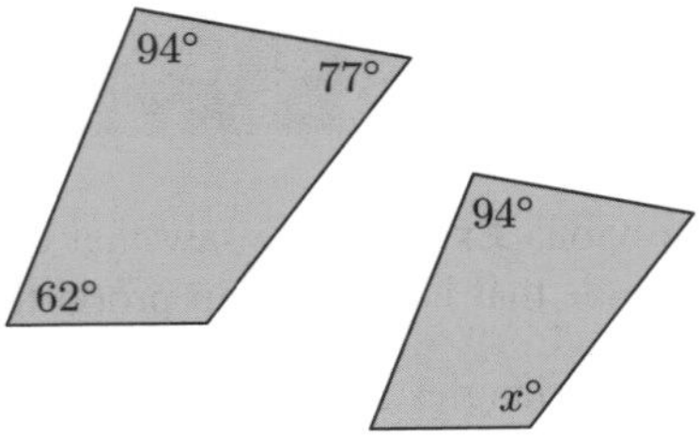

5 Narelle is drawing a scale diagram of her bedroom, which is a rectangle 4.2 m long by 3.6 m wide. On her diagram she draws her room 7 cm long.

- **a** How wide will her bedroom be on her diagram?
- **b** What is the scale factor for the diagram?

6 Find x given that triangle ABC is similar to triangle A′B′C′:

a

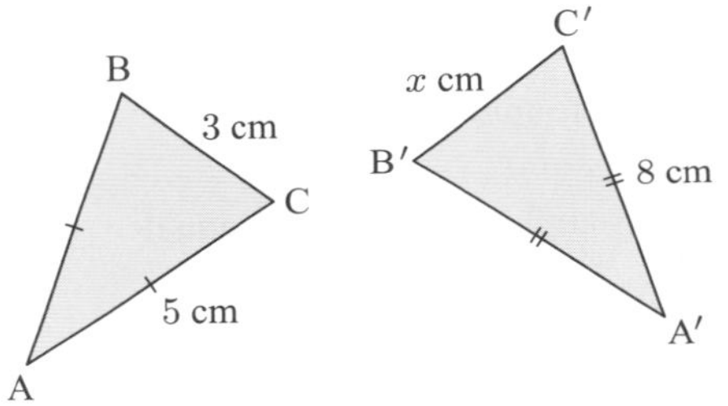

b

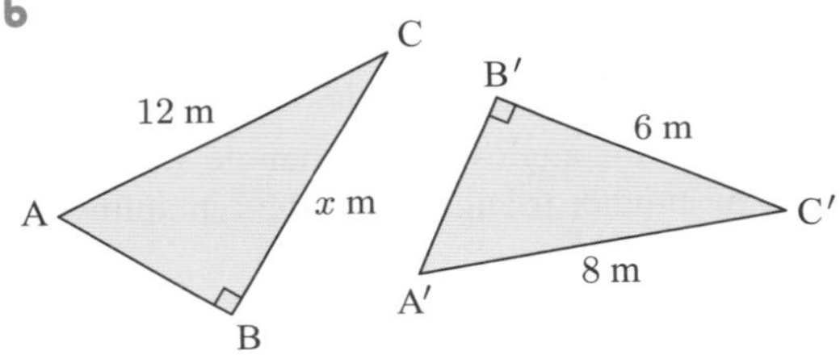

c

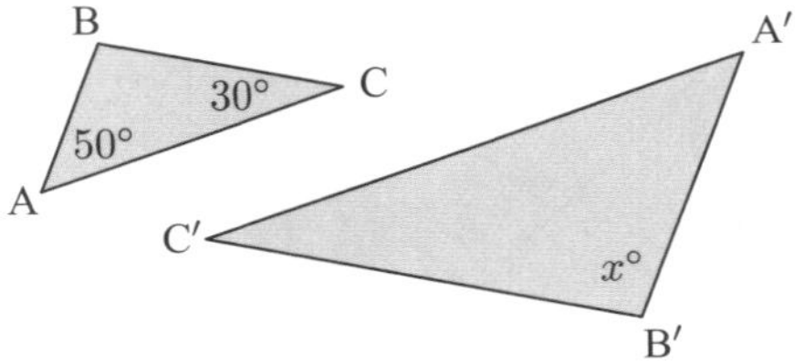

d

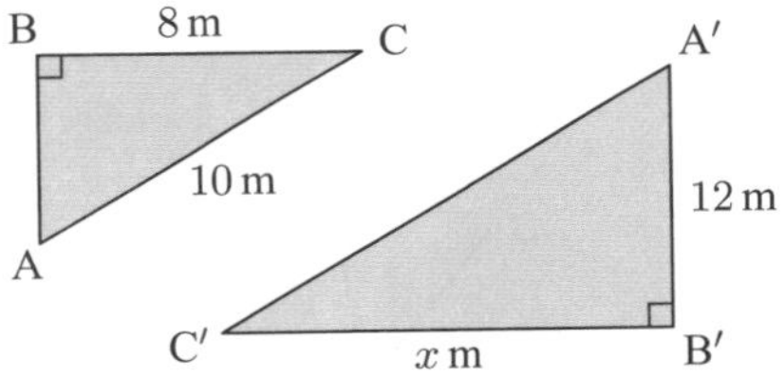

7 Sketch two quadrilaterals that:

- **a** are equiangular, but not similar
- **b** have sides in proportion, but are not similar.

8 Can you draw two triangles which are equiangular but not similar?

9

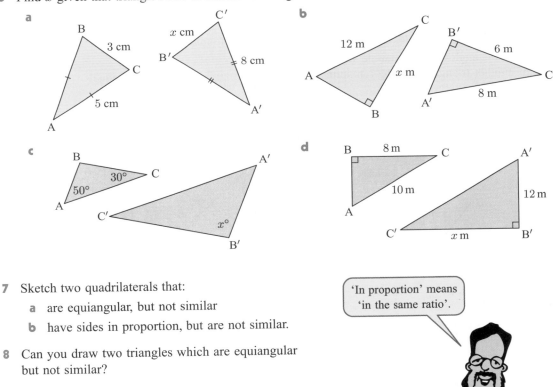

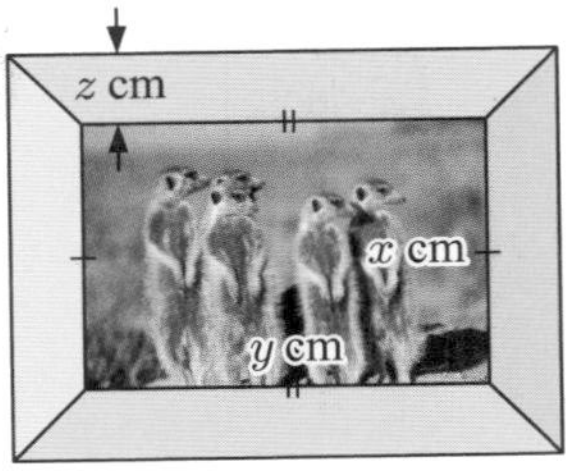

A picture x cm $\times$ y cm is surrounded by a frame z cm wide, as illustrated.
Prove that the rectangles in the figure are similar only if the picture is a square.

C SIMILAR TRIANGLES

In the previous **Exercise** we saw that quadrilaterals that are equiangular are not necessarily similar, and quadrilaterals that have sides in proportion are not necessarily similar.

However, if triangles are equiangular, then their corresponding sides *must* be in the same ratio, and vice versa. So, to show that two triangles are similar, we only need to show that **one** of these properties is true.

TESTS FOR TRIANGLE SIMILARITY

Two triangles are similar if either:
- they are equiangular *or* • their side lengths are in the same ratio.

Notice that:
- either of these properties is sufficient to prove that two triangles are similar
- since the angles of any triangle add up to 180°, if two angles of one triangle are equal to two angles of another triangle, then the remaining angles of the triangles must also be equal.

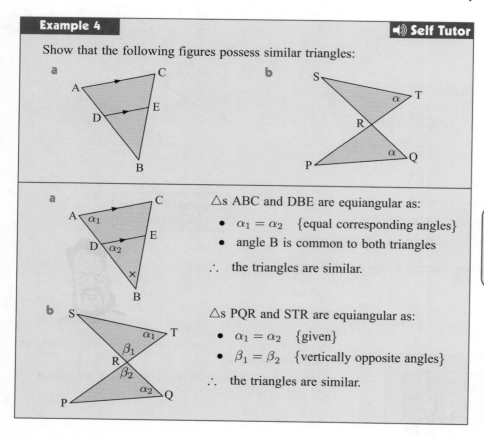

Example 4 Self Tutor

Show that the following figures possess similar triangles:

a

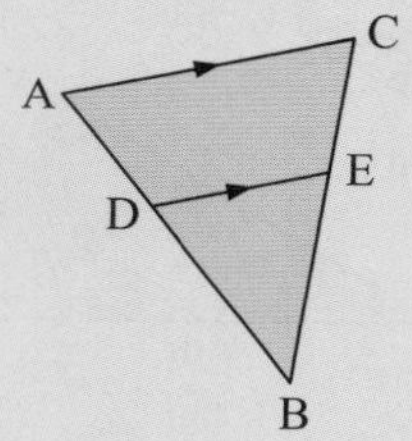

b

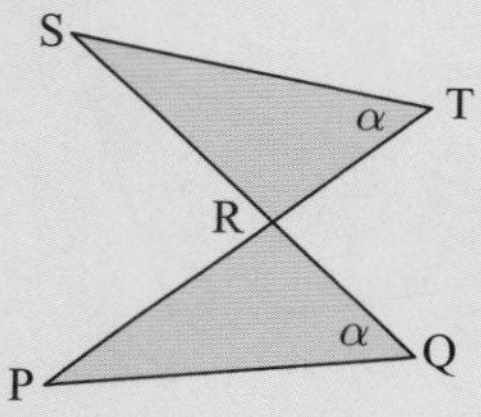

a

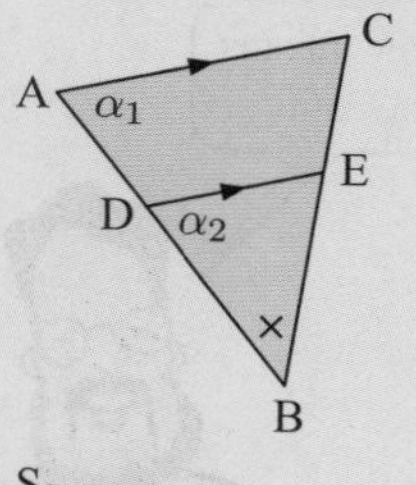

Δs ABC and DBE are equiangular as:
- $\alpha_1 = \alpha_2$ {equal corresponding angles}
- angle B is common to both triangles

$\therefore$ the triangles are similar.

b

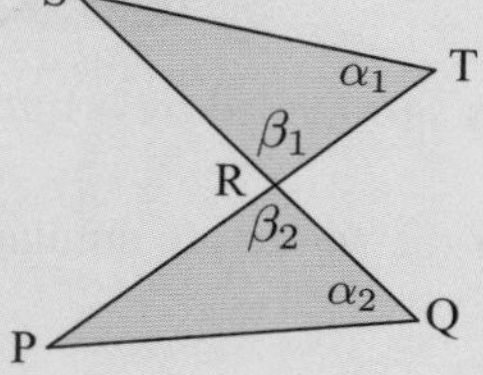

Δs PQR and STR are equiangular as:
- $\alpha_1 = \alpha_2$ {given}
- $\beta_1 = \beta_2$ {vertically opposite angles}

$\therefore$ the triangles are similar.

If two triangles are similar, we list corresponding vertices in the same order.

EXERCISE 18C.1

1 Show that the following figures possess similar triangles:

a

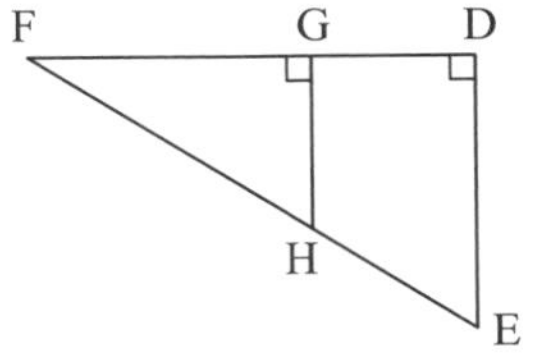

b

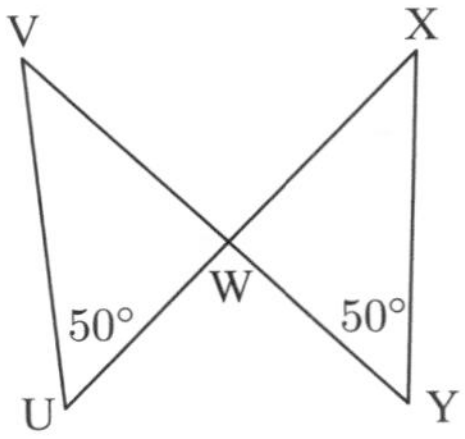

c

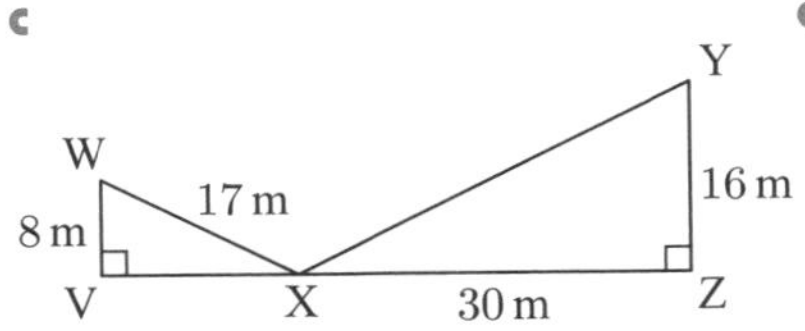

d

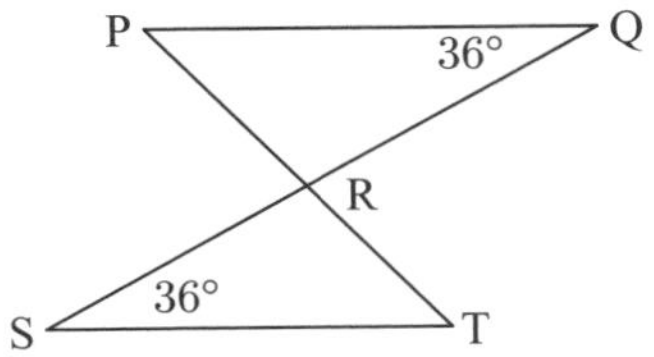

e

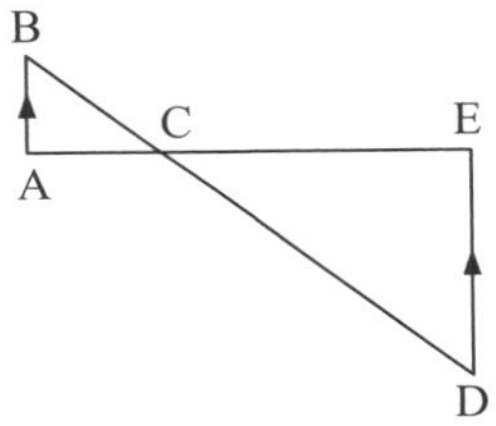

f

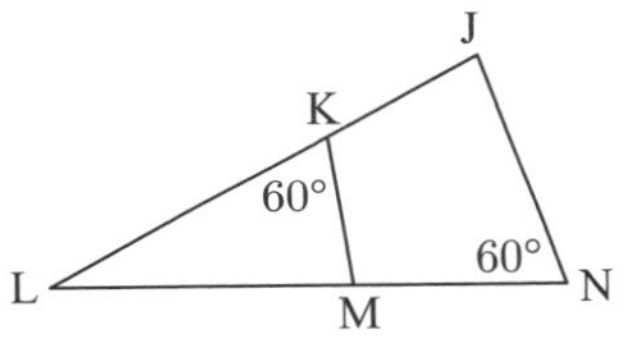

If two angles of one triangle are equal in size to two angles of another triangle, then the remaining angles of the triangles must also be equal.

2 Show that the three triangles in the given figure are all similar to each other.

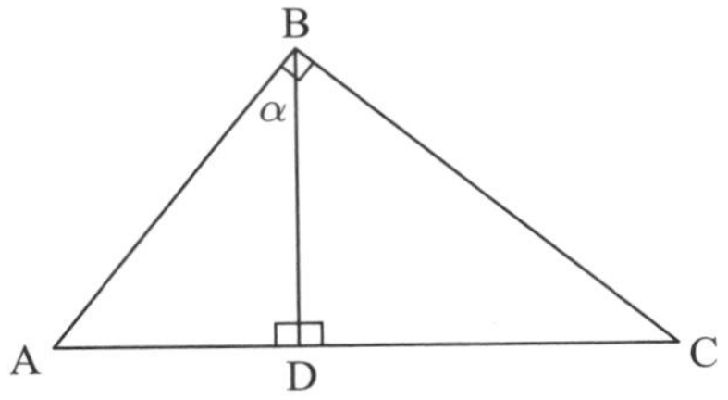

FINDING SIDE LENGTHS

Once we have established that two triangles are similar, we may use the fact that corresponding sides are in the same ratio to find unknown lengths.

Example 5 **Self Tutor**

Establish that a pair of triangles is similar, and find x:

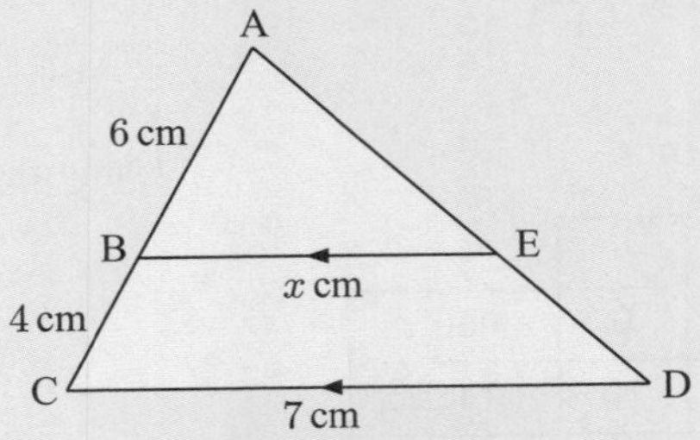

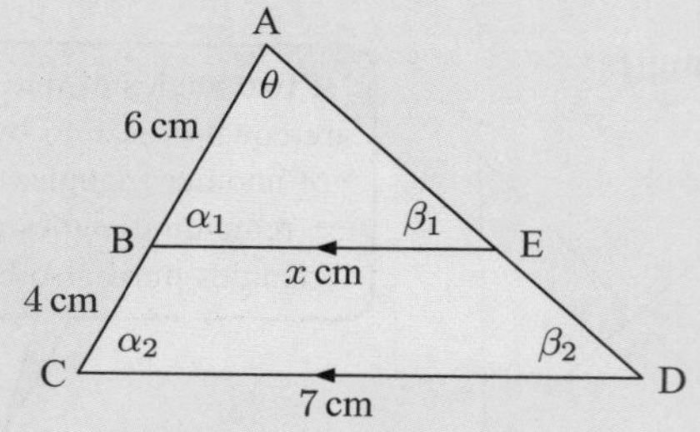

$\triangle$s ABE and ACD are equiangular as:

- $\alpha_1 = \alpha_2$ {corresponding angles}
- $\beta_1 = \beta_2$ {corresponding angles}

$\therefore$ the triangles are similar.

$\therefore \dfrac{BE}{CD} = \dfrac{AB}{AC}$ {same ratio}

$\therefore \dfrac{x}{7} = \dfrac{6}{6+4}$

$\therefore x = \dfrac{6}{10} \times 7 = 4.2$

When solving similar triangle problems, it may be useful to use a table. Consider the following method, written in the context of the example above:

Step 1: Label equal angles.
Step 2: Show that the triangles are equiangular, and hence similar.
Step 3: Put the information in a table, showing the equal angles and the side lengths opposite these angles.
Step 4: Use the columns to write down the equation for the ratio of the corresponding sides.
Step 5: Solve the equation.

α	β	θ	
-	6	x	small $\triangle$
-	10	7	large $\triangle$

from which $\dfrac{6}{10} = \dfrac{x}{7}$

$\therefore x = 4.2$

Example 6 **Self Tutor**

Establish that a pair of triangles is similar, and hence find x.

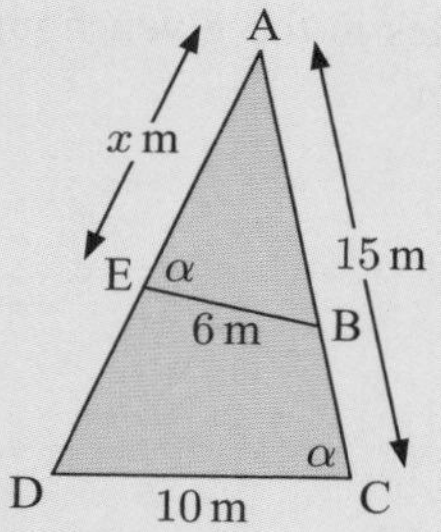

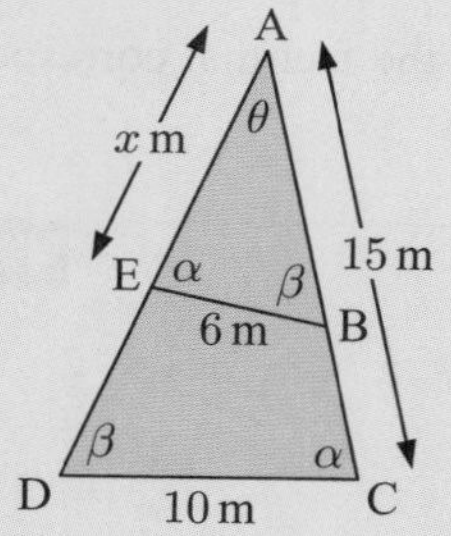

α	β	θ	
-	x	6	small $\triangle$
-	15	10	large $\triangle$

$\triangle$s ABE and ADC are equiangular since:

- $A\widehat{E}B = A\widehat{C}D$ {given}
- $\widehat{A}$ is common

$\therefore$ the triangles are similar.

$\therefore A\widehat{B}E = A\widehat{D}C$, and we call this angle β.

Using the table, $\dfrac{x}{15} = \dfrac{6}{10}$ {same ratio}

$\therefore x = 15 \times \dfrac{6}{10}$

$\therefore x = 9$

EXERCISE 18C.2

1 In each of the following figures, establish that a pair of triangles is similar. Hence find x.

a
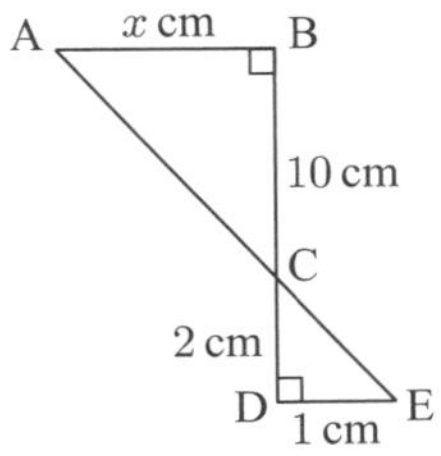

b
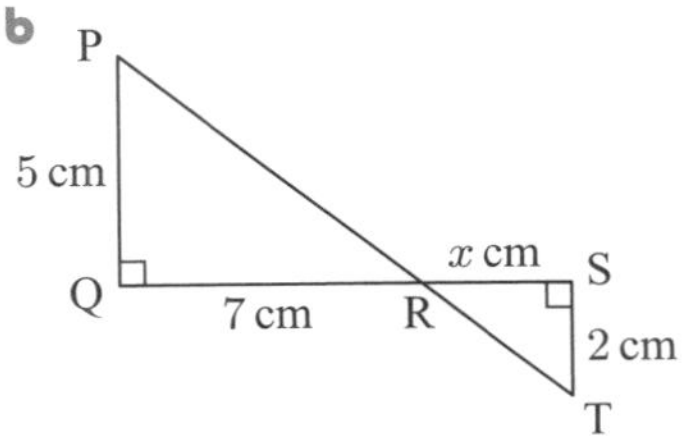

c
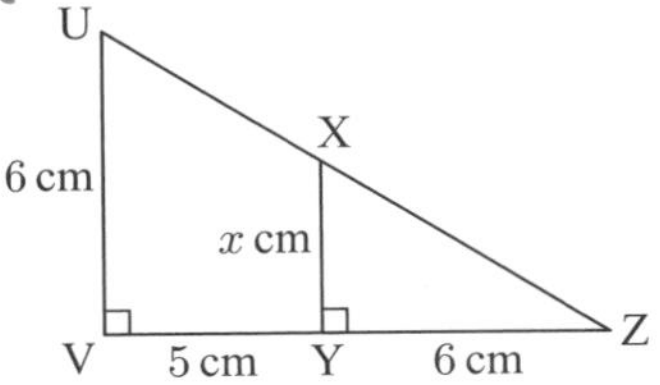

d
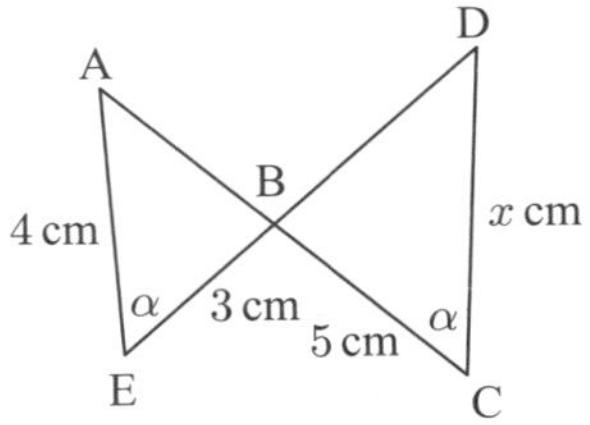

e
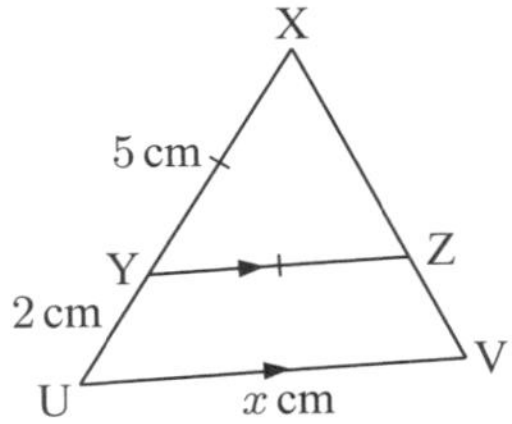

f
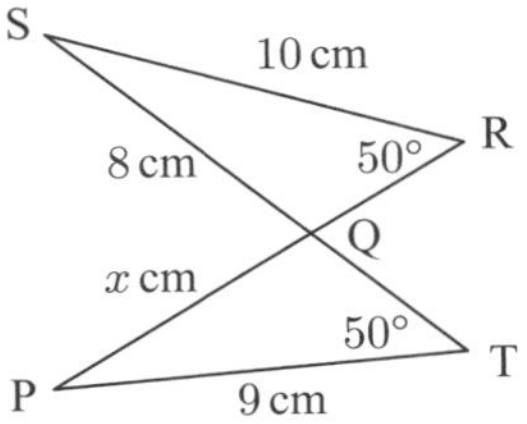

2 Given the figure alongside, find the length of [BF].

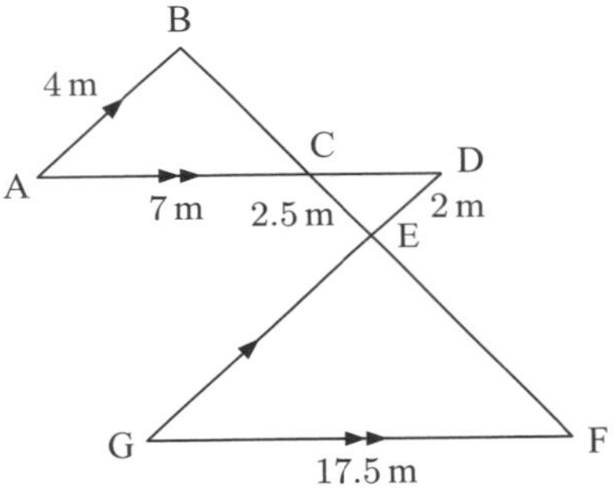

D PROBLEM SOLVING

The properties of similar triangles have been known since ancient times. However, even with the technologically advanced measuring instruments available today, similar triangles are still important for finding heights and distances which would otherwise be difficult to measure.

Step 1: Read the question carefully. Draw a sketch showing all of the given information.

Step 2: Introduce a variable such as x, for the unknown quantity to be found.

Step 3: Establish that a pair of triangles are similar, and hence set up an equation involving the variable.

Step 4: Solve the equation.

Step 5: Answer the question in a sentence.

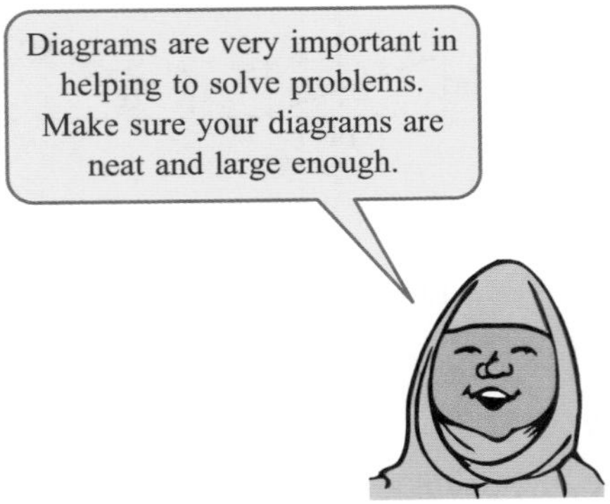

Diagrams are very important in helping to solve problems. Make sure your diagrams are neat and large enough.

Example 7

Self Tutor

When a 30 cm stick is stood vertically on the ground, it casts a 24 cm shadow.
At the same time a man casts a shadow of length 152 cm. How tall is the man?

The sun shines at the same angle on both the stick and the man.
We suppose this is angle $\alpha°$ to the horizontal.
Let the man be h cm tall.

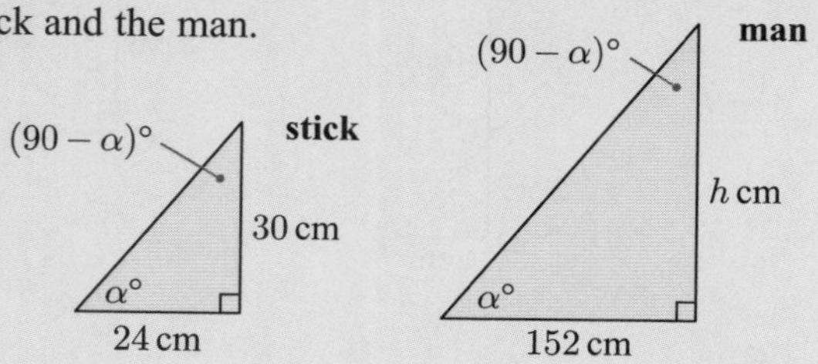

The triangles are equiangular and therefore similar.

$\therefore \quad \frac{h}{30} = \frac{152}{24}$ {same ratio}

$\therefore \quad h = \frac{152}{24} \times 30$

$\therefore \quad h = 190$

The man is 190 cm tall.

$\alpha°$	$(90-\alpha)°$	$90°$	
30 cm	24 cm	-	small △
h cm	152 cm	-	large △

Example 8

Self Tutor

Hester places a small mirror on the flat, horizontal ground 15 m from a tree. She stands where she can just see the top of the tree in the mirror. Hester is now 4 m from the mirror, and her eyes are 160 cm off the ground. How tall is the tree?

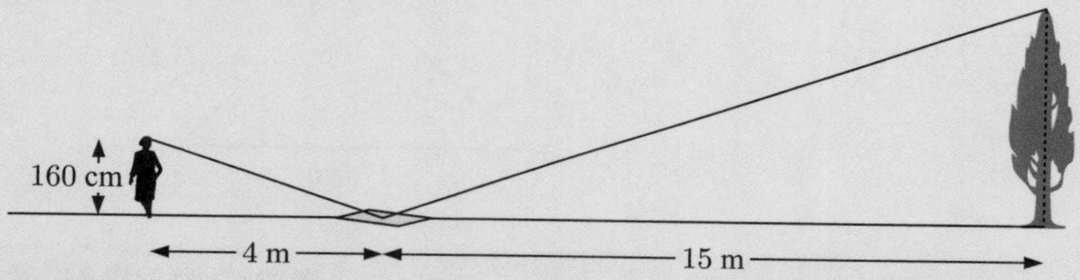

Suppose the angle from the mirror to the top of the tree is α from the horizontal.
The reflection of the tree comes off the mirror at the same angle α.

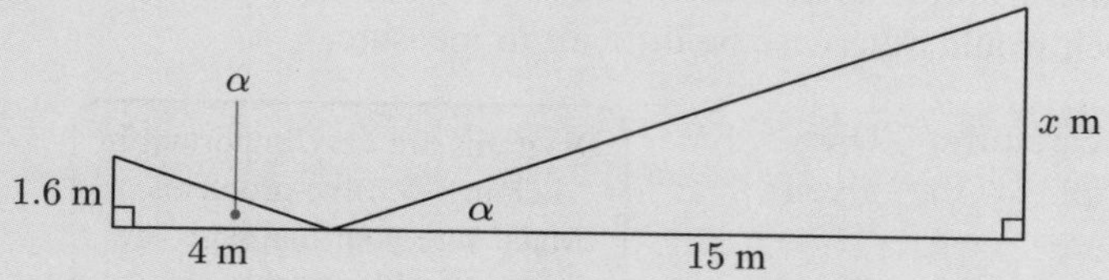

The two triangles are equiangular and so they are similar.

$\therefore \quad \frac{x}{1.6} = \frac{15}{4}$ {same ratio}

$\therefore \quad x = \frac{15}{4} \times 1.6$

$\therefore \quad x = 6$

So, the tree is 6 m high.

Always check your distances have the same units.

EXERCISE 18D

1 Find the height of the pine tree:

a

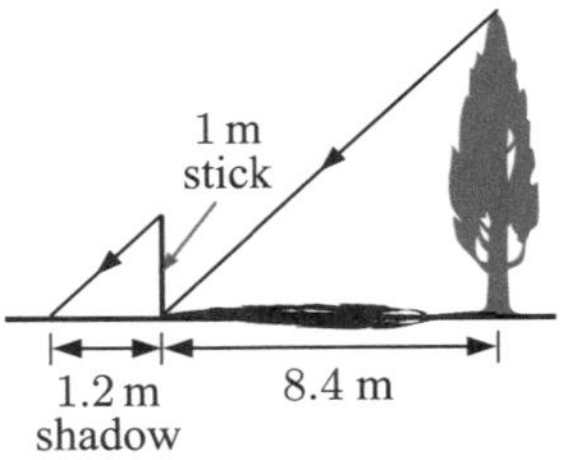

b

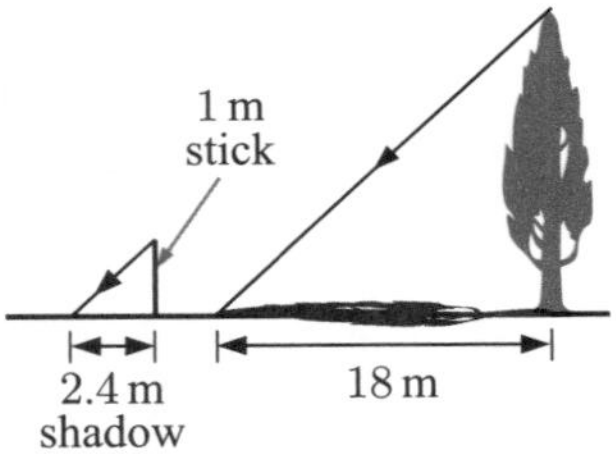

2 A ramp is built to enable wheelchair access to a building that is 24 cm above ground level. The ramp has a constant slope of 2 in 15, which means that for every 15 cm horizontally it rises 2 cm. Calculate the length of the base of the ramp.

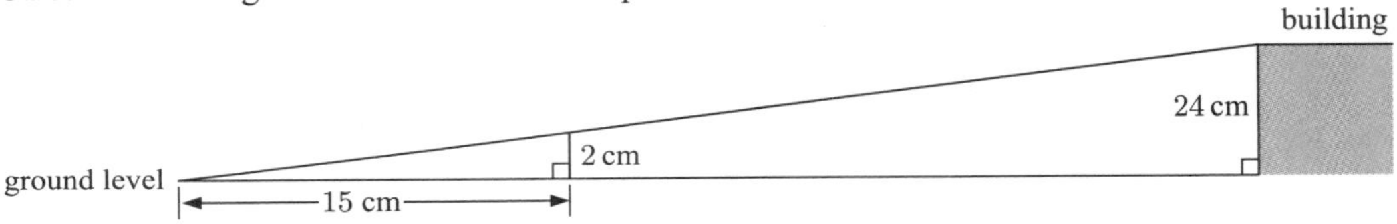

3 A piece of timber rests against both the top of a fence and the wall behind it, as shown.

- **a** Find how far up the wall the timber reaches.
- **b** Find the length of the timber.

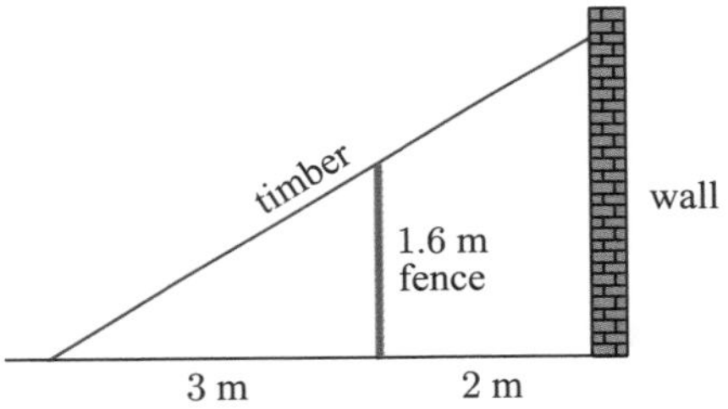

4

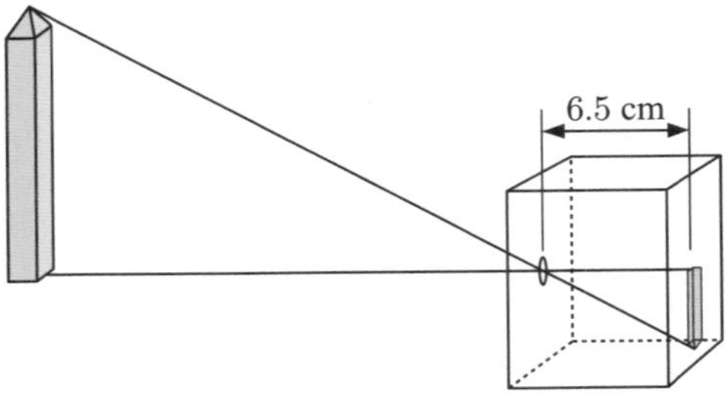

A pinhole camera displays an image on a screen as shown alongside. The monument shown is 21 m tall, and its image is 3.5 cm high. The distance from the pinhole to the image is 6.5 cm.
How far is the pinhole from the monument?

5 Ryan is standing on the edge of the shadow cast by a 5 m tall building. Ryan is 4 m from the building, and is 1.8 m tall. How far must Ryan walk towards the building to be completely shaded from the sun?

6

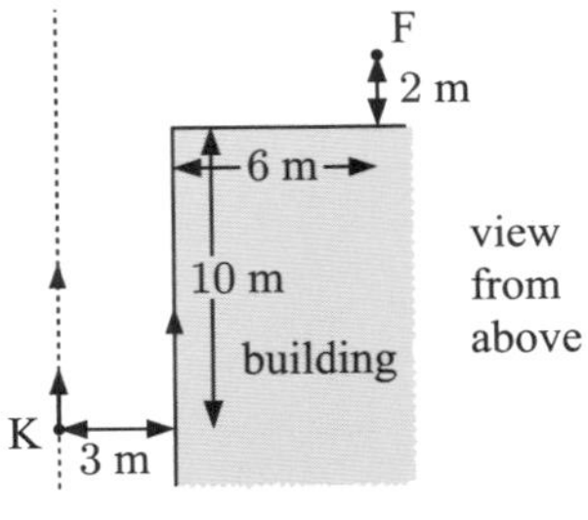

Kalev is currently at K. He is walking at 1 m/s, parallel to the side of a building. A flagpole is located at F. How long will it be before Kalev will be able to see the flagpole?

7 A, B, C, and D are pegs on the bank of a canal which has parallel straight sides. C and D are directly opposite each other. AB = 30 m and BC = 140 m.
When I walk from A directly away from the bank, I reach a point E, 25 m from A, where E, B, and D line up.
How wide is the canal?

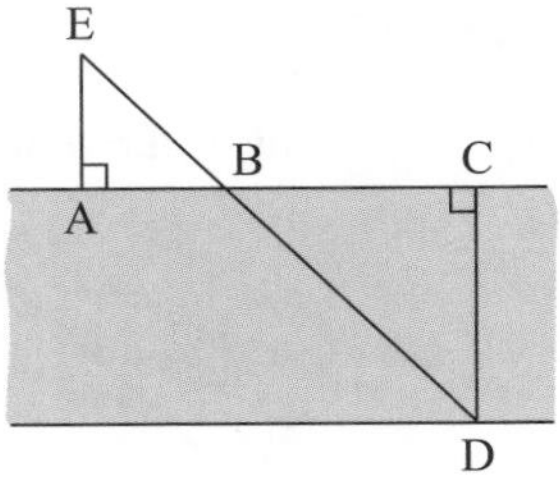

8 Two spheres of diameter 6 cm and 4 cm touch each other at A as they rest on a horizontal table. How high is A above the table?

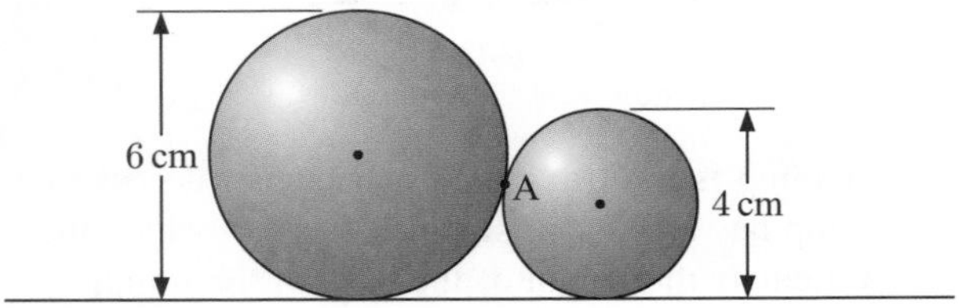

9 A cone of base radius 5 cm and height 12 cm is placed over a solid rubber ball. The fit is 'perfect', so the cone touches the floor and the ball touches the cone.
Find the radius of the ball.
Hint: Show that triangles ABY and AXC are similar.

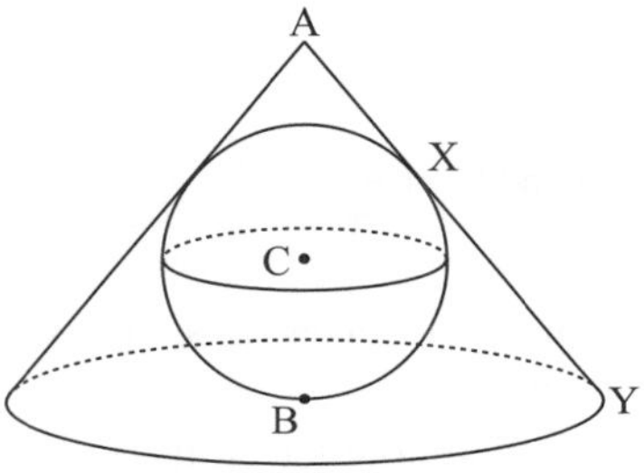

ACTIVITY 1 — PAPER FOLDING

You will need:

A square piece of paper with side length 10 cm.

DEMO

What to do:

1 Take the bottom left corner D of your paper, and fold it up so that it touches M, the midpoint of the top edge.

2 Mark the point X where the fold is on [AD].

3 Mark the point Y where the edge [C′M] crosses [BC].

4 Unfold your piece of paper. *Estimate* the positions of X and Y on the vertical edges. For example, are they halfway down the edge, $\frac{1}{3}$ of the way down, or something else?

5 Suppose AX = x cm and BY = y cm.
Explain why:
a AM = 5 cm **b** XM = $(10 - x)$ cm.

6 Use Pythagoras' theorem to find the value of x.

7 Use similar triangles to find the value of y.

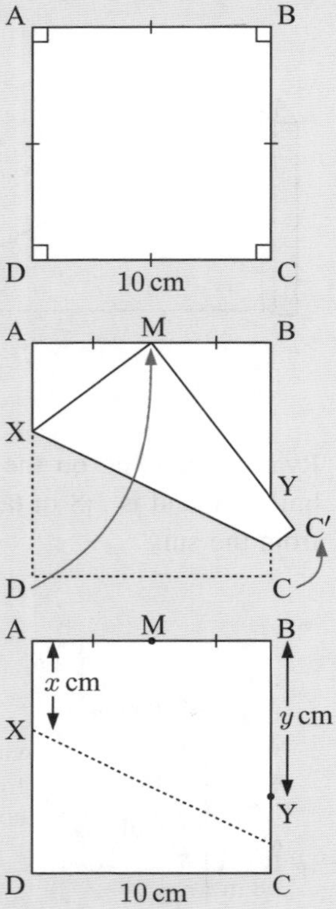

8 Hence, determine the positions of X and Y on the vertical edges.
Compare your answers with your estimates in **4**.

E CONGRUENT FIGURES

Two figures are **congruent** if they are identical in size and shape. They do not need to have the same orientation.

For example, the figures alongside are congruent even though one is a rotation of the other.

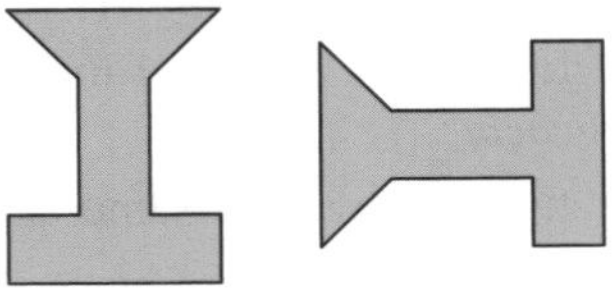

congruent figures

ACTIVITY 2 CREATING CONGRUENT FIGURES

You will need: Two sheets of card, scissors.

What to do:

1. Draw a shape on one of the sheets of card.
2. Place the second sheet of card behind it, and hold them together tightly. Carefully cut out the shape, cutting through both sheets of card. This will give you two congruent figures.

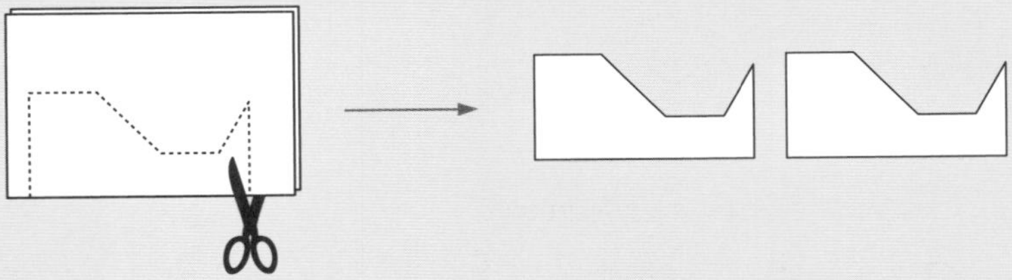

3. In a group or as a class, place both figures from each student in a box, and mix the figures up.
4. Try to pair up the congruent figures. How can you tell that two figures are congruent?

Two figures are **congruent** if:
- the figures are **equiangular** *and*
- the corresponding side lengths are equal.

The figures alongside are congruent. The corresponding sides and angles in the figures are identical. If we were to place one figure on top of the other, they would match each other perfectly.

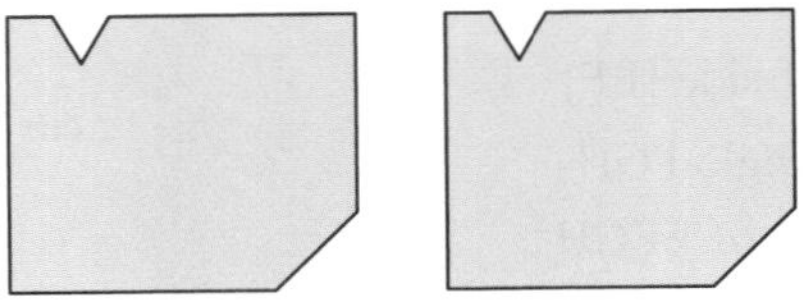

DEMO

Example 9 **Self Tutor**

Are the following pairs of figures congruent?

a

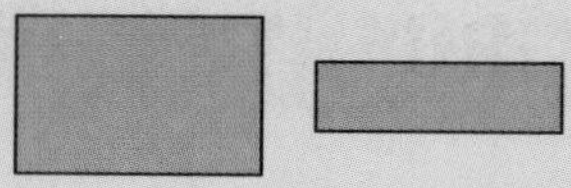

b

c

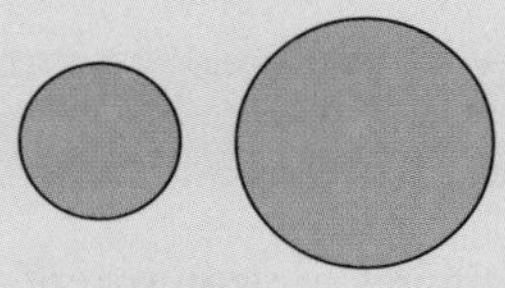

a The figures do not have the same shape, so they are *not congruent.*

b The figures are identical in size and shape even though one is rotated. They are therefore *congruent.*

c The figures have the same shape, but they are not the same size. They are therefore *not congruent.*

EXERCISE 18E

1 Are the following pairs of figures congruent?

a

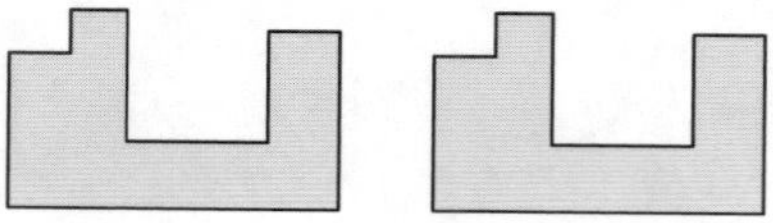

b

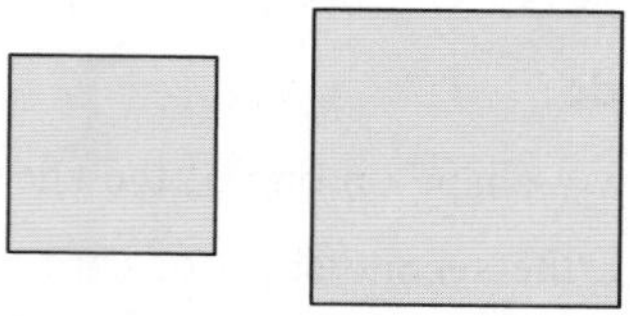

c

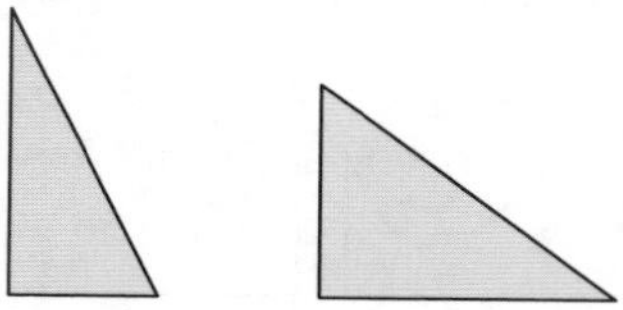

d

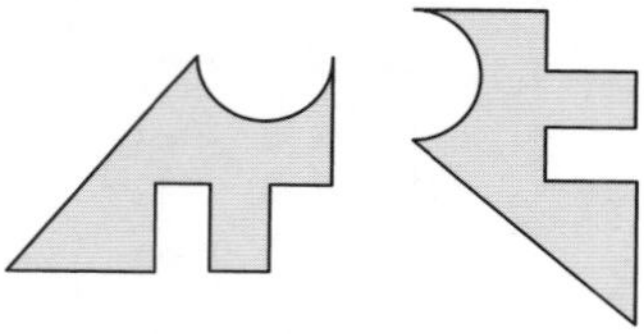

2 Which two of these figures are congruent?

A

B

C

D

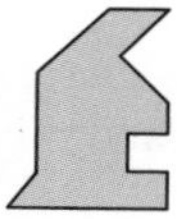

E

3 Which three of these figures are congruent?

A

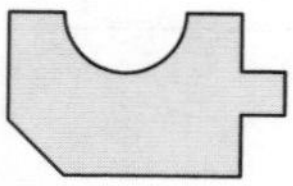

B

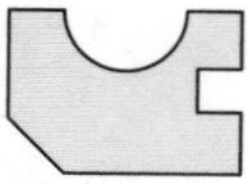

C

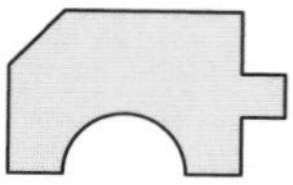

D

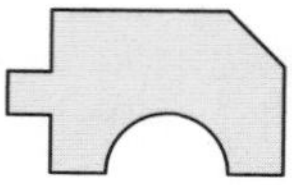

E

4 Quadrilaterals EFGH and ABCD are congruent.
Determine the:

a length of side [EF]

b size of angle $F\widehat{G}H$

c perimeter of EFGH.

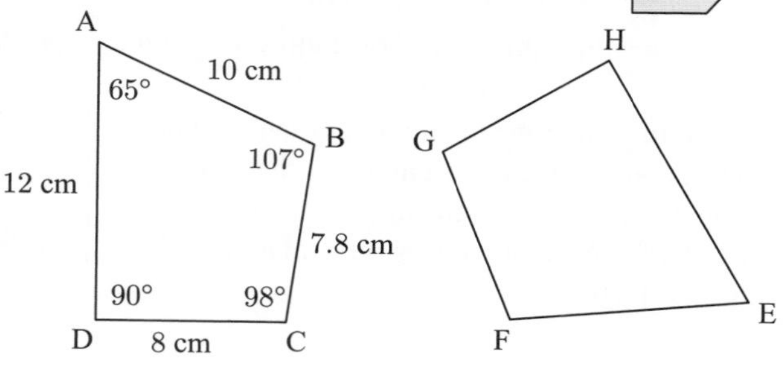

F CONGRUENT TRIANGLES

The triangles alongside have identical side lengths and angles, so the triangles are **congruent**.

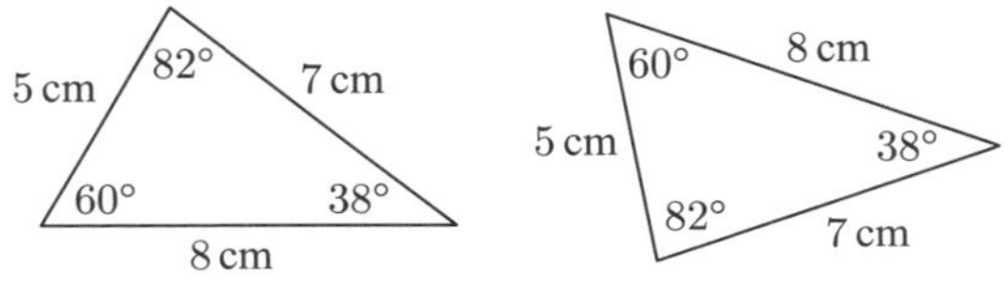

However, we do not necessarily need to know all of the information given to conclude that the triangles are congruent.

For example, if we know that two triangles have the same side lengths, then these triangles *must* be **congruent**.

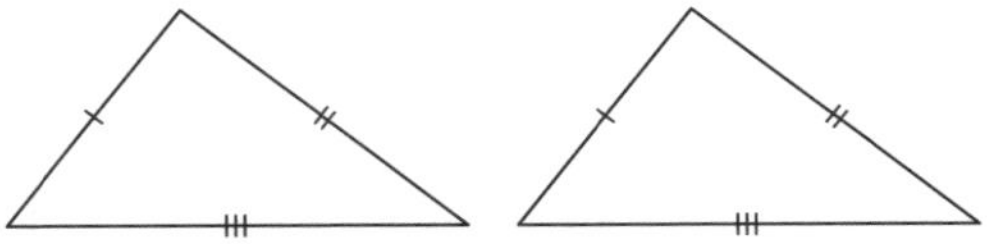

DEMO

INVESTIGATION — CONSTRUCTING TRIANGLES

In this Investigation we will discover other conditions which allow us to conclude that two triangles are congruent.

You will need: Paper, ruler, protractor.

What to do:

1. **Two sides and an included angle**
   Draw a triangle with two side lengths 8 cm and 12 cm, with an angle of 25° between these sides. How many different triangles can be constructed?

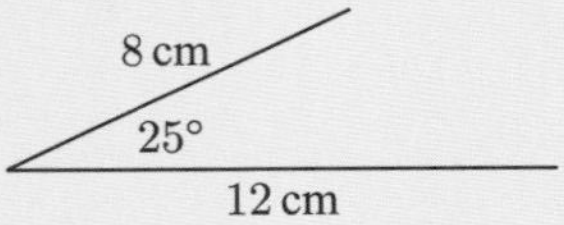

2. **Two angles and a corresponding side**
   Draw a triangle with two angles measuring 70° and 45°, with the side between these angles being 10 cm long. How many different triangles can be constructed?

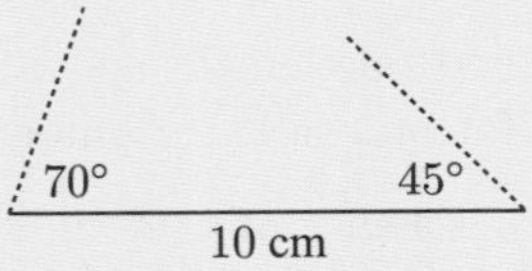

3. **Right angle, hypotenuse, and a side**
   Draw a right angled triangle with hypotenuse 10 cm, and one other side 6 cm long. How many different triangles can be constructed?

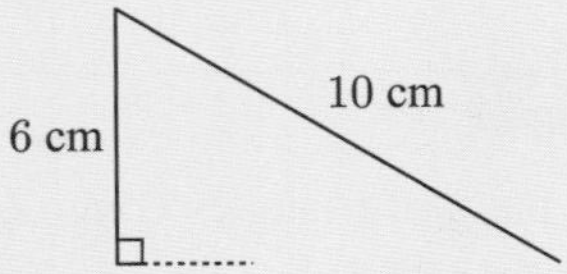

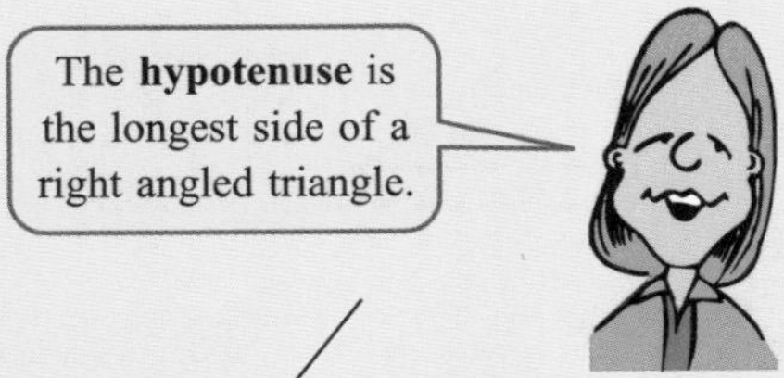

The **hypotenuse** is the longest side of a right angled triangle.

4. **Two sides and a non-included angle**
   Draw a triangle with two side lengths 8 cm and 12 cm, with an angle of 25° between the 12 cm side and the third side as shown. How many different triangles can be constructed?

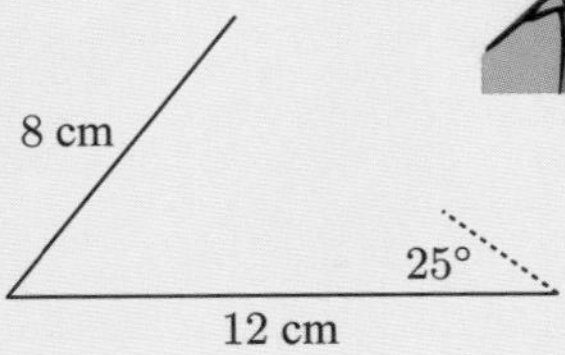

5 Three angles

Draw a triangle with angles 50°, 60°, and 70°. How many different triangles can be constructed?

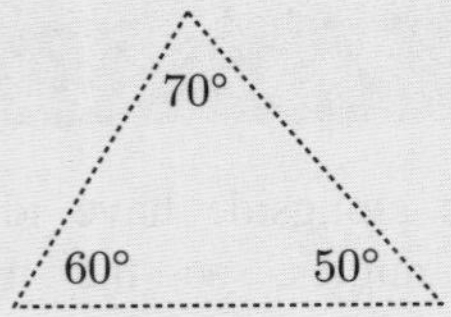

You should have made the following discoveries:

Two triangles are **congruent** if any one of the following is true:

- All corresponding sides are equal in length. **(SSS)**

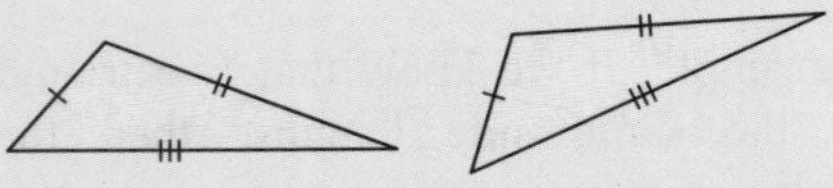

- Two sides and the **included angle** are equal. **(SAS)**

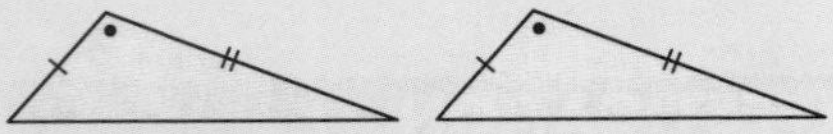

- Two angles and a pair of **corresponding sides** are equal. **(AAcorS)**

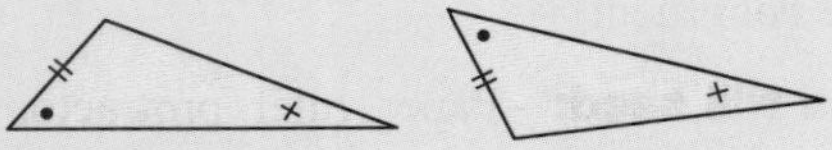

- For right angled triangles, the hypotenuses and one pair of sides are equal. **(RHS)**

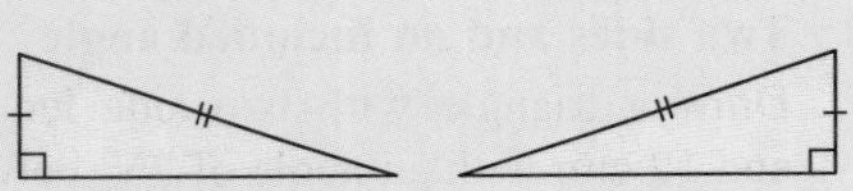

We usually indicate our reason why two triangles are congruent by writing one of the abbreviations given above in bold.

If we know two side lengths and a non-included angle, there may be two ways to construct the triangle. This is therefore *not* sufficient information to show that two triangles with these properties are congruent.

If we know all angles of a triangle, the triangle may still vary in size. This is therefore *not* sufficient information to show that two triangles with these angles are congruent.

Example 10 **Self Tutor**

Are these pairs of triangles congruent? Give reasons for your answers.

a

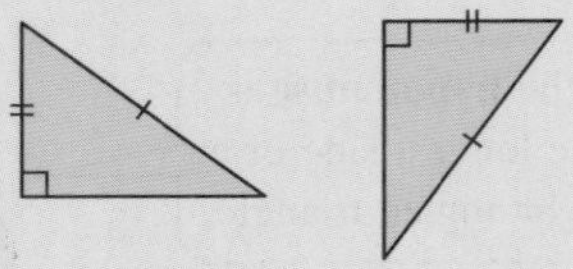

b

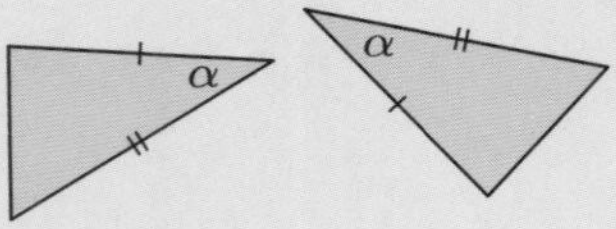

c

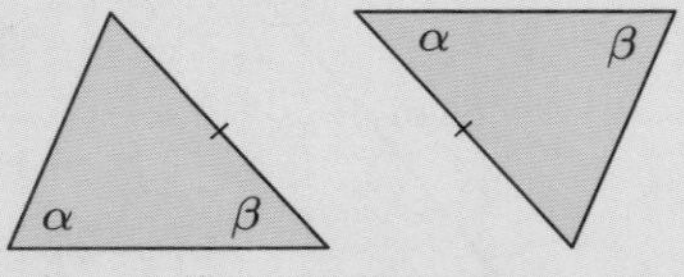

d

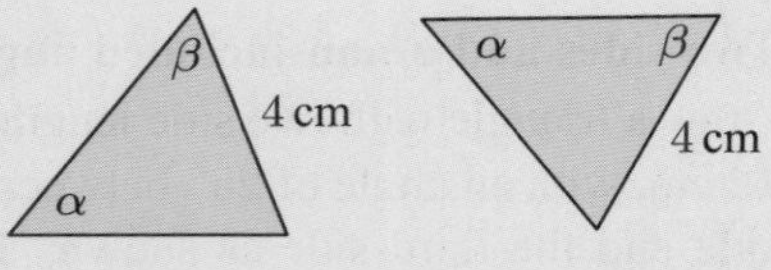

a Yes {RHS} **b** Yes {SAS}

c No. This is **not** AAcorS as the equal sides are not in corresponding positions. One is opposite angle α, the other is opposite angle β.

d Yes {AAcorS}

Once we have established that two triangles are congruent, we can deduce that the remaining corresponding sides and angles of the triangles are equal.

Example 11 **Self Tutor**

a Show that these triangles are congruent.

b What can be deduced from this congruence?

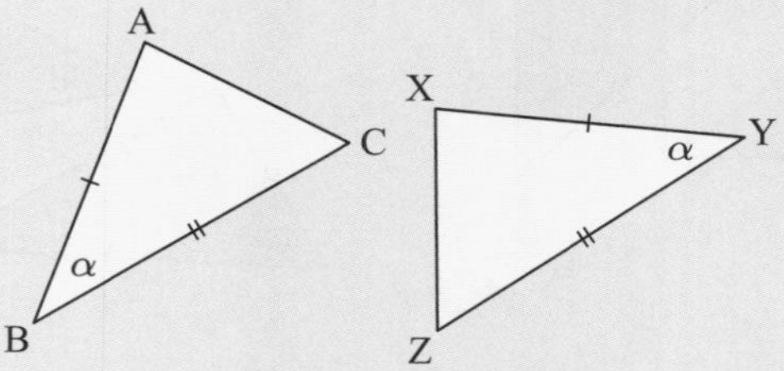

a In $\triangle$s ABC and XYZ:
- AB = XY
- BC = YZ
- $A\widehat{B}C = X\widehat{Y}Z$

$\therefore$ $\triangle ABC \cong \triangle XYZ$ {SAS}

b $AC = XZ$
$B\widehat{A}C = Y\widehat{X}Z$
and $A\widehat{C}B = X\widehat{Z}Y$

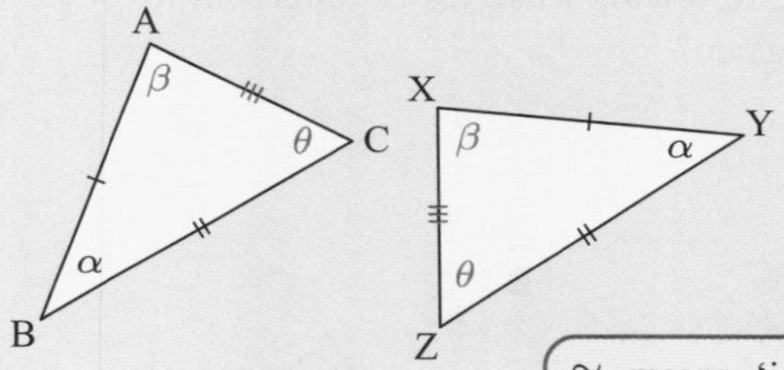

When we describe congruent triangles, we label the vertices that are in corresponding positions in the same order. For instance, in the previous Example, we write $\triangle ABC \cong \triangle XYZ$, not $\triangle ABC \cong \triangle YZX$.

EXERCISE 18F

1 State whether these pairs of triangles are congruent, giving reasons for your answers:

a

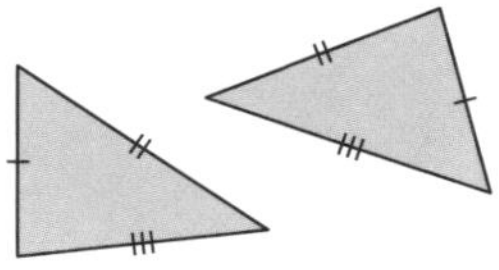

b

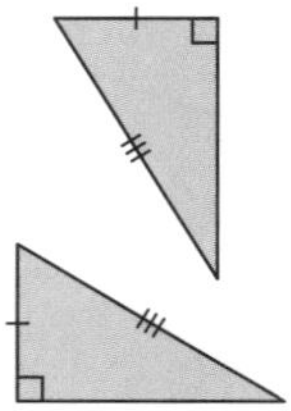

c

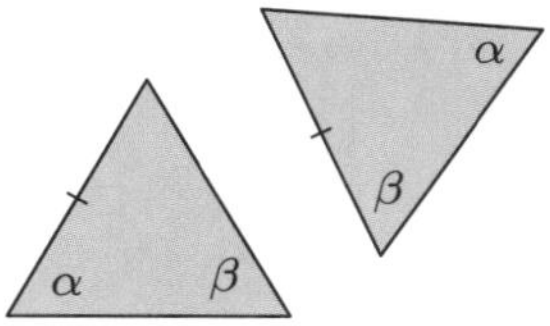

d

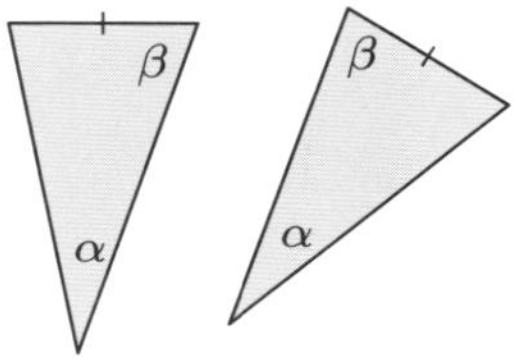

e

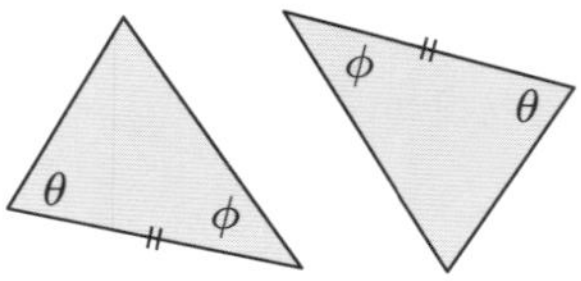

f

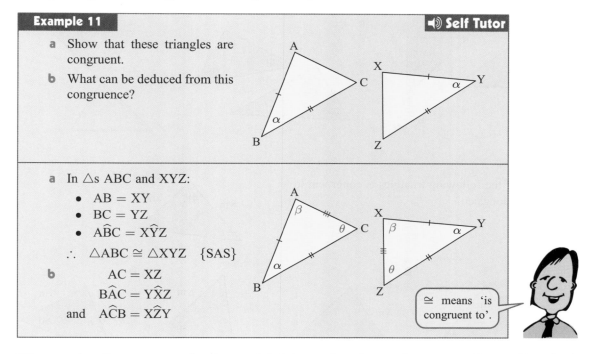

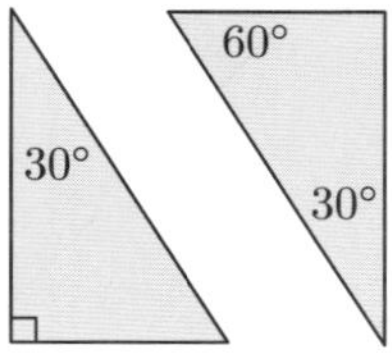

2 State whether these pairs of triangles are congruent, giving reasons for your answers:

a

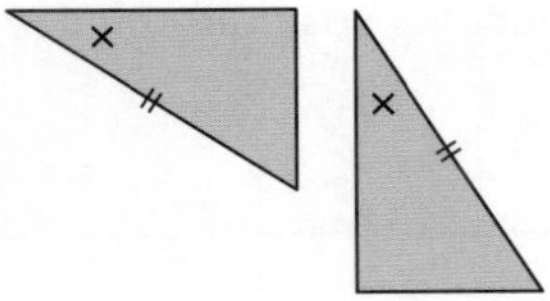

b

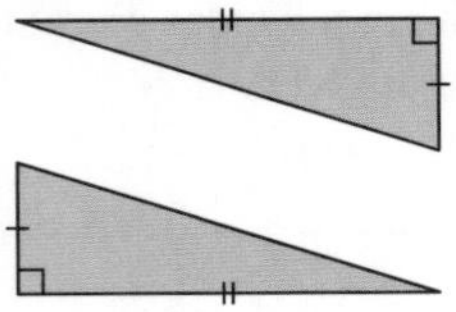

c

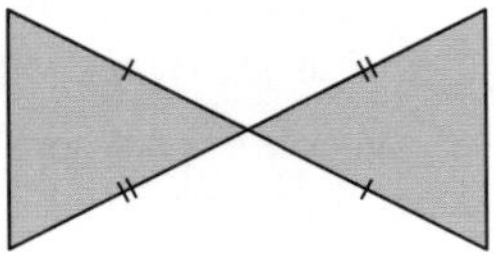

d

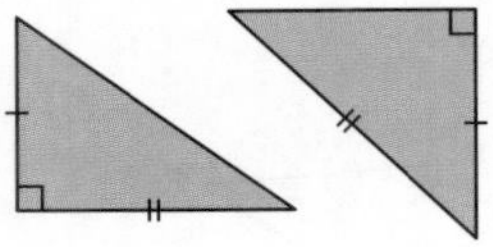

e

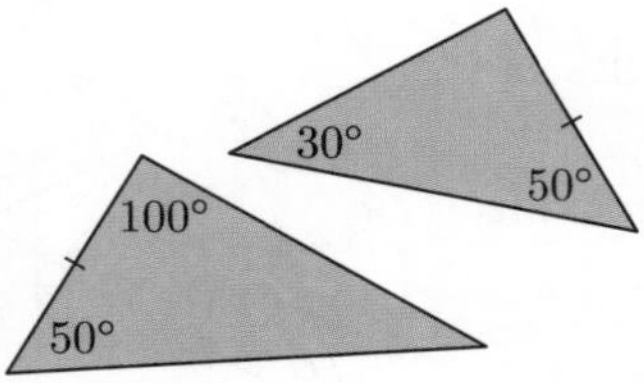

f

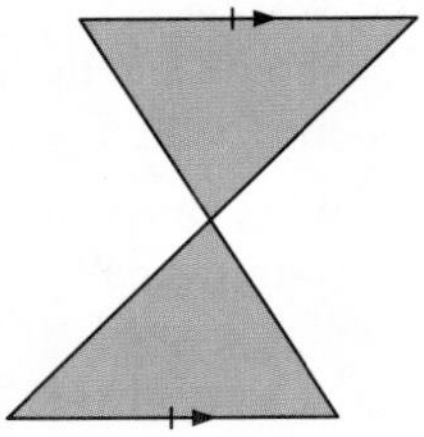

3 Which of the following triangles is congruent to the one alongside?

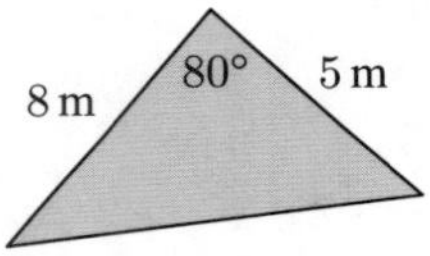

A

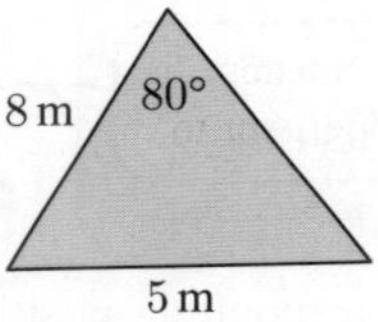

B

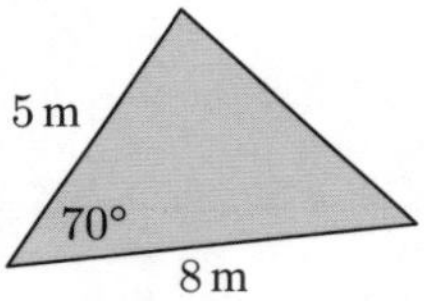

C

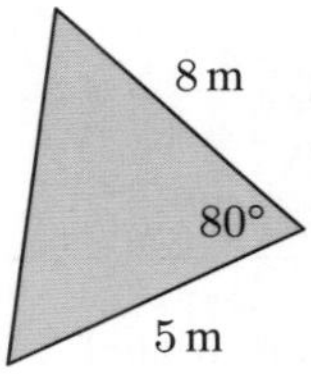

D

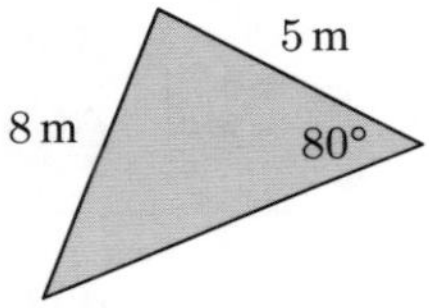

4 Which of these triangles are congruent to each other?

A

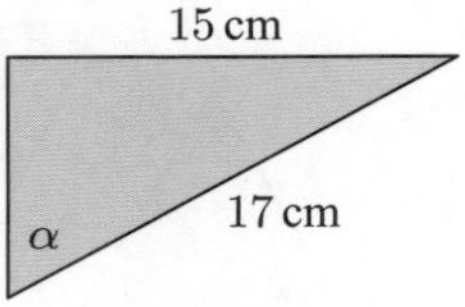

B

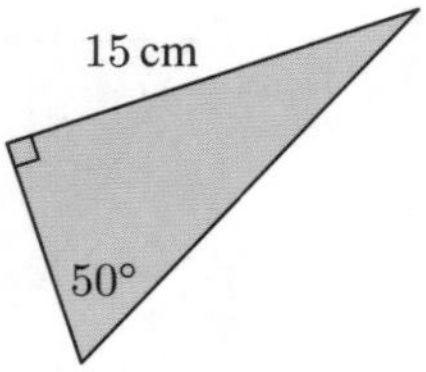

C

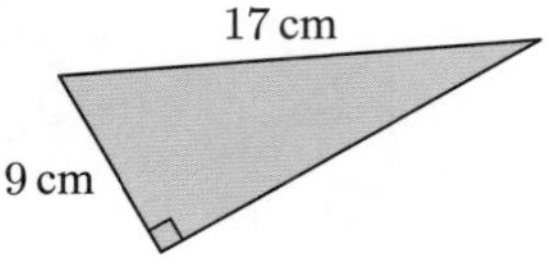

D

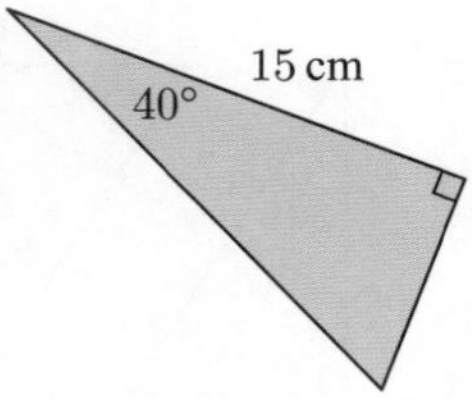

E

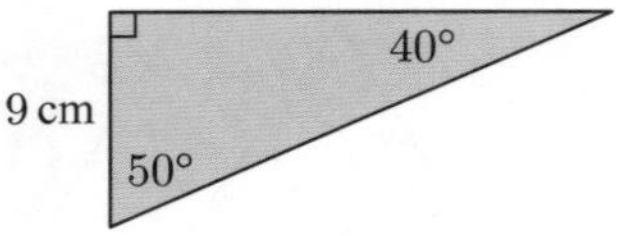

F

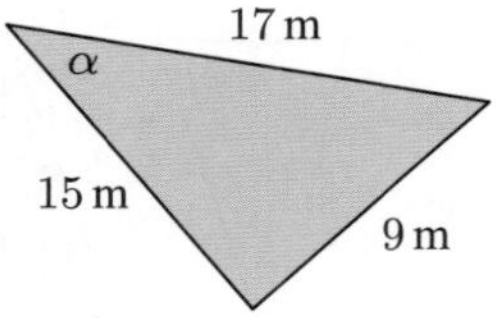

5 The following pairs of triangles are not drawn to scale, but the information on them is correct.

- **i** Determine whether the triangles are congruent.
- **ii** If the triangles are congruent, what else can we deduce about them?

a

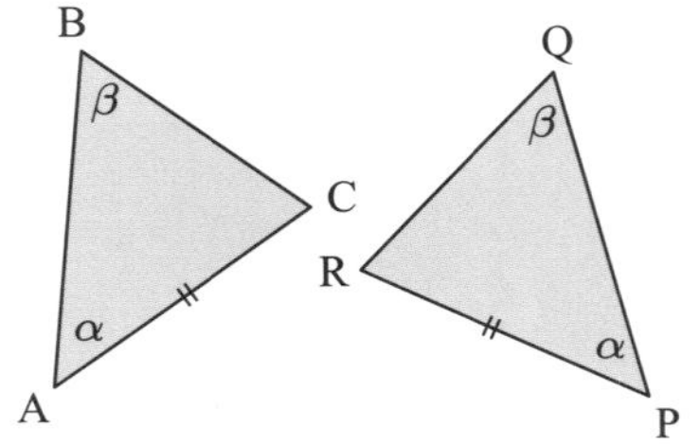

b

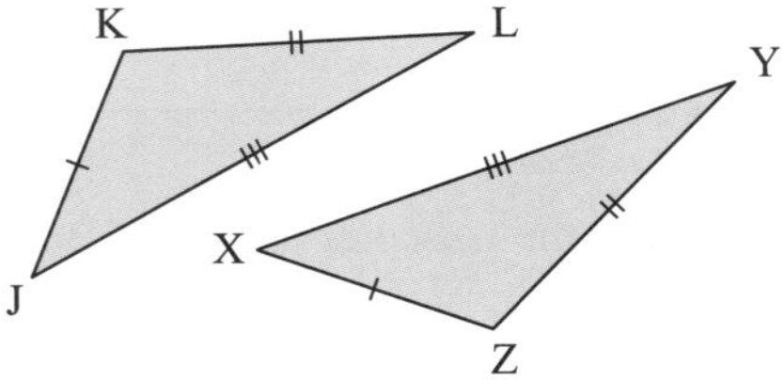

c

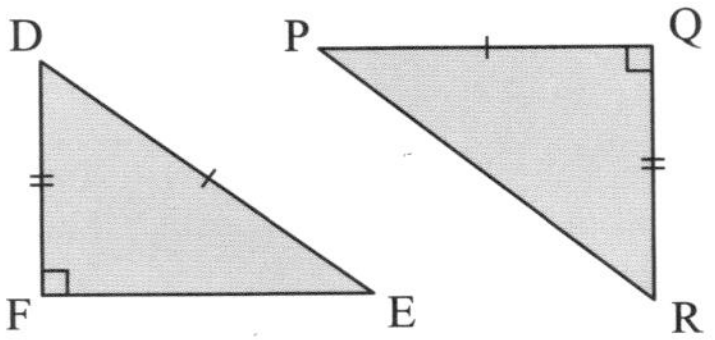

d

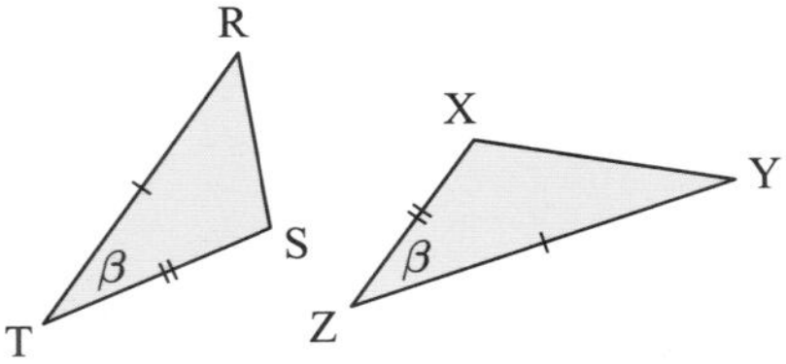

e

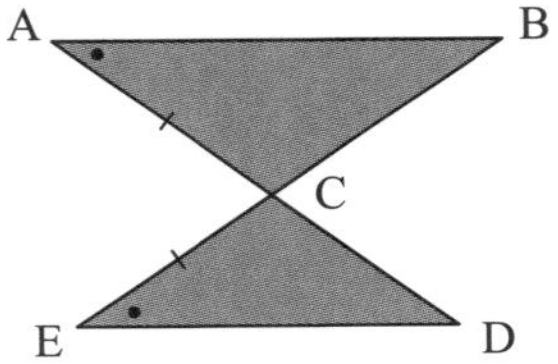

f

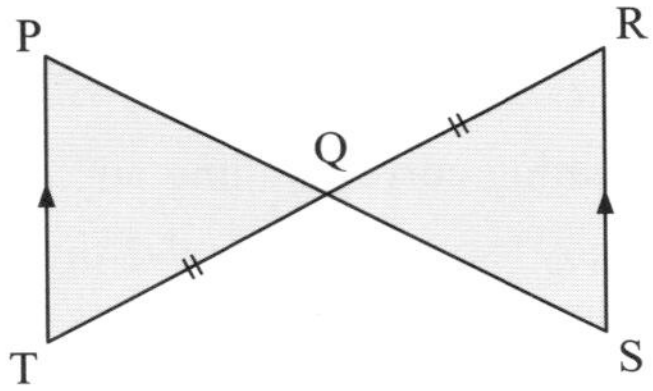

g

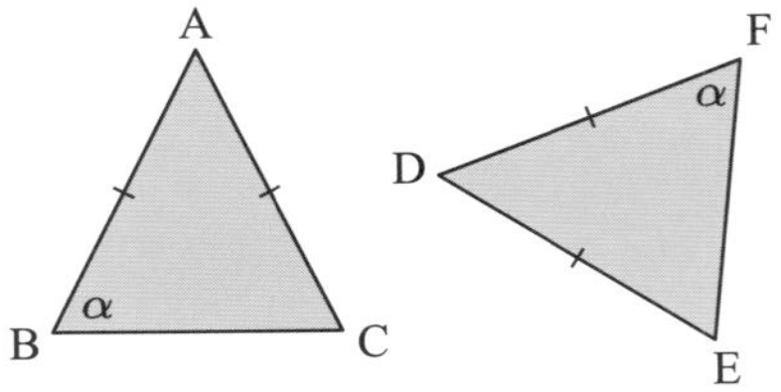

h

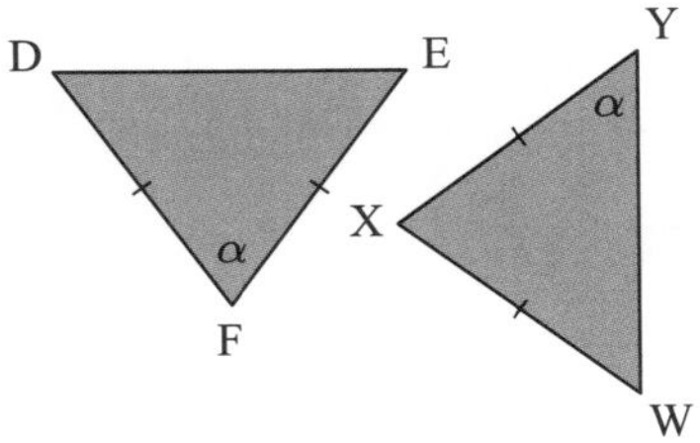

DISCUSSION

We have seen that if two *triangles* have equal corresponding sides, then they are congruent.

Is the same true for *quadrilaterals*? Can we say that the quadrilaterals alongside are congruent?

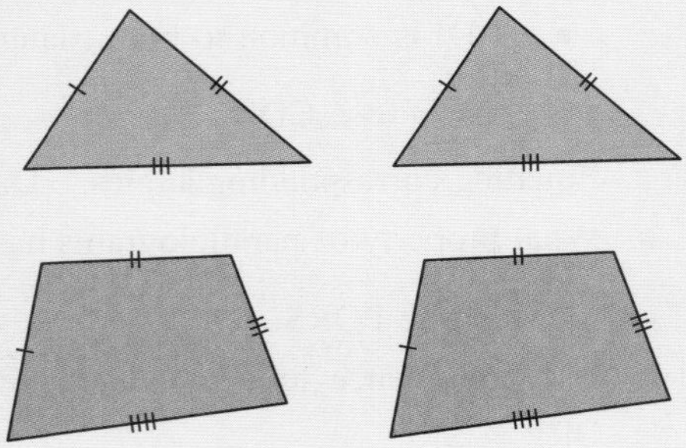

G PROOF USING CONGRUENCE

In **Chapter 9**, we studied the properties of isosceles triangles and special quadrilaterals. We can use congruence to prove many of these properties.

Example 12 Self Tutor

Consider the isosceles triangle ABC.

M is the midpoint of [BC].

a Use congruence to show that $B\widehat{A}M = C\widehat{A}M$.

b What property of isosceles triangles has been proven?

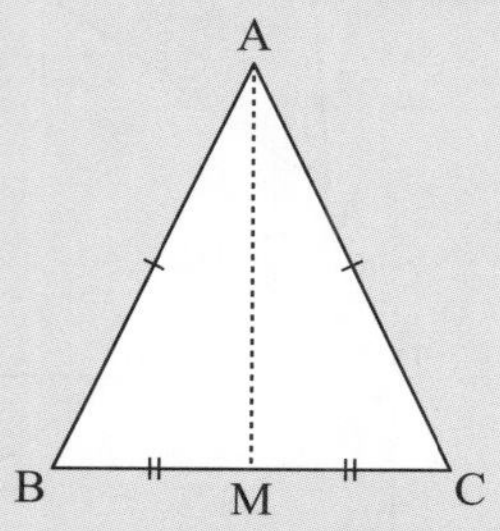

a In triangles ABM and ACM:
- AB = AC {△ABC is isosceles}
- BM = CM {M is the midpoint of [BC]}
- [AM] is common to both triangles.

$\therefore$ △ABM ≅ △ACM {SSS}

Equating corresponding angles, $B\widehat{A}M = C\widehat{A}M$. (×)

b In any isosceles triangle, the line joining the apex to the midpoint of the base bisects the vertical angle.

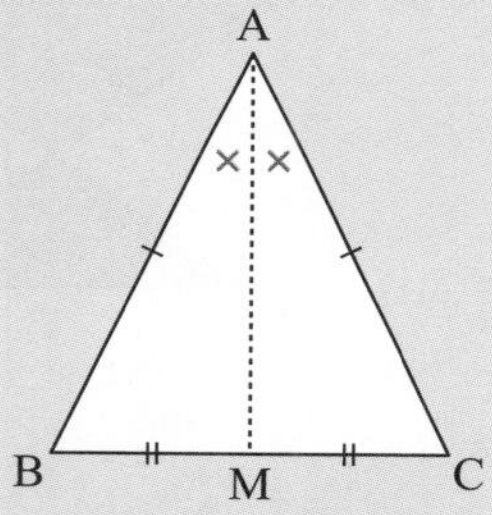

EXERCISE 18G

1 Consider the parallelogram ABCD.

a Copy and complete:
In triangles ABD and CDB:
- $A\widehat{D}B$ = ... {equal alternate angles}
- $A\widehat{B}D$ = ... {equal alternate angles}
- [BD] is common to both triangles

$\therefore$ △ABD ≅ △CDB {......}

Equating corresponding angles, $D\widehat{A}B$ = ...

b What property of parallelograms has been proven in **a**?

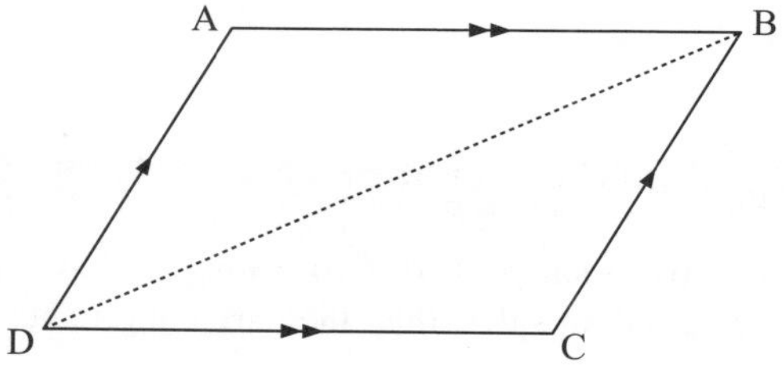

2 Consider the kite PQRS.

a Use congruence to show that $Q\widehat{P}R = S\widehat{P}R$ and $Q\widehat{R}P = S\widehat{R}P$.

b What property of kites has been proven?

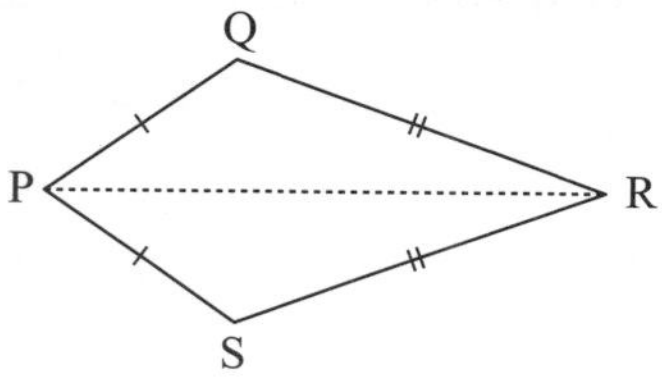

3 Consider the square ABCD.

- **a** Show that $\triangle ABC \cong \triangle DAB$.
- **b** Hence, show that $AC = DB$.
- **c** What property of squares has been proven?

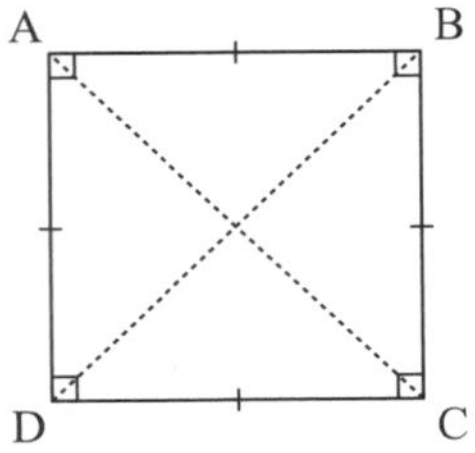

4

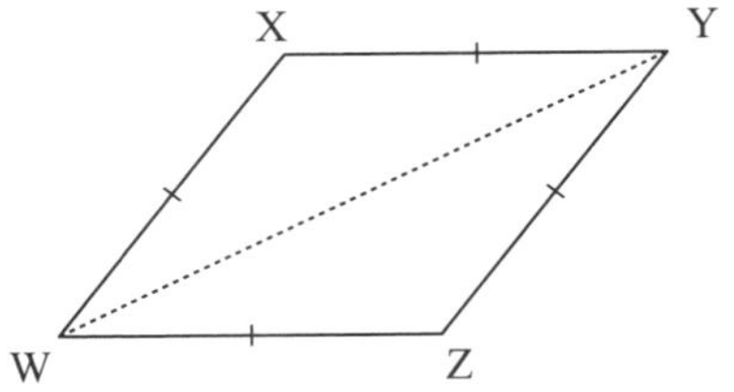

Consider the rhombus WXYZ.

- **a** Show that $\triangle WXY \cong \triangle YZW$.
- **b** Hence, show that $X\widehat{Y}W = Z\widehat{W}Y$.
- **c** Hence, show that [XY] is parallel to [WZ].
- **d** Likewise, show that [XW] is parallel to [YZ].
- **e** What property of rhombuses has been proven?

5 The diagonals of rhombus PQRS meet at M.

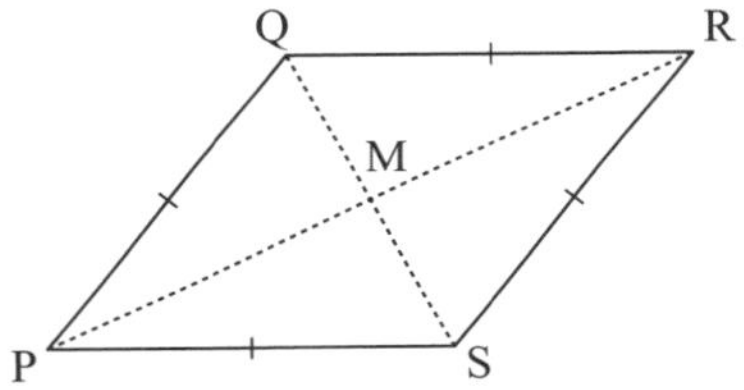

- **a** Show that $\triangle PSQ \cong \triangle RSQ$.
- **b** Hence, show that $P\widehat{S}Q = R\widehat{S}Q$.
- **c** What property of rhombuses has been proven?
- **d** Explain why $\triangle PSM \cong \triangle RSM$.
- **e** Hence: **i** show that $PM = RM$
  - **ii** find the sizes of $S\widehat{M}P$ and $S\widehat{M}R$.
- **f** Use **e** to show that $\triangle SMP \cong \triangle QMR$, and therefore $SM = QM$.
- **g** What property of rhombuses has been proven in **e** and **f**?

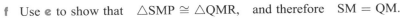

6 Use congruence to show that:

- **a** the opposite sides of a parallelogram are equal in length
- **b** the base angles of an isosceles triangle are equal
- **c** the diagonals of a kite intersect at right angles.

Global context

click here

Create your own pyramids

Statement of inquiry:	Investigating the monuments of ancient civilisations can help us to understand their cultures.
Global context:	Personal and cultural expression
Key concept:	Form
Related concepts:	Measurement, Quantity, Space
Objective:	Knowing and understanding
Approaches to learning:	Thinking, Self-management

REVIEW SET 18A

1 Copy the given figure and reduce it by a factor of $k = \frac{2}{3}$.

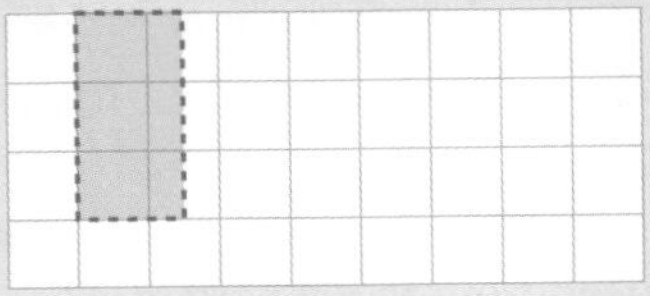

2 Are all rhombuses similar? Explain your answer.

3 Find x:

a

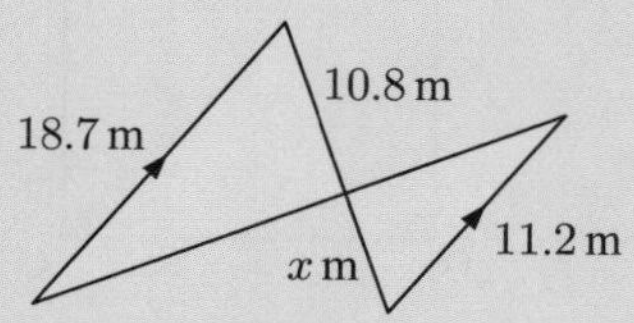

b

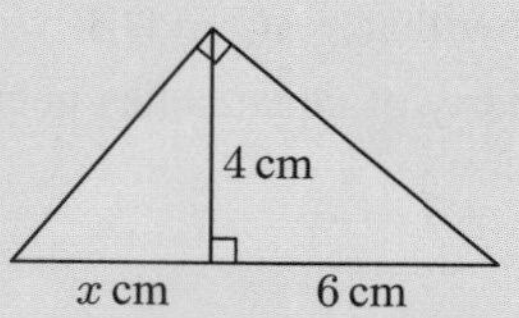

4

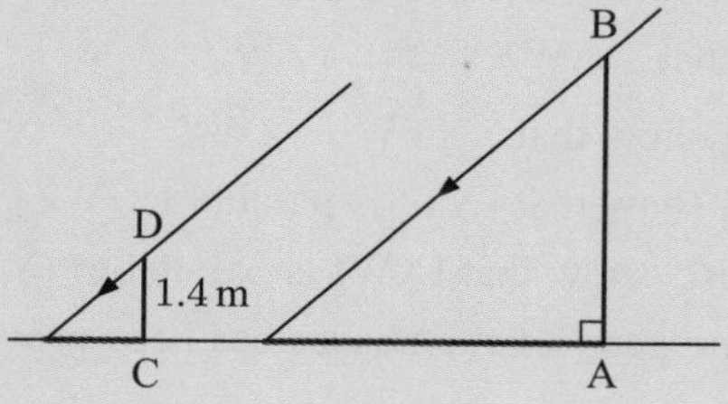

[AB] is a vertical flagpole of unknown height.
[CD] is a vertical stick.
When the shadow of the flagpole is 12.3 m long, the shadow of the stick is 1.65 m long.
Find, rounded to 3 significant figures, the height of the flagpole.

5 Find the value of x:

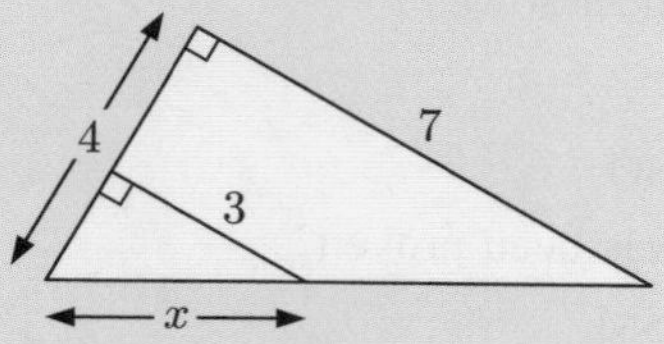

6 State whether each pair of figures is congruent:

a

b

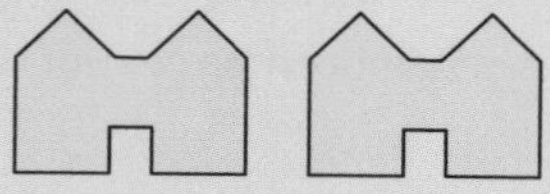

c

7 State whether each pair of triangles is congruent, giving reasons for your answers.

a

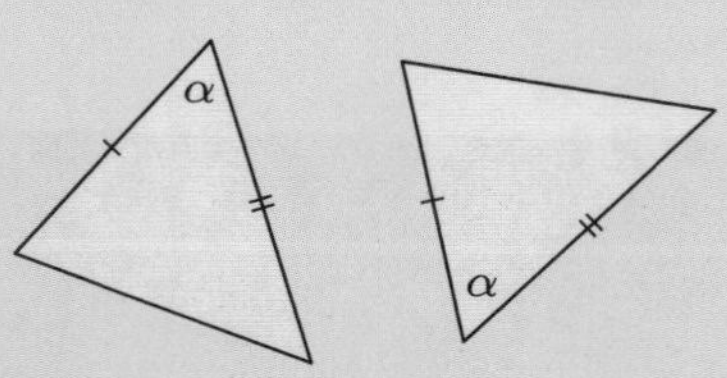

b

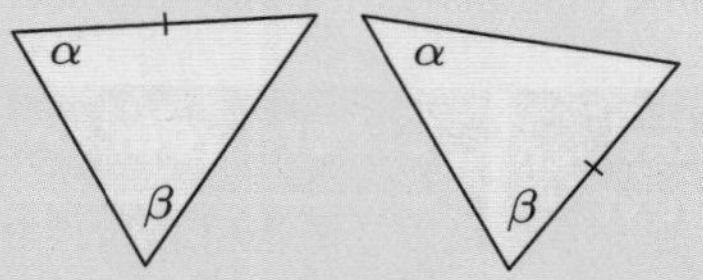

8 Consider the kite ABCD.
Use congruence to show that $A\widehat{B}C = A\widehat{D}C$.
What property of kites has been proven?

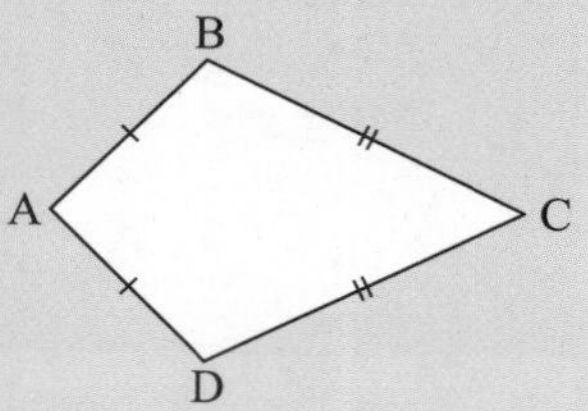

9 These triangles are not drawn to scale, but the information on them is correct.

a Determine whether the triangles are congruent.

b If the triangles are congruent, what can be deduced from the congruence?

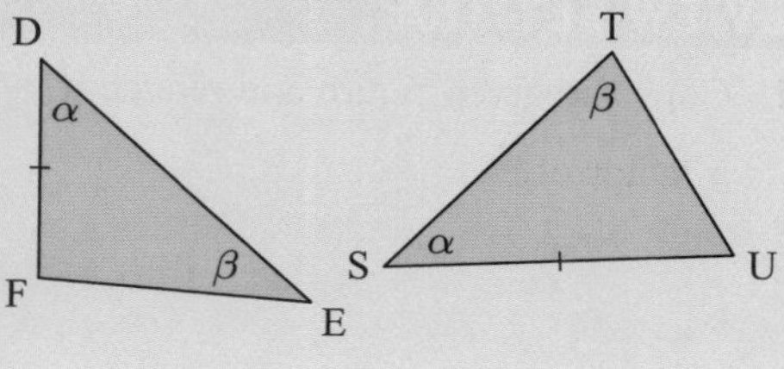

10 A square piece of paper is divided into four triangles as shown.

- **a** Show that triangles A and D are congruent.
- **b** Hence, show that triangles B and C are congruent.
- **c** Find the area of each triangle.

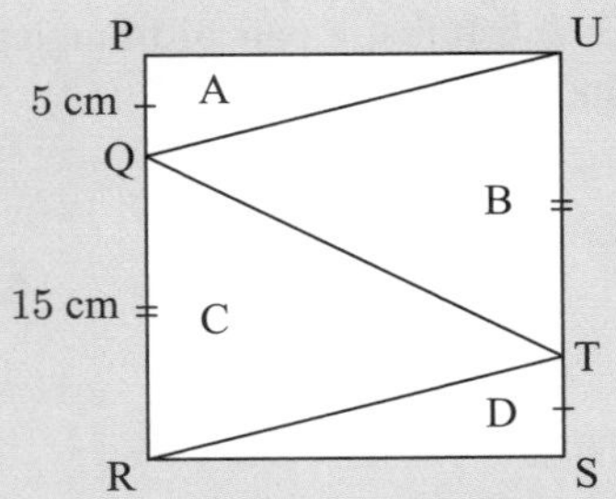

REVIEW SET 18B

1 Copy and enlarge the shape with a scale factor $k = \frac{5}{2}$.

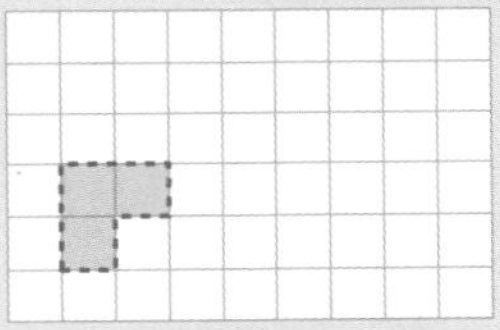

2 Find x, given that the figures are similar:

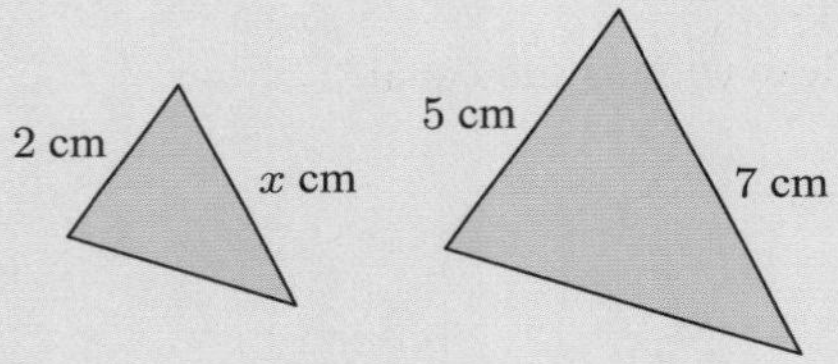

3 Which two of these figures are congruent?

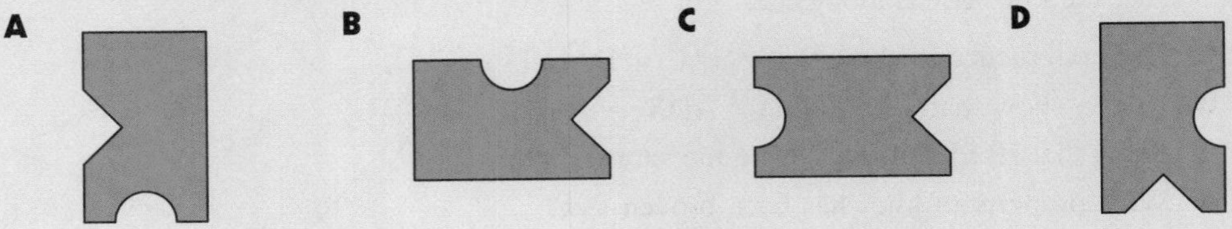

4 Show that the following figures possess similar triangles:

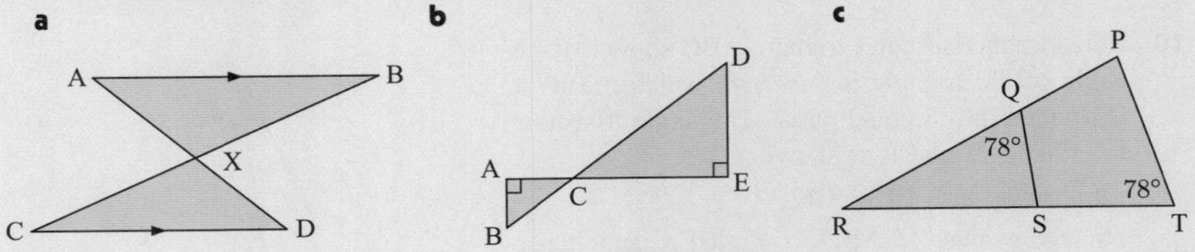

5 State whether these pairs of triangles are congruent, giving reasons for your answers:

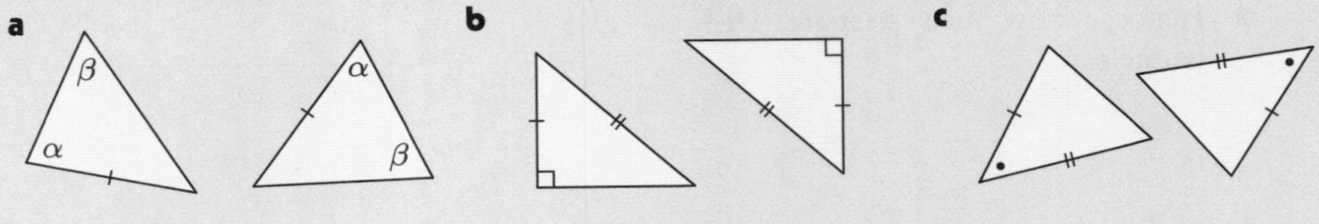

6 Use congruence to prove that, in an isosceles triangle, the line joining the apex to the midpoint of the base meets the base at right angles.

7 Establish that a pair of triangles is similar, and hence find x:

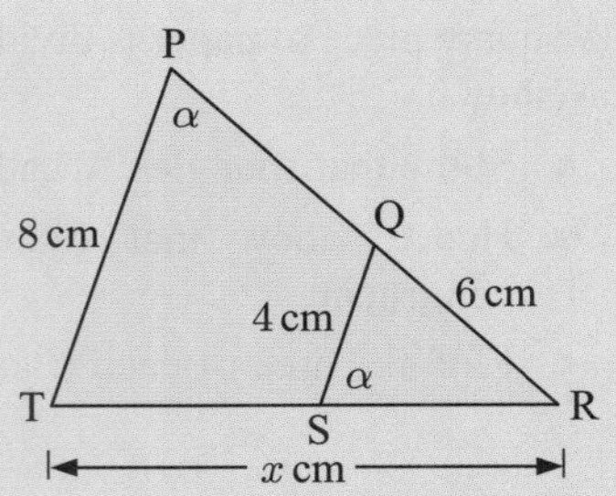

8 P and Q are markers on the bank of a canal which has parallel sides. R and S are telegraph poles which are directly opposite each other. PQ = 30 m and QR = 100 m.
When I walk 20 m from P directly away from the bank, I reach the point T such that T, Q, and S line up.
How wide is the canal?

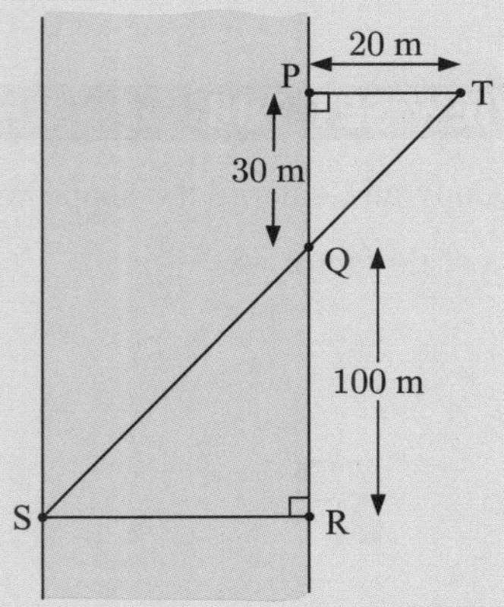

9 Consider the kite ABCD alongside.

a Use congruence to show that $B\widehat{A}C = D\widehat{A}C$.

b Hence, show that $\triangle ABX \cong \triangle ADX$.

c Show that [BX] and [DX] have the same length.

d What property of kites has been proven in **c**?

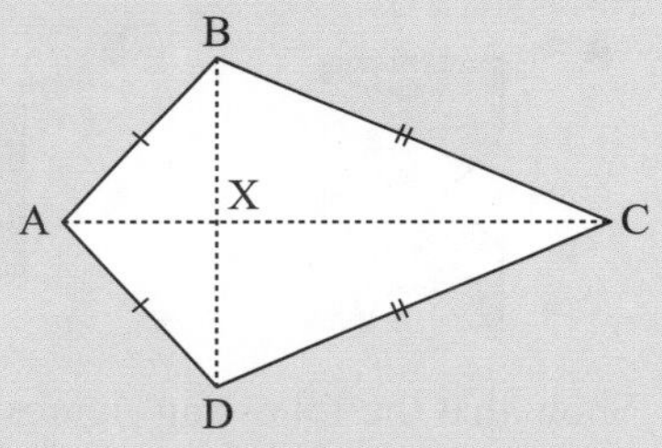

10 Consider the isosceles triangle ABC shown. Each angle of the triangle is *trisected*, which means it is divided into 3 equal parts. The angle trisectors meet at D, E, and F as shown.

a Show that BF = CF.

b Show that $\triangle ABD \cong \triangle ACE$, and hence BD = CE.

c Show that $\triangle BDF \cong \triangle CEF$.

d Hence, show that triangle DEF is also isosceles.

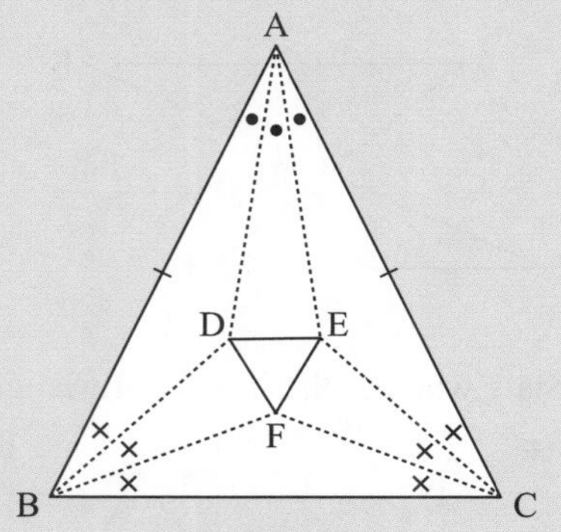

Chapter 19

Algebraic factorisation

Contents:

OPENING PROBLEM

A circular pond will be surrounded by a path as shown. The landscaper needs to know the area of the path so he knows how many pavers to buy.

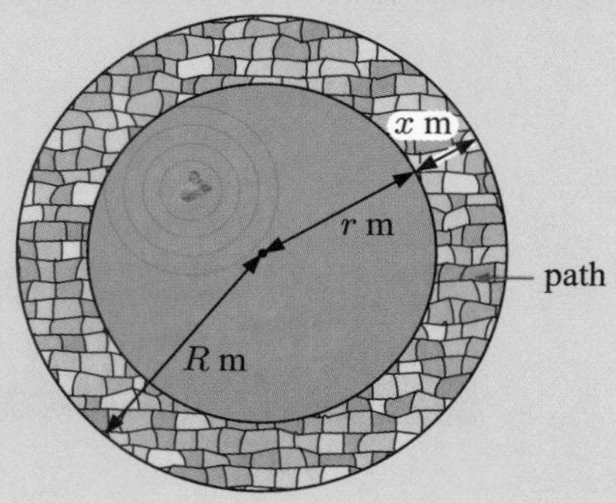

Things to think about:

Can you show that the area of the path is:

a $\pi x(2r + x)$ m^2

b $\pi(R + r)(R - r)$ m^2?

In **Chapter 7** we learnt how to perform algebraic **expansions** such as $3(x + 2) = 3x + 6$.

In this chapter we will learn how to **factorise** algebraic expressions.

Factorisation is the reverse process of expansion.

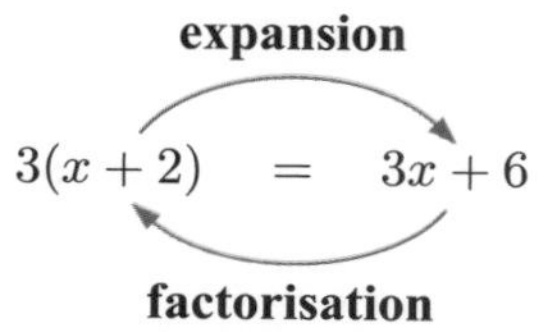

A COMMON FACTORS

In previous years we have seen how numbers can be expressed as the product of factors.

A number which is a factor of two or more numbers is called a **common factor** of these numbers.

The **highest common factor** or **HCF** of a set of numbers is the largest factor that is common to all of them.

For example, $30 = 2 \times 3 \times 5$ and $140 = 2 \times 2 \times 5 \times 7$. We see that 2 and 5 are the common factors of 30 and 140.

$\therefore$ the HCF of 30 and 140 is $2 \times 5 = 10$.

We can find the HCF of **algebraic products** in the same way.

Example 1 Self Tutor

Find the highest common factor of:

a $8a$ and $12b$ **b** $4x^2$ and $6xy$

a
$$8a = 2 \times 2 \times 2 \times a$$
$$12b = 2 \times 2 \times 3 \times b$$
$$\therefore \text{HCF} = 2 \times 2 = 4$$

b
$$4x^2 = 2 \times 2 \times x \times x$$
$$6xy = 2 \times 3 \times x \times y$$
$$\therefore \text{HCF} = 2 \times x = 2x$$

Write each term as a product of its factors!

EXERCISE 19A

1 Find the highest common factor of:

- **a** $3x$ and 6
- **b** $2b$ and b
- **c** $7b$ and 28
- **d** $4q$ and $5q$
- **e** $9c$ and $27c$
- **f** $8d$ and $12d$
- **g** $11x$ and 12
- **h** $16z$ and $20z$
- **i** $42x$ and $70x$

2 Find the HCF of:

- **a** $15ab$ and $13ba$
- **b** st and $3st$
- **c** $12x$ and $18xy$
- **d** f and f^2
- **e** c^3 and $5c$
- **f** r^3 and r^2
- **g** $8d$ and $2d^2$
- **h** $5a^3$ and $25a$
- **i** $7b^2$ and $14b^3$
- **j** $26gh$ and $39hg$
- **k** $6jk$ and $12jk^2$
- **l** $8x^2y$ and $18xy^2$
- **m** $10x$, $20xy$, and $30y^2$
- **n** $5abc$, $10a^2b$, and $15bc$
- **o** $22p^2q$ and $48pq^2$

Example 2 — **Self Tutor**

Find the HCF of $3(x+3)$ and $(x+3)(x+1)$.

$$3(x+3) = 3 \times (x+3)$$
$$(x+3)(x+1) = (x+3) \times (x+1)$$
$$\therefore \text{ HCF} = (x+3)$$

3 Find the HCF of:

- **a** $3(b+6)$ and $(b+5)(b+6)$
- **b** $7(1+b)^2$ and $7(2+b)(1+b)$
- **c** $y^2(y-3)$ and $y(y-3)$
- **d** $16(x-4)^2$ and $8(x-4)(x-2)$
- **e** $9(x-8)^2$ and $12(x-7)(x-8)$
- **f** $5d(d+1)$ and $15d(d+1)^2$

4 Find the HCF of:

- **a** $x+1$ and x^2+1
- **b** x^2 and $x-1$
- **c** $x(1-x)$ and $(x+1)(x-1)$

If there are no common factors, the HCF is 1.

ACTIVITY 1

Click on the icon to run a game involving algebraic common factors.

GAME

B FACTORISING WITH COMMON FACTORS

Factorisation is the process of writing an expression as a **product** of its **factors**.

Factorisation is the reverse process of **expansion**.

When we expand an expression, we remove its brackets.

When we factorise an expression, we insert brackets.

Notice that $5(x-1)$ is the *product of the two factors*, 5 and $x-1$.

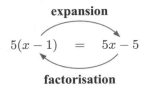

expansion

$$5(x-1) \quad = \quad 5x-5$$

factorisation

To factorise an algebraic expression involving a number of terms, we look for the HCF of the terms. We write it in front of a set of brackets. We then use the reverse of the distributive law to complete the factorisation.

For example: $6x^2$ and $2xy$ have HCF $= 2x$,

$$\begin{aligned}\therefore\ 6x^2+2xy &= 2x \times 3x + 2x \times y \\ &= 2x(3x+y)\end{aligned}$$

Example 3 — Self Tutor

Fully factorise:

a $3a+6$ **b** $ab-2bc$

a $3a+6$
$= 3 \times a + 3 \times 2$
$= 3(a+2)$ {HCF is 3}

b $ab-2bc$
$= a \times b - 2 \times b \times c$
$= b(a-2c)$ {HCF is b}

With practice, the middle line is not necessary.

EXERCISE 19B

1 Fully factorise:

a $3x-6$	**b** $8d+40$	**c** $10x-30$	**d** $4+2x$
e $5p+5q$	**f** $ab+ad$	**g** $42-35x$	**h** $gh+h$
i $y+yz$	**j** $p-pq$	**k** $3e+ef$	**l** $9x-xy$
m $jk-3hk$	**n** $rs-st$	**o** $3xy-2yz$	**p** $4mn+lm$

Example 4 — Self Tutor

Fully factorise: **a** $8x^2 + 12x$ **b** $3y^2 - 6xy$

a $8x^2 + 12x$
$= 2 \times 4 \times x \times x + 3 \times 4 \times x$
$= 4x(2x + 3)$ {HCF is $4x$}

b $3y^2 - 6xy$
$= 3 \times y \times y - 2 \times 3 \times x \times y$
$= 3y(y - 2x)$ {HCF is $3y$}

2 Fully factorise:

a $x^2 + 7x$ **b** $3x^2 + 9x$ **c** $8x - 4x^2$
d $5x - 25x^2$ **e** $6x^2 + 15x$ **f** $x^3 + 2x^2$
g $x^3 + 3x$ **h** $8x^3 - x^2$ **i** $x^2y - xy^2$
j $2xy^2 + 8x^2y$ **k** $4x^2 - 8x + 12$ **l** $9x^2 - 45x - 27x^3$

3 Write an expression for the total area of the shape in:

a factorised form **b** expanded form.

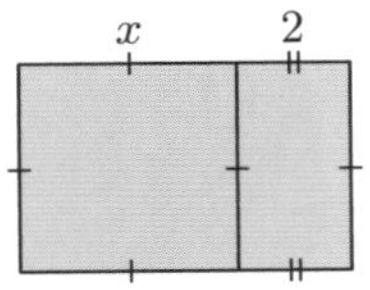

Example 5 — Self Tutor

Fully factorise: $-2a + 6ab$

$-2a + 6ab$
$= 6ab - 2a$ {Rewrite with $6ab$ first.}
$= 2 \times 3 \times a \times b - 2 \times a$
$= 2a(3b - 1)$ {HCF is $2a$}

4 Fully factorise:

a $-5a + 10$ **b** $-20 + 12b$ **c** $-8c + 16d$
d $-ab + 3a$ **e** $-p + pq$ **f** $-y^2 + y$
g $-14y + 7y^2$ **h** $-cd + 2d^2$ **i** $-z^2 + z$

Example 6 — Self Tutor

Fully factorise: $-2x^2 - 4x$

$-2x^2 - 4x$
$= -2 \times x \times x + -2 \times 2 \times x$
$= -2x(x + 2)$ {HCF is $-2x$}

5 Fully factorise:

a $-6x - 24$ **b** $-8 - 8x$ **c** $-2x - 2y$
d $-10p - 5q$ **e** $-ab - a$ **f** $-7a - 21a^2$
g $-16g^2 - 8g$ **h** $-18t^2 - 12st$ **i** $-22e^2 - 33e$

Example 7 — Self Tutor

Fully factorise:

a $2(x+3)+x(x+3)$ b $x(x+4)-(x+4)$

a $2(x+3)+x(x+3)$ $\{\text{HCF} = (x+3)\}$
$= (x+3)(2+x)$

b $x(x+4)-(x+4)$
$= x(x+4)-1(x+4)$ $\{\text{HCF} = (x+4)\}$
$= (x+4)(x-1)$

6 Fully factorise:

a $a(a+2)+3(a+2)$
b $4(x-1)+x(x-1)$
c $5(x+4)-x(x+4)$
d $x(x-9)+(x-9)$
e $a(c+d)-b(c+d)$
f $x(x-3)-3(x-3)$
g $t(r+s)-(r+s)$
h $y(y-6)+y-6$

Example 8 — Self Tutor

Fully factorise $(x-1)(x+2)+3(x-1)$

$(x-1)(x+2)+3(x-1)$ $\{\text{HCF} = (x-1)\}$
$= (x-1)[(x+2)+3]$
$= (x-1)(x+5)$

We use square brackets in the second line to help distinguish them.

7 Fully factorise:

a $(x+4)(x+5)+3(x+4)$
b $2(x+1)+(x+1)(x-3)$
c $(x-6)(x+2)-2(x+2)$
d $(x-10)^2+4(x-10)$
e $(d+7)^2+(d+6)(d+7)$
f $(x-y)(y-1)-5(y-1)$
g $15(a+1)^2-10(a+1)$
h $3(n-3)-7(n-3)^2$
i $n(n-3)-2(n-3)(n+1)$
j $(x-14)^2-3(x-14)(x+8)$

8 Jake has factorised $12x^2-18xy$ as $6(2x^2-3xy)$.

a Explain why Jake has not factorised the expression fully.
b Fully factorise $12x^2-18xy$.

9 All of the regions in the diagram are rectangles. Write an expression for the area of each of the following regions, fully factorising your answers.

a blue b red c total

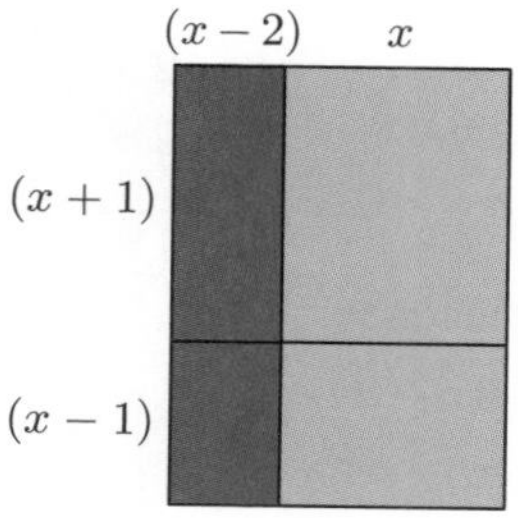

C DIFFERENCE OF TWO SQUARES FACTORISING

INVESTIGATION THE DIFFERENCE OF TWO SQUARES

In the diagram alongside, a square with side length b
has been cut from a square with side length a.

WORKSHEET

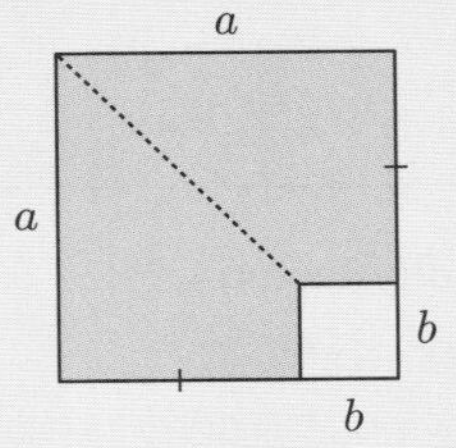

What to do:

1 Explain why the green shaded area is given by $a^2 - b^2$.

2 Copy the above diagram, or print the **worksheet** by clicking on
 the icon. Cut along the dotted line.

3 Rearrange the two trapezia to form a rectangle as shown.

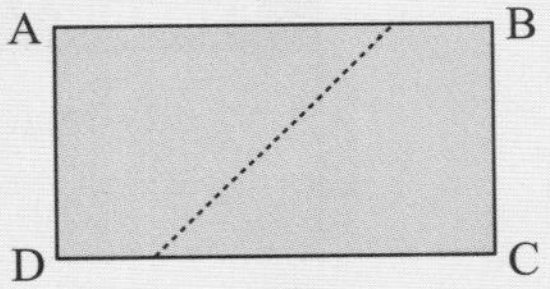

4 Find, in terms of a and b, the lengths of [AB] and [BC].

5 Hence find the area of the rectangle in the form $(\ldots\ldots)(\ldots\ldots)$.

6 What can be deduced by comparing the areas in **1** and **5**?

Using the FOIL rule, $(a + b)(a - b) = a^2 - ab + ab - b^2$
$$= a^2 - b^2$$

We can factorise expressions of the form $a^2 - b^2$ by reversing this process:

$$a^2 - b^2 = (a + b)(a - b)$$

Example 9 ◆)) Self Tutor

Fully factorise:

 a $x^2 - 4$ b $1 - 25y^2$

a $x^2 - 4$ $= x^2 - 2^2$ $= (x + 2)(x - 2)$	b $1 - 25y^2$ $= 1^2 - (5y)^2$ $= (1 + 5y)(1 - 5y)$

Write each term
as a square.

EXERCISE 19C

1 Fully factorise:

 a $d^2 - e^2$ b $p^2 - q^2$ c $q^2 - p^2$ d $x^2 - y^2$

 e $x^2 - 9$ f $x^2 - 100$ g $y^2 - 49$ h $16x^2 - 9$

 i $4b^2 - 1$ j $36y^2 - 49$ k $81 - d^2$ l $121 - 9y^2$

Example 10 **Self Tutor**

Fully factorise:

a $2x^2 - 18$ **b** $x^3 - xy^2$

a $2x^2 - 18$
$= 2(x^2 - 9)$
$= 2(x+3)(x-3)$

b $x^3 - xy^2$
$= x(x^2 - y^2)$
$= x(x+y)(x-y)$

Always look for common factors first.

2 Fully factorise:

a $3x^2 - 75$ **b** $8x^2 - 32$ **c** $5a^2 - 20$ **d** $5x^2 - 5$
e $9b^2 - 900$ **f** $80 - 5t^2$ **g** $6k^2 - 24$ **h** $15 - 15y^2$
i $r^3 - 49r$ **j** $z^3 - z$ **k** $x^5 - x^3$ **l** $x^3y - xy^3$

Example 11 **Self Tutor**

Fully factorise:

a $4a^2 - 9b^2$ **b** $x^2y^2 - 16$

a $4a^2 - 9b^2$
$= (2a)^2 - (3b)^2$
$= (2a + 3b)(2a - 3b)$

b $x^2y^2 - 16$
$= (xy)^2 - 4^2$
$= (xy + 4)(xy - 4)$

3 Fully factorise:

a $25a^2 - b^2$ **b** $x^2 - 81y^2$ **c** $16x^2 - 49y^2$ **d** $25p^2 - 36q^2$
e $81j^2 - k^2$ **f** $s^2t^2 - 9$ **g** $49x^2 - y^2z^2$ **h** $4d^2 - 25e^2$

Example 12 **Self Tutor**

Fully factorise:

a $(x+2)^2 - 9$ **b** $25 - (x-2)^2$

a $(x+2)^2 - 9$
$= (x+2)^2 - 3^2$
$= [(x+2)+3][(x+2)-3]$
$= [x+2+3][x+2-3]$
$= (x+5)(x-1)$

b $25 - (x-2)^2$
$= 5^2 - (x-2)^2$
$= [5 + (x-2)][5 - (x-2)]$
$= [5 + x - 2][5 - x + 2]$
$= (x+3)(7-x)$

Notice the use of the square brackets.

4 Fully factorise:

a $(x+2)^2 - 4$ **b** $(x-3)^2 - 36$ **c** $100 - (x-11)^2$
d $81 - (x-8)^2$ **e** $(x+7)^2 - 1$ **f** $9 - (x+4)^2$

5 **a** Write 391 as the difference of two squares. **b** Hence show that 17 is a factor of 391.

6 Answer the **Opening Problem** on page **384**.

D PERFECT SQUARE FACTORISATION

We have seen that

$$(a+b)^2 = (a+b)(a+b) = a^2+ab+ab+b^2 = a^2+2ab+b^2$$

and

$$(a-b)^2 = (a-b)(a-b) = a^2-ab-ab+b^2 = a^2-2ab+b^2$$

We can reverse this process to factorise expressions of the form $a^2+2ab+b^2$ or $a^2-2ab+b^2$.

$$\mathbf{a^2+2ab+b^2=(a+b)^2} \quad \text{and} \quad \mathbf{a^2-2ab+b^2=(a-b)^2}$$

Expressions such as $a^2+2ab+b^2$ and $a^2-2ab+b^2$ are called **perfect squares** because they factorise into the product of two identical factors.

For example, x^2+6x+9 and x^2-6x+9 are perfect squares because they factorise into two identical factors:

$x^2+6x+9=(x+3)^2$ and $x^2-6x+9=(x-3)^2$

Check these factorisations by expanding $(x+3)^2$ and $(x-3)^2$.

IDENTIFYING PERFECT SQUARES

Notice that $(a+b)^2 = a^2+2ab+b^2$ (squares: a^2, b^2) and $(a-b)^2=a^2-2ab+b^2$ (squares: a^2, b^2).

A perfect square must contain two squares a^2 and b^2, and a middle term which is $\pm 2ab$. The sign of the middle term indicates whether the perfect square is $(a+b)^2$ or $(a-b)^2$.

We can see that $x^2+10x+25$ is a perfect square because $x^2+10x+25$ contains two squares x^2 and 5^2 and a middle term $2\times x\times 5$.

$x^2+11x+25$ does not satisfy these conditions, because $11x \neq 2\times x\times 5$.

Example 13 — Self Tutor

Determine whether the following expressions are perfect squares:

a $x^2+12x+36$ **b** x^2-4x+9

a $x^2+12x+36 = x^2+12x+6^2$

The expression contains two squares x^2 and 6^2, and the middle term $12x = 2\times x\times 6$.

So, $x^2+12x+36$ is a perfect square.

b $x^2-4x+9=x^2-4x+3^2$

The expression contains two squares x^2 and 3^2, but the middle term $-4x \neq -2\times x\times 3$.

So, x^2-4x+9 is *not* a perfect square.

Example 14 — Self Tutor

Factorise:

a $x^2 + 20x + 100$ b $x^2 - 8x + 16$

a
$$\begin{aligned} & x^2 + 20x + 100 \\ &= x^2 + 2 \times x \times 10 + 10^2 \\ &= (x + 10)^2 \end{aligned}$$

b
$$\begin{aligned} & x^2 - 8x + 16 \\ &= x^2 - 2 \times x \times 4 + 4^2 \\ &= (x - 4)^2 \end{aligned}$$

EXERCISE 19D

1 Determine whether the following expressions are perfect squares:

a $x^2 + 16x + 64$ b $x^2 + 14x + 36$ c $a^2 - 6a + 9$

d $x^2 - 12x + 49$ e $t^2 - 2t + 1$ f $x^2 + 10x + 100$

2 Factorise:

a $x^2 - 2x + 1$ b $x^2 + 10x + 25$ c $x^2 + 8x + 16$

d $x^2 - 14x + 49$ e $x^2 + 22x + 121$ f $x^2 - 20x + 100$

g $x^2 + 12x + 36$ h $x^2 - 6x + 9$ i $x^2 + 24x + 144$

Example 15 — Self Tutor

Factorise:

a $16x^2 + 24x + 9$ b $4x^2 - 20x + 25$

a
$$\begin{aligned} & 16x^2 + 24x + 9 \\ &= (4x)^2 + 2 \times 4x \times 3 + 3^2 \\ &= (4x + 3)^2 \end{aligned}$$

b
$$\begin{aligned} & 4x^2 - 20x + 25 \\ &= (2x)^2 - 2 \times 2x \times 5 + 5^2 \\ &= (2x - 5)^2 \end{aligned}$$

3 Factorise:

a $4x^2 - 4x + 1$ b $25x^2 + 20x + 4$ c $64x^2 - 48x + 9$

d $9x^2 + 42x + 49$ e $36x^2 - 60x + 25$ f $16x^2 - 40x + 25$

4 Determine whether each expression is a perfect square, and factorise those which are:

a $x^2 + 18x + 81$ b $x^2 - 8x + 25$ c $4x^2 + 6x + 1$

d $9x^2 - 24x + 16$ e $16x^2 + 28x + 49$ f $49x^2 + 14x + 1$

g $1 - 2x + x^2$ h $x^2 - 4xy + 4y^2$ i $4x^2 + 9y^2 - 12xy$

Example 16 — Self Tutor

Fully factorise:

a $3x^2 - 18x + 27$ b $-2x^2 + 8x - 8$

a
$$\begin{aligned} & 3x^2 - 18x + 27 \\ &= 3(x^2 - 6x + 9) \\ &= 3(x^2 - 2 \times x \times 3 + 3^2) \\ &= 3(x - 3)^2 \end{aligned}$$

b
$$\begin{aligned} & -2x^2 + 8x - 8 \\ &= -2(x^2 - 4x + 4) \\ &= -2(x^2 - 2 \times x \times 2 + 2^2) \\ &= -2(x - 2)^2 \end{aligned}$$

Look for common factors first!

5 Fully factorise:

a $2x^2+12x+18$	**b** $2x^2-4x+2$	**c** $3x^2+12x+12$
d $4x^2-32x+64$	**e** $5x^2+50x+125$	**f** $-x^2+12x-36$
g $-x^2-16x-64$	**h** $-2x^2+40x-200$	**i** $-3x^2+30x-75$

6 Evaluate $30^2+2\times30\times1+1^2$, and hence find the square root of 961.

7

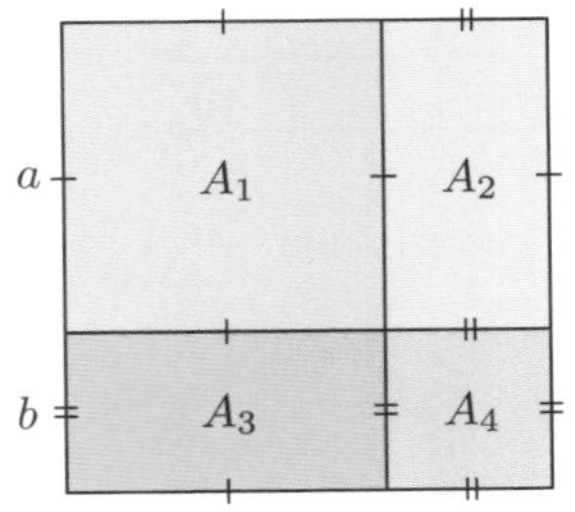

a Write expressions for the areas A_1, A_2, A_3, and A_4.

b Hence explain why $(a+b)^2=a^2+2ab+b^2$.

8 Use the perfect square factorisation to factorise:

a $x^2+2\sqrt{3}x+3$ **b** $2x^2+3y^2-2\sqrt{6}xy$

E FACTORISING QUADRATIC TRINOMIALS

A **quadratic trinomial** is an algebraic expression of the form ax^2+bx+c where x is a variable and a, b, c are constants, $a\neq0$.

We have previously used the FOIL rule to expand expressions of the form $(x+a)(x+b)$.

For example, $(x+5)(x+3)=x^2+3x+5x+15=x^2+8x+15$

Firsts **Outers** **Inners** **Lasts**

We now consider the reverse process. If we are given the expression $x^2+8x+15$, how can we deduce that it can be factorised as $(x+5)(x+3)$?

To do this, notice that the coefficient of x, which is 8, is the **sum** of 5 and 3. The constant term, which is 15, is the **product** of 5 and 3.

So, to factorise $x^2+8x+15$, we need two numbers whose sum is 8 and whose product is 15. The numbers are 5 and 3, so $x^2+8x+15=(x+5)(x+3)$.

$x^2+px+q=(x+a)(x+b)$
where a and b are two numbers whose sum is p, and whose product is q.

This process is sometimes called **sum and product** factorisation.

Example 17 Self Tutor

Factorise: $x^2 + 11x + 24$

We need to find two numbers with sum 11 and product 24.

We list pairs of numbers with product 24, and find their sum.

Number pair	1, 24	2, 12	3, 8	4, 6
Sum	25	14	11	10

(↑ this one: 3, 8 with sum 11)

The numbers we want are 3 and 8.

$\therefore \quad x^2 + 11x + 24 = (x+3)(x+8)$

Most of the time we can find these two numbers mentally. We then don't need to show all of the working.

If we try all of the number pairs with a particular product but none of the pairs have the correct sum, then we cannot use this method for factorisation.

EXERCISE 19E

1 Find two numbers which have:

a sum 8 and product 7
b sum 11 and product 30
c sum 17 and product 60
d sum 2 and product -8
e sum -1 and product -20
f sum -15 and product 56
g sum -22 and product -48
h sum -9 and product -10

2 Factorise:

a $x^2 + 7x + 10$
b $x^2 + 14x + 33$
c $x^2 + 19x + 34$
d $x^2 + 24x + 23$
e $x^2 + 16x + 48$
f $x^2 + 9x + 20$
g $x^2 + 21x + 54$
h $x^2 + 29x + 100$
i $x^2 + 16x + 63$

Example 18 Self Tutor

Factorise: $x^2 - 7x + 12$

sum $= -7$ and product $= 12$

$\therefore$ the numbers are -3 and -4

$\therefore \quad x^2 - 7x + 12 = (x-3)(x-4)$

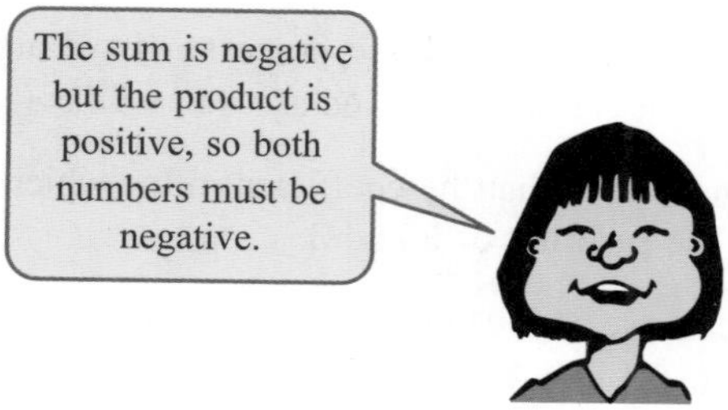

The sum is negative but the product is positive, so both numbers must be negative.

3 Factorise:

a $x^2 - 9x + 20$
b $x^2 - 18x + 56$
c $x^2 - 13x + 42$
d $x^2 - 11x + 28$
e $x^2 - 3x + 2$
f $x^2 - 16x + 63$
g $x^2 - 20x + 96$
h $x^2 - 17x + 30$
i $x^2 - 8x + 15$

4 Explain why the following quadratic trinomials cannot be factorised using the 'sum and product' method:

a $x^2 + 3x - 2$
b $x^2 + 2$

Example 19 Self Tutor

Factorise: **a** $x^2 - 2x - 15$ **b** $x^2 + x - 6$

a sum $= -2$ and product $= -15$

$\therefore$ the numbers are -5 and $+3$

$\therefore$ $x^2 - 2x - 15 = (x-5)(x+3)$

b sum $= 1$ and product $= -6$

$\therefore$ the numbers are -2 and $+3$

$\therefore$ $x^2 + x - 6 = (x-2)(x+3)$

Since the product is negative, the numbers must be opposite in sign.

5 Factorise:

a $x^2 - 5x - 6$ **b** $x^2 - 7x - 18$ **c** $x^2 + 11x - 80$

d $x^2 + x - 72$ **e** $x^2 + 8x - 33$ **f** $x^2 - 4x - 77$

g $x^2 + 16x - 57$ **h** $x^2 - x - 90$ **i** $x^2 - 17x - 84$

j $x^2 - 3x - 10$ **k** $x^2 + 4x - 45$ **l** $x^2 + 6x - 72$

Example 20 Self Tutor

Fully factorise by first removing a common factor: $3x^2 + 6x - 72$

$3x^2 + 6x - 72$ {look for a **common factor**}

$= 3(x^2 + 2x - 24)$ {sum $= 2$, product $= -24$

$= 3(x+6)(x-4)$ $\therefore$ the numbers are 6 and -4}

6 Fully factorise by first removing a common factor:

a $2x^2 + 6x + 4$ **b** $4x^2 + 28x + 40$ **c** $3x^2 + 12x + 9$

d $4x^2 - 8x - 12$ **e** $9x^2 + 27x - 36$ **f** $5x^2 - 20x + 15$

g $7x^2 - 28x - 35$ **h** $5x^2 - 45x - 110$ **i** $6x^2 - 72x + 120$

j $3x^2 - 15x - 18$ **k** $2x^2 - 14x - 36$ **l** $10x^2 - 10x - 200$

F MISCELLANEOUS FACTORISATION

In the following **Exercise** you will need to determine which factorisation method to use.

The flowchart below may be useful:

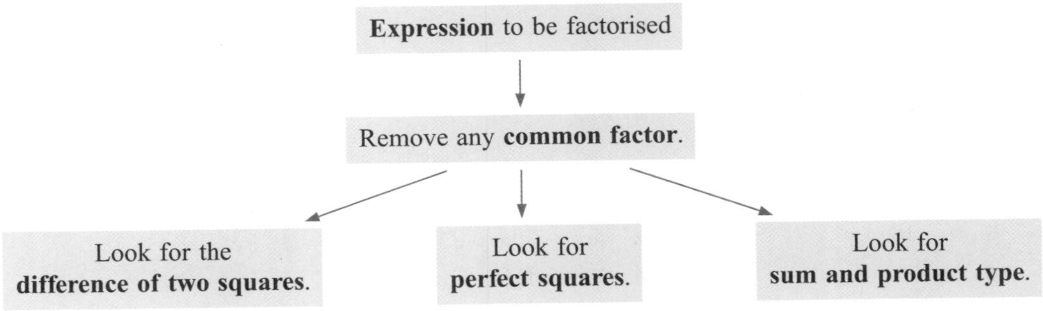

EXERCISE 19F

1 Fully factorise:

- **a** $4a^2 + 8a$
- **b** $3b^2 + 15$
- **c** $6x - 36y$
- **d** $p^2 + 12p + 35$
- **e** $x^2 - 17x - 18$
- **f** $x^2 - 3x - 4$
- **g** $-x^2 - 49x$
- **h** $h^2 + 2h^3$
- **i** $st^2 - 2st$
- **j** $-2x^2 - 18$
- **k** $r^2 + r - 42$
- **l** $20x - 5x^3$
- **m** $3z - 21yz$
- **n** $a^2 + 16ab$
- **o** $y^2 - 7y + 12$
- **p** $9x^2 - 9x - 18$
- **q** $6y^2 - 36y + 54$
- **r** $x^3 + 4x^2 + 4x$

2 Fully factorise:

- **a** $x^2 - 10x + 25$
- **b** $x^2 - 169$
- **c** $4c^2 - 16$
- **d** $10 - 10y^2$
- **e** $5x^2 - 125$
- **f** $12f^2 + 24f + 12$
- **g** $81y^2 - 49x^2$
- **h** $d^2 - 11d + 24$
- **i** $2x^2 - 32x + 128$

3 Fully factorise:

- **a** $pq^2 - p^2q - pq$
- **b** $4b^3 - 4b^2$
- **c** $c^2d^2 - 8cd$
- **d** $16y - 9y^3$
- **e** $(x+1)^2 - 2(x+1)$
- **f** $e^2f - fg^2$
- **g** $2(x-5) - x(x-5)$
- **h** $9(x+y) - y(x+y)$
- **i** $s(s+t) - t(s+t)$
- **j** $k^2 - 100k$
- **k** $6x^2 + 30x - 84$
- **l** $49mn^2 - m^3$

ACTIVITY 2

Click on the icon to play a game involving factorisation.

Shoot the correct expression, and advance through the rounds.

GAME

REVIEW SET 19A

1 Find the HCF of:

- **a** $3a^2b$ and $6ab$
- **b** $3(x+1)$ and $6(x+1)^2$

2 Fully factorise:

- **a** $x^2 - 3x$
- **b** $3mn + 6n^2$
- **c** $ax^3 + 2ax^2$

3 Fully factorise:

- **a** $-2x^2 - 32x$
- **b** $d(t+2) - 4(t+2)$
- **c** $(x-1)^2 - (x-1)$
- **d** $2x(x+3) - 5(x+3)$
- **e** $3(g+1)^2 - 9(g+1)$
- **f** $b(b-c) - c(b-c)$

4 Determine whether the following are perfect squares:

- **a** $x^2 - 4x + 9$
- **b** $16x^2 + 24x + 9$

5 Fully factorise:

- **a** $x^2 - 25$
- **b** $100 - k^2$
- **c** $x^2 + 14x + 49$
- **d** $9 - 16x^2$
- **e** $4x^2 + 20x + 25$
- **f** $9x^2 - 6x + 1$
- **g** $5x^2 - 20x + 20$
- **h** $9a^2 - 4b^2$
- **i** $6x^2 - 24$

6 Fully factorise:

a $x^2 + 10x + 21$ **b** $x^2 + 4x - 21$ **c** $x^2 - 4x - 21$
d $6 - 5x + x^2$ **e** $4x^2 + 8x - 12$ **f** $x^2 + 13x + 36$
g $20 + 9x + x^2$ **h** $2x^2 - 2x - 60$ **i** $3x^2 - 30x + 48$

REVIEW SET 19B

1 Find the HCF of:

a $6y^2$ and $8y$ **b** $4(x-2)$ and $2(x-2)(x+3)$

2 Fully factorise:

a $2x^2 + 6x$ **b** $-2xy - 4x$ **c** $(x+1)(x+3) - 2(x+3)$

3 Fully factorise:

a $xy^3 - 16xy$ **b** $3x^2 - 60x + 300$ **c** $p(a+2) - q(a+2)$
d $4cd^2 - 6c^2d$ **e** $(k-3) + (k-3)^2$ **f** $x(x-1) + 3x$

4 Explain why $x^2 - 2x + 4$ cannot be factorised by the 'sum and product' method.

5 Fully factorise:

a $2x^2 - 50$ **b** $x^2 - 12x + 36$ **c** $n^2 - 6n + 9$
d $49 - 9z^2$ **e** $2x^2 + 4x + 2$ **f** $x^3 - 16x$

6 Fully factorise:

a $x^2 + 12x + 35$ **b** $x^2 + 2x - 35$ **c** $x^2 - 12x + 35$
d $2x^2 - 4x - 70$ **e** $30 - 11x + x^2$ **f** $x^2 - 8x - 20$
g $x^2 - 14x + 33$ **h** $4x^2 - 36x - 88$ **i** $2x^2 + 10x - 72$

HISTORICAL NOTE GRACE CHISHOLM YOUNG 1868 - 1944

Grace Chisholm was born in 1868 near London, England. Her father held the prestigious position of Warden of the Standards, which meant he was in charge of the Department of Weights and Measures for the British Government. She was therefore brought up in a well educated upper-class environment.

In early childhood, Grace suffered from headaches and nightmares. As a result, she only studied mental arithmetic and music, with her mother as tutor. Initially she wished to study medicine, but her mother forbade it. Instead, with the encouragement of her father, she won a scholarship to study mathematics at Girton College, Cambridge.

Grace found the mathematical atmosphere at Cambridge stifling, but she still managed to qualify for a first class degree. Despite her outstanding performance, her hopes of pursuing a career as a mathematician were small because women could not at that time be admitted to graduate schools in England.

After completing another final honours year at Oxford, Grace moved to the University of Gottingen in Germany. Here she qualified for her doctorate and was the first woman to be officially awarded that degree in any subject in Germany.

Her former tutor William Young read her thesis and suggested that they write an astronomy book together. Eventually they married, and continued to work together, with Grace performing research and William teaching mathematics. Despite Grace doing most of the research, William convinced her that most of the papers should appear under his name.

Whilst raising six children she continued to produce high quality mathematical research. At the time of her death in 1944, Grace had been proposed as an honorary fellow of Girton College.

Chapter 20

Statistics

Contents:

OPENING PROBLEM

Chan-juan wanted to find the mean number of people living in the apartments on her block. Her block is quite large, so instead of surveying every apartment, she only visited the apartments in her own building. She obtained the following results for the number of people living in each apartment:

1 2 2 4 3 2 1 3 5 2 1 4 1 2 2 3 2 4 1 2
2 3 1 2 5 1 2 4 1 3 5 2 8 4 1 3 4 2 3 1

Things to think about:

a What is the most commonly occurring number of people in an apartment?

b Can you find the mean number of people per apartment?

c Can Chan-juan use this data to predict the mean number of people per apartment for the whole block? What factors would she need to consider?

Statistics is the art of solving problems and answering questions by collecting and analysing data.

The facts or pieces of information we collect are called **data**.

One piece of information is known as *datum* (singular), whereas lots of pieces of information are called *data* (plural).

A list of information is called a **data set**. If it is not in an organised form, it is called **raw data**.

The data that we collect is either **categorical data** or **numerical data**. We will study both types of data in this chapter.

A CATEGORICAL DATA

A **categorical variable** describes a particular quality or characteristic. The data is divided into **categories**, and the information collected is called **categorical data**.

Examples of categorical variables are:

- *Method of getting to school*: the categories could be train, bus, car, and walking.
- *Colour of eyes*: the categories could be blue, brown, hazel, green, and grey.

Consider the following example:

Jordan wanted to know which season his classmates liked most. The variable *favourite season* is a categorical variable, and the possible categories are autumn, winter, spring, and summer.

Jordan collected the following categorical data from the 30 students in his class. He recorded the data using A $\equiv$ autumn, W $\equiv$ winter, Sp $\equiv$ spring, and Su $\equiv$ summer:

Sp A A Su W   Su Sp A Sp W   A Sp W Su A
A Sp Su W Sp   Su W Sp A Sp   Sp A Sp Sp Su

TALLY AND FREQUENCY TABLES

We can record the results of a survey in a **tally and frequency table**. We place a tick mark in the tally column for each of the data. A set of five ticks is grouped together as 𝍸 .

The *frequency* column alongside shows the total number of students who prefer each of the seasons.

Season	*Tally*	*Frequency*
autumn	𝍸 |||	8
winter	𝍸	5
spring	𝍸 𝍸 |	11
summer	𝍸 |	6
	Total	30

The **mode** of a set of categorical data is the category that occurs most frequently. The mode for this data set is *spring*.

DISPLAYING CATEGORICAL DATA

Once we have recorded the frequency of each category, we can **graph** the data. Appropriate graphs for displaying categorical data are:

Vertical column graph

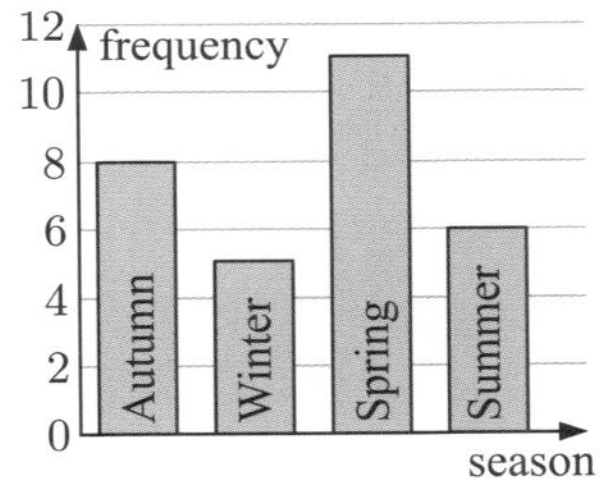

Horizontal bar chart

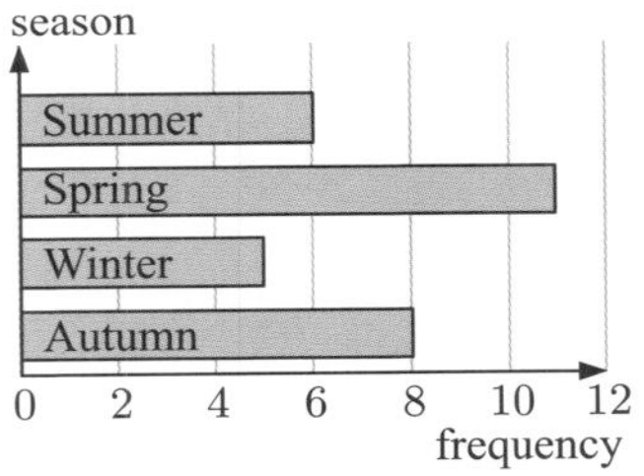

Pie chart

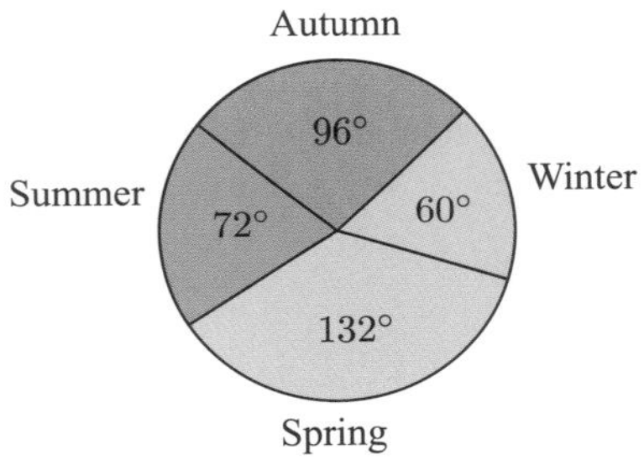

To calculate the sector angles in the pie chart, notice that each student represents $\frac{1}{30}$th of the pie chart, which is $\frac{1}{30} \times 360° = 12°$. So, the sector angle for *autumn* is $8 \times 12° = 96°$, and so on.

Click on the icon to run software which can be used to draw:

- a vertical column graph
- a horizontal bar chart
- a pie chart.

STATISTICS PACKAGE

EXERCISE 20A

1 Write down possible categories for the following categorical variables:

a flavours of ice cream
b methods of transport
c families of musical instruments in a band
d methods of communication.

2 50 students were asked their favourite way of spending time with their friends.
The responses are given below, where $B \equiv$ going to the beach, $M \equiv$ going to the movies, $P \equiv$ going to a park, $S \equiv$ shopping, and $V \equiv$ playing video games.

V V S B P   M S B V S   M M M B S   M S M B B   V P V S M
P S S M M   V S V M S   B B S V M   B S M P P   M V S M P

a Complete a tally and frequency table for this data.
b How many students chose shopping?
c Find the mode of the data.

3 Guests of a hotel in Paris were asked which country they lived in. The results are shown in the vertical column graph.

- **a** How many guests were surveyed?
- **b** Find the mode of the data. Explain what this means.
- **c** What percentage of the guests surveyed were from Spain?

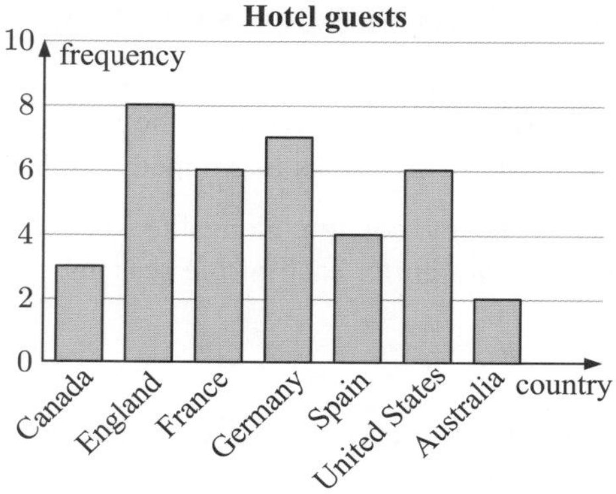

4 Students at a school took part in a Mathematics competition. Their results are illustrated in the pie chart alongside.

- **a** Which result was achieved by the least number of students?
- **b** Which result was achieved by more than half of the students?

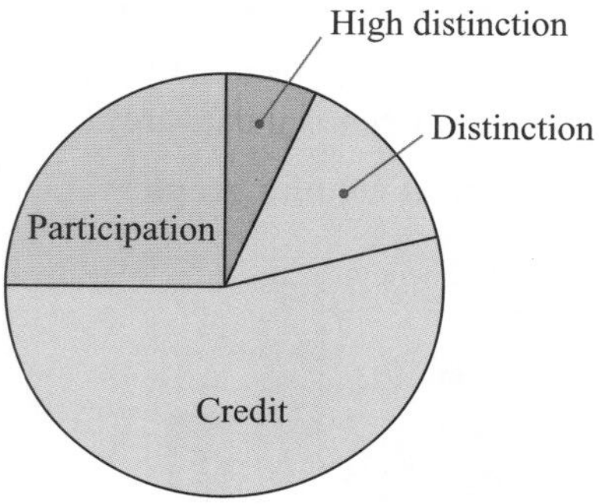

5 A class of 25 students is having a party for multicultural week. The class captain conducts a survey to determine which cuisine is most desired for the party.

The choices were: Chinese (C), Greek (G), Indian (In), Italian (It), and Thai (T).

The votes were:

In It It G It   C T G G It   T G C In In
G It It C T   It It T In It

- **a** Draw a tally and frequency table for the data.
- **b** Construct a column graph to display the data.
- **c** According to the data, which cuisine should the class captain organise for the party?

6 A member of each household in one street was asked which brand of washing machine they owned. The data collected is summarised alongside.

- **a** How many households were surveyed?
- **b** Find the mode of the data. Explain what this means.
- **c** Construct a horizontal bar chart for the data.
- **d** What percentage of households own a brand E washing machine?

Brand	*Frequency*
A	11
B	5
C	13
D	8
E	7
F	6

7 Sixty students were asked which elective subject they would like to learn next semester.
Their first preferences are given in the frequency table alongside.

- **a** Draw a pie chart to display this data.
- **b** What percentage of the students want to learn Art?
- **c** Which two subjects account for more than half of the students' choices?

Subject	*Frequency*
Art	11
Design	8
Music	17
Performing Arts	15
Textiles	9

DISCUSSION

When analysing categorical data, what information is easiest to obtain from:

- a vertical column graph or horizontal bar chart
- a pie chart?

B NUMERICAL DATA

A **numerical variable** describes a quantity which takes a value which is a number.
The **numerical data** is either counted or measured.

For example, a numerical variable could be the *number of pins in a pin cushion.*
There could be 0, 1, 2, 3, 4, ... pins in the cushion.

We can organise numerical data using a tally and frequency table. For example, for the data in the **Opening Problem** we obtain this table:

Notice that the data value '8' is separated from the rest of the data. We call this data value an **outlier**.

Number of people	*Tally*	*Frequency*
1	卌 卌	10
2	卌 卌 |||	13
3	卌 ||	7
4	卌		6
5					3
6		
7		
8			1
	Total	40

We can display numerical data using a **column graph** or a **dot plot**.

Column graph

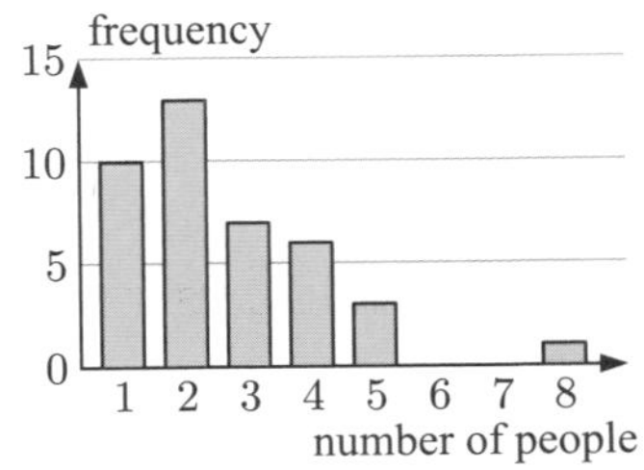

Dot plot

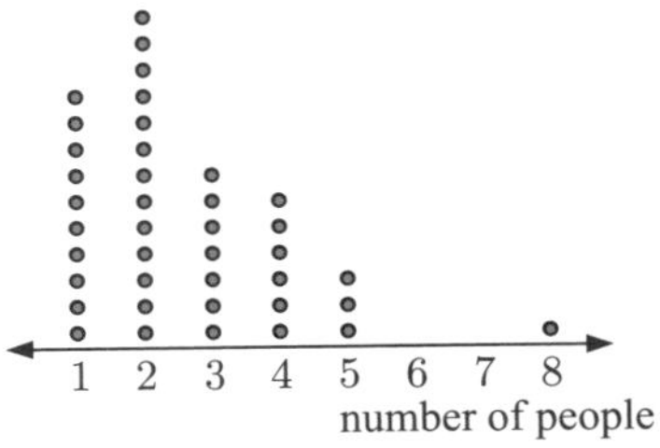

In a dot plot, each dot represents a data value.

Example 1 **Self Tutor**

Every time Ashley buys something at the canteen, he has to wait in line. On his last 20 visits to the canteen, he counted the number of people in front of him when he arrived:

7	10	6	5	5	8	10	7	9	7
8	6	1	7	9	11	5	8	9	8

a Draw a dot plot of the data.

b Are there any outliers in the data?

c On what percentage of visits were there more than 8 people in front of Ashley?

a

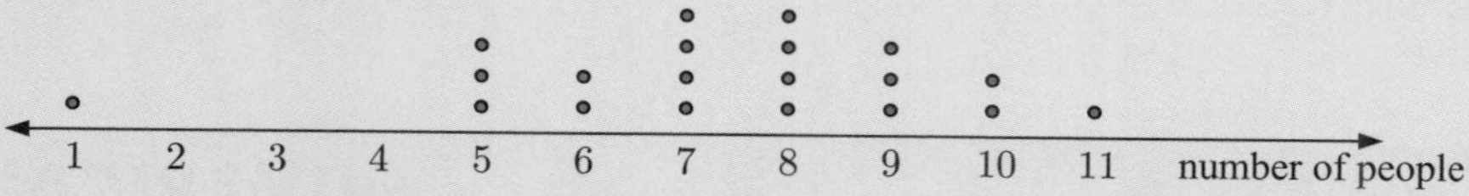

b Yes, the data value '1' is an outlier.

c There were more than 8 people in front of Ashley on $3+2+1=6$ occasions.

This is $\frac{6}{20} \times 100\% = 30\%$ of his visits.

You can use the **statistics package** or your **calculator** to graph numerical data.

STATISTICS PACKAGE

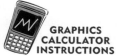

GRAPHICS CALCULATOR INSTRUCTIONS

EXERCISE 20B

1 Classify the following variables as either categorical or numerical:

a the number of text messages you send in a day

b the places where you access the internet

c the brands of breakfast cereal

d the heights of students in your class

e the number of road fatalities each day

f the breeds of horses

g the number of hours you sleep each night.

2 A randomly selected sample of teenagers was asked "How many times per week do you eat red meat?" A column graph has been constructed from the results.

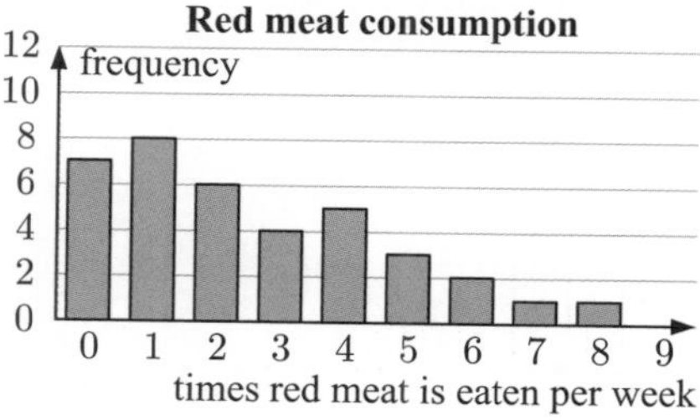

a How many teenagers answered the survey?

b How many of the teenagers ate red meat at least once per week?

c What percentage of the teenagers ate red meat more than twice per week?

3 25 randomly selected residents of a retirement village were asked "How many great-grandchildren do you have?" The following dot plot was constructed from the data.

- **a** How many residents do not have any great-grandchildren?
- **b** What percentage of residents have more than one great-grandchild?
- **c** How would you describe the data value of 9?

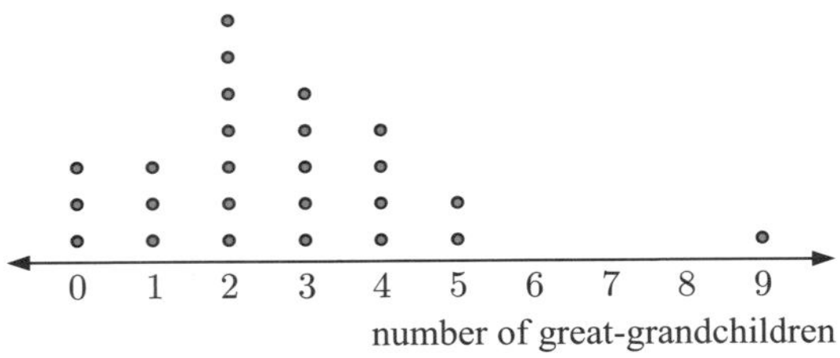

4 Bernadette counts the number of tomatoes on each of her tomato plants. The results are shown in the table alongside.

- **a** How many tomato plants does Bernadette own?
- **b** Draw a column graph to display the data.
- **c** Are there any outliers?

Number of tomatoes	*Frequency*
5	2
6	7
7	8
8	5
9	3
10	1

5 Rosie owns a small bakery. She records the number of doughnuts sold each day for four weeks:

15	14	12	8	16	17	12	14	13	18	12	11	13	15
14	16	17	11	18	12	15	13	15	16	12	15	11	14

- **a** Construct a tally and frequency table for this data.
- **b** Display the data using a column graph.
- **c** On what percentage of days were 15 or more doughnuts sold?
- **d** State any outliers in this data.

6 30 customers in a supermarket were asked how many litres of milk they bought each week. The following data was collected:

3	2	1	4	5	0	2	6	3	2	1	1	2	2	3
2	4	0	1	1	2	3	5	0	1	2	4	2	10	2

- **a** Construct a dot plot to display the data.
- **b** Are there any outliers in the data?
- **c** What percentage of the customers do not buy milk?
- **d** What percentage of the customers buy 3 or more litres of milk each week?

C GROUPED DATA

In situations where there are large numbers of different data values, it is not sensible to organise the data in a frequency table. It is also often inappropriate to display the data by dot plot or column graph.

For example, a local kindergarten was concerned about the number of vehicles passing by between 8:45 am and 9:00 am. Over 30 consecutive week days they recorded data:

27	30	17	13	46	23	40	28	38	24	23	22	18	29	16
35	24	18	24	44	32	52	31	39	32	9	41	38	24	32

In situations like this, it is appropriate to group the data in **class intervals**. In this case we use class intervals of length 10 in the tally and frequency table:

The **modal class** is the class with the highest frequency. In this case the modal class is 20 to 29 cars.

Number of cars	*Tally*	*Frequency*
0 to 9	|	1
10 to 19	𝍸	5
20 to 29	𝍸 𝍸	10
30 to 39	𝍸 ||||	9
40 to 49	||||	4
50 to 59	|	1
	Total	30

DISPLAYING GROUPED DATA

We can display grouped data using a **column graph** as before, except that the columns correspond to the class intervals, rather than individual values.

Passing traffic

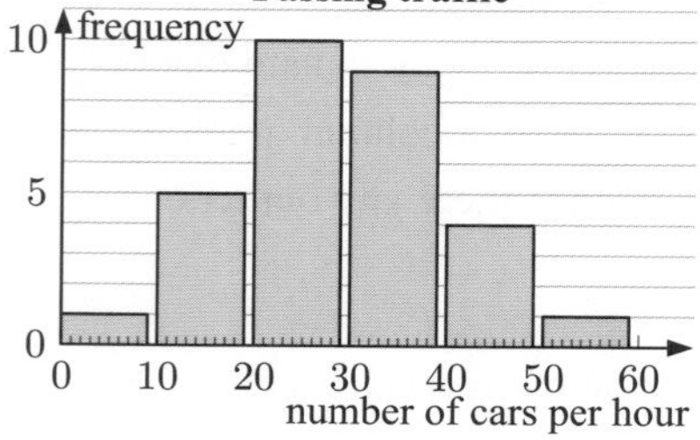

DISCUSSION

- If we are given a set of raw data, how can we efficiently find the lowest and highest data values?
- If the data values are grouped in classes on a frequency table or column graph, do we still know what the highest and lowest values are?
- Is there another way to display data in groups without 'losing' information about the highest and lowest values?

STEM-AND-LEAF PLOTS

A **stem-and-leaf plot** or **stem plot** is a method of writing data in groups without losing information about the actual data values. However, it still allows us to compare the frequencies of each group.

For numbers with two digits, the first digit forms part of the **stem** and the second digit forms a **leaf**.

For example, for the first vehicle data value which is 27, the stem is 2 and the leaf is 7.

Once a stem-and-leaf plot has been constructed, we can write the leaves in order to form an **ordered stem-and-leaf plot**.

For the data on vehicles passing the kindergarten, we have:

Stem-and-leaf plot

Stem	*Leaf*
0	9
1	7 3 8 6 8
2	7 3 8 4 3 2 9 4 4 4
3	0 8 5 2 1 9 2 8 2
4	6 0 4 1
5	2

Scale: 1 | 7 = 17

Ordered stem-and-leaf plot

Stem	*Leaf*
0	9
1	3 6 7 8 8
2	2 3 3 4 4 4 4 7 8 9
3	0 1 2 2 2 5 8 8 9
4	0 1 4 6
5	2

Scale: 1 | 7 = 17

Notice that:

- we write a **scale** to show the place value of each leaf
- the lowest data value is 9 and the highest data value is 52
- the modal class is 20 to 29 cars.

Example 2 — Self Tutor

The ages of guests at a 21st birthday party were:

22	20	18	27	35	21	48	19	21	47	17	26	49
16	21	48	19	22	31	20	18	21	19	45	22	

a Draw a stem-and-leaf plot for the data.
b Redraw the stem-and-leaf plot so that it is ordered.
c How many guests attended the party?
d How old was the youngest guest?
e How many guests were at least 30 years old?
f What percentage of guests were in their twenties?

a The stem-and-leaf plot is:

Stem	*Leaf*
1	8 9 7 6 9 8 9
2	2 0 7 1 1 6 1 2 0 1 2
3	5 1
4	8 7 9 8 5

1 | 8 means 18

b The ordered stem-and-leaf plot is:

Stem	*Leaf*
1	6 7 8 8 9 9 9
2	0 0 1 1 1 1 2 2 2 6 7
3	1 5
4	5 7 8 8 9

c 25 guests attended the party.

d The youngest guest was 16 years old.

e 7 guests were at least 30 years old.

f 11 guests were in their twenties.
The percentage of guests who were in their twenties $= \frac{11}{25} \times 100\% = 44\%$

EXERCISE 20C

1 Dave plays golf almost every day. The data set given shows his scores for his last 40 rounds:

72	81	78	77	82	78	89	82
85	76	75	81	74	87	84	77
80	83	79	82	75	74	74	71
75	79	72	76	71	75	82	78
76	76	81	77	72	84	87	83

a Construct a tally and frequency table for this data using the class intervals 70 - 74, 75 - 79, 80 - 84, and 85 - 89.
b How many of Dave's scores were more than 84?
c What percentage of Dave's scores were less than 75?
d Copy and complete:
More scores were in the interval ...... than in any other interval.

2 An English teacher asked her students to write a brief description of themselves. The teacher recorded the number of words each student used, and displayed the results in a column graph.

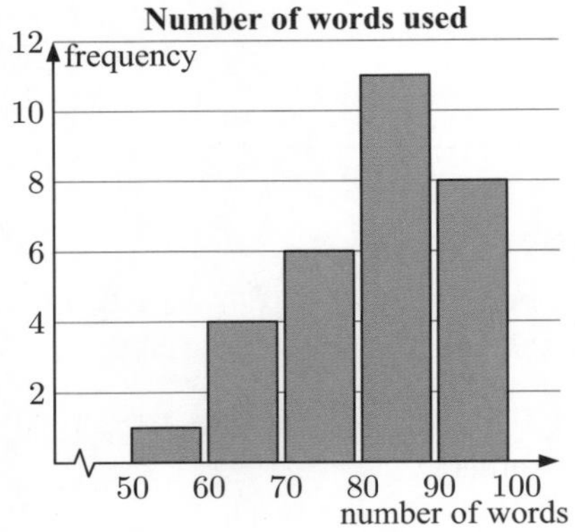

The -∿- in the horizontal axis indicates a break in the values.

- **a** How many students are in the class?
- **b** Find the modal class of the data.
- **c** How many students did not reach the minimum word limit of 70 words?
- **d** Is it possible to determine the highest number of words used?

3 A delicatessen records how many customers it has each day for 50 days. The results are given below:

81	82	75	83	104	92	112	124	110	92
111	105	78	87	99	86	129	115	121	76
109	75	104	96	74	104	98	114	106	109
101	110	92	86	122	118	115	117	84	71
73	116	119	122	94	81	107	109	115	127

- **a** Construct a tally and frequency table for this data using the class intervals 70 - 79, 80 - 89, 90 - 99, 100 - 109, 110 - 119, and 120 - 129.
- **b** Draw a column graph of the data.
- **c** Find the modal class of the data.
- **d** On what percentage of the days did the delicatessen have at least 100 customers?

4 For the data in this stem-and-leaf plot, find:

- **a** the value indicated by the shaded number
- **b** the maximum value
- **c** the number of values greater than 50.

Stem	*Leaf*
2	5 6 9
3	1 2 7 7
4	0 3 4 6 9
5	2 5 6

2 | 6 means 26

5 **a** Draw an unordered stem-and-leaf plot for the following data using the stems 1, 2, 3, 4, and 5:

27	34	19	36	52	34	42	51	18	48
29	27	33	30	46	19	35	24	21	56

- **b** Redraw the stem-and-leaf plot from **a** so that it is ordered.
- **c** State the modal class for the data.

6 For the ordered stem-and-leaf plot given, find:

- **a** the minimum value
- **b** the maximum value
- **c** the number of data with values greater than 90
- **d** the number of data with values of at least 100
- **e** the percentage of data with values less than 75.

Stem	*Leaf*
7	3 4 6 7 8 9 9
8	0 0 1 1 2 3 3 5 5 6 7 8 8
9	1 1 2 4 4 5 8 9
10	2 3 7
11	
12	2

9 | 1 means 91

7 The number of students absent from City Bay High School is recorded for 40 days during winter:

21	16	23	24	18	29	35	37	41	38	33	28	29	34
25	23	17	26	34	33	10	27	49	52	43	41	31	
24	20	25	23	19	22	12	16	17	15	14	14	32	

- **a** Construct a stem-and-leaf plot for this data using 1, 2, 3, 4, and 5 as the stems.
- **b** Redraw the stem-and-leaf plot so that it is ordered.
- **c** What was the **i** highest **ii** lowest number of absences for the period?
- **d** On what percentage of the days were there 40 or more students absent?
- **e** Attendance is described as 'good' if there are less than 25 absences per day in winter. On what percentage of the days was the attendance 'good'?

8 Mandy's netball team went undefeated for the season. The winning margins for each game were:

32	20	1	7	5	13	14	9	23	12	6	55
14	23	30	16	6	13	24	10	4	19	8	27

- **a** Construct an unordered stem-and-leaf plot using the stems 0, 1, 2, 3, 4, and 5.
- **b** Order the stem-and-leaf plot.
- **c** Find the maximum and minimum winning margins.
- **d** Find the modal class of the data.
- **e** In how many games was the winning margin less than 20 points?
- **f** Are there any outliers in this data set?

D MEASURING THE CENTRE AND SPREAD

We can gain a better understanding of a data set by locating the **middle** or **centre** of the data, and by measuring its **spread**. Knowing one of these without the other is often of little use.

MEASURING THE CENTRE

There are *three statistics* that are used to measure the **centre** of a data set. These are the **mean**, the **median**, and the **mode**.

THE MEAN

The **mean** of a data set is the arithmetic average of the data.

$$\textbf{mean} = \frac{\textbf{the sum of all data values}}{\textbf{the number of data values}}$$

The mean gives us a single number which indicates a centre of the data set. It is not necessarily a member of the data set.

For example, suppose the mean success rate of a basketball team from the free throw line is 78%. It is likely that several of the players score less than 78%, and several score more than 78%. It does not necessarily mean that any of the players score exactly 78% from the free throw line.

THE MEDIAN

An ordered data set is obtained by listing the data, usually from smallest to largest.

The **median** is the *middle value* of an ordered data set.

The median splits the data in two halves. Half of the data are less than or equal to the median, and half are greater than or equal to the median.

For example, if the median success rate of a basketball team from the free throw line is 78%, then half of the team scores less than or equal to 78%, and half scores greater than or equal to 78%.

For an **odd number** of data, the median is one of the data.

For an **even number** of data, the median is the average of the two middle values. It may therefore not be one of the original data.

Here is a rule for finding the median:

If there are n data values, find the value of $\frac{n+1}{2}$.

The median is the $\left(\frac{n+1}{2}\right)$th data value.

For example:

When $n = 9$, $\frac{n+1}{2} = 5$, so the median is the 5th ordered data value.

When $n = 12$, $\frac{n+1}{2} = 6.5$, so the median is the average of the 6th and 7th ordered data values.

THE MODE

The **mode** is the most frequently occurring value in the data set.

There may be two data values which are the most frequently occurring. In this case both values are modes, and we say the data is **bimodal**.

Example 3

◀) Self Tutor

The numbers of games won by a football team over the last 9 seasons have been:

$$5 \quad 7 \quad 3 \quad 6 \quad 5 \quad 9 \quad 8 \quad 7 \quad 5.$$

For this data set, find:

 a the mean **b** the median **c** the mode.

a mean $= \dfrac{5+7+3+6+5+9+8+7+5}{9}$ ⟵ sum of the data

 9 ⟵ 9 data values

 $= \dfrac{55}{9}$

 ≈ 6.11 wins

b The ordered data set is: $\cancel{3} \ \cancel{5} \ \cancel{5} \ \cancel{5} \ 6 \ \cancel{7} \ \cancel{7} \ \cancel{8} \ \cancel{9}$ $\{ n = 9, \ \frac{n+1}{2} = 5 \}$

 \therefore the median $= 6$ wins

c 5 is the score which occurs most often

 \therefore the mode $= 5$ wins

Suppose the team in **Example 3** wins 7 games in the next season.

We would expect the mean to increase because the new data value is greater than the old mean.

In fact, the new mean $= \dfrac{55+7}{10}$

 $= \dfrac{62}{10}$

 $= 6.2$ wins

If a data set has more than two modes, we say that the mode is undefined.

The new ordered data set is: $\cancel{3} \ \cancel{5} \ \cancel{5} \ \cancel{5} \ \underbrace{6 \ 7}_{} \ \cancel{7} \ \cancel{7} \ \cancel{8} \ \cancel{9}$

 two middle scores

\therefore the new median $= \dfrac{6+7}{2} = 6.5$ wins

This new data set is bimodal with modes 5 and 7 wins.

MEASURING THE SPREAD

In this course we will use the **range** to measure the spread of a data set.

> The **range** of a data set is the difference between the **maximum** or largest data value, and the **minimum** or smallest data value.
>
> **range = maximum value − minimum value**

Example 4

◀) Self Tutor

The number of bedrooms in the houses on a street are listed below:

 2 3 1 3 2 2 4 3 2 2 5 1 2 1 3 1

Find the range of this data set.

The minimum value is 1, and the maximum value is 5.

\therefore the range $= 5 - 1 = 4$.

You can use the **statistics package** or your **calculator** to find the measures of centre and spread.

STATISTICS PACKAGE

GRAPHICS CALCULATOR INSTRUCTIONS

EXERCISE 20D.1

1 Find the mean, median, mode, and range for the data set:

- **a** 1, 3, 4, 5, 9, 9, 11
- **b** 10, 12, 12, 15, 15, 17, 18, 18, 18, 19
- **c** 8, 4, 17, 11, 10, 10, 12, 11, 9, 18, 11, 6, 17, 7, 8
- **d** 127, 123, 115, 105, 145, 133, 142, 115, 135, 148, 129, 127, 103, 130, 146, 140, 125, 124, 119, 128, 141, 116

2 In a survey, 25 randomly selected women were asked to give their shoe size. The results were:

7.5	7	6.5	8.5	9	10	11	6.5	8.5	9	8	8	9.5
8.5	7.5	5	7	9	8.5	8	8	9.5	10	6	7.5	

- **a** Find the range of the data. Explain what this means.
- **b** Find the median of the data.
- **c** Find the mode of the data. Explain what this means.
- **d** If you were a shoe store owner, would you stock the same number of shoes for each size? Explain your answer.

3 The prices of 20 cars in a used car dealership are:

\$4800	\$7900	\$12 950	\$3000	\$4950	\$9800	\$12 000
\$11 000	\$6200	\$5250	\$8750	\$6900	\$9900	\$7500
\$8250	\$6900	\$5800	\$10 000	\$8500	\$7600	

- **a** Calculate the mean price of cars in the dealership.
- **b** Calculate the median price of cars in the dealership.
- **c** A luxury car is now being sold at the dealership for \$45 000.
  Find the new **i** mean **ii** median price of the cars in the dealership.
- **d** Which measure of centre was most affected by the inclusion of the value \$45 000?
- **e** How would you describe the value \$45 000 relative to the other data?

Example 5 Self Tutor

Find the median and mean of the data set illustrated:

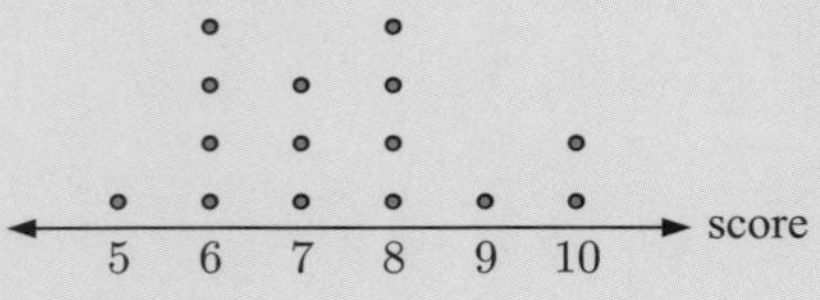

In order, the data values are:

~~5, 6, 6, 6, 6, 7, 7,~~ 7, ~~8, 8, 8, 8, 9, 10, 10~~

Now $n = 15$ so $\frac{n+1}{2} = 8$

$\therefore$ the median is 7.

$$\text{The mean} = \frac{5+6+6+....+9+10+10}{15} = \frac{111}{15} = 7.4$$

4 Find the median and mean of the data set:

a

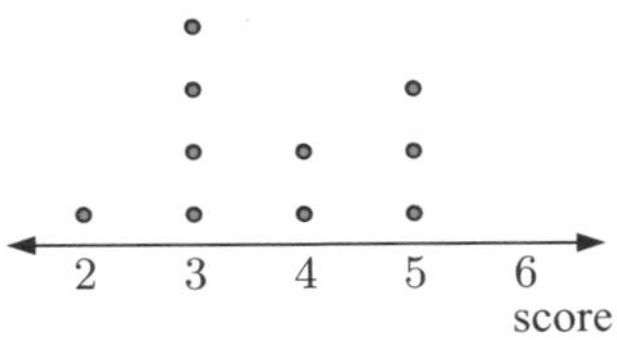

b

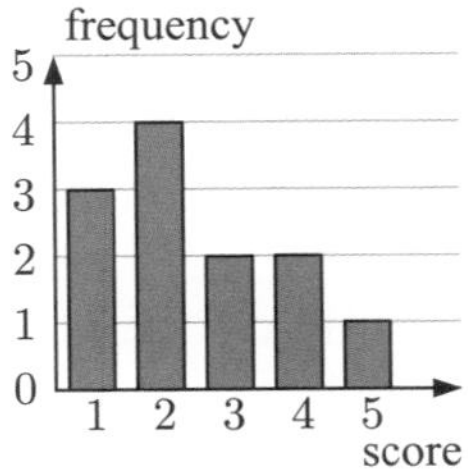

c

Stem	*Leaf*
2	1 3
3	2 5 6
4	3 4 4 5 8
5	1 5 7

2 | 1 means 21

Example 6 **Self Tutor**

A set of 7 data values has a mean of 9. Find the sum of the data values.

$$\text{mean} = \frac{\text{sum of data values}}{\text{number of data values}}$$

$$\therefore\ 9 = \frac{\text{sum of data values}}{7}$$

$\therefore$ the sum of the data values $= 9 \times 7 = 63$

5 A set of 12 data values has a mean of 6. Find the sum of the data values.

6 Huang does casual work at a petrol outlet. On average, he has earned €214.50 per week for the last 6 weeks. How much has he earned in total?

7 It started raining on Sunday October 1st. 11 mm of rain fell that day. On the next 5 days 24 mm, 28 mm, 22 mm, 16 mm, and 13 mm of rain fell.

a Find the mean rainfall from Sunday to Friday.

b How much rain would need to fall on Saturday for the mean to rise to 20 mm?

c If 10 mm of rain fell on Saturday, calculate the mean rainfall for the week.

8 Helen rolled a die eight times. The numbers she rolled had a mean of 4, a median of 3.5, a mode of 3, and a range of 4. List the results of Helen's rolls, from smallest to largest.

ACTIVITY — A MEAN GAME

Use the bridges to move from the Start circle to the Finish circle. The mean of the numbers you have landed on must never drop below 5 or rise above 10. You cannot land on the same island more than once.

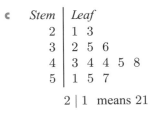

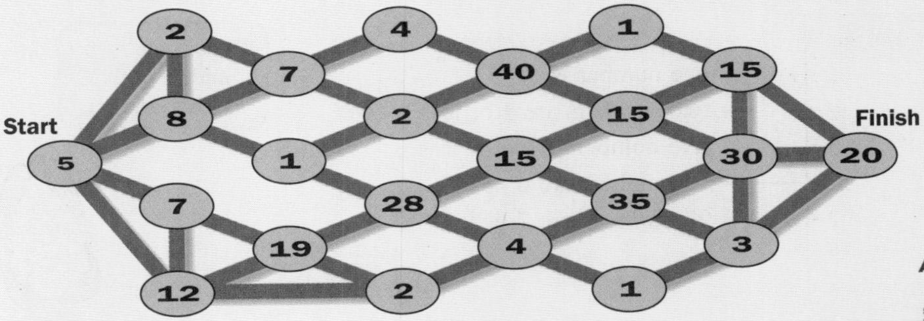

ACTIVITY

Click on the icon to run this Activity as a computer game.

DISCUSSION

Does it make sense to find the mean or median of categorical data?

MEASURES OF THE CENTRE AND SPREAD FROM A FREQUENCY TABLE

When the same data appear many times, we often summarise the data in a frequency table.

We can find the measures of the centre and spread directly from the table, without having to list the individual data values.

Consider the data opposite.

Score	*Frequency*
3	1
4	1
5	3
6	7
7	15
8	8
9	5
Total	40

THE MODE

There are 15 of data value 7, which is more than any other data value.

The mode is therefore 7.

THE MEAN

Adding a 'Product' column to the table helps to add all of the scores.

For example, the data value 7 occurs 15 times, and these total $7 \times 15 = 105$.

By adding all of the products, we find the sum of the scores is 278.

So, the mean $= \frac{278}{40} = 6.95$.

Score	*Frequency*	*Product*
3	1	$3 \times 1 = 3$
4	1	$4 \times 1 = 4$
5	3	$5 \times 3 = 15$
6	7	$6 \times 7 = 42$
7	15	$7 \times 15 = 105$
8	8	$8 \times 8 = 64$
9	5	$9 \times 5 = 45$
Total	40	278

THE MEDIAN

The sample size $n = 40$, so $\frac{n+1}{2} = \frac{41}{2} = 20.5$

$\therefore$ the median is the average of the 20th and 21st data values.

In the table below, the blue numbers show us accumulated values.

Score	*Frequency*		
3	1	1	one number is 3
4	1	2	two numbers are 4 or less
5	3	5	five numbers are 5 or less
6	7	12	12 numbers are 6 or less
7	15	27	27 numbers are 7 or less
8	8		
9	5		
Total	40		

The median is the middle of the ordered data set.

The 20th and 21st data values (in order) are both 7s, so the median $= \frac{7+7}{2} = 7$.

THE RANGE

The largest data value is 9, and the smallest data value is 3. So, the range $= 9 - 3 = 6$.

Example 7 Self Tutor

A class of 20 students take a spelling test. Their results out of 10 are shown in the table.

Score	*Number of students*
5	1
6	2
7	4
8	7
9	4
10	2
Total	20

Calculate the:

a mean
b median
c mode
d range of the scores.

a

Score	*Number of students*	*Product*
5	1	$5 \times 1 = 5$
6	2	$6 \times 2 = 12$
7	4	$7 \times 4 = 28$
8	7	$8 \times 7 = 56$
9	4	$9 \times 4 = 36$
10	2	$10 \times 2 = 20$
Total	20	157

The mean score
$= \dfrac{\text{sum of the scores}}{\text{number of scores}}$
$= \dfrac{157}{20}$
$= 7.85$

b There are 20 scores, so the median is the average of the 10th and 11th scores.

Score	*Number of students*	
5	1	← 1st student
6	2	← 2nd and 3rd student
7	4	← 4th, 5th, 6th, and 7th student
8	7	← 8th, 9th, **10th**, **11th**, 12th, 13th, 14th student
9	4	
10	2	
Total	20	

The 10th and 11th students both scored 8, so the median $= 8$.

c The highest frequency is 7 when the score is 8, so the mode $= 8$.

d The highest score is 10, and the lowest score is 5.
So, the range $= 10 - 5 = 5$.

EXERCISE 20D.2

1 A class of 28 students was asked how many televisions they had in their home. The following data was obtained. Calculate the:

a mode **b** median
c mean **d** range of the data.

Number of televisions	*Frequency*
0	1
1	8
2	12
3	7
Total	28

2 Sarah recorded the number of occupants in each car that drove down her street in one hour. The results are shown in the column graph.

a Construct a frequency table from the graph.
b How many cars did Sarah record data for?
c Find the:
  i mode **ii** median
  iii mean **iv** range of the data.

Occupancy in cars

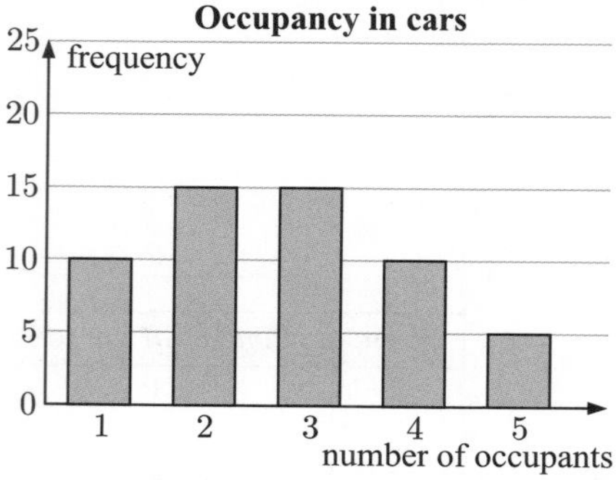

3 60 Danish students were asked how many times they had travelled to another country for a holiday. The results are given in the frequency table.

a For this data, find the:
  i mode **ii** median **iii** mean.
b Construct a column graph of the data. Show the positions of the mode, median, and mean on the horizontal axis.
c One extra student was surveyed, who had been on 21 international holidays. Recalculate the mode, median, and mean of the data.
d Which of the measures of centre was most affected by the outlier?

Number of international holidays	*Frequency*
0	8
1	9
2	11
3	12
4	8
5	5
6	3
7	2
8	2

E COMPARING NUMERICAL DATA

In statistics, we want to be able to **compare** two sets of data so we can tell which set is on average larger or smaller, or more spread.

Data sets can be compared graphically using a **back-to-back stem-and-leaf plot**. One data set is displayed on the left of the stem, and the other data set is displayed on the right of the stem.

Back-to-back stem-and-leaf plots allow us to make a visual comparison of the data sets.

For example, we can see that the values in data set A are generally larger than those in data set B.

Data set A	*Stem*	**Data set B**
	2	7
8	3	0 1 8
9 5 3 3 0	4	2 5 6 7 7 9
9 6 4 4 2 2 2 1 1	5	0 1 2 3 3 3 5 7 7 8
9 8 7 6 4 4 2 0	6	4 5 5 9
9 9 8 8 6 6 5	7	0 8
8 5 5 3	8	1

Scale: 2 | 7 means 27

We can also compare the centres of data sets by calculating their means and medians.

Example 8 Self Tutor

Two football teams, Northfield and Southbeach, are due to play against each other in the grand final. To determine if either team has a height advantage, the heights of the players from each team were recorded, in centimetres.

Northfield:	172	183	177	167	185	180	174	177	172	188
	191	175	165	182	173	172	192	188	174	182
Southbeach:	174	177	162	184	178	158	179	191	170	168
	180	172	172	165	157	177	186	178	167	176

a Construct a back-to-back stem-and-leaf plot for this data, using 15, 16, 17, 18, and 19 as the stems.

b Compare the mean and median heights of the teams.

c Copy and complete: "In general, the players from Southbeach are ...... than the players from Northfield."

a

Northfield		**Southbeach**
	15	7 8
7 5	16	2 5 7 8
7 7 5 4 4 3 2 2 2	17	0 2 2 4 6 7 7 8 8 9
8 8 5 3 2 2 0	18	0 4 6
2 1	19	1

19 | 1 means 191 cm

b We calculate the following statistics:

	mean (cm)	median (cm)
Northfield	178.5	177
Southbeach	173.6	175

Northfield has a higher mean and median height.

c "In general, the players from Southbeach are **shorter** than the players from Northfield."

EXERCISE 20E

1 Maura owns an ice cream store. In an attempt to improve sales, she decides to renovate her store and expand her outdoor seating area. She records her daily ice cream sales before and after the work is completed.

Before

40	51	42	37	32	36	54	42	31	36	58
41	62	53	34	45	39	56	65	53	42	37
49	32	44	50	35	48	54	42	55		

After

62	73	62	34	76	82	77	64	35	54	78
64	44	95	57	78	85	64	60	88	56	77
93	79	69	78	82	58	62	83	70		

a Construct a back-to-back stem-and-leaf plot for this data.

b Compare the mean and median of the data sets.

c Did the ice cream sales generally increase after the work was completed?

2 Two professional tennis players, Andre and Andrew, want to find out who has the faster serve. Each player serves 25 times. The speeds are recorded in km per hour:

Andre:	192	201	199	212	182	191	203	194	187	195	206	215	197
	217	208	187	222	195	208	192	204	218	206	188	213	
Andrew:	209	213	198	219	223	197	205	217	216	203	188	224	211
	219	206	192	215	200	220	217	206	224	191	207	219	

a Construct a back-to-back stem-and-leaf plot for this data.

b Are there any outliers in the data?

c Compare the mean and median of each data set.

d Copy and complete:
"...... generally serves the ball faster than ......"

3 Mary drives her car to and from work each day. She wants to know if she takes longer getting to work in the mornings, or getting home in the evenings. Every work day for a month she records how long it takes her to get to and from work. The results, in minutes, are shown below:

Going to work:	16.7	18.9	17.3	17.7	16.5	15.8	17.2	18.2	17.3	17.8	16.6
	15.7	16.9	17.8	16.7	15.7	17.1	18.5	17.1	16.6	17.4	16.3
Returning from	18.8	17.6	16.5	18.7	19.2	18.9	17.9	17.6	18.5	17.7	18.5
work:	17.2	18.2	19.7	18.9	17.9	16.8	17.6	22.3	18.8	17.4	16.6

a Construct a back-to-back stem-and-leaf plot for this data, using 15, 16, 17, ... as the stems.

b Are there any outliers in the data?

c Compare the mean and median of each data set.

d Copy and complete: "In general it takes Mary ...... time to get to work than it does to return home from work."

F DATA COLLECTION

Data collection is an important part of any statistical investigation. We can collect data by:

- **asking questions**: either face-to-face, or in a questionnaire
- **measuring**: for example, measuring the weight of goats on a farm
- **counting**: for example, counting the number of items bought by customers in a shop.

Before collecting data for an investigation, we must first consider the **target population**. This is the group of things or people that we want to find information about.

For example, Zhen wants to know the average height of the students at his school. The target population is all of the students at the school.

When we collect data, we can either perform a **census**, or take a **sample**.

A **census** involves collecting data about *every* individual in the target population.

In Zhen's investigation, a census would involve measuring the height of every student in his school. Depending on the size of his school, this is likely to be time-consuming and impractical.

An alternative is to take a **sample** from the population.

A **sample** involves collecting data about a *part* of the target population only.

For example, Zhen may randomly select 50 students from his school as they leave assembly, and measure their heights. Taking a sample from the population is quicker and more practical than taking a census, but it is not as detailed or accurate.

Since samples do not provide information about the whole population, the statistics calculated from a sample can only be used to *estimate* the statistics for the population.

We can make sure this estimate is accurate in two ways:

- **Choosing an unbiased sample**
  For example, if Zhen chose to sample 50 Grade 12 students, his sample would not be representative of all the students at the school. This is a **biased sample**. The average height of the sample would be much higher than the average height of *all* the school students.
- **Choosing a sufficiently large sample**
  For example, if Zhen only sampled 5 students, the average height of the sample is an unreliable estimate of the average height of *all* the students.

EXERCISE 20F

1 State whether a census or a sample would be used to investigate:
  a the ages of people in a shopping centre
  b the weights of coins produced at a mint
  c the prices of items on a restaurant menu.

2 

A research company wants to survey people on whether smoking should be banned in all public places. They ask people standing outside buildings in the city during office hours. Explain why the data collected is likely to be biased.

3 A school has 820 students. 40 of the students are randomly selected to complete a survey on their school uniform.
  a Find the size of the:
    i target population
    ii sample.
  b Explain why data collected in the following ways may not produce a sample representative of the population:
    i the surveyor's ten best friends are asked to complete the survey
    ii all of the students in one class are surveyed
    iii volunteers are asked to complete the survey.

4 A polling agency is employed to survey the voting intentions of residents of a particular district in the coming election. From the data collected they are to predict the election result in that district. Explain why each of the following situations may produce a biased sample:

- **a** a random selection of people in the local large shopping complex is surveyed between 1 pm and 3 pm on a weekday
- **b** all of the members of the local golf club are surveyed
- **c** a random sample of people at the local train station are surveyed between 7 am and 9 am
- **d** a doorknock is undertaken, surveying every voter in a particular street.

5 A newspaper invited readers to respond to a poll by phone. The results are displayed alongside.

- **a** Explain why a sample of data collected in this manner may be biased.
- **b** State another reason why the result of this poll is not reliable.

Should helmets be compulsory for cyclists?

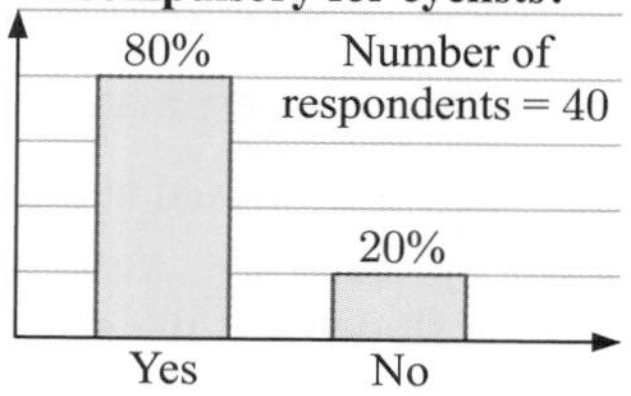

6 Grant was interested in the number of children in each household in his neighbourhood. He randomly sampled 100 houses and apartments. The results are displayed in the table alongside.

- **a** Construct a column graph to display the data.
- **b** Use the data to estimate the average number of children in each household in his neighbourhood.
- **c** Discuss the reliability of your estimate.

Number of children	*Frequency*
0	27
1	22
2	25
3	17
4	8
5	1
Total	100

7 Jill suspects that the scores in NFL games were higher in 2013 than they were in 2012. She researched the results from the first game in each week of the competition in 2012 and 2013, and recorded the winning team's score for each. The results were:

2012: 24 23 36 23 17 26 13 36 31 27 19 34
23 26 34 31 22

2013: 49 13 26 35 37 27 34 31 22 34 30 17
40 27 27 42 34

- **a** Construct a back-to-back stem-and-leaf plot to display the data.
- **b** Find the mean and median of each data set.
- **c** Does Jill's suspicion appear correct? Explain your answer.
- **d** How could Jill improve the accuracy of her investigation?

INVESTIGATION — EVALUATING STATISTICS

Reports on television, the internet, and newspapers, frequently use statistics such as a mean or median to explain a particular viewpoint. These statistics are often estimates based on a sample.

We need to understand how the data for these statistics has been obtained, to establish whether the statistics are reliable.

What to do:

1. Find a report on the internet, or in a newspaper or magazine, which includes a mean or median statistic.
2. Find out what data was used to calculate the statistic.
3. Discuss whether the statistics used in the report are reliable. Consider any possible bias in the sampling method, and the sample size.

Global context

click here

Calculating the age of a population

Statement of inquiry:	Presenting data in tables can help us to perform calculations more efficiently.
Global context:	Identities and relationships
Key concept:	Relationships
Related concepts:	Change, Justification
Objectives:	Communicating, Applying mathematics in real-life contexts
Approaches to learning:	Thinking, Communication

REVIEW SET 20A

1 For each of the following investigations, classify the variable as categorical or numerical:

- **a** the area of each block of land in a town
- **b** the marital status of people in a suburb
- **c** the number of matches in a match box.

2 Forty football players at a training camp were asked what position they played. The results are given below, where S ≡ striker, M ≡ midfielder, D ≡ defender, and G ≡ goalkeeper:

S D M M S M D S G M
M D S D M D S M D G
S G M D S D M D S M
D G M S M D G M M S

- **a** Summarise the data in a tally and frequency table.
- **b** Find the mode of the data. Explain what this means.
- **c** What percentage of the players were defenders or goalkeepers?
- **d** Display the data on a horizontal bar chart.

3 For the following sample of weights of Grade 8 students, find:

- **a** the minimum weight
- **b** the maximum weight
- **c** the median weight
- **d** the range of weights
- **e** the number of students who weigh at least 70 kg
- **f** the percentage of students who weigh less than 48 kg.

Stem	*Leaf*
3	2 4 8
4	0 4 4 7 9 9 9
5	0 0 1 2 2 3 3 5 5 6 8 8
6	0 1 2 4 4 5 7 9
7	0 2 6
8	4
9	1

9 | 1 means 91 kg

4 The column graph alongside shows the number of assists per game in a basketball player's international career.

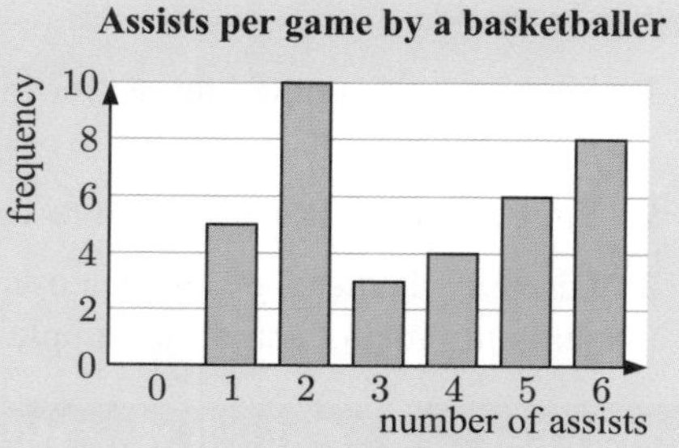

a Construct a frequency table for the data.

b Determine the total number of assists.

c Find the:

i mode **ii** median

iii mean **iv** range of the data.

5 A set of 19 data values has average 14. When a 20th data value is added, the average is now 14.4. What was the 20th value?

6 This data shows the number of camping trips taken by students in a class:

2	0	4	1	3	4	0	2	1	4	1	5	7	0	5
6	2	5	3	4	0	5	4	6	3	12	1	5	1	4

a Draw a dot plot to display the data.

b What is the mode of the data? What does it mean?

c Is there an outlier in the data?

d How many students have been camping 5 times?

e What percentage of students have been camping less than 3 times?

7

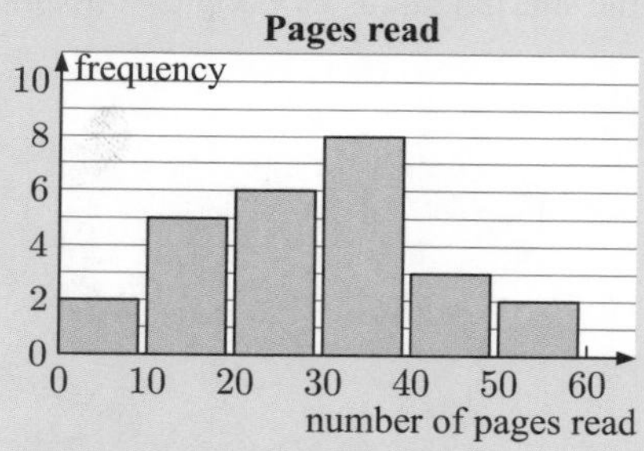

An English class was asked how many pages they had read so far of their class novel. The results are given alongside.

a What is the modal class for the data?

b How many students have read 40 or more pages?

c The class was supposed to read the first 30 pages for homework. How many students did not complete their homework?

8 25 randomly selected adults were asked how many hot beverages they drank per day. The results are listed below:

4	2	1	0	0	3	5	4	3	2	2	2	1
1	10	1	2	4	2	0	1	1	3	4	2	

a Draw a tally and frequency table of the data.

b Construct a column graph to display the data.

c Find the mean and median of the data.

d Identify the outlier in the data.

e Calculate the mean and median with the outlier removed.

f Which of the measures of centre is most affected by the outlier?

9 A survey is conducted to determine the number of motor vehicles passing through two suburban intersections in a given time period during peak hour traffic.

Intersection A

49	37	47	42	51	54	46	59
59	48	64	53	57	46	62	65
54	45	47	51	62	59	43	55

Intersection B

48	25	29	48	47	40	53	58
62	66	51	64	37	43	51	47
41	64	46	55	37	52	57	37

a Construct a back-to-back stem-and-leaf plot comparing the two data sets.

b Find the median of each data set.

c Find the mean of each data set.

d Copy and complete: "More vehicles generally pass through ...... than ...."

10 Explain why each of the following situations may produce a biased sample:

a A researcher uses the members of a country town's Under 14 athletics team to test the claim that boys in that town are overweight.

b A shop manager wants to know what customers think of the services the shop provides. He introduces himself and questions the first 10 customers who enter the shop on Monday morning.

REVIEW SET 20B

1 Classify the following variables as either categorical or numerical:

a the type of food ordered by a family in a food court

b the number of books sold by a publisher each week.

2 Of the 60 passengers on a bus, 15 were children, 11 were students, 22 were adults, and 12 were pensioners.

a Display this data on a pie chart. **b** Find the mode of the data.

3 An office kept a record of the number of phone calls it received each day for 30 days:

18 32 25 37 24 28 35 42 31 16 28 38 30 41 27
31 46 17 35 26 32 14 44 37 48 23 19 33 15 36

a Record the data in a tally and frequency table, using the class intervals 10 - 19, 20 - 29, 30 - 39, and 40 - 49.

b Display the data on a column graph.

c Find the modal class of the data.

d On what percentage of days did the office receive at least 30 calls?

4 The table shows the scores in a fitness test for a class of 13 year old Canadians.

a Calculate the:

i median **ii** mean score.

b The average score for all 13 year old Canadians was 7.2. How does this class compare with the national average?

Score	*Frequency*
6	2
7	4
8	7
9	12
10	5
Total	30

5

Stem	*Leaf*
3	8 9
4	2 2 5
5	0 1 1 7 9
6	1 3 4
7	0

3 | 8 means 3.8

For the data displayed in the stem-and-leaf plot, find the:

a mode **b** median **c** range.

6 The dot plot shows the number of goals scored by a group of netballers in 10 attempts.

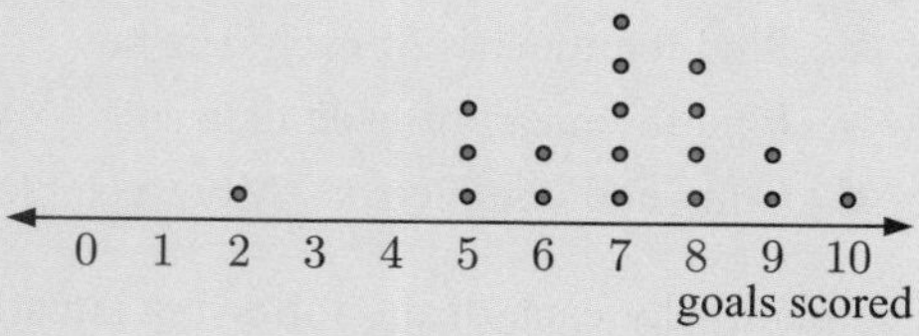

- **a** How many netballers are in the group?
- **b** Are there any outliers?
- **c** Find the median number of goals scored.

7 The test scores out of 40 marks were recorded for a group of 30 students:

25	18	35	32	34	28	24	39	29	33	22	34	39	31	36
35	36	33	35	40	26	25	20	18	9	40	32	23	28	27

- **a** Construct a stem-and-leaf plot for this data using 0, 1, 2, 3, and 4 as the stems.
- **b** Redraw the stem-and-leaf plot so that it is ordered.
- **c** What advantage does the stem-and-leaf plot have over a column graph?
- **d** What is the **i** highest **ii** lowest mark scored for the test?
- **e** If an 'A' was awarded to students who scored 36 or more for the test, what percentage of students scored an 'A'?

8 To find out students' views on changing the library borrowing system, the principal asked 60 Grade 12 students.
Explain why this sample is likely to be biased.

9 State whether a census or a sample would be used to investigate:

- **a** the most popular ride at a fair
- **b** the favourite holiday destination of Europeans.

10 To find out whether doctors or lawyers work longer hours, 20 doctors and 20 lawyers were each asked how many hours they worked in an average month.
The following data was collected:

Doctors:	212	203	228	215	200	194	216	222	210	232
	211	225	209	217	217	199	213	235	219	207
Lawyers:	227	216	238	221	206	228	233	214	229	232
	220	210	197	238	224	226	219	171	225	236

- **a** Draw a back-to-back stem-and-leaf plot comparing the two data sets.
- **b** Are there any outliers in the data?
- **c** Compare the mean and median of each data set.
- **d** Copy and complete:
  "From the samples above, it appears that ...... generally work longer hours than ...."

Chapter 21

Quadratic equations

Contents:

OPENING PROBLEM

Matheus has a piece of paper 15 cm $\times$ 20 cm. His friend Gabriela challenges him to divide it into two sections of equal area, one of which is an L-shaped region with constant width x cm, as shown.

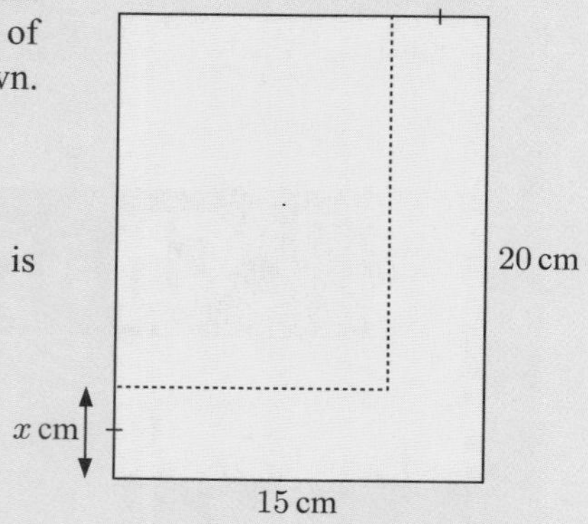

Things to think about:

- **a** What possible values can x take?
- **b** Can you explain why the area of the L-shaped section is given by $(-x^2 + 35x)$ m^2?
- **c** Can you hence explain why $x^2 - 35x + 150 = 0$?
- **d** How many solutions does the equation $x^2 - 35x + 150 = 0$ have?
- **e** How wide should the L-shaped section be?

The equation in the **Opening Problem** is an example of a **quadratic equation**. Solving quadratic equations is harder than solving linear equations because, while linear equations generally have one solution, quadratic equations may have two, one, or zero solutions.

In this chapter we will study some strategies for solving quadratic equations.

A QUADRATIC EQUATIONS

A **quadratic equation** is an equation which can be written in the form $ax^2 + bx + c = 0$, where a, b, and c are constants, $a \neq 0$.

For example, $2x^2 - 3x + 5 = 0$ and $x^2 + 3x = 0$ are quadratic equations, whereas $x^2 + 5 + \frac{1}{x} = 0$ is not.

Quadratic equations may have two, one, or zero solutions. For example, consider the table below:

Equation	$ax^2 + bx + c = 0$ *form*	*Solutions*	
$x^2 - 4 = 0$	$x^2 + 0x - 4 = 0$	$x = 2$ or $x = -2$	**two solutions**
$(x-2)^2 = 0$	$x^2 - 4x + 4 = 0$	$x = 2$	**one solution**
$x^2 + 4 = 0$	$x^2 + 0x + 4 = 0$	none, as x^2 is always $\geqslant 0$	**zero solutions**

Consider the quadratic equation $x^2 + 3x - 10 = 0$.

If $x = 2$,
$$\begin{aligned} &x^2 + 3x - 10 \\ &= 2^2 + 3 \times 2 - 10 \\ &= 4 + 6 - 10 \\ &= 0 \end{aligned}$$

If $x = -5$,
$$\begin{aligned} &x^2 + 3x - 10 \\ &= (-5)^2 + 3 \times (-5) - 10 \\ &= 25 - 15 - 10 \\ &= 0 \end{aligned}$$

So, the solutions to $x^2 + 3x - 10 = 0$ are $x = 2$ and $x = -5$.

EXERCISE 21A

1 State whether each of the following is a quadratic equation:

a $x^2 - x + 6 = 0$ **b** $2x^3 + 5x - 4 = 0$ **c** $4x^2 - 7 = 8x$

d $-6x^2 - 11 = 0$ **e** $3x^2 + x - \dfrac{2}{x} = 0$ **f** $\frac{2}{3}x^2 - \frac{1}{2}x = 0$

2 For each of the following quadratic equations, determine which of the numbers in brackets are solutions.

a $x^2 - 7x + 6 = 0$ $\{1, 2, 4, 6, 7\}$ **b** $x^2 + 2x - 8 = 0$ $\{-5, -4, -1, 1, 2\}$

c $x^2 - 5x = 0$ $\{-2, 0, 3, 5, 7\}$ **d** $x^2 - 6x + 9 = 0$ $\{-3, 1, 3, 4, 6\}$

e $2x^2 + 3x - 2 = 0$ $\{-2, -1, -\frac{1}{2}, \frac{1}{2}, 1\}$

3 Explain why the quadratic equation $x^2 + 5 = 0$ has no solutions.

B THE NULL FACTOR LAW

In the previous Section we used trial and error to find solutions to quadratic equations. To find solutions in a more systematic way, we can use the **Null Factor law**.

INVESTIGATION 1 THE NULL FACTOR LAW

What to do:

1 Complete the following products:

a $3 \times 5 =$ **b** $0 \times 5 =$ **c** $1 \times 2 =$ **d** $1 \times 0 =$

e $2 \times -4 =$ **f** $-6 \times -7 =$ **g** $0 \times -9 =$ **h** $-5 \times 8 =$

i $-10 \times 0 =$ **j** $7 \times -11 =$ **k** $2 \times 4 \times 5 =$ **l** $3 \times -6 \times 4 =$

m $7 \times 5 \times 0 =$ **n** $4 \times 4 \times 5 =$ **o** $-8 \times 0 \times 7 =$ **p** $0 \times 13 \times 0 =$

2 Circle the products which have a value of zero.

3 Look at the numbers in the products which you have circled. What do you notice?

WORKSHEET

In the previous **Investigation**, you should have discovered the **Null Factor law**:

> When the product of two or more numbers is zero, at least one of them must be zero.
>
> So, if $ab = 0$ then $a = 0$ or $b = 0$.

For example:
- If $2xy = 0$ then $x = 0$ or $y = 0$.
- If $x(x - 2) = 0$ then $x = 0$ or $x - 2 = 0$.
- If $xyz = 0$ then $x = 0$, $y = 0$, or $z = 0$.

Therefore, if we are given an equation where the LHS is a factorised expression, and the RHS is zero, we can use the Null Factor law to find solutions.

Example 1 — Self Tutor

Solve for x:

a $5x(x+2)=0$ **b** $(x+4)(x-1)=0$

a
$$5x(x+2)=0$$
$\therefore\ 5x=0$ or $x+2=0$ {Null Factor law}
$\therefore\ x=0$ or $x=-2$ {solving linear equations}
So, $x=0$ or -2

b
$$(x+4)(x-1)=0$$
$\therefore\ x+4=0$ or $x-1=0$ {Null Factor law}
$\therefore\ x=-4$ or $x=1$ {solving linear equations}
So, $x=-4$ or 1

EXERCISE 21B

1 Explain what can be deduced from:

a $ac=0$ **b** $bd=0$ **c** $abc=0$ **d** $3x=0$
e $x(x-3)=0$ **f** $x^2=0$ **g** $(x-5)y=0$ **h** $x^2y=0$

2 Solve for x:

a $2x(x-1)=0$ **b** $x(x+5)=0$ **c** $3x(x+2)=0$
d $(x-1)^2=0$ **e** $-x(x-4)=0$ **f** $-2x(x+3)=0$
g $x(2x+1)=0$ **h** $3x(4x-3)=0$ **i** $-x(3x+5)=0$

3 Solve for x:

a $(x-1)(x-5)=0$ **b** $(x+2)(x-4)=0$ **c** $(x+3)(x+7)=0$
d $(x+7)(x-11)=0$ **e** $2x(x-8)=0$ **f** $(x+12)(x-5)=0$
g $-3x(x+7)=0$ **h** $(2x+1)(x-3)=0$ **i** $(x+6)(3x-1)=0$
j $(2x+1)(x+6)=0$ **k** $4(x-3)^2=0$ **l** $(x-31)(x+11)=0$
m $(x+4)(4x-1)=0$ **n** $-3x(7x+3)=0$ **o** $(2-x)(3x+4)=0$

C SOLVING QUADRATIC EQUATIONS

For quadratic equations written in other forms, we cannot apply the Null Factor Law directly. Before we can solve the quadratic equation, we first need to factorise the quadratic using the techniques studied in **Chapter 19**.

Step 1: If necessary, rearrange the equation so one side is **zero**.
Step 2: **Fully factorise** the other side (usually the LHS).
Step 3: Use the **Null Factor law**: if $ab=0$ then $a=0$ or $b=0$.
Step 4: **Solve** the resulting linear equations.

EQUATIONS IN THE FORM $ax^2 + bx = 0$

To solve quadratic equations of the form $ax^2+bx=0$ where $a \neq 0$, we first take out x as a common factor. We can then use the Null Factor law.

Example 2 Self Tutor

Solve for x: $x^2 = 4x$

$x^2 = 4x$

$\therefore\ x^2 - 4x = 0$ {subtracting $4x$ from both sides to make RHS $= 0$}

$\therefore\ x(x-4) = 0$ {factorising the LHS}

$\therefore\ x = 0$ or $x - 4 = 0$ {Null Factor law}

$\therefore\ x = 0$ or $x = 4$

WARNING ON INCORRECT CANCELLING

Given the equation $x^2 = 4x$ in the example above, we may be tempted to divide both sides by x, giving $x = 4$.

While $x = 4$ is a solution to the equation, it is not the only solution. By dividing both sides by x, we have lost the solution $x = 0$.

From this example we conclude that:

We should never cancel a common factor involving a variable unless we are sure that this factor is non-zero.

EXERCISE 21C.1

1 Solve for x:

a $x^2 - x = 0$
b $x^2 - 13x = 0$
c $x^2 + 8x = 0$
d $x^2 + 3x = 0$
e $2x + x^2 = 0$
f $5x - x^2 = 0$
g $12x - x^2 = 0$
h $x^2 + 7x = 0$
i $x^2 - 4x = 0$
j $2x^2 - 7x = 0$
k $3x^2 - 15x = 0$
l $2x^2 + 8x = 0$

2 Solve for x:

a $x^2 = 3x$
b $x^2 = 10x$
c $a^2 = a$
d $x^2 = -6x$
e $2x^2 = -7x$
f $5x = x^2$
g $8x = x^2$
h $3y^2 = 18y$
i $5x^2 = 6x$
j $7x + x^2 = x$
k $x^2 - 4 = 2x - 4$
l $2x^2 + x = 3x$

SOLVING EQUATIONS USING THE DIFFERENCE OF TWO SQUARES

In both the equations $x^2 - 9 = 0$ and $4x^2 - 1 = 0$, the LHS can be factorised as the **difference of two squares**:

$$a^2 - b^2 = (a+b)(a-b)$$

Example 3 — Self Tutor

Solve for x:

a $x^2 - 4 = 0$ **b** $4x^2 - 25 = 0$

a
$$x^2 - 4 = 0$$
$$\therefore (x+2)(x-2) = 0$$
$$\therefore x+2 = 0 \quad \text{or} \quad x-2 = 0$$
$$\therefore x = -2 \quad \text{or} \quad x = 2$$
$$\therefore x = \pm 2$$

b
$$4x^2 - 25 = 0$$
$$\therefore (2x)^2 - 5^2 = 0$$
$$\therefore (2x+5)(2x-5) = 0$$
$$\therefore 2x+5 = 0 \quad \text{or} \quad 2x-5 = 0$$
$$\therefore x = -\frac{5}{2} \quad \text{or} \quad x = \frac{5}{2}$$
$$\therefore x = \pm\frac{5}{2}$$

EXERCISE 21C.2

1 Solve for x:

a $x^2 - 16 = 0$ **b** $x^2 - 49 = 0$ **c** $x^2 - 144 = 0$
d $2x^2 - 8 = 0$ **e** $3x^2 - 27 = 0$ **f** $5x^2 - 20 = 0$
g $-3x^2 + 12 = 0$ **h** $-2x^2 + 8 = 0$ **i** $x^2 + 4 = 0$

2 Solve:

a $9x^2 - 4 = 0$ **b** $1 - 9x^2 = 0$ **c** $4 - 25x^2 = 0$ **d** $4t^2 - 1 = 0$
e $4x^2 - 9 = 0$ **f** $2 - 8x^2 = 0$ **g** $3x^2 + 12 = 0$ **h** $16z^2 - 25 = 0$

EQUATIONS OF THE FORM $x^2 + bx + c = 0$

For quadratic equations in the general form $x^2 + bx + c = 0$, we look for **perfect squares** or else use **sum and product** factorisation.

For example, to solve $x^2 - 5x + 6 = 0$ we must first factorise $x^2 - 5x + 6$.

The numbers -2 and -3 have a sum of -5 and a product of 6.

$\therefore x^2 - 5x + 6 = (x-2)(x-3)$.

Example 4 — Self Tutor

Solve for x:

a $x^2 - 3x + 2 = 0$ **b** $x^2 = x + 12$ **c** $x^2 + 4 = 4x$

a
$$x^2 - 3x + 2 = 0$$
$$\therefore (x-1)(x-2) = 0 \quad \{\text{the numbers } -1 \text{ and } -2 \text{ have sum } -3 \text{ and product } 2\}$$
$$\therefore x-1 = 0 \quad \text{or} \quad x-2 = 0$$
$$\therefore x = 1 \text{ or } 2$$

b
$$x^2 = x + 12$$
$$\therefore x^2 - x - 12 = 0 \quad \{\text{subtracting } x+12 \text{ from both sides to make RHS} = 0\}$$
$$\therefore (x-4)(x+3) = 0 \quad \{\text{the numbers } -4 \text{ and } 3 \text{ have sum } -1 \text{ and product } -12\}$$
$$\therefore x-4 = 0 \quad \text{or} \quad x+3 = 0$$
$$\therefore x = 4 \text{ or } -3$$

c
$$x^2 + 4 = 4x$$
$$\therefore\ x^2 - 4x + 4 = 0 \quad \{\text{subtracting } 4x \text{ from both sides to make RHS} = 0\}$$
$$\therefore\ x^2 - 2 \times x \times 2 + 2^2 = 0$$
$$\therefore\ (x-2)^2 = 0 \quad \{\text{perfect square factorisation}\}$$
$$\therefore\ x - 2 = 0$$
$$\therefore\ x = 2$$

Sometimes each term in an equation contains a **constant common factor**. To solve these equations we first remove the common factor.

Example 5 — Self Tutor

Solve for x: $3x^2 + 21x + 30 = 0$

$$3x^2 + 21x + 30 = 0 \quad \{\text{common factor} = 3\}$$
$$\therefore\ 3(x^2 + 7x + 10) = 0$$
$$\therefore\ 3(x+2)(x+5) = 0 \quad \{\text{the numbers 2 and 5 have sum 7 and product 10}\}$$
$$\therefore\ x + 2 = 0 \text{ or } x + 5 = 0$$
$$\therefore\ x = -2 \text{ or } -5$$

EXERCISE 21C.3

1 Solve for x:

a $x^2 - 7x + 10 = 0$
b $x^2 + 6x + 8 = 0$
c $x^2 + 11x + 10 = 0$
d $x^2 - 8x + 12 = 0$
e $x^2 - 5x + 4 = 0$
f $x^2 - 11x + 24 = 0$
g $x^2 + 10x + 25 = 0$
h $x^2 - 3x - 18 = 0$
i $x^2 + 7x - 18 = 0$
j $x^2 - 22x + 121 = 0$
k $x^2 - 6x + 9 = 0$
l $x^2 - 5x - 6 = 0$
m $x^2 + 11x - 60 = 0$
n $x^2 + 18x - 63 = 0$
o $x^2 - 12x - 64 = 0$
p $x^2 - 19x + 70 = 0$

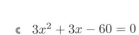

Look for factorisations which are perfect squares.

2 Solve for x:

a $2x^2 + 4x - 30 = 0$
b $-x^2 + 12x - 36 = 0$
c $3x^2 + 3x - 60 = 0$
d $-3x^2 + 21x - 36 = 0$
e $5x^2 - 5x - 210 = 0$
f $-4x^2 - 32x - 48 = 0$

3 Solve for x:

a $x^2 - 14x = 15$
b $x^2 + 2 = 3x$
c $d^2 = 3d + 28$
d $x^2 = 20 + x$
e $8 = x^2 + 7x$
f $x^2 = 5x + 24$
g $2x^2 + 2x = 24$
h $k^2 = 4k + 45$
i $3x^2 = 30x - 48$
j $x^2 + 1 = 2x$
k $y^2 = 19y + 20$
l $5x^2 = 20(x + 8)$

4 Solve for x:

a $x(x + 2) = 15$
b $x(x - 2) = 5(x + 12)$
c $2x - 6 = x(x - 5)$
d $x^2 - 4 = x + 2$
e $2(x + 5) = x^2 + 11$
f $5 - x^2 = 2x - 3$

ACTIVITY

Click on the icon to practise solving quadratic equations.

QUADRATIC EQUATIONS

D PROBLEM SOLVING WITH QUADRATIC EQUATIONS

Many problems expressed in words, and geometric problems involving right angled triangles, can be described in algebra by a **quadratic equation**.

PROBLEM SOLVING METHOD

- Carefully **read the question** until you understand it. A **sketch** may be useful.
- Decide on the **unknown** quantity. Label it with a variable such as x.
- Use the given information to construct an **equation**.
- **Solve** the equation using **factorisation** and the **Null Factor law**.
- **Check** that any solutions satisfy the original problem.
- Where appropriate, write your answer to the question in **sentence form**.

Example 6 — Self Tutor

The sum of a number and its square is 30. Find the number.

Let the number be x.

So, $x + x^2 = 30$ {the number plus its square is 30}

$\therefore\ x^2 + x = 30$ {rearranging}

$\therefore\ x^2 + x - 30 = 0$ {making RHS $= 0$}

$\therefore\ (x+6)(x-5) = 0$ {factorising}

$\therefore\ x + 6 = 0$ or $x - 5 = 0$ {Null Factor law}

$\therefore\ x = -6$ or $x = 5$

$\therefore$ the numbers are -6 and 5.

Check: If $x = -6$, we have $-6 + (-6)^2 = -6 + 36 = 30$ ✓

If $x = 5$, we have $5 + 5^2 = 5 + 25 = 30$ ✓

EXERCISE 21D

1 The sum of a number and its square is 42. Find the number.

2 When a number is squared, the result is five times the original number. Find the number.

3 When a number is subtracted from its square, the result is 56. Find the number.

Example 7 — Self Tutor

Two numbers have a sum of 10, and the sum of their squares is 58. Find the numbers.

Let one of the numbers be x.

$\therefore$ the other number is $10 - x$. {their sum is 10}

So, $x^2 + (10 - x)^2 = 58$ {the sum of the squares is 58}

$\therefore x^2 + 100 - 20x + x^2 = 58$ {expanding the brackets}

$\therefore 2x^2 - 20x + 42 = 0$ {making RHS = 0}

$\therefore 2(x^2 - 10x + 21) = 0$ {common factor = 2}

$\therefore 2(x - 3)(x - 7) = 0$ {factorising LHS}

$\therefore x - 3 = 0$ or $x - 7 = 0$ {Null Factor law}

$\therefore x = 3$ or 7

If $x = 3$, $10 - x = 7$.
If $x = 7$, $10 - x = 3$.
$\therefore$ the numbers are 3 and 7.

4 Two numbers have a sum of 9, and the sum of their squares is 153. Find the numbers.

5 The product of two consecutive integers is 156. Find the integers.

6 The sum of the squares of two consecutive odd numbers is 290. Find the numbers.

7 Two numbers differ by 4. The product of the two numbers is 221. What are the numbers?

Example 8 — Self Tutor

A rectangle has length 3 cm greater than its width, and the area of the rectangle is 28 cm^2. Find the dimensions of the rectangle.

If the rectangle has width x cm, then its length is $(x + 3)$ cm.

$\therefore x(x + 3) = 28$ {width × length = area}

$\therefore x^2 + 3x = 28$ {expanding}

$\therefore x^2 + 3x - 28 = 0$ {making RHS = 0}

$\therefore (x + 7)(x - 4) = 0$ {factorising LHS}

$\therefore x + 7 = 0$ or $x - 4 = 0$ {Null Factor law}

$\therefore x = -7$ or 4

$\therefore x = 4$ {lengths must be positive}

$\therefore$ the rectangle is $4 \text{ cm} \times 7 \text{ cm}$.

8 The length of a rectangle is 4 cm more than its width, and the area of the rectangle is 96 cm^2. Find the width of the rectangle.

9 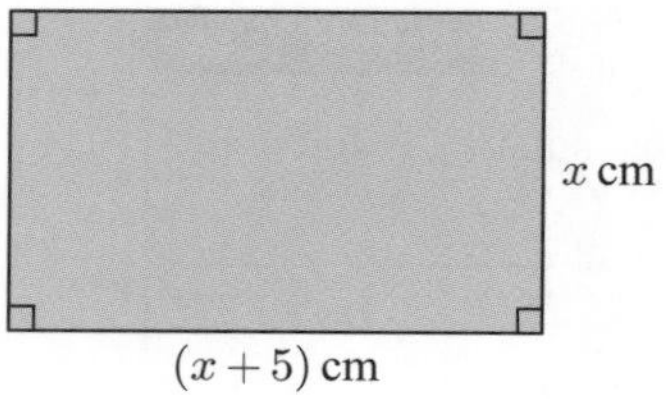

a Write an expression for the rectangle's:
  i area **ii** perimeter.

b If the perimeter is 21.6 cm, find the area of the rectangle.

c If the area is 176 cm^2, find the perimeter of the rectangle.

10 A triangle has altitude 4 cm less than its base. If the area of the triangle is $38\frac{1}{2}$ cm^2, find the length of its base.

11 A rectangle has sides which differ in length by 3 cm. If the area of the rectangle is 154 cm^2, find its perimeter.

Example 9 **Self Tutor**

Find x:

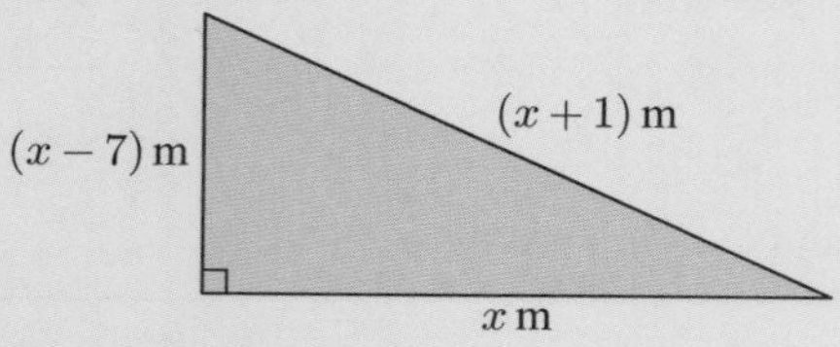

Using Pythagoras' theorem,

$$x^2 + (x-7)^2 = (x+1)^2$$
$$\therefore \; \cancel{x^2} + x^2 - 14x + 49 = \cancel{x^2} + 2x + 1$$
$$\therefore \; x^2 - 16x + 48 = 0 \qquad \{\text{making RHS} = 0\}$$
$$\therefore \; (x-4)(x-12) = 0 \qquad \{\text{factorising LHS}\}$$
$$\therefore \; x - 4 = 0 \quad \text{or} \quad x - 12 = 0 \qquad \{\text{Null Factor law}\}$$
$$\therefore \; x = 4 \text{ or } 12$$
$$\text{But } \; x \neq 4 \; \text{ as } \; x - 7 > 0 \qquad \{\text{all lengths are positive}\}$$
$$\therefore \; x = 12$$

12 Find x:

a

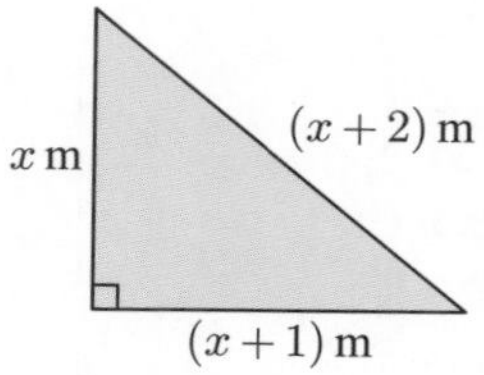

b

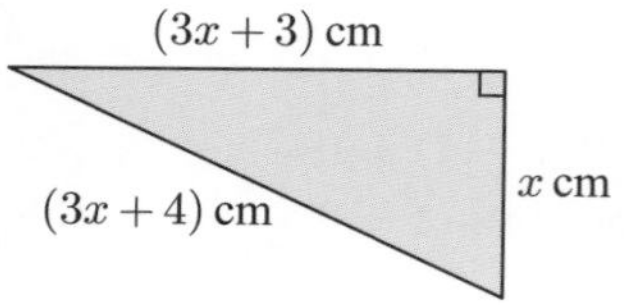

c

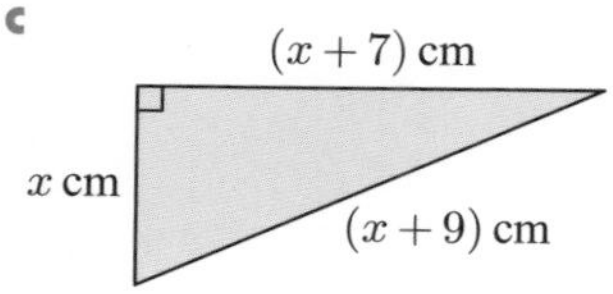

d

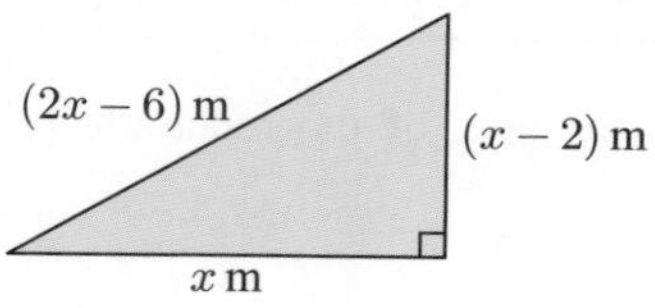

e

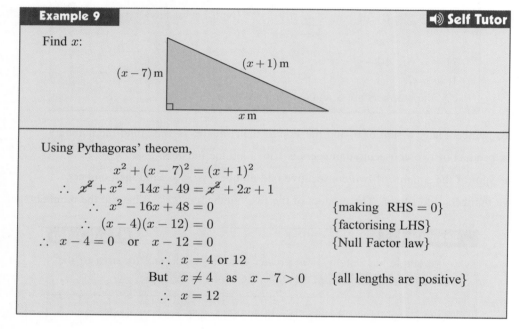

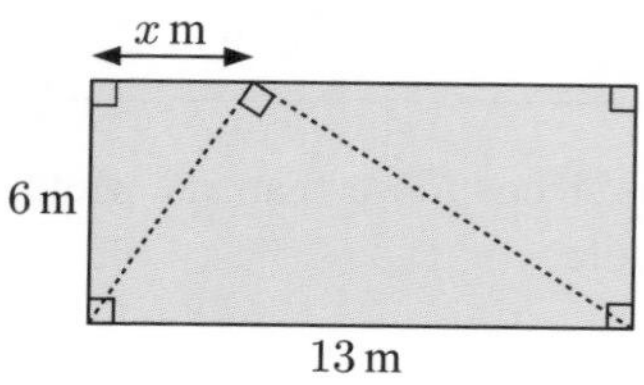

13 Answer the **Opening Problem** on page **426**.

14 In a right angled triangle, the hypotenuse is 6 cm longer than the shortest side. The third side is the average of the other two. Find the:

a perimeter of the triangle **b** area of the triangle.

15

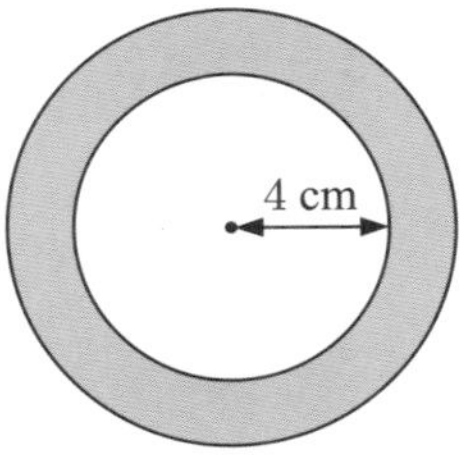

The shaded region has area 33π cm^2.
Find the radius of the outer circle.

16 **a** Kelly knows that $x^2 + ax + b = 0$ has solutions $x = 2$ and $x = -5$, but she has forgotten the values of a and b. Find a and b to help Kelly.

b Fredrik knows that $x^2 + ax + b = 0$ has only one solution, and this is $x = -\frac{3}{2}$. Find the values of a and b.

17 The sum of the squares of three consecutive integers is 110.

a **i** Let the *smallest* integer be x, and find a quadratic equation involving x.
ii Solve the quadratic equation, and hence write down the three integers.

b **i** Now suppose the *middle* integer is x, and find a quadratic equation involving x.
ii Solve the quadratic equation, and hence write down the three integers.

c Is the problem easier to solve letting x be the smallest number or the middle number? Explain your answer.

18 The sum of the squares of three consecutive odd numbers is 371. What are the numbers?

19

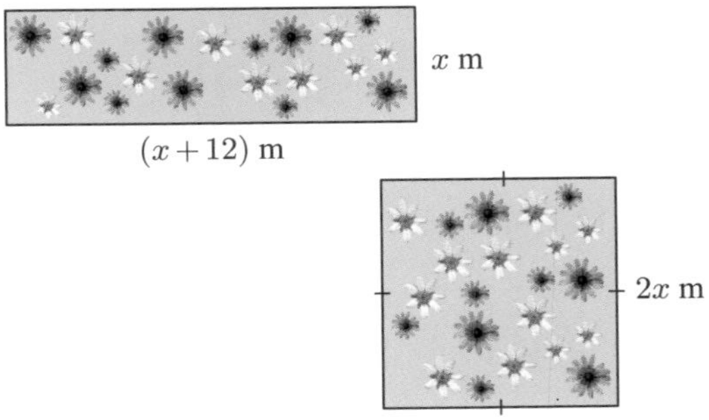

Alongside are the dimensions of two flower beds of equal area.

a Find their dimensions.

b Find the total length of border needed to enclose the two flower beds.

20 A circle is drawn so that it just fits in the corner of a page. Point A is 1 cm from one edge of the page, and 2 cm from the other edge. Find the radius of the circle.

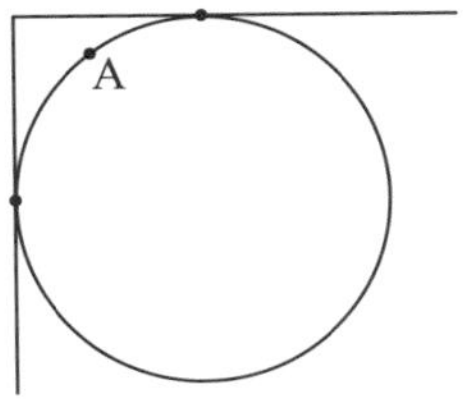

INVESTIGATION 2 COMPLETING THE SQUARE

Many quadratic equations cannot be solved by factorisation. For example, we cannot solve the quadratic equation $x^2 + 10x - 1 = 0$ by factorising the LHS.

We can use the method of **completing the square** to solve the equation:

$$x^2 + 10x - 1 = 0$$
$$\therefore\ x^2 + 10x = 1 \quad \text{\{moving the constant to the RHS\}}$$
$$\therefore\ x^2 + 10x + 25 = 1 + 25 \quad \text{\{adding 25 to both sides to complete a perfect square on LHS\}}$$
$$\therefore\ (x+5)^2 = 26 \quad \text{\{factorising the LHS\}}$$
$$\therefore\ x + 5 = \pm\sqrt{26} \quad \{\text{If } a^2 = k \text{ then } a = \pm\sqrt{k}\}$$
$$\therefore\ x = -5 \pm \sqrt{26}$$

So, the exact solutions to the equation are $x = -5 + \sqrt{26}$ and $x = -5 - \sqrt{26}$.

What to do:

1 Use the method of completing the square to solve:

a $x^2 + 6x + 5 = 0$ **b** $x^2 - 4x + 3 = 0$ **c** $x^2 - 8x - 20 = 0$

Solve the equations by factorisation to check your answers.

2 Use the method of completing the square to solve:

a $x^2 + 2x - 5 = 0$ **b** $x^2 - 6x - 2 = 0$ **c** $x^2 + 12x + 7 = 0$

3 Try to solve the following equations by completing the square:

a $x^2 + 8x + 20 = 0$ **b** $x^2 - 4x + 11 = 0$

Comment on your results.

REVIEW SET 21A

1 Determine whether the following are quadratic equations:

a $4x^2 - 8x = 0$ **b** $x^2 = x + \frac{1}{x}$ **c** $2x + 7 = 0$

2 Consider the quadratic equation $x^2 = 6 + x$. Determine which of the numbers $\{-3, -2, -1, 0, 1, 2, 3, 4\}$ are solutions.

3 Solve for x:

a $-5x^2 = 0$ **b** $2(x+2)(x-8) = 0$ **c** $-2(2x-1)^2 = 0$

d $4x^2 + 8x = 0$ **e** $x^2 - 5x - 24 = 0$ **f** $x^2 = 7x + 18$

4 Solve for x:

a $x(x-3) = 10$ **b** $(x+2)(x-3) = 2x(x-3) - 2$

5 When the square of a number is subtracted from the original number, the result is -110. Find the number.

6 The difference between two numbers is 3, and the sum of their squares is 5. Find the numbers.

7 A square has sides of length $3x$ cm. A rectangle is $2x$ cm by $(x+7)$ cm. The area of the square is twice the area of the rectangle. Find the dimensions of each figure.

8 A rectangular plot has length 5 m more than its width. If the area of the plot is 84 m^2, find its dimensions.

9 Solve for x:

a $x(x-16)=0$ **b** $9x^2-27x-90=0$ **c** $(x+1)(x-1)=2(7x-17)$

10 Find x, and hence find the perimeter of the triangle.

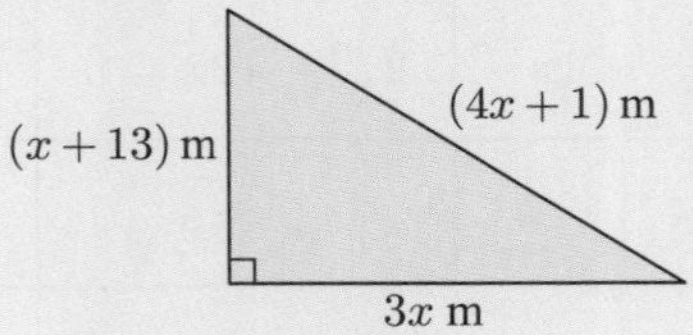

REVIEW SET 21B

1 What can be deduced from $2pqr=0$?

2 For the equation $5x^2-2x-3=0$, determine which of the numbers $\{-\frac{7}{10}, -\frac{3}{5}, -1, 0, 1, \frac{3}{5}, \frac{4}{5}, \frac{9}{10}\}$ are solutions.

3 Explain why the quadratic equation $x^2+9=0$ has no solutions.

4 Solve for x:

a $2x^2+x=0$ **b** $7x^2=14x$ **c** $4x^2-64=0$ **d** $25x^2-9=0$

5 Solve for x:

a $x^2=14x-33$ **b** $(1-3x)^2=0$ **c** $x^2-9=x+3$ **d** $x(x+4)=8x-3$

6 The sum of the squares of three consecutive even numbers is 308. What are the integers?

7 A rectangle has one side 4 m longer and the other side 2 m shorter than the side of a square. The rectangle's area is 14 m^2 more than the area of the square. What is the area of the rectangle?

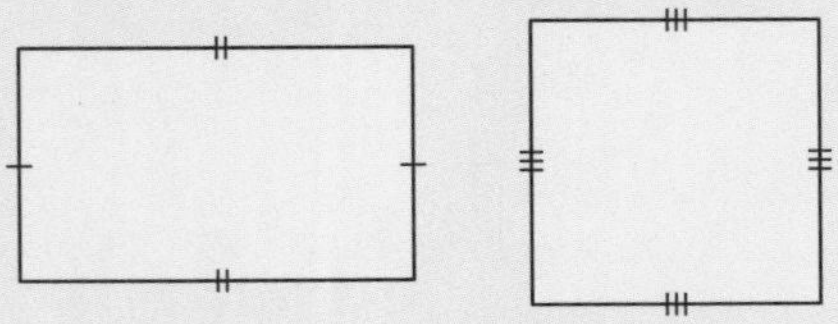

8 Two numbers have a product of -6. One of the numbers is 5 more than the other. Find the numbers.

9 Solve for x:

a $x^2-15x+26=0$ **b** $x^2+42=13x$ **c** $2x^2-12x-54=0$

d $5x^2-20x=25$ **e** $x(x-2)=48$ **f** $2x^2+4x=x^2+45$

10 Two small circles fit perfectly inside a large circle of diameter 20 m. The total shaded area is 52π m^2. Find the radius of each of the smaller circles.

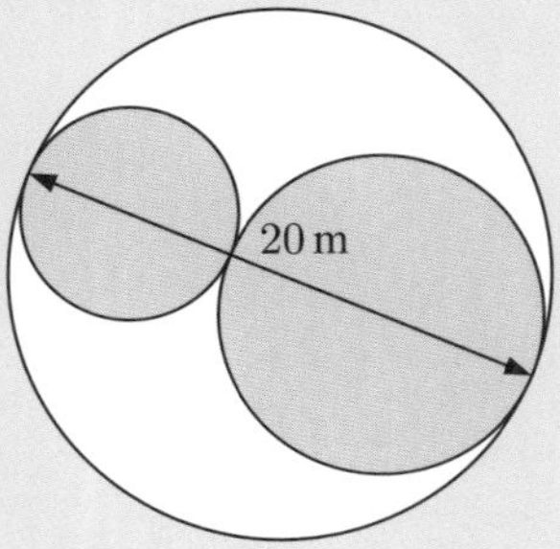

PUZZLE — QUADRATIC EQUATIONS MAZE

Your task is to find your way from the Start to the Finish of the maze. You may move horizontally or vertically, but not diagonally.

You may only move from one square to another if the quadratic equations in the two squares share a common solution.

PRINTABLE MAZE

Start ↓ (top right square)

$x^2 + x - 18 = 4x$	$2x^2 - 12x = 0$	$x^2 - x = 2$	$x^2 - 8x + 15 = 0$
$(x+3)(x-7) = 0$	$x^2 = x$	$x^2 + 4 = 5x$	$(x-3)(x+2) = 0$
$x^2 + 8x + 12 = x$	$x^2 + 12 = 7x$	$-x^2 + 8x - 16 = 0$	$5x^2 - 40 = 10x$
$-2x^2 + 10x + 72 = 0$	$x(x-7) = 18$	$x^2 - 25 = 0$	$x^2 - 9x = 70$
$2x^2 - x - 20 = x^2$	$x^2 = -4(x+1)$	$3x^2 - 30 = 9x$	$x^2 - 8x + 42 = 9x$

↓ Finish (bottom right square)

Chapter 22

Trigonometry

Contents:

OPENING PROBLEM

Sometimes it is difficult or even impossible to measure angles, heights, and distances directly.

Suppose you are in a boat at sea. You look up at a mountain in front of you and wonder how high it is.

You have no way of measuring the height directly, but what you *can* do is measure the angle from horizontal to the top of the mountain.

So, you make two measurements from points A and B which are 300 m apart in a direct line with the mountain.

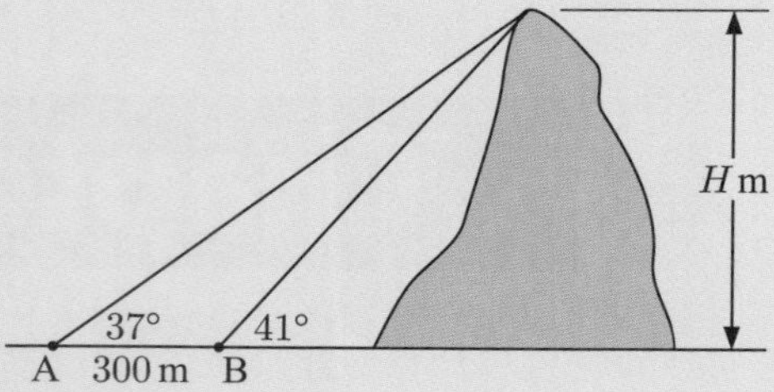

Things to think about:

a How could you use these measurements to *estimate* the mountain's height?

b How accurate would you expect your estimation to be?

c Is there a mathematical method for calculating the height of the mountain to greater accuracy?

Trigonometry is the study of the relationship between lengths and angles of a triangle.

HISTORICAL NOTE

The word *trigonometry* is derived from the Greek word *trigonometria*, meaning "triangle measuring".

This subject was first studied in ancient Egypt and Babylon in the 2nd millennium BC. The Egyptians used trigonometry in the construction of the pyramids, and the scribe **Ahmes** included a problem of trigonometry in the *Rhind Mathematical Papyrus*. The Babylonian astronomers, meanwhile, studied the relationships between angles and distances in their astronomy.

Hipparchus

The Greek mathematician **Hipparchus of Nicaea** (180 - 125 BC) compiled the first trigonometric table, including the corresponding measurements of arc and chord for a series of angles. His work was extended by **Menelaus of Alexandria**, who recorded Menelaus' theorem in his book *Sphaerica*, and **Claudius Ptolemy**, who expanded Hipparchus' table of values in his book *Almagest.*

We use trigonometry alongside algebra, arithmetic, and geometry to find unknown lengths and angles of triangles. In this course we will consider only trigonometry of right angled triangles.

A SCALE DIAGRAMS IN GEOMETRY

Scale diagrams can be used to estimate side lengths and angles in geometrical figures.

Example 1 — Self Tutor

Jake has been contracted to install lights to shine on the front of a hotel. He wants to install the lights at ground-level at a point A on the near side of a drain. The drain is 36.5 m from the base of the hotel. From this point, the angle up to the top of the hotel is 50°. How high is the hotel?

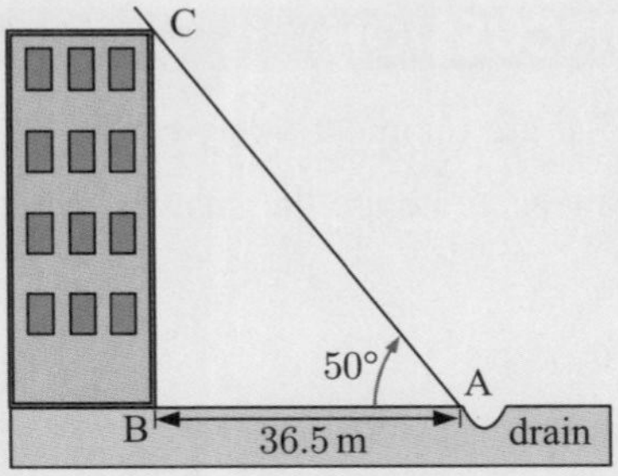

We choose a suitable *scale*, in this case $1 \text{ mm} \equiv 1 \text{ m}$.

We draw a horizontal line [BA] 36.5 mm long, and from point B draw a vertical line.

We then use a protractor to draw a 50° angle at A, and extend the line to meet the vertical. The point C, at the top of the hotel, is where the two lines meet.

Using a ruler, we find that $\text{BC} \approx 43.5$ mm

$\therefore$ the building is approximately 43.5 metres high.

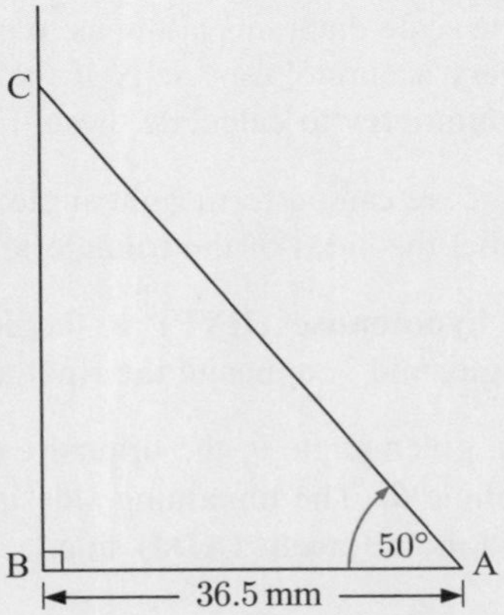

EXERCISE 22A

1 **a** Convert this rough sketch into an accurate scale diagram. Use a scale of $1 \text{ cm} \equiv 1 \text{ m}$.

b Use your scale diagram to find the actual length of:

i [BC] ii [AC]

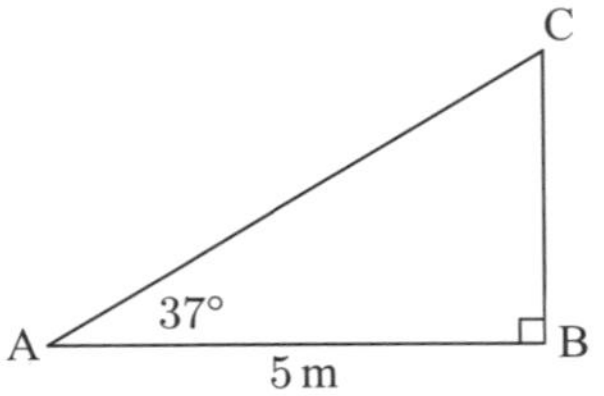

2 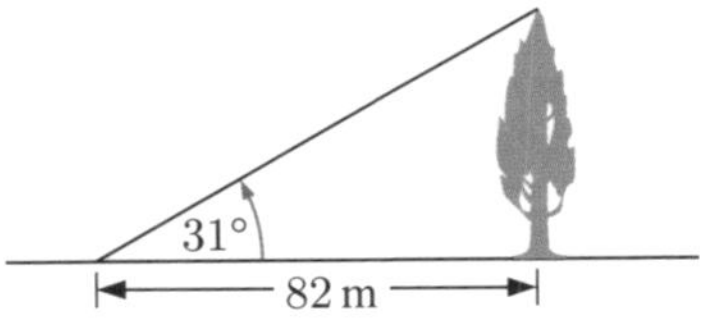

Use a scale diagram with scale $1 \text{ cm} \equiv 10 \text{ m}$ to find the height of the tree.

3 The triangular garden ABC has $AB = 8$ m, $BC = 7.2$ m, and $AC = 5.9$ m.
Use a scale diagram of the garden with scale $1 \text{ cm} \equiv 1 \text{ m}$ to find the measures of the garden's angles.

4 Use a scale diagram to estimate the height of the mountain in the **Opening Problem**.

DISCUSSION

What are the most likely causes of error when using scale diagrams?

How accurate are the answers when using scale diagrams?

B LABELLING RIGHT ANGLED TRIANGLES

While scale diagrams allow us to estimate the side lengths and angles of triangles, our estimates may not be very accurate, especially if the scale diagram is much smaller than the actual situation. We can use **trigonometry** to calculate these triangle properties more accurately.

Before we can perform right angled triangle trigonometry, we need to label the sides of the triangle in a systematic way.

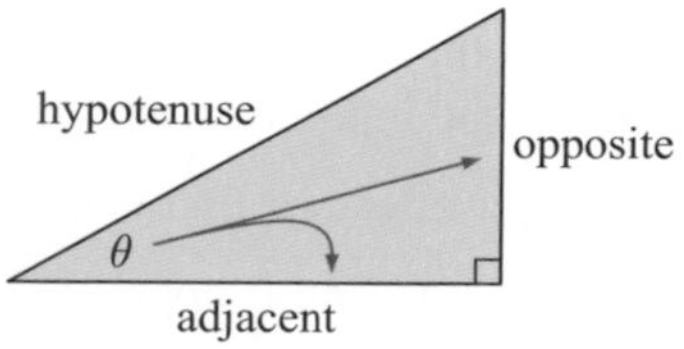

The **hypotenuse (HYP)** is the longest side of a right angled triangle, and is opposite the right angle.

For a given angle θ, the **opposite (OPP)** side is the side opposite the angle θ. The remaining side is next to the angle θ, and so is called the **adjacent (ADJ)** side.

Example 2 **Self Tutor**

For the triangle given, name the:

a hypotenuse
b side opposite θ
c side adjacent to θ.

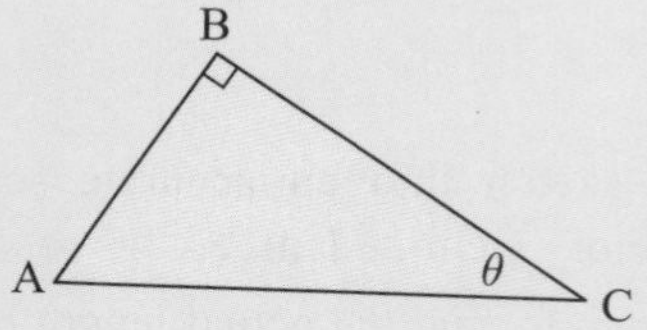

a The hypotenuse is [AC].
b The side opposite θ is [AB].
c The side adjacent to θ is [BC].

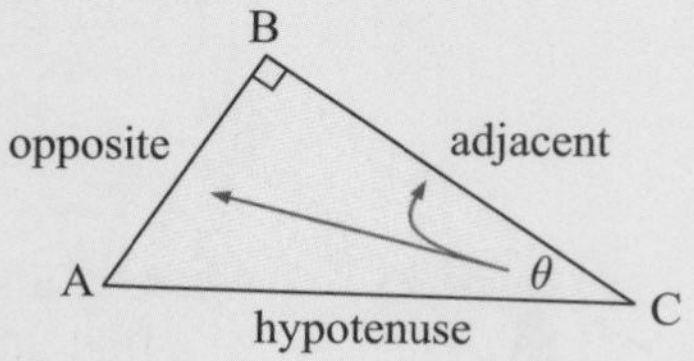

Locate the hypotenuse first. Then locate the opposite and adjacent sides for the angle you are working with.

EXERCISE 22B

1 For each diagram below, name the:

i hypotenuse **ii** side opposite angle θ **iii** side adjacent to angle θ.

a

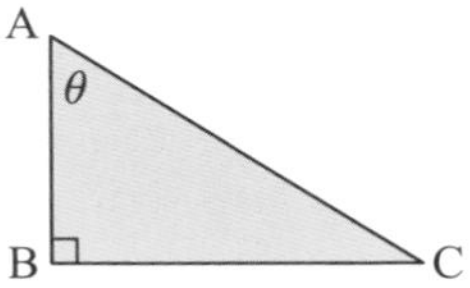

b

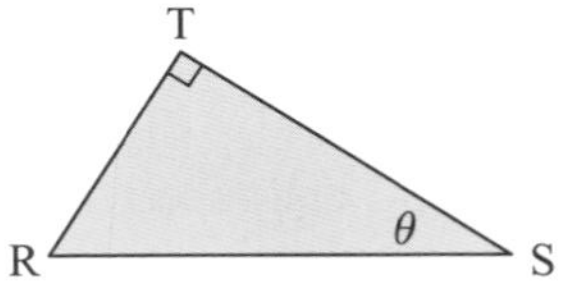

c

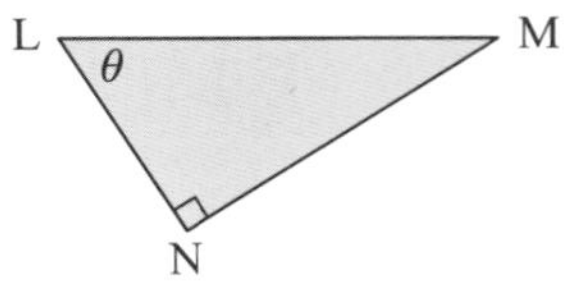

2 The hypotenuse of the right angled triangle shown has length a units. The other sides have lengths b units and c units. θ and ϕ are the two acute angles.
Find the length of the side:

a opposite θ **b** adjacent to θ

c opposite ϕ **d** adjacent to ϕ.

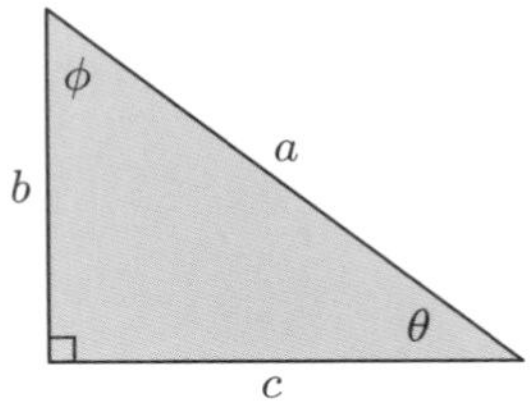

C THE TRIGONOMETRIC RATIOS

Having agreed on a consistent way to label right angled triangles, we can define three basic **trigonometric ratios**. These are the ratios of the side lengths of the triangle.

Consider a right angled triangle with one angle θ.

The **sine** of angle θ is $\sin\theta = \dfrac{\text{OPP}}{\text{HYP}}$.

The **cosine** of angle θ is $\cos\theta = \dfrac{\text{ADJ}}{\text{HYP}}$.

The **tangent** of angle θ is $\tan\theta = \dfrac{\text{OPP}}{\text{ADJ}}$.

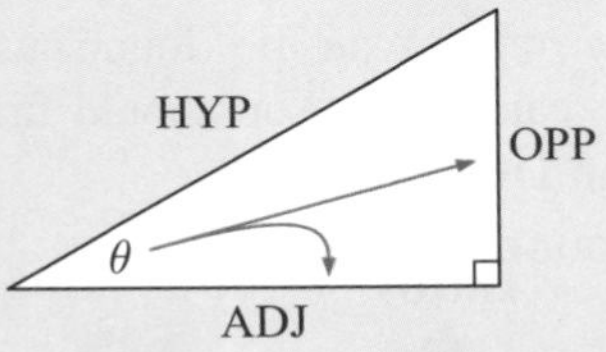

INVESTIGATION 1 TRIGONOMETRIC RATIOS

In this Investigation we explore the trigonometric ratios for triangles which are *similar*.

Consider the right angled triangle alongside.
It contains one angle of $39°$.

What to do:

1 Use a ruler to check that:
- the hypotenuse (HYP) is 5.4 cm long
- the side opposite the $39°$ angle (OPP) is 3.4 cm long
- the side adjacent to the $39°$ angle (ADJ) is 4.2 cm long.

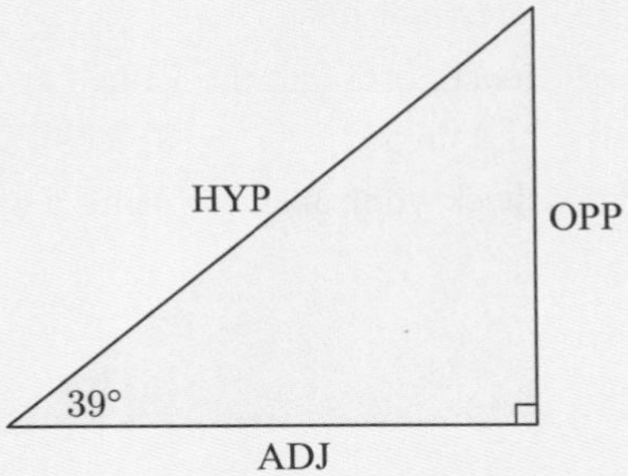

2 Copy and complete this table:

HYP	OPP	ADJ	$\frac{\text{OPP}}{\text{HYP}}$	$\frac{\text{ADJ}}{\text{HYP}}$	$\frac{\text{OPP}}{\text{ADJ}}$
5.4	3.4	4.2	$\frac{3.4}{5.4} \approx 0.63$		

3 **a** Use a ruler and protractor to construct a different right angled triangle with one angle of 39°.

b Measure the sides of the triangle, and repeat step **2**. Comment on your results.

c Compare your results with those of your classmates. Does the size of the triangle affect the trigonometric ratios?

4 Consider the triangles ABC and A′B′C′.

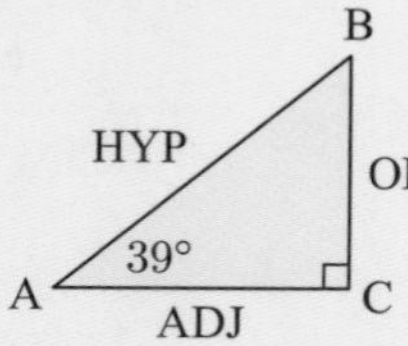

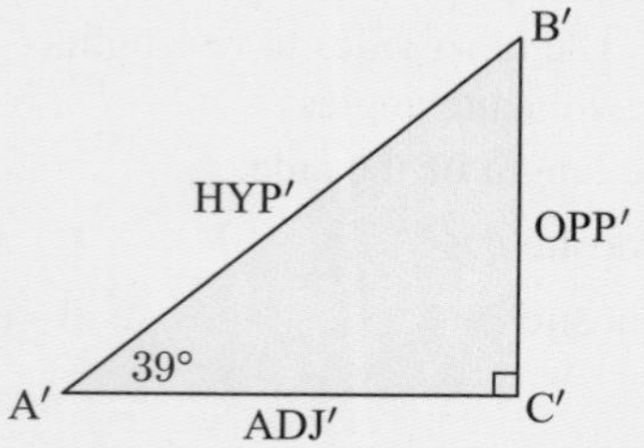

a Show that the triangles are similar.

b Hence, show that:

i $\frac{\text{OPP}}{\text{HYP}} = \frac{\text{OPP}'}{\text{HYP}'}$ **ii** $\frac{\text{ADJ}}{\text{HYP}} = \frac{\text{ADJ}'}{\text{HYP}'}$ **iii** $\frac{\text{OPP}}{\text{ADJ}} = \frac{\text{OPP}'}{\text{ADJ}'}$

You should have discovered that for any right angled triangle with one angle 39°, the trigonometric ratios are constant. In particular, $\sin 39° \approx 0.63$, $\cos 39° \approx 0.78$, $\tan 39° \approx 0.81$.

Trigonometric ratios can be found using the software provided or a calculator. You should first check that your calculator is in DEGREE mode.

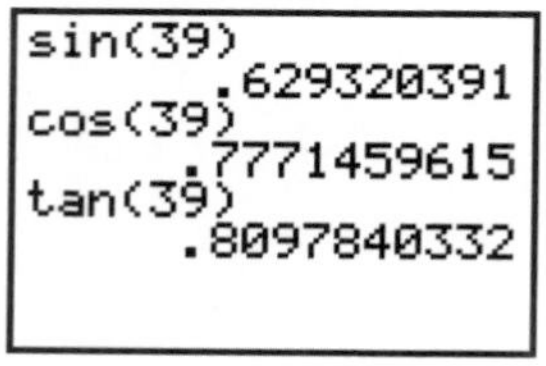

EXERCISE 22C

1 Consider the right angled triangle ABC given.

a Use a ruler to find the length of each side, rounded to 1 decimal place.

b Hence, estimate the value of:

i $\sin 57°$ **ii** $\cos 57°$ **iii** $\tan 57°$

c Check your answers using a calculator.

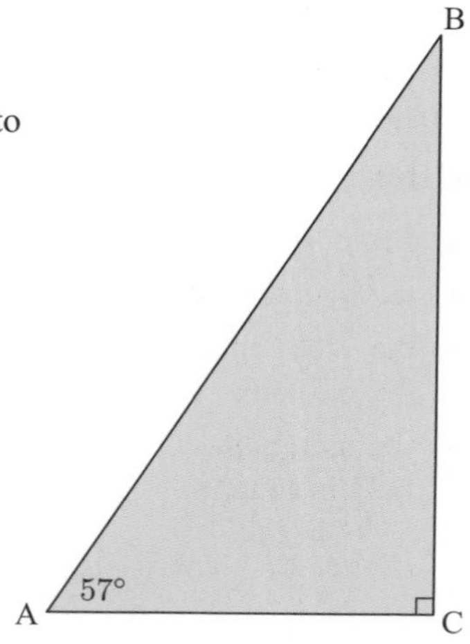

2 **a** Use Pythagoras' theorem to find the length of the hypotenuse of this triangle. Round your answer to 2 decimal places.

b Hence, estimate the value of:

i $\sin 28°$ ii $\cos 28°$ iii $\tan 28°$

c Check your answers using a calculator.

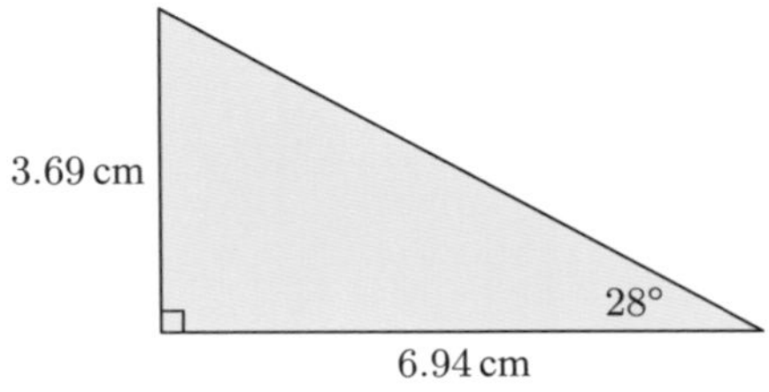

3 **a** Use the diagram alongside to determine which is greater:

i $\tan 55°$ or $\tan 65°$

ii $\cos 55°$ or $\cos 65°$.

b Check your answers using a calculator.

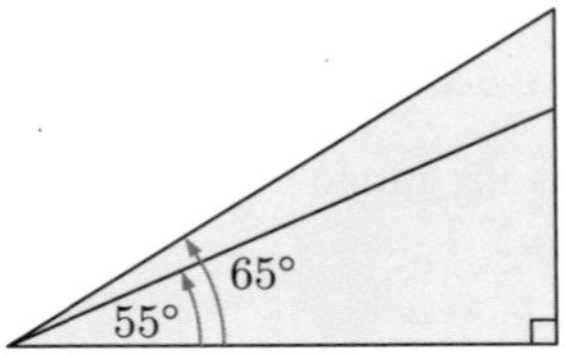

4

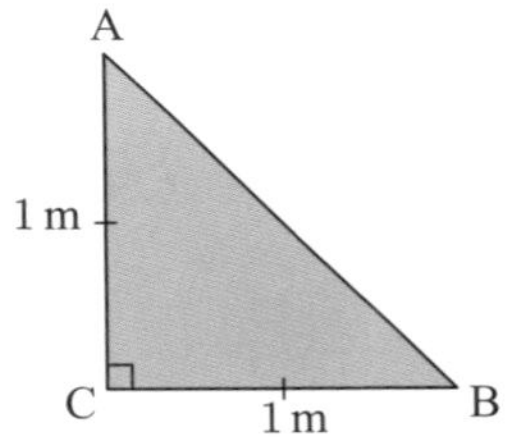

Consider the right angled isosceles triangle given.

a Explain why $A\widehat{B}C = 45°$.

b Find the exact length of [AB].

c Hence, find exact values for:

i $\sin 45°$ ii $\cos 45°$ iii $\tan 45°$

5 ABC is an equilateral triangle with side lengths 2 m.

a Explain why:

i BM = 1 m ii $A\widehat{B}M = 60°$.

b Find the exact length of [AM].

c Hence, find exact values for:

i $\sin 60°$ ii $\cos 60°$ iii $\tan 60°$

d Show that $B\widehat{A}M = 30°$.

e Hence, find exact values for:

i $\sin 30°$ ii $\cos 30°$ iii $\tan 30°$

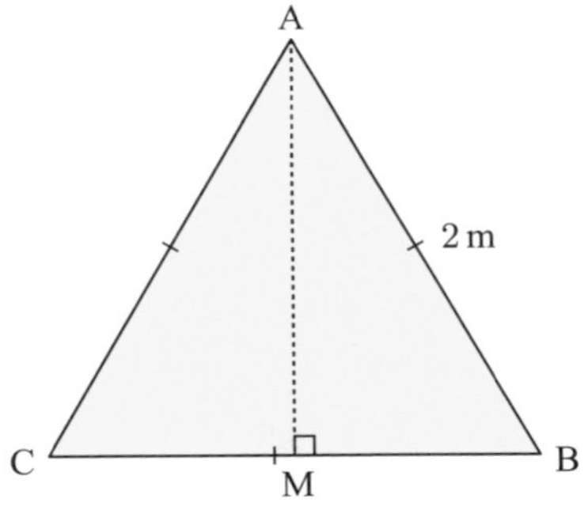

6 **a** Use your calculator to find:

i $\sin 70°$ ii $\cos 70°$ iii $\sin 20°$ iv $\cos 20°$

Comment on your results.

b Use the diagram alongside to show that, for $0° < \theta < 90°$:

i $\sin(90° - \theta) = \cos\theta$

ii $\cos(90° - \theta) = \sin\theta$.

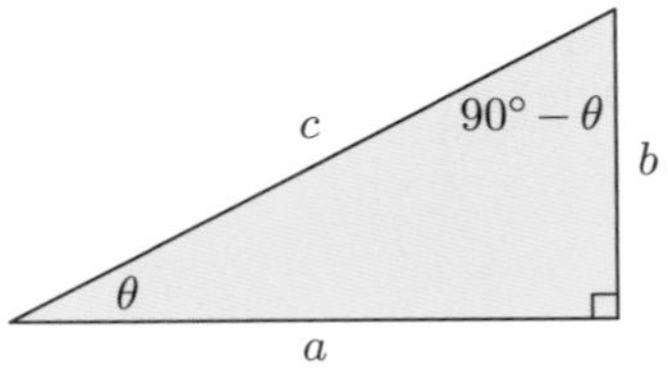

7 **a** Use your calculator to find:

i $\sin 52°$ ii $\cos 52°$ iii $\dfrac{\sin 52°}{\cos 52°}$ iv $\tan 52°$

b Explain why $\tan\theta = \dfrac{\sin\theta}{\cos\theta}$.

8 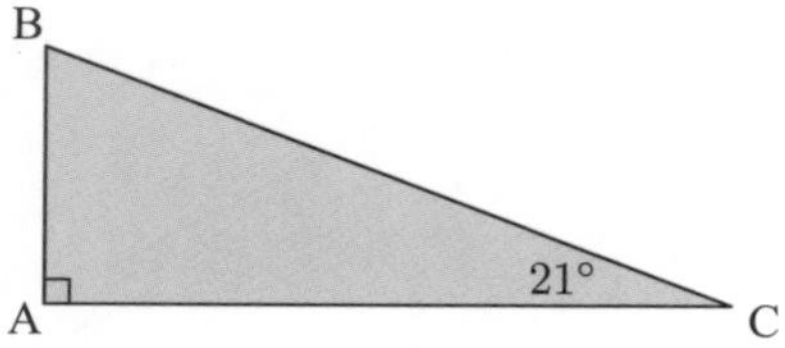

Use your calculator to find the following ratios:

a $\dfrac{AB}{BC}$ **b** $\dfrac{AC}{BC}$ **c** $\dfrac{AB}{AC}$

DISCUSSION

Suppose θ is one angle of a right angled triangle.

What is the range of possible values that $\sin\theta$ and $\cos\theta$ can take?

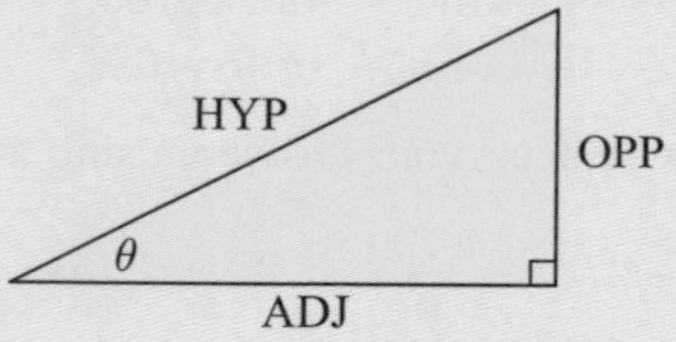

INVESTIGATION 2 $\cos^2\theta + \sin^2\theta$

$\cos^2\theta$ is shorthand notation for $\cos\theta \times \cos\theta$.

Likewise, $\sin^2\theta = \sin\theta \times \sin\theta$.

Your task is to examine the value of $\cos^2\theta + \sin^2\theta$ for various values of θ.

What to do:

1 Copy the table below, and use your calculator to fill in the missing values.

θ	$\cos^2\theta$	$\sin^2\theta$	$\cos^2\theta + \sin^2\theta$
45°			
30°			
15°			
26°			
37.8°			
64°			

2 Draw a general conclusion from your results in **1**.

3 Use the figure alongside to prove that your conclusion is true for all values of θ, where $0° < \theta < 90°$.

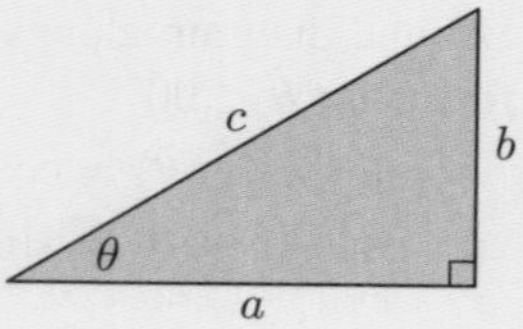

D FINDING SIDE LENGTHS

If we know the angles of a right angled triangle, the trigonometric ratios give us the ratios of its side lengths. For example, in the triangle alongside, we know that $\frac{\text{PQ}}{\text{PR}} = \cos 36° \approx 0.809$.

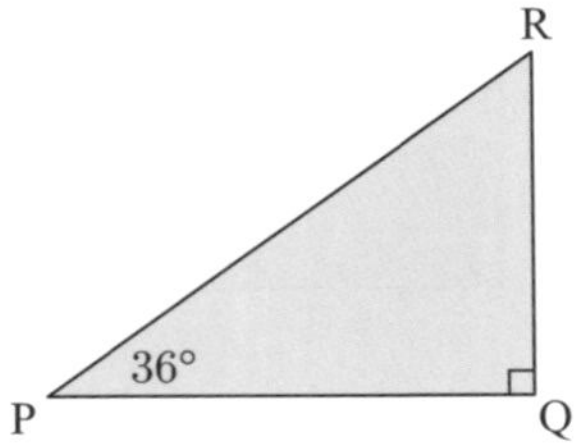

So, if we also know one of the side lengths, we can use the trigonometric ratios to find the other side lengths.

Step 1: Redraw the figure and mark on it HYP, OPP, and ADJ relative to a given angle.
Step 2: Choose an appropriate trigonometric ratio, and construct an equation.
Step 3: Solve the equation to find the unknown side length.

Example 3 **Self Tutor**

Find x, rounding your answer to 2 decimal places:

a

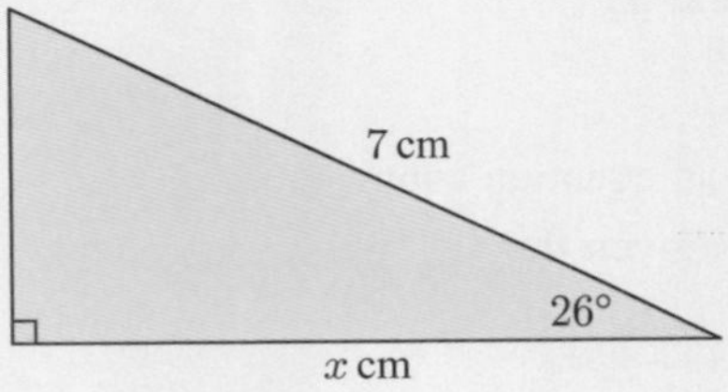

b

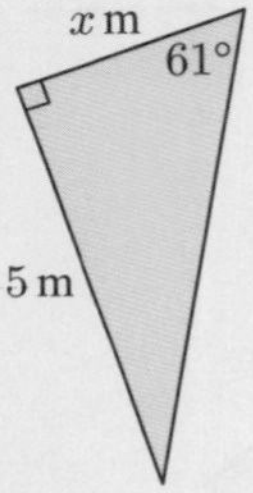

a

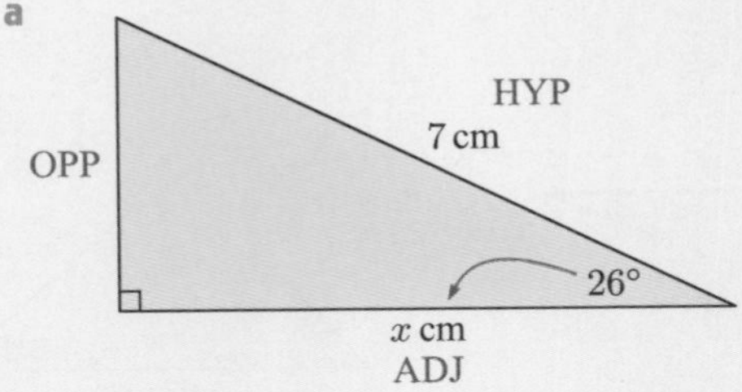

The relevant sides are ADJ and HYP, so we use the *cosine* ratio.

Now $\cos 26° = \frac{x}{7}$ $\{\cos\theta = \frac{\text{ADJ}}{\text{HYP}}\}$

$\therefore\ x = 7 \times \cos 26°$ {multiplying both sides by 7}

$\therefore\ x \approx 6.29$ {calculator}

b

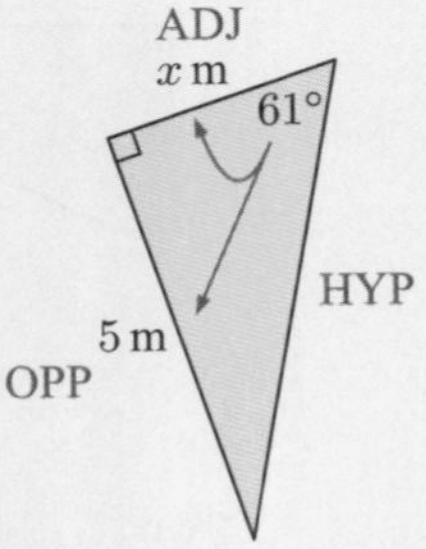

The relevant sides are OPP and ADJ, so we use the *tangent* ratio.

Now $\tan 61° = \frac{5}{x}$ $\{\tan\theta = \frac{\text{OPP}}{\text{ADJ}}\}$

$\therefore\ x \times \tan 61° = 5$ {multiplying both sides by x}

$\therefore\ x = \frac{5}{\tan 61°}$ {dividing both sides by $\tan 61°$}

$\therefore\ x \approx 2.77$ {calculator}

EXERCISE 22D

1 Write a trigonometric equation connecting the angle and the sides given:

a
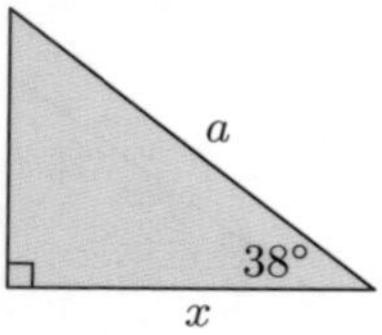

b
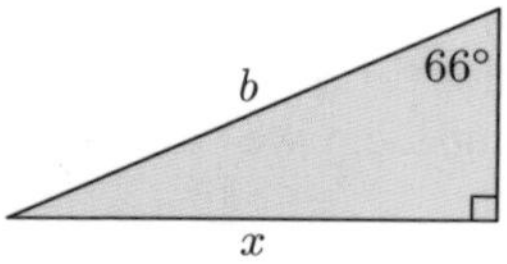

c
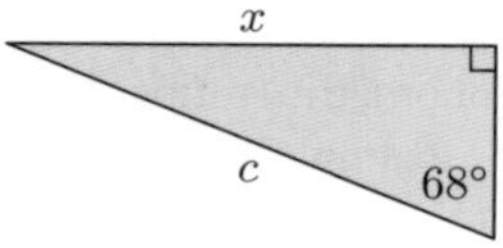

d
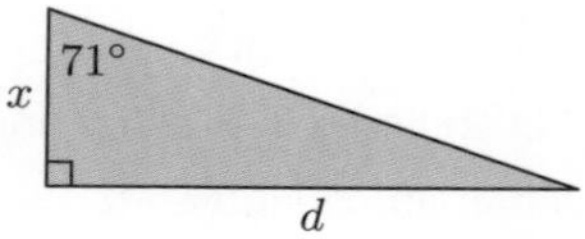

e
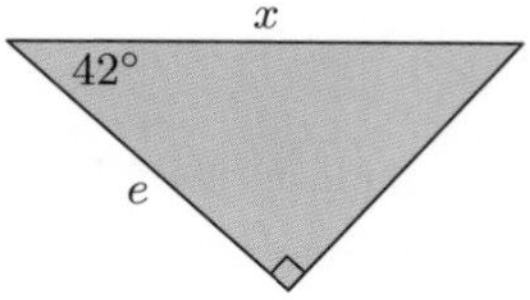

f
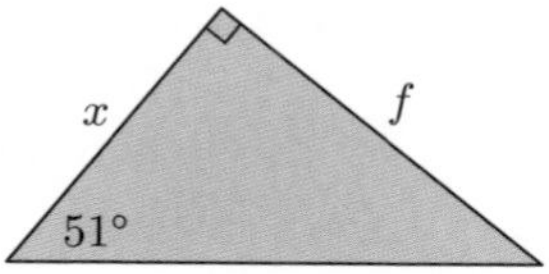

g
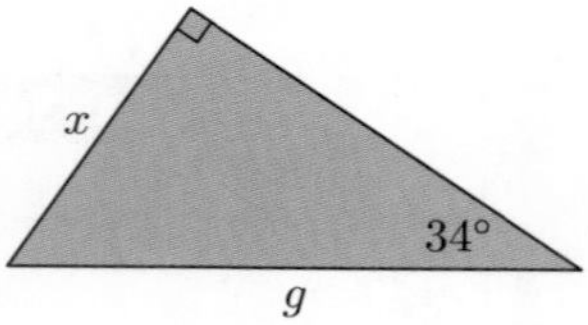

h
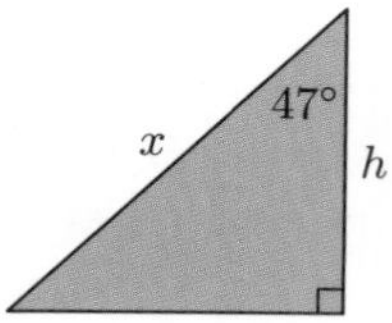

i
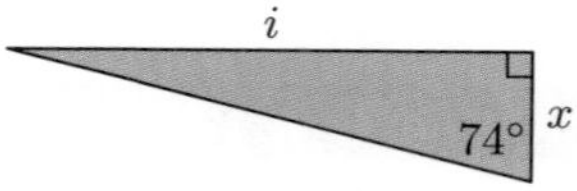

2
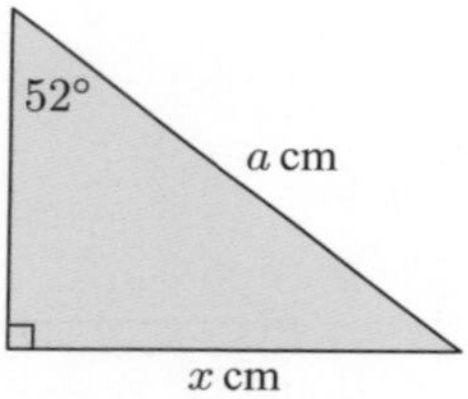

a Write an equation connecting x and a.

b Find x given that $a = 6$.

3 Find x, rounding your answer to 2 decimal places:

a
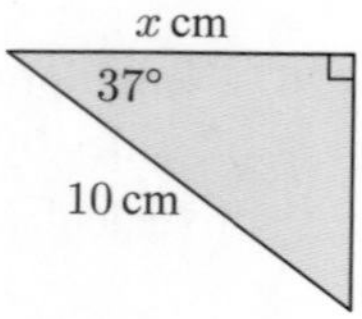

b
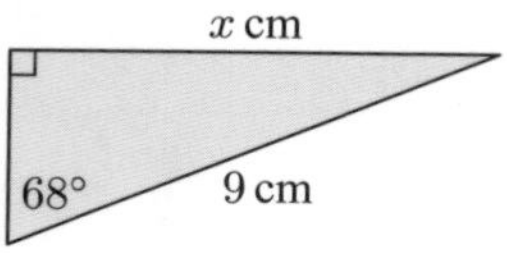

c
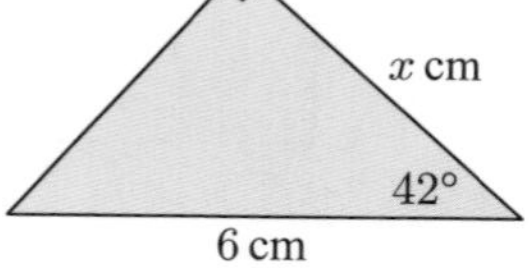

d
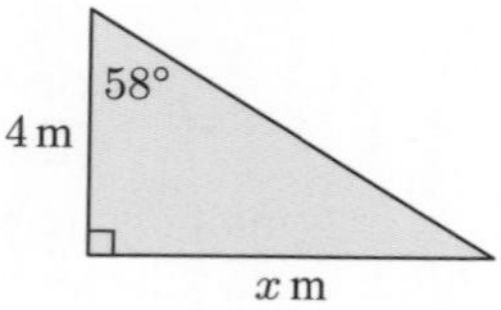

e
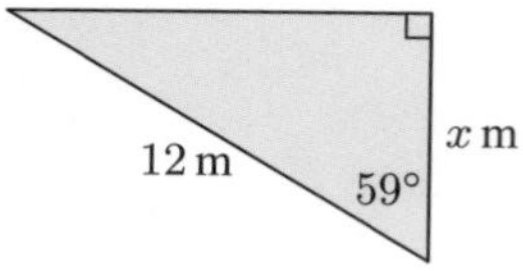

f
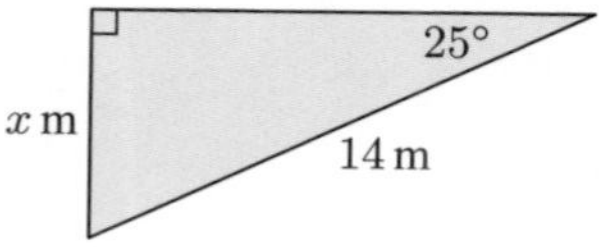

g
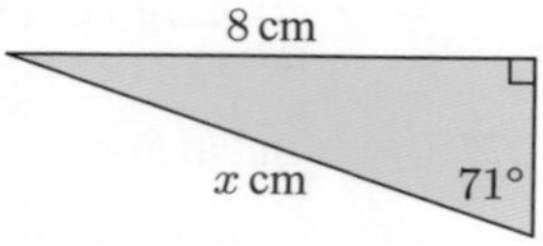

h
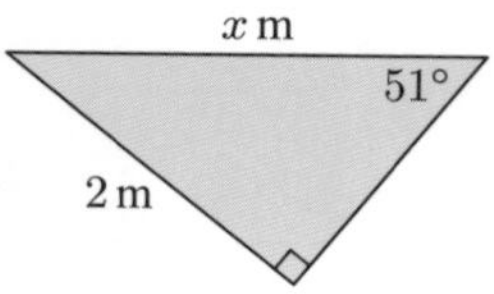

i
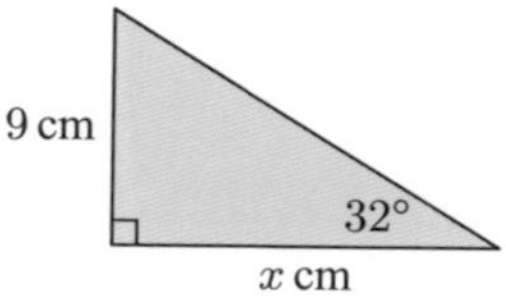

j

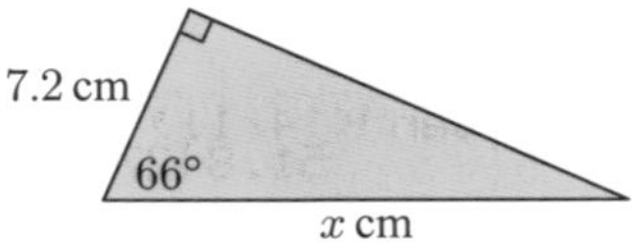

k

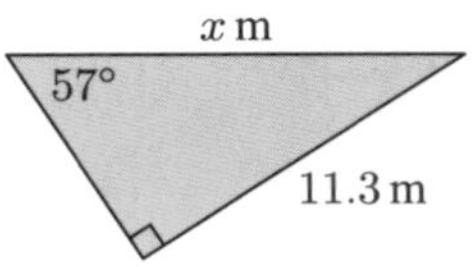

l

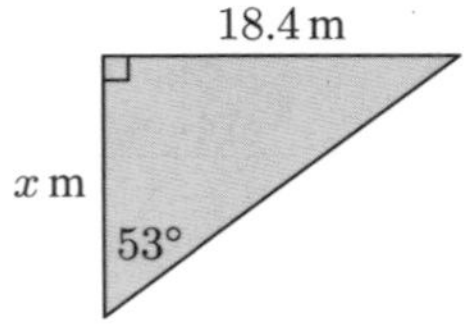

4 Find, to 1 decimal place, *all* the unknown angles and sides of:

a

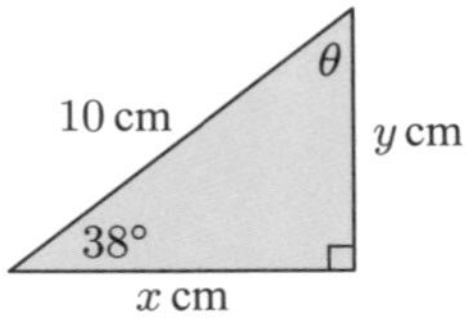

b

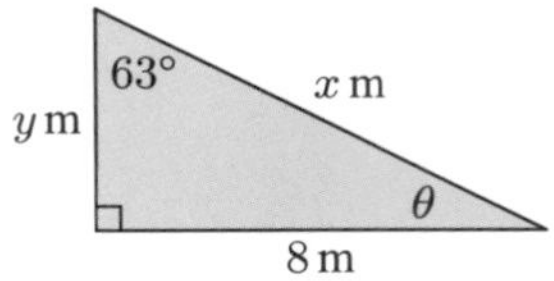

c

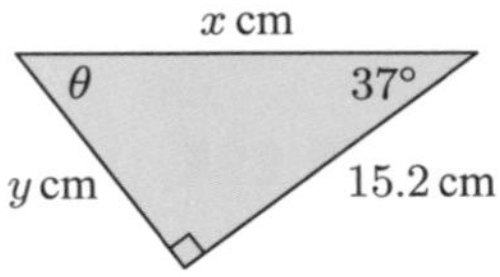

E FINDING ANGLES

If we are given two side lengths of a right angled triangle, we can find the other angles of the triangle.

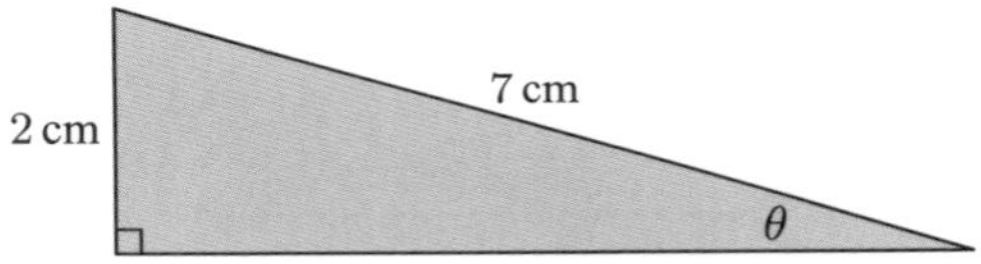

In the triangle alongside, $\sin\theta = \frac{2}{7}$.

So, θ is the angle whose sine is $\frac{2}{7}$. We say θ is the **inverse sine** of $\frac{2}{7}$, and write $\theta = \sin^{-1}\left(\frac{2}{7}\right)$.

We can use a calculator to evaluate inverse sines. Click on the icon for instructions.

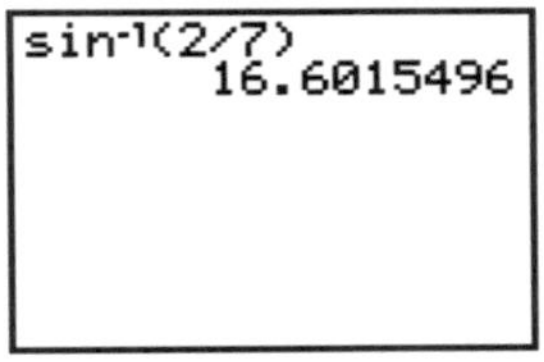

For the right angled triangle with hypotenuse 7 cm and opposite side 2 cm, $\theta \approx 16.6°$.

We define **inverse cosine** and **inverse tangent** in a similar way.

Example 4 — Self Tutor

Find, to 1 decimal place, the measure of the angle marked θ.

a

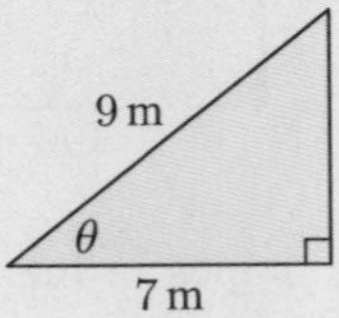

b

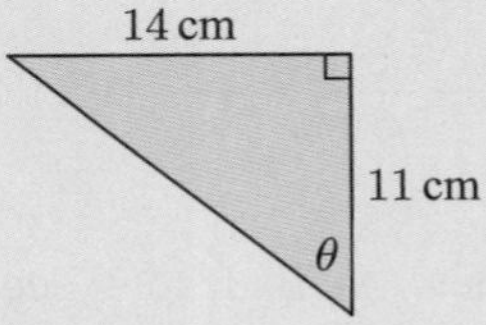

a

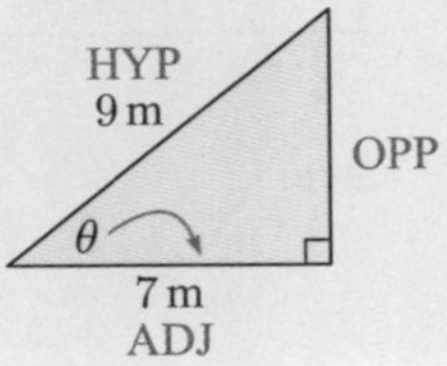

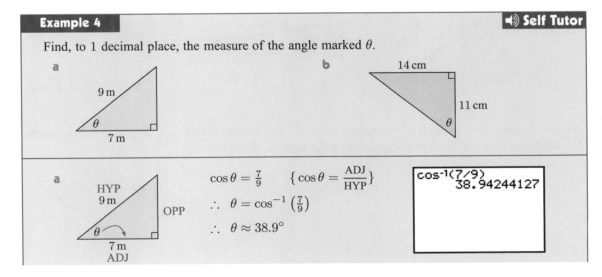

$\cos\theta = \frac{7}{9}$ $\quad \left\{\cos\theta = \frac{\text{ADJ}}{\text{HYP}}\right\}$

$\therefore\ \theta = \cos^{-1}\left(\frac{7}{9}\right)$

$\therefore\ \theta \approx 38.9°$

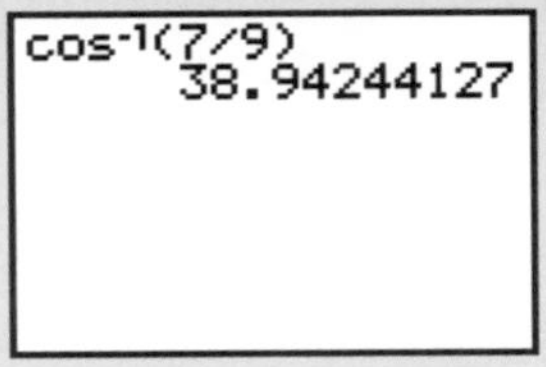

b

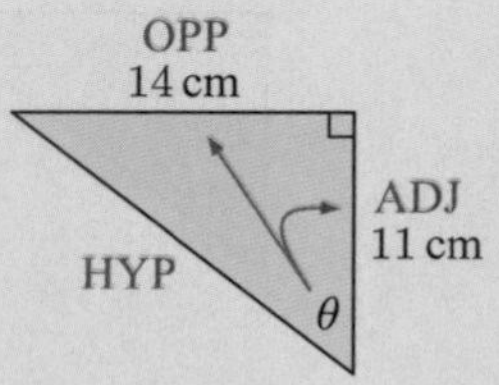

$\tan\theta = \frac{14}{11}$ $\{\tan\theta = \frac{\text{OPP}}{\text{ADJ}}\}$

$\therefore \quad \theta = \tan^{-1}\left(\frac{14}{11}\right)$

$\therefore \quad \theta \approx 51.8°$

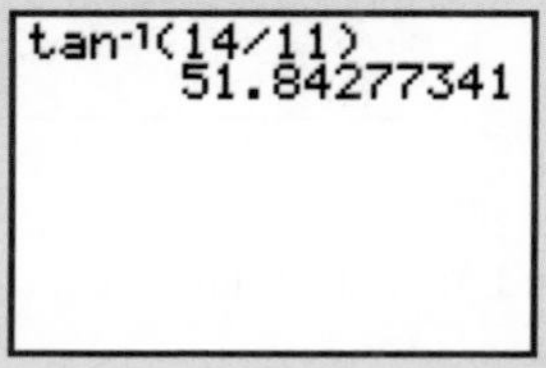

EXERCISE 22E

1 Find, to 1 decimal place, the measure of the angle marked θ:

a
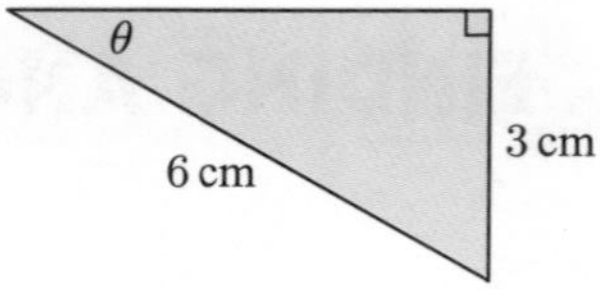

b
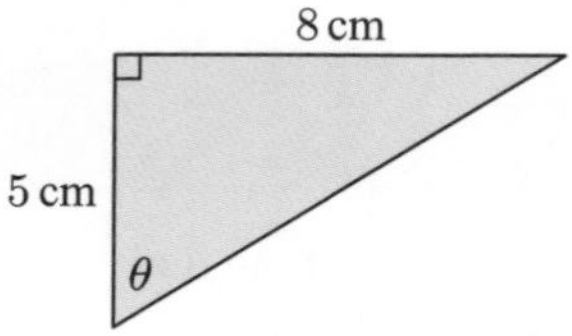

c
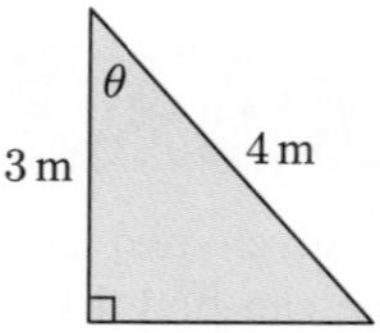

d
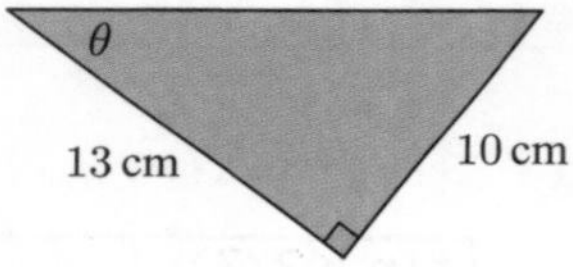

e
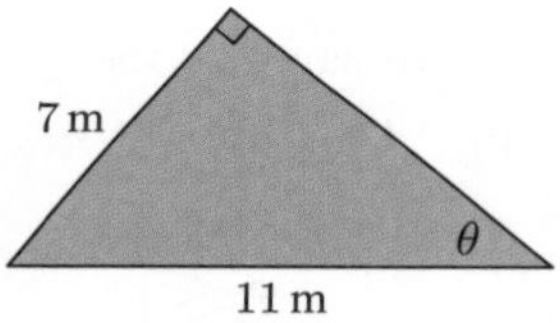

f
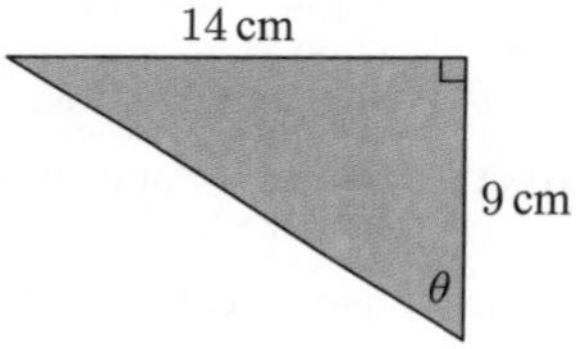

g
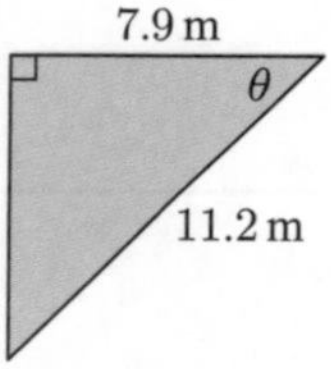

h
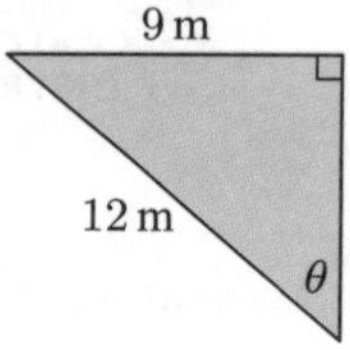

i
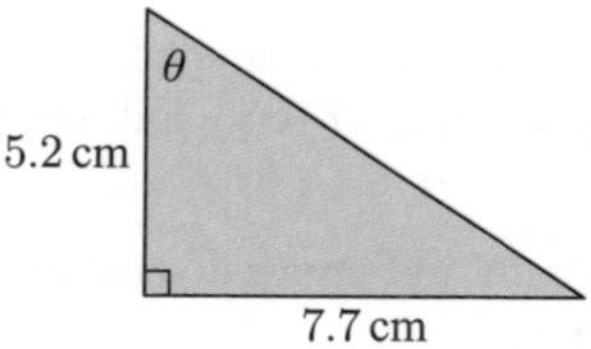

j
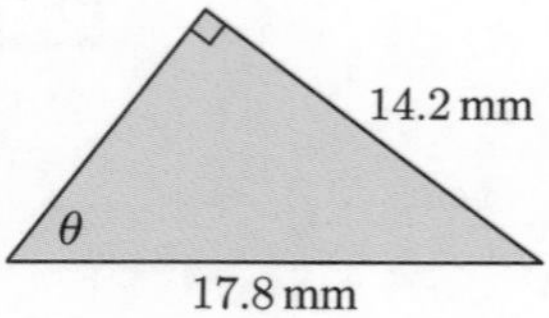

k
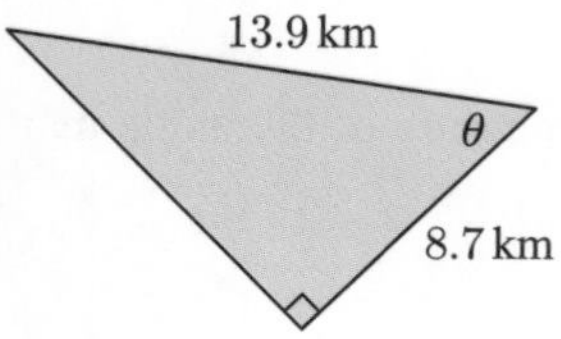

l
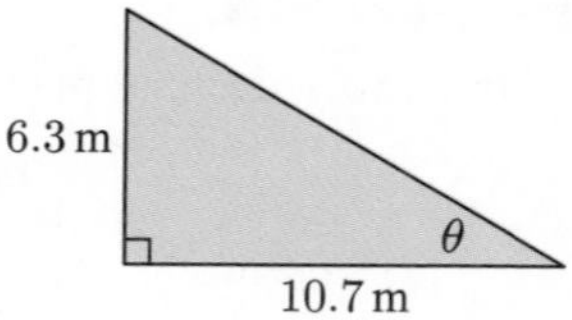

2 Use trigonometry to find, to 1 decimal place, all the unknown sides and angles in the following triangles. Check your answers for x using Pythagoras' theorem.

a
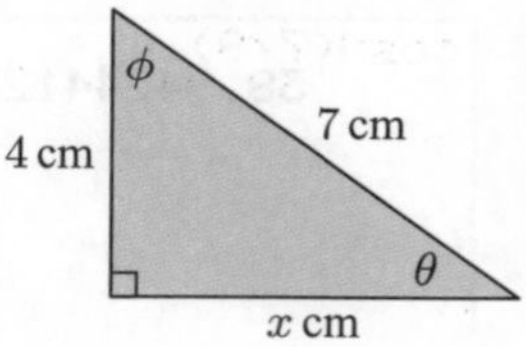

b
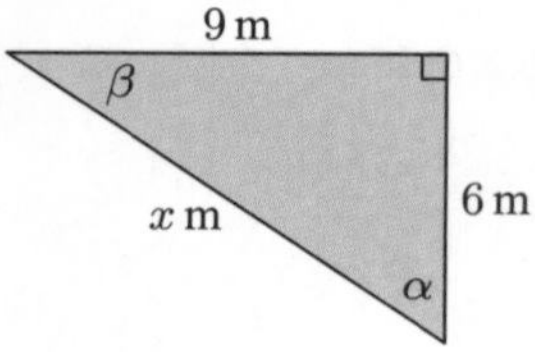

c
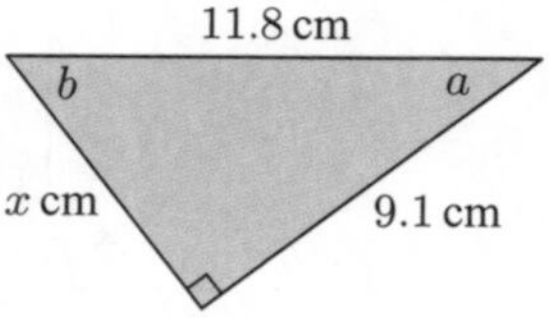

PUZZLE **THE SPIRAL OF THEODORUS**

The **spiral of Theodorus** consists of a series of right angled triangles.

The initial triangle ABC is isosceles with legs of length 1.

For each subsequent triangle, one of the legs is the hypotenuse of the previous triangle, and the other leg has length 1.

How many triangles can be drawn before they start to overlap?

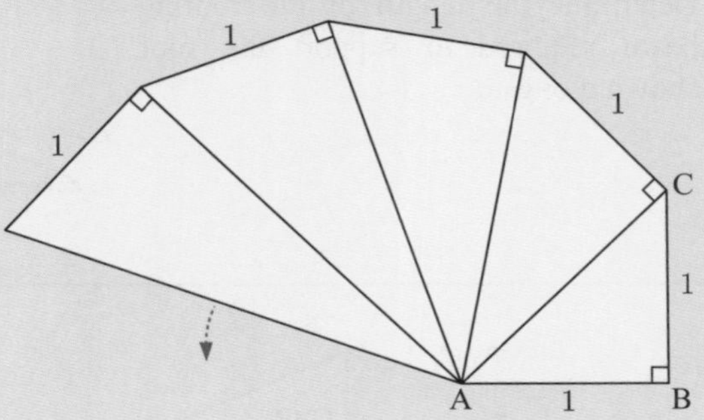

F PROBLEM SOLVING WITH TRIGONOMETRY

The trigonometric ratios can be used to solve problems involving right angled triangles.

When solving these problems, you should follow the steps below:

Step 1: Draw a **diagram** to illustrate the situation.

Step 2: Mark on the diagram the **unknown** angle or side that needs to be calculated. We often use x for a length and θ for an angle.

Step 3: Locate a **right angled triangle** in your diagram.

Step 4: Write an **equation** connecting an angle and two sides of the triangle using one of the trigonometric ratios.

Step 5: **Solve** the equation to find the unknown.

Step 6: **Write** your answer in sentence form.

Example 5 **Self Tutor**

A ladder leaning against a vertical wall reaches 3.5 m up the wall, and makes an angle of 55° with the ground. Find the length of the ladder.

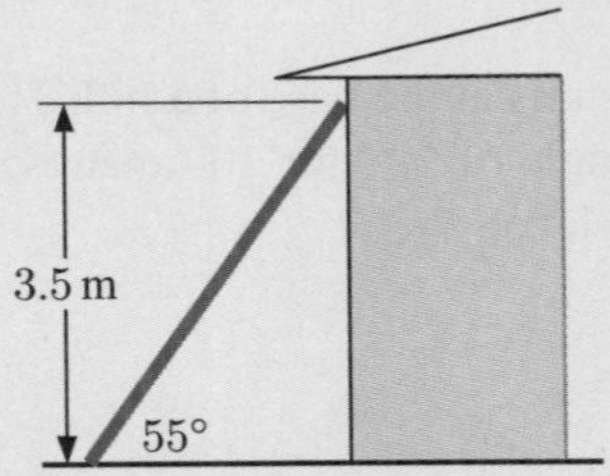

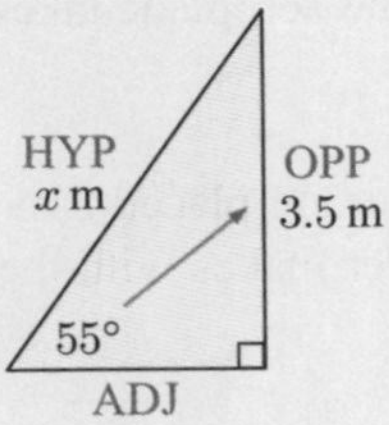

Let the ladder be x m long.

$$\sin 55° = \frac{3.5}{x} \qquad \{\sin\theta = \frac{\text{OPP}}{\text{HYP}}\}$$

$$\therefore \ x \times \sin 55° = 3.5$$

$$\therefore \ x = \frac{3.5}{\sin 55°}$$

$$\therefore \ x \approx 4.27$$

$\therefore$ the ladder is about 4.27 m long.

Example 6 — Self Tutor

Determine the length of the roofing beam required to support the roof shown alongside:

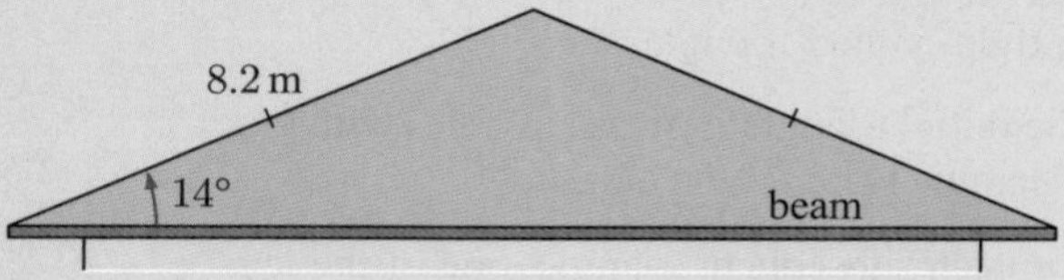

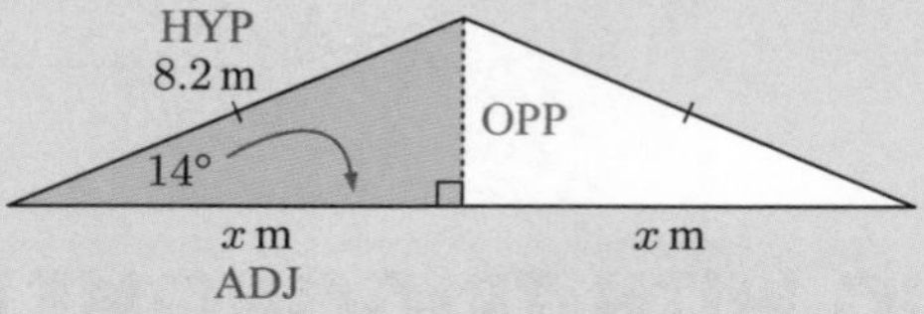

Suppose the beam is $2x$ m long.

$\cos 14° = \frac{x}{8.2}$ $\{\cos\theta = \frac{\text{ADJ}}{\text{HYP}}\}$

$\therefore\ x = 8.2 \times \cos 14°$

$\therefore\ 2x = 2 \times 8.2 \times \cos 14°$

≈ 15.9

$\therefore$ the beam is about 15.9 m long.

We can use the properties of isosceles triangles to locate a right angle.

EXERCISE 22F

1 From a point 25 metres from the base of a flagpole, the angle to the top of the pole is 35°. Find the height of the flagpole.

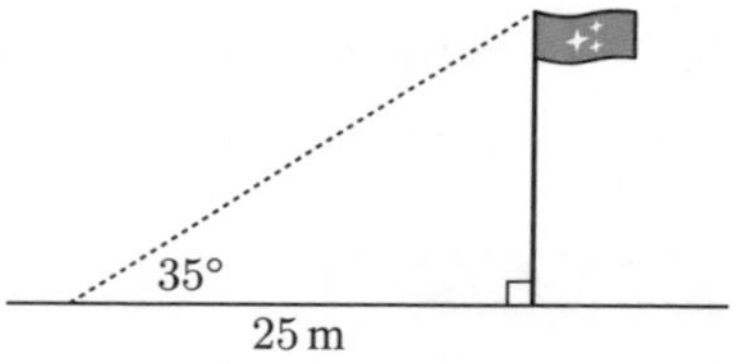

2 Lucas starts at the base of a hill. He walks up a steep path at an angle of 22° for 100 metres. Find his height above ground level.

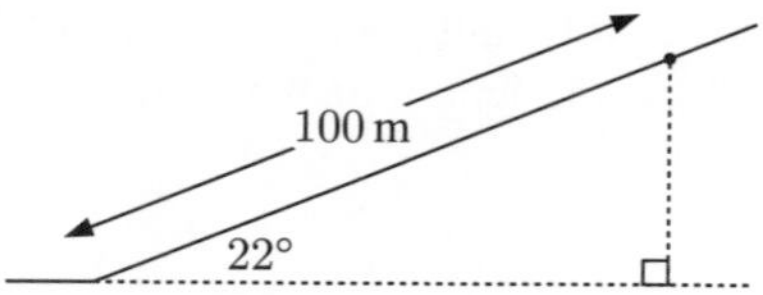

3

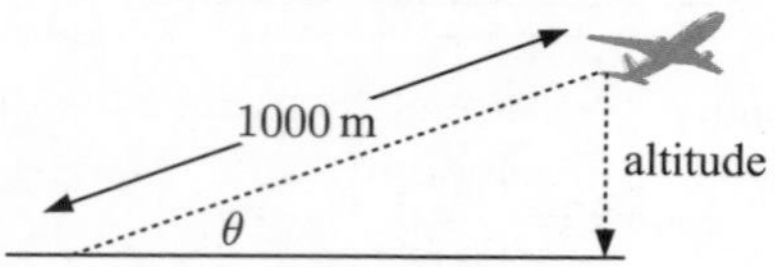

An aeroplane takes off at a constant angle to the ground. At the time when it has flown 1000 m, its altitude is 320 m. Find the angle θ at which the aeroplane takes off.

4

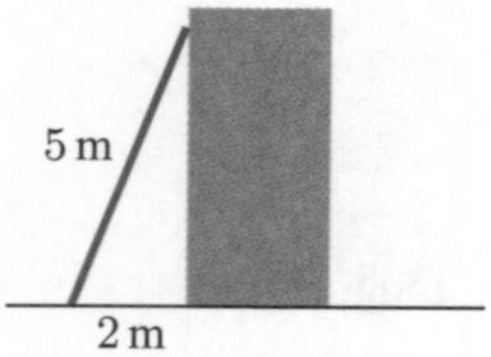

The feet of a 5 m long ladder are placed 2 m from a wall. Find the angle that the ladder makes with the ground.

5 A beam of length 4.8 metres supports a garage roof. The pitch of the roof is 12°. Find the length of the sloping sides.

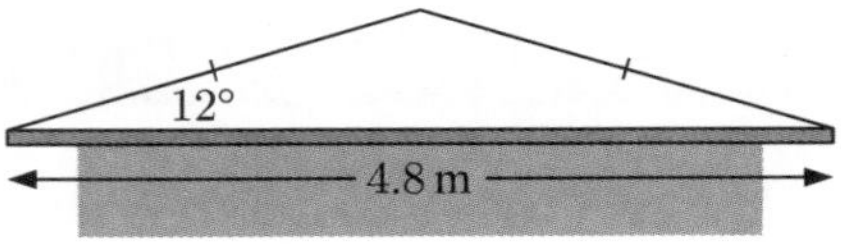

6 A parasailer is towed behind a boat. The towing cable is 40 metres long, and makes an angle of 50° with the deck of the boat. How high is the parasailer above the water?

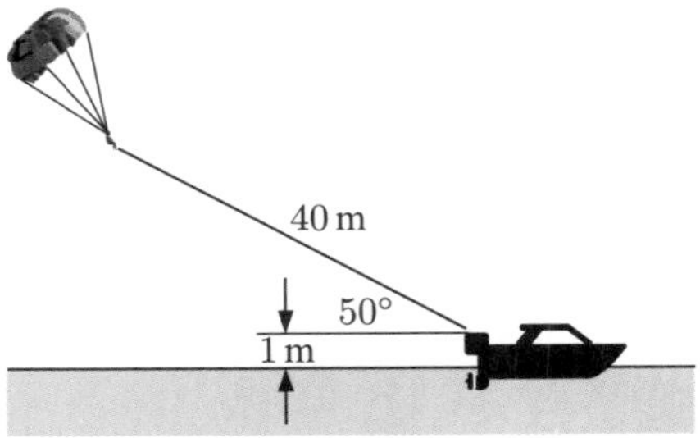

7 Find the perimeter of this rectangle.

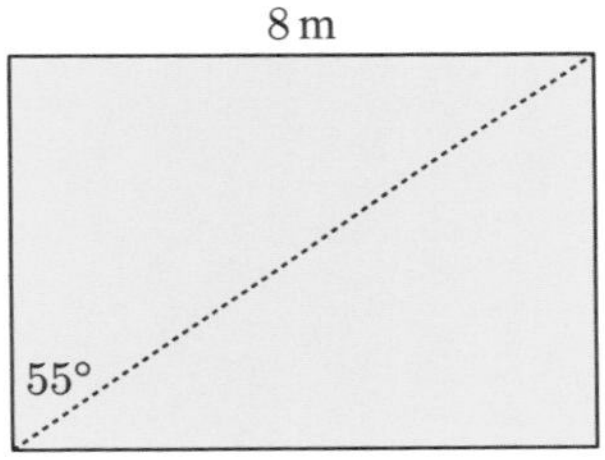

8 An isosceles triangle has sides 7 cm, 7 cm, and 8 cm in length. Find the measure of the base angles.

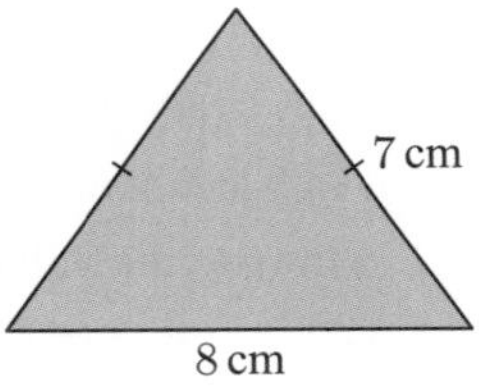

9 An isosceles triangle has equal sides of length 13 cm, and base angles of 40°. Find the length of the base of the triangle.

10 A rhombus has sides of length 15 cm, and one diagonal of length 20 cm. Find the measure of the angles of the rhombus.

11 One angle of a rhombus measures 70°, and the shorter diagonal is 12 cm long. Find the perimeter of the rhombus.

12 A 7 m long ladder leaning against a vertical wall makes an angle of 50° to the horizontal. The foot of the ladder is pushed towards the wall until an angle of 65° is obtained. How much further up the wall does the ladder now reach?

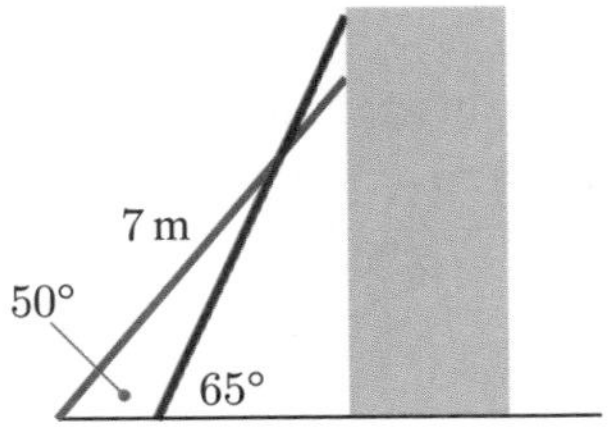

13 From a point A that is 40 m from the base of a building B, the angle to the top of the building T is 41°, and the angle to the top of the flagpole F is 47°. Find the height of the flagpole [FT].

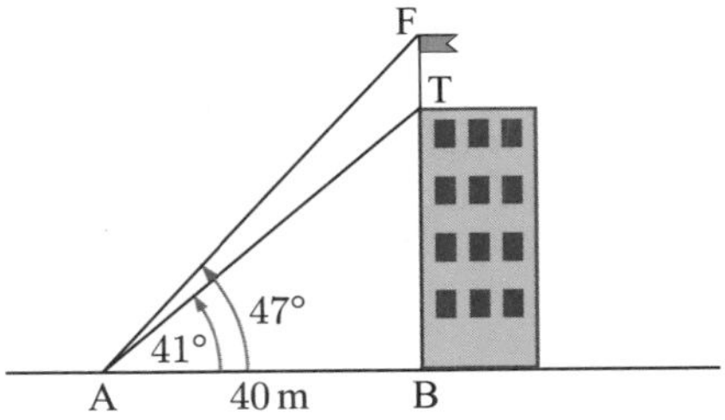

14 Find the height of the mountain in the **Opening Problem** on page **440**.

REVIEW SET 22A

1 **a** Convert this sketch into an accurate scale diagram using a scale of 1 cm ≡ 1 m.

b Use the scale diagram to estimate the length of [PQ].

c Use trigonometry to find the length of [PQ], rounded to 2 decimal places.

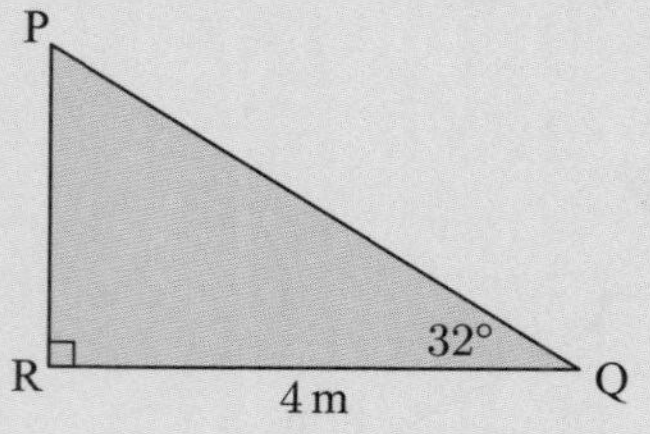

2 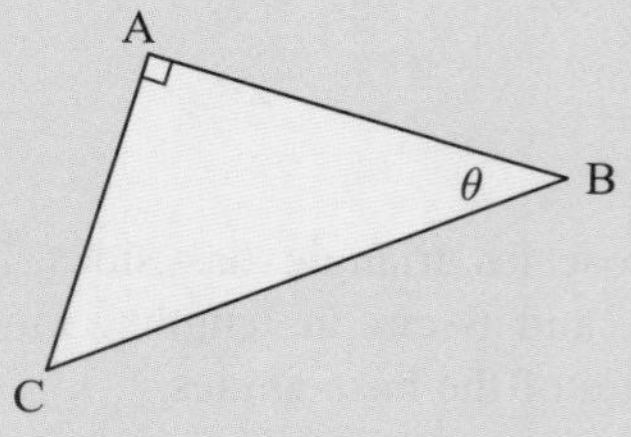

For this right angled triangle, name the:

a hypotenuse

b side opposite angle θ

c side adjacent to angle θ.

3 Consider the right angled triangle PQR given.

a Use a ruler to find the length of each side, rounded to 1 decimal place.

b Hence, estimate the value of:

i $\sin 26°$ **ii** $\cos 26°$ **iii** $\tan 26°$

c Check your answer using a calculator.

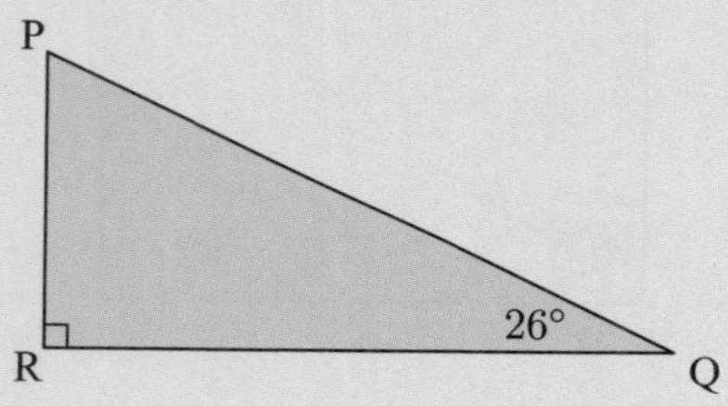

4 Write a trigonometric equation connecting the angle and the sides given.

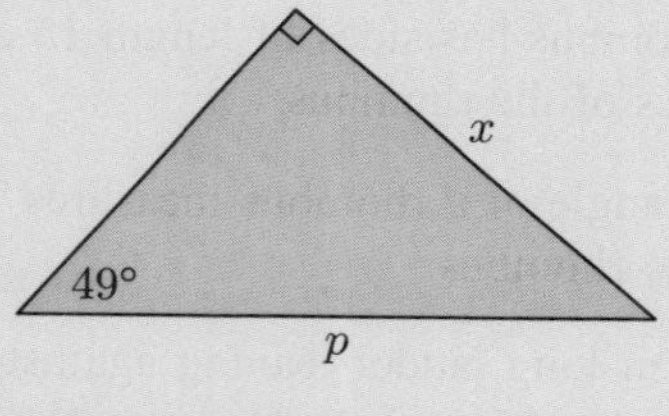

5 Find x in the following figures, rounding your answers to 1 decimal place:

a 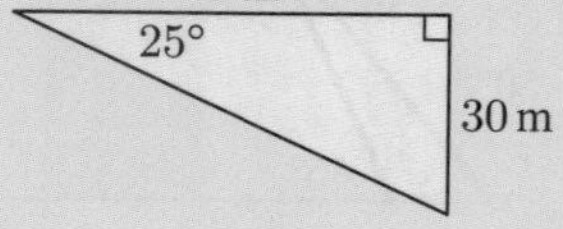

b 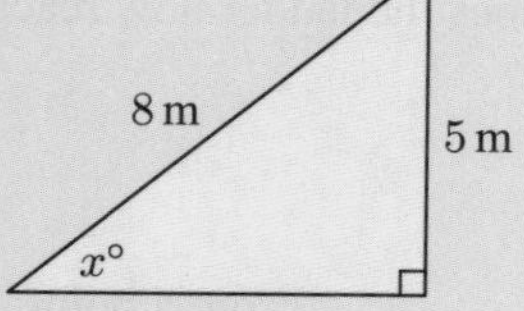

c 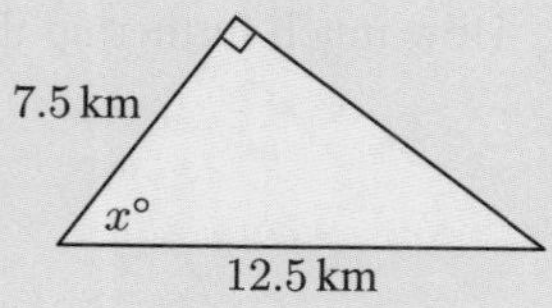

6 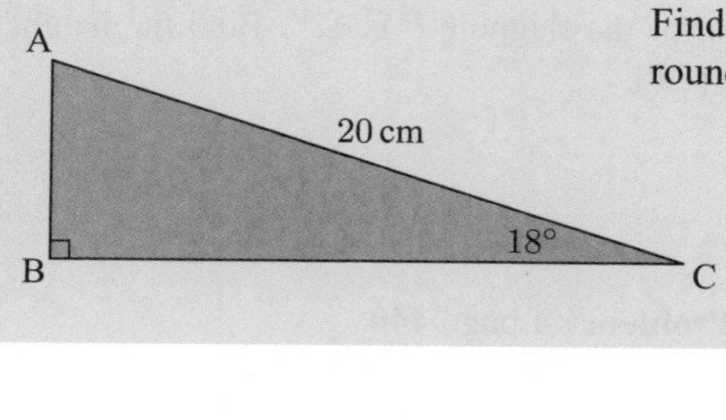

Find the remaining side lengths in the given triangle, rounding your answers to 2 decimal places.

7 Find, to 1 decimal place, all the unknown sides and angles in this triangle.

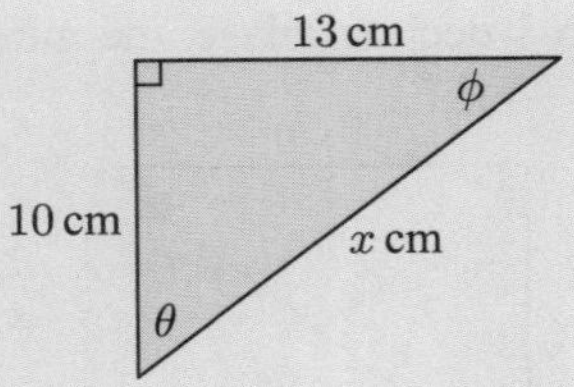

8 The shadow of a tree is 17.5 m in length. The angle from the end of the shadow to the tree top is 38°. Find the height of the tree.

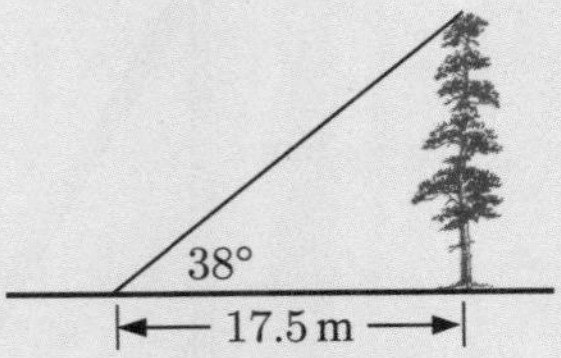

9 A 95 cm long ramp is needed to climb a step of height 30 cm. Find the angle of incline θ of the ramp.

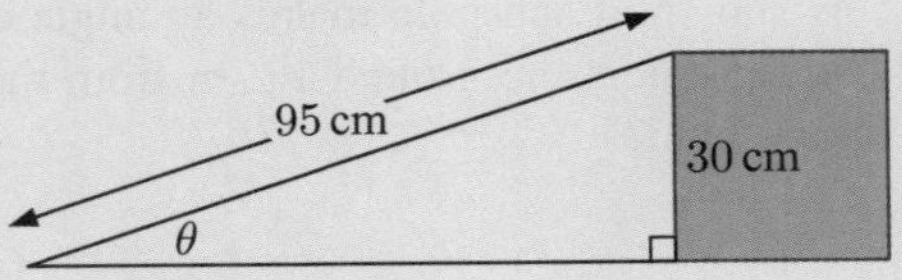

10 An isosceles triangle has equal sides of length 12 cm, and the base angles are 58°. Find the length of the base of the triangle.

REVIEW SET 22B

1 **a** Use a compass and a ruler to construct a scale diagram of a triangular field with sides 100 m, 100 m, and 60 m. Use a scale of $1 \text{ cm} \equiv 20 \text{ m}$.

b Use a protractor to measure the smallest angle of the triangle, to the nearest degree.

c Use trigonometry to find the smallest angle of the triangle you constructed, rounding your answer to 1 decimal place.

2 Find the length of the side:

a opposite θ **b** adjacent to θ

c opposite ϕ **d** adjacent to ϕ.

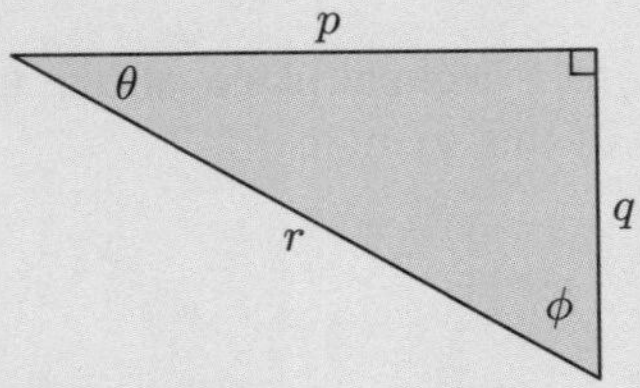

3

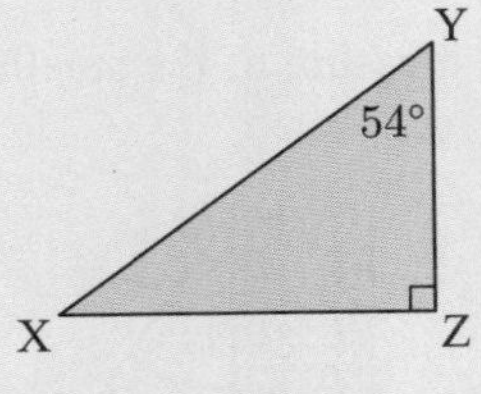

Use your calculator to find the following ratios:

a $\dfrac{\text{YZ}}{\text{XY}}$ **b** $\dfrac{\text{XZ}}{\text{XY}}$ **c** $\dfrac{\text{XZ}}{\text{YZ}}$

4 Find x, rounding your answer to 2 decimal places:

a

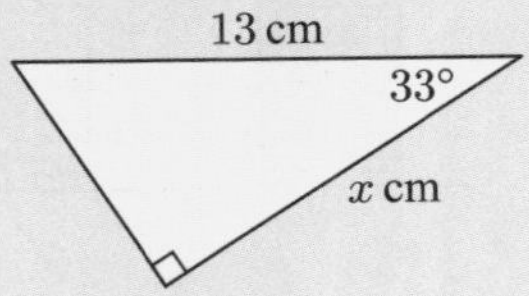

b

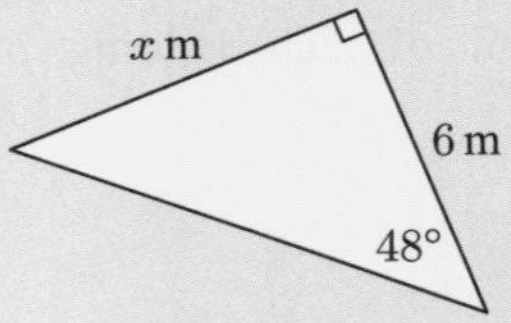

c

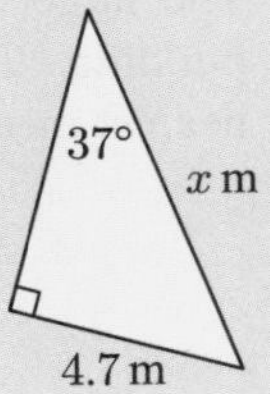

5 Find, to 1 decimal place, the measure of the angle marked θ:

a

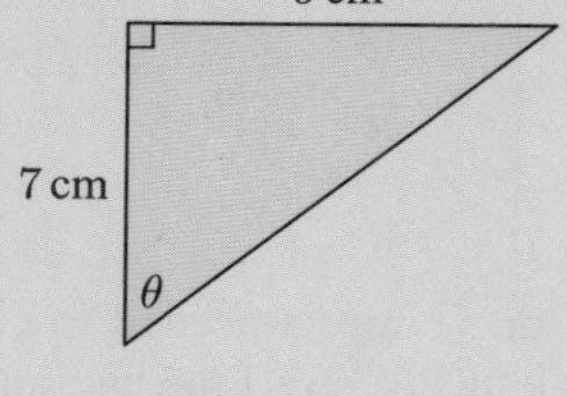

b

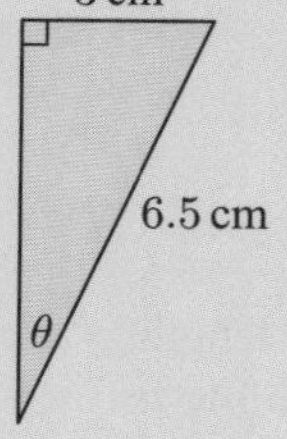

c

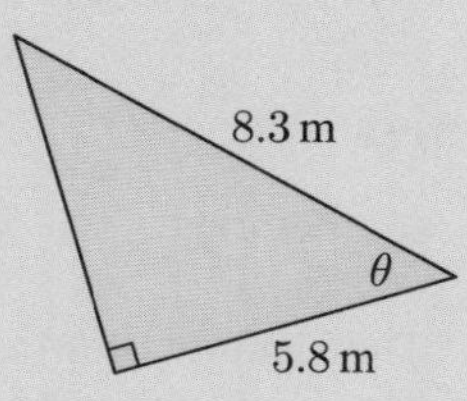

6 A boundary fence is reinforced with a series of metal poles as shown. Each pole makes an angle of 65° to the ground, and it enters the ground 1.2 m from the fence. How long is each pole?

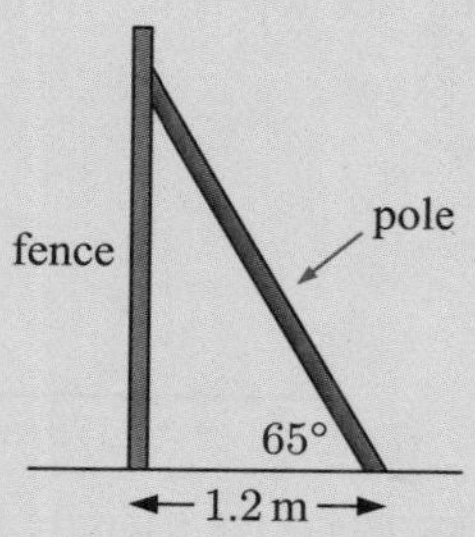

7 Find the value of y, rounded to 1 decimal place:

a

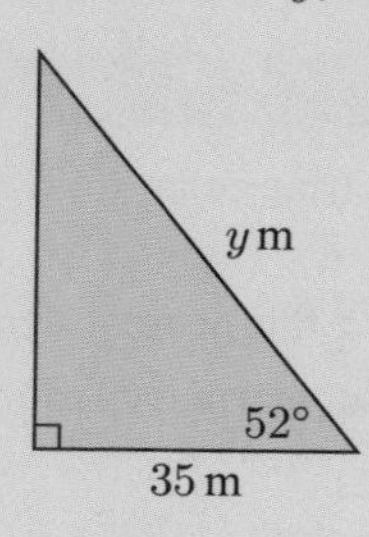

b

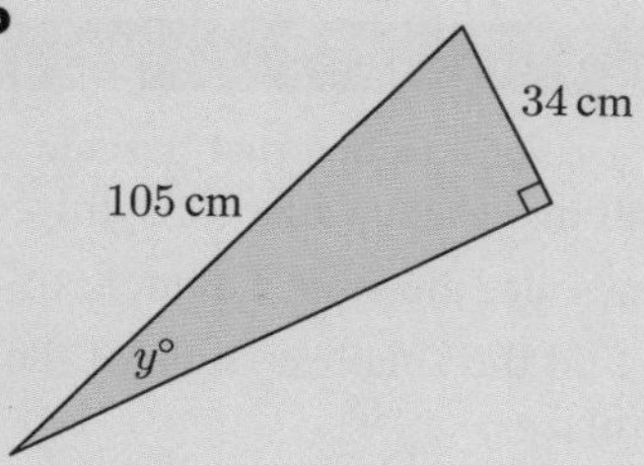

c

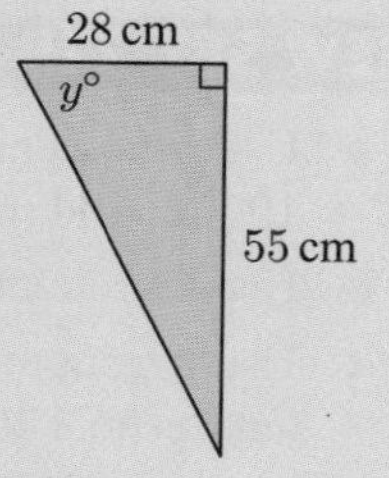

8 Find, to 1 decimal place, all the unknown angles and sides of this triangle.

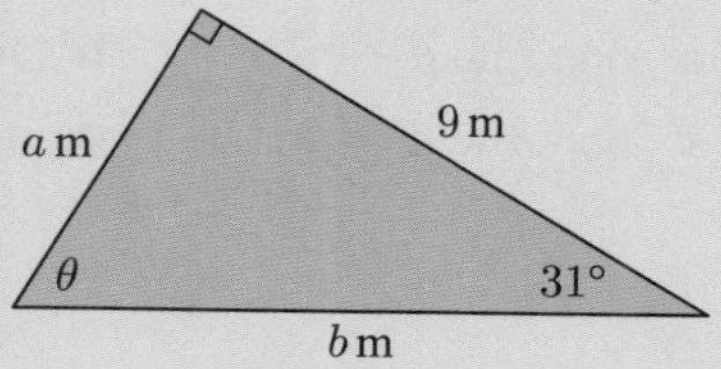

9 A rhombus has diagonals of length 8 cm and 11 cm. Find the measure of the smaller angles of the rhombus.

10 Two office buildings are located 10 m apart. A cable is strung between the two buildings as shown. The angle made between the cable and the taller building is 11°.

a How long is the cable?

b The larger building is twice as tall as the shorter building. Find the height of each building, to the nearest metre.

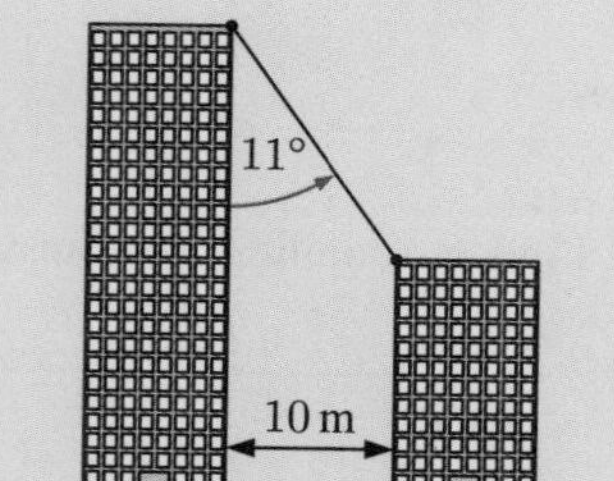

NDEX